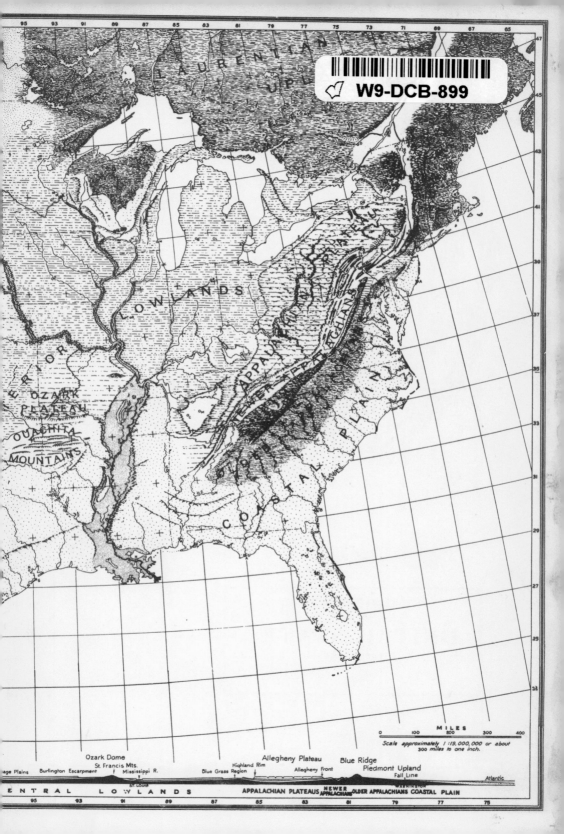

Geology: Principles and Processes

GEOLOGY
Principles and Processes

WILLIAM H. EMMONS
Late Professor of Geology, University of Minnesota

GEORGE A. THIEL
Professor of Geology, University of Minnesota

CLINTON R. STAUFFER
Professor Emeritus of Geology, University of Minnesota
Research Associate, California Institute of Technology

IRA S. ALLISON
Professor of Geology, Oregon State College

FOURTH EDITION

1955   *New York   Toronto   London*
McGRAW-HILL BOOK COMPANY, INC.

Mount Robson and Emperor Falls, British Columbia. (*Photograph by Canadian National Railways.*)

Garrie L. Tufford
MNO 620900 8199

Preface

In its fourth edition, "Geology: Principles and Processes" has been revised and reset. The revision retains the major plan of organization of the earlier editions, but several sections have been completely reorganized. This was deemed advisable because geological science now employs various new techniques, and many positive experimental data have accumulated to replace former speculations with specific geologic facts. Furthermore, during the years since the third edition was published (1949) a large volume of new geologic literature has been made available, and distinct advances have been made in various aspects of geology. Many of the new concepts have been incorporated in this fourth edition.

The revision is designed to challenge the interest of the student looking for a cultural course in natural science, and at the same time provides a sound basic presentation for the student who plans a major in earth sciences. In many liberal arts colleges it is not practical to separate the students taking beginning geology into different sections or groups according to their fields of major interest, and consequently all take the same course. It is desirable, therefore, that the first course be comprehensive in order to acquaint the students with the basic framework of a vast and, to most of them, an unfamiliar field of science. The essential, major concepts of earth science should form a framework that is not concealed in a maze of details.

Chapter 1 has been expanded to include a discussion of the broad scope of the activities of geologists. Chapter 2 is for the most part new subject matter. It gives a preview of the earth's gross features and the interrelation between geologic forces and processes acting on the surface of the earth and those reflecting internal forces. This represents an amplification of the introductory material in the text and should help the student to understand the relation between diastrophism and gradation.

As in the earlier editions, the authors hold the view that the basic concepts involved in the operation of many geologic processes cannot be fully appreciated without some knowledge of the nature of the materials being acted upon. Therefore, Chapter 3 describes the common elements, compounds, minerals, and rocks. This chapter is revised to give a clearer and more complete presentation of the structure of atomic matter and of the union of atoms to form molecules and compounds which in turn form minerals. Detailed chemical formulae and chemical equations are avoided, however, throughout the text.

More emphasis than in the previous editions has been placed on the influence of climate on chemical weathering and soil formation. Erosion and the work of the wind in desert regions have been expanded, and the unit on the erosion of folds has been transferred to a position following the description of folds, faults, and other structural features.

During the past decade numerous reports on the polar and subpolar regions of the earth have been published, and high-latitude glaciation has been studied extensively. In order to include some of these recent observations, the chapter on ice and glaciers has been expanded and presented as two chapters. The chapter on the ocean has been reorganized and the discussion on earthquakes has been transferred from the chapter on diastrophism to one dealing with the nature of the earth's interior.

Some instructors would prefer to have the final chapter on mineral resources deleted because of a lack of time to cover the subject matter adequately. Others have indicated that a more comprehensive presentation would be welcomed. In deference to the latter group this chapter has been expanded to include more data on the non-metals.

The order of presentation of the subject matter is considered a logical sequence, but individual instructors may choose to shift some of the chapters to different positions in a topical outline. Most of the chapters are sufficiently complete units to allow for such transpositions.

The authors have endeavored to acknowledge the sources of all photographic illustrations and drawings. They realize, however, that it is impracticable to acknowledge fully all sources of information. They wish especially to express their indebtedness to their colleagues and scores of others for the many courtesies in connection with the preparation of the manuscript for this revision.

George A. Thiel
Clinton R. Stauffer
Ira S. Allison

Contents

CHAPTER 1

The Scope and Methods of Geology

Geology, the science of the earth, is comparatively young, but despite its youth it already has done much to stimulate the thinking of mankind. Man always has been interested in the earth on which he lives, and he long has speculated about places and regions beyond the horizon. Several centuries ago men's thoughts were warped by dogmas which led the early natural philosophers to argue about numerous speculative concepts based largely on assumptions. In the early part of the nineteenth century, however, many students of earth science began to realize the importance of field observations, and thus gradually the observed facts began to invalidate many of the earlier speculations in regard to the structure of the earth and the mode of origin of the rocks of its outer crust.

In the days of the natural philosophers, the observations regarding the earth were very superficial, but gradually more and more of the earth's surface was observed, described, and recorded, and the observations became progressively more comparative and more quantitative. Thus, in general, earth science has advanced primarily through reasoning based on accurate field observations. These observations included such elements of the natural environment as (1) surface features, (2) climate, (3) soil, (4) surface waters, (5) underground water, (6) oceans and coasts, (7) subsurface structures, and (8) mineral resources. However, many geologic phenomena originate deep within the earth's crust, and the hypotheses advanced to explain them must be based largely or entirely upon indirect evidence. Even now some of the deep-seated processes are only partially understood, and they may have to remain so because of the impossibility of bringing them under direct observation, but others can be inferred from the results that have been produced.

We are accustomed to thinking of the earth's crust as relatively stable, except in zones where earthquakes or explosive volcanoes suddenly and visibly dislocate it. However, the earth is continually changing. There is much evidence that less spectacular but nevertheless very definite motion is taking place slowly in many parts of the world. Careful

FIG. 1. An erosion remnant known as Mormon Temple in Bryce Canyon National Park. Degradational agents such as wind and water have removed the rocks that surrounded it. (*Courtesy of Union Pacific Railroad.*)

observations on lake levels show that the land is rising in the area to the north of the Great Lakes at a rate of approximately 16 inches per century, and in the region of the Baltic Sea tidal gauges show that certain localities are rising at a rate of more than 3 feet per century.

Geology is the fundamental earth science which attempts an intelligent interpretation of the products resulting from these natural processes acting on and in the earth (Figs. 1, 2, and 6). Familiarity with present earth processes and conditions enables the geologist to reconstruct the sequence of past events and thus to interpret the history of the earth and its inhabitants. This interpretation requires a knowledge of the materials and of the structure of the earth, as well as a proper conception of the agencies and processes which continually are altering it. Since many of the agencies involve physical and chemical changes, not only does geology enlist the aid of other sciences, such as chemistry and physics, but its field overlaps those of many other sciences. The earliest earth history deals with the form, size, and physical condition of the earth as a planet, and thus the subject matter is closely related to astronomy. Later the varied forms of plant and animal life made their appearance on earth in a very definite order. Their study is to a large extent botany and zoology. It is evident, therefore, that no sharp boundary separates earth science from the other major fields of science. As a matter of fact the various fields of science are so interrelated that a problem in any one of them may require crossing over into another many times before a satisfactory solution is attained.

Branches of Geology. Geology is a very broad science and therefore has a number of subdivisions, each of which emphasizes certain phases of the subject. One branch of the study (cosmology) treats of the early history of the earth and the relation of the earth to other heavenly bodies in the Universe, such as the sun, the other planets, and other stars; another (petrology) is devoted to the study of the character and origin of all types of rock; still another (structural geology) deals with the arrangement or the structural relations of rocks and particularly with their relations to each other. Other special branches are concerned with the

FIG. 2. Deeply incised, or entrenched, stream meanders formed by degradation in a semiarid region of southeastern Utah. View along Grand Gulch to its outlet into San Juan River. (*Photograph by National Park Service.*)

forces and movements (dynamic geology) that have affected the rocks and the results of these movements and with the various land forms (geomorphology) or contour of the surface of the earth and the origin of the mountains, valleys, and plains. A biological branch (paleontology) is the study of the remains of ancient life that are found in the rocks and the evidences of the gradual development of that life throughout the known eras of geologic time. It is closely related to a study of the history of the earth (historical geology) as shown by its rocks and particularly the record of events that is revealed in the rocks. An economic branch (economic geology) treats of the occurrence, origin, and distribution of the materials of the earth that are valuable to man. It includes the study of deposits of the metals, coal, petroleum, and many other substances. The extent of the uses of these materials is indicated by the fact that mining and allied activities now represent one of the four basic industries which furnish the raw materials needed in our modern world, the other basic industries being agriculture, lumbering, and fishing. According to the U.S. Bureau of Mines the total value of the mineral production of the United States in 1951 was approximately 10 billion dollars.

There are other branches of earth science less closely related to geology as it is taught today. These are meteorology, which is a study of the atmosphere, its composition, movements, and effects on and relation to the other parts of the earth; climatology, which is the study of the various earth climates and their causes; and hydrology, which treats of the surface and subsurface waters in their relation to the surface on which they lie or to the rock media through which they travel. More closely related to dynamic geology is a study of the ocean waters, oceanography. This branch treats of the composition, movement, and influence of the waters of the oceans on the coast lines and on the floor of the sea.

Geology and Human Welfare. The science of geology long has been closely related to the activities and welfare of man. Primitive man made his first rude weapons and utensils from stone, wood, bone, and other materials, and then as he became more adept in the working of stone into various shapes, he entered what is now known as the Stone Age. Overhanging cliffs and caves were his first dwelling places, the springs and streams furnished his water supply, and rivers served as highways for his travel. With the discovery of the methods for isolating the metals from their ores, man passed successively into the Copper, Bronze, and Iron Ages, and with each stage minerals assumed a progressively greater importance. Today modern man has found thousands of uses for many materials of the earth. Metals, fuels, fertilizers, structural materials, abrasives, medicines, and almost countless other substances that affect our daily lives have been made available through geologic research.

A geologist may be called upon for many services, not merely to locate and classify minerals, rocks, and ores, for there are many aspects of geology besides those concerned with the use of mineral resources. For instance, today the matter of soil conservation deservedly receives much attention, and an understanding of basic geologic principles is vital in any soil-conservation program, for the soil itself is based on disintegrated and decomposed rocks. It follows, therefore, that the physical characteristics of a soil are determined to a considerable extent by the source rock from which it was derived and the geological environment in which it was formed. Furthermore, in the southern Great Plains area and in the desert regions of the Southwest, geologists have been called upon to locate the sites for many artesian wells which are used to irrigate soils or to furnish water supplies for cities and for industries. Geologists are asked also to give counsel regarding dam sites, tunnels, foundations, control of floods, and other engineering projects.

Besides the great scientific discoveries geologists have made, perhaps the greatest contribution earth science makes to man is to teach him a greater appreciation of his physical environment. When a person learns that hills and valleys, lakes and streams are not permanent features of the landscape, they become more and more interesting and fascinating, especially as he begins to understand the geologic processes which have brought them into existence. When his travels take him to such scenic features as the Rainbow Bridge, Niagara Falls, the Grand Canyon, the Painted Desert, and many others (Figs. 2 to 7), he takes pride and satisfaction in being able to analyze the changes and processes that produce them.

Processes Acting on the Earth. The processes which are now in operation on the surface of the earth include:

1. Gradation:
    a. Degradation, or the wearing down of rocks by water, air, and ice.
    b. Aggradation, or the building up of rock formations by deposition of the degraded material.
2. Diastrophism, or the movements of parts of the solid earth with respect to each other.
3. Vulcanism, or the movements of molten rocks or lavas and the formation of their products.

Gradation. Rocks exposed at the surface of the earth are continually subject to gradation. The waves beat upon the coasts and wear away the land. The rain falls upon the land, and the water flows to the creeks and rivers and thence to lakes and seas. The water carries with it particles of rock, and these finally are dropped in lakes, along rivers (Fig. 3) and in the ocean, where they form beds of sand and mud. The wind carries rock particles and rolls them along the surface of the earth.

FIG. 3. Stream aggradation. Alluvial fans along east side of Death Valley, California. (*Photograph by Fairchild Aerial Surveys, Los Angeles.*)

depositing them as sand dunes or layers and films of dust. Sand and dust deposits of this sort are very thick in parts of China and the central portion of the United States. Ice in motion carries rock fragments; and when the ice melts, these are deposited. The process of gradation is generally slow, but it is continuous, and in long periods of time its results are very great.

  Diastrophism. Diastrophism includes all movements of solid parts of the earth with respect to other parts. At many places rocks that were un-

FIG. 4. Horizontal bedding in sedimentary rocks near Hamlin, Texas. (*Photograph by N. H. Darton, U.S. Geological Survey.*)

FIG. 5. Steeply tilted sedimentary rocks near Gallup, New Mexico. Diastrophism tilted them from an originally horizontal position such as that shown in Fig. 4. (*Photograph by N. H. Darton, U.S. Geological Survey.*)

doubtedly formed as sediments on the sea bottom and contain the remains of marine animals and plants are found high above the sea. Such rocks have been raised by diastrophism. A study of the rocks and their relations to each other shows that large areas of the earth's surface have been submerged below sea level and elevated above sea level many times. Diastrophism commonly determines the nature of gradation. Above sea level the dominant process is degradation; below sea level the dominant process is aggradation. When sediments are laid down in the sea, they are nearly flat-lying (Fig. 4); if they are found to be folded or on edge (Fig. 5), the inference is warranted that they have been disturbed by diastrophic movements. Degradation tears down the rocks and re-

FIG. 6. Sedimentary beds arched into a fold (anticline) by diastrophism near Lead, Black Hills, South Dakota. (*Photograph by A. J. Tieje.*)

moves their particles to the sea, where new beds are formed from them. By diastrophism these beds are raised above the sea and exposed again to degradation. By diastrophism beds are folded (Fig. 6) and fractured.

Vulcanism. Vulcanism includes all the phenomena that are connected with molten rock matter and its movements. Large parts of the earth's surface are made up of rocks that have solidified from the molten state. Such rocks are igneous. Some of them are extrusive rocks that have been ejected from the throats of volcanoes (Fig. 7); others, intrusive rocks, solidified at depths. The deep-seated intrusive igneous rocks were not exposed at the surface of the earth until erosion had removed the material that covered them (Fig. 8). When igneous rocks are exposed above the

FIG. 7. Parícutin Volcano in Mexico as it appeared in 1943. A young cinder and lava cone that is now more than 2,000 feet high. (*Photograph courtesy of American Museum of Natural History.*)

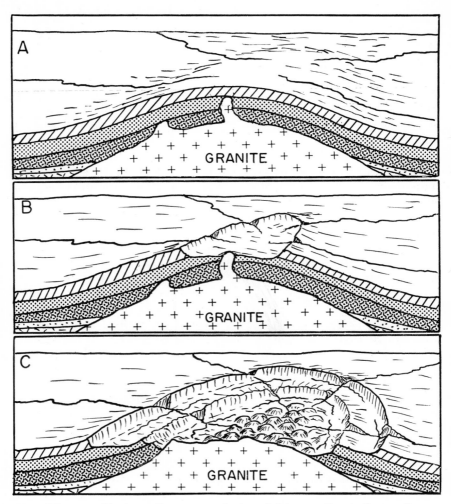

FIG. 8. Diagrams showing sedimentary rocks intruded by granite. *A*, the granite was formed at great depth and is not exposed at the surface; *B*, erosion has removed some of the strata, but the granite is not exposed; *C*, erosion has removed the sedimentary strata, and the granite is now exposed to the view of man. (*Modified after Lobeck.*)

sea at the surface of the earth, they are attacked by air and water and are broken down. Their fragments, together with other material, are carried away by streams and are deposited to form sands and muds.

Methods of Study. The geologic history of the earth should be interpreted in the light of the processes that are observed to be operating on the earth today. These processes—gradation, diastrophism, and vulcanism—are studied and their results are noted as a means of interpreting the geologic past.

The methods of geology are very simple if the steps are taken singly. As sediments are laid down in the lake or sea to which a stream has transported them, they are deposited over the bottom of the quiet water in sheets or layers, one on top of the other, and it is obvious that the lowest one was laid down first. If these beds are not disturbed over a long period of time, anybody can still be sure that the lowest was formed first and hence is the oldest of the series of sedimentary beds shown at this particular place. Moreover the beds above it are successively younger toward the top, and so the relative ages of the different layers are established. The same holds true even if these sediments have been compressed and cemented into a solid rock.

In rocks of sedimentary origin are found the remains of plants and animals that were living while the rocks were being formed. The remains in one set of beds may be different from those in other beds of the same group of rocks, but they may resemble the remains of organisms that are found in beds located far away. Thus a bed carries a "label" that states its age. By studying hundreds of sections of rocks and mapping them, the extent of the area over which a bed was deposited may be learned, and thus it is possible to chart the ancient sea in which a bed was deposited many ages ago.

Where sediments are laid down in water, they are nearly flat (Fig. 4); where beds formed from sediments have been disturbed by diastrophism, they are found to be tilted and folded (Figs. 5, 6). Where an igneous mass intrudes a group of beds, it is known to be later than the beds intruded. Thus by studying large areas—the beds, their attitudes, and their relations to each other and to igneous bodies—it is possible to ascertain the times at which the major events have taken place in the area containing the rocks and to interpret the geological history of the area.

With an increase in our knowledge of earth's history there comes an extension of our conception of geologic time. Processes and forces which seem to have but slight effect when observed from day to day are capable of producing tremendous results when continued over long periods of geologic time. The geologist looks upon the duration of geologic time as comparable with the vast expanses of space recognized by the astronomer.

CHAPTER 2

Gross Features of the Earth

THE EARTH IN RELATION TO THE UNIVERSE

The earth is one of the planets of our solar system, which consists of the sun, nine known planets and their satellites, numerous asteroids, comets, and meteorites. The sun is one of billions of stars within our stellar system, or galaxy, which is known as the Milky Way system. This system of stars occupies a lens-shaped portion of space which has a diameter of about 70,000 light-years. One light-year is the distance light travels in 365¼ days, traveling at a velocity of approximately 186,200 miles per second. The average distance between stars is 8 to 10 light-years. Such great distances are utterly beyond our comprehension, but to try to visualize the enormous distances in the Milky Way system, consider the group of stars known as the Great Cluster of Hercules, which is 36,000 light-years distant. The light which we receive from this cluster today left its surface 360 centuries ago. If a news dispatch could be flashed by radio from that cluster of stars to the earth today, it would be ancient history before it reached this planet.

Beyond our own galaxy are a large number of other systems of stars of approximately the same size. These systems, known as extragalactic nebulae (Fig. 9), are scattered fairly uniformly through space, the nearest to the earth being the nebula in the constellation of Andromeda at a distance of 1 million light-years.

The spectra of these extragalactic nebulae show a displacement of their lines toward the red end of the spectrum which is interpreted to indicate that the nebulae are moving away from the solar system. This observation has led to the theory of the expanding universe, which postulates that all the matter in the Universe was once concentrated into a smaller region and has expanded to its present proportions. With certain assumptions as to the rate of expansion the age of the Universe has been computed to be several billion years.

The millions of bright stars within the confines of our own galactic

12

system are spheres of glowing gas. They vary in size from a globe as small as the earth to one 1,000 times larger than the sun. In density the stars differ from 10,000 times rarer than our atmosphere to several hundred thousand times denser than water. These exceedingly dense stars are small and are classified as "white dwarfs." The very large stars are red and have a high mass and volume but low density, whereas the dwarfs have low mass and volume but high density.

Unlike stars, the planets do not produce light. They simply reflect part of the light they receive from the star we call the sun. A star shines because it has a certain mass and a certain composition. All stars contain abundant hydrogen, and the conversion of hydrogen into helium releases radiant energy in the form of heat and light. Thus a star cannot help shining, for if it did not, the mutual gravitation of its particles would cause it to contract and the energy liberated by the contraction would soon heat the interior sufficiently to start the hydrogen-helium transformation. Once started, the radiation would maintain itself as long as sufficient hydrogen remained. The planets do not contain a sufficiently high percentage of hydrogen, nor are they at a high enough temperature to produce such radiation.

FIG. 9. Photograph of spiral nebula in Ursa Major taken with 200-inch Hale reflector. (*Courtesy of Mount Wilson and Palomar Observatories.*)

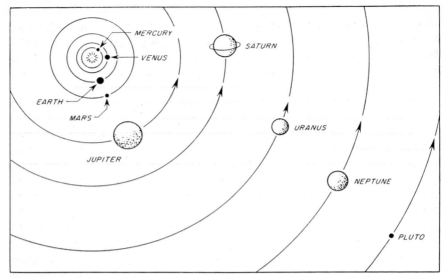

FIG. 10. Diagram showing the planets of the solar system in the order of their distances from the sun. The distance from earth to sun is approximately 93 million miles. All the planets revolve in elliptical orbits that are in approximately the same plane.

SOLAR SYSTEM

The solar system is of primary importance to us (Fig. 10), but it is inconspicuous within our galaxy and insignificant in size in relation to the Universe as a whole. The sun contains more than 99.8 per cent of the mass of the system, and spectroscopic analyses of its light indicate that it is composed of the same chemical elements as those found in the earth, although differences in surface temperatures doubtless cause different states and different combinations of these elements. Light from even more distant stars, some of which are hotter than the sun, is similar but shows much of the matter to be in a simpler atomic state. Hence the earth, although relatively small, appears to offer a fair sample of the matter composing not only the solar system but also our galaxy and perhaps even the entire Universe. In geology it may well be that we are dealing with the end products of matter as it exists under the temperatures and pressures of earth conditions and that there is no other kind of matter anywhere, but merely a difference in its condition.

Sixty-six of the more than 90 elements recognized on earth have been identified in the sun's spectrum, and there is no reason to conclude that any element is really absent, as the others may be unobservable because of the small percentage present or because of the absorption of their wave lengths by the atmosphere of the earth.

Seen through the telescope, the sun appears as a yellowish disk, noticeably darker near the edge than at the center. The darkening toward the edge suggests that the material of the sun is gaseous for a considerable depth, inasmuch as a solid or liquid surface would appear illuminated more uniformly. From a variety of measurements it has been found that the distance from the earth to the sun is about 93 million miles.

All stars travel at very high speeds, and the sun is no exception. It is rushing through space in the general direction of the bright star Vega at a rate of 12 miles per second. Since the planets and their satellites revolve around the sun, it follows that they are carried with the sun as they continue to journey around it. There are 9 planets, more than 2,000 smaller bodies known as asteroids, or planetoids, which revolve around the sun, and 27 satellites, or moons, which accompany certain planets. All the planets revolve about the sun approximately in the same plane and in the same direction. Their average rate of speed around the sun is approximately 13 miles per second. The earth completes one revolution each year at an average velocity of about 18.5 miles per second. Since the outer planets have less speed and greater distances to travel, their periods of revolution around the sun are longer. The planets also rotate on their polar axes; the earth rotates once every 24 hours.

The planets show a rather regular spacing in two contrasted groups: an inner group of small planets (Mercury, Venus, earth, and Mars), which are called the terrestrial planets, and an outer group of large planets (Jupiter, Saturn, Uranus, Neptune, and Pluto), which are called the major planets. The small terrestrial planets all have densities which indicate that they are composed of minerals and rocks closely related to those in the earth. Mercury has no atmosphere, but Venus, our nearest neighbor, has a very dense atmosphere, consisting almost entirely of carbon dioxide, which conceals its surface. Mars has polar icecaps which increase in size during its cold seasons and melt during its summer seasons; so its atmosphere must contain some water vapor. The major planets have low densities and thick atmospheres that completely conceal their other features.

The moon is the earth's satellite. It is approximately 2,160 miles in diameter and revolves around the earth at a distance of about 240,000 miles, which is less than ten times the distance around the earth. Like the earth, the moon rotates as it revolves, but the rotation keeps pace with the revolution so that the moon turns completely around only once during each circuit of the earth. This means that the same face of the moon is always turned toward the earth, while the other side remains forever hidden. The moon is so near that the side toward the earth is clearly shown, and an ordinary telescope reveals much of its surface to be covered by lofty mountains, wide plains, and very large pits which resemble volcanic craters on the earth (Fig. 11). The largest of these

FIG. 11. Photograph of part of the moon taken with 100-inch reflector telescope at Mount Wilson Observatory.

craters is 56 miles in diameter, and the height of its surrounding rim, measured by its shadows, is 12,000 feet. It has been suggested that these craters, or pits, may have been formed by the infall of large meteorites rather than by vulcanism (Figs. 12, 13).

Because of its low gravity, the moon lacks an atmosphere, and its surface is therefore dry, dead, and desolate, dazzling with light in the sunshine but black in the shadows. Even though its attractive power is low, the moon is so near the earth that its gravitative pull upon the earth is greater than that of other heavenly bodies except the sun. Its pull upon the side nearest the earth is greater than its pull on the far side, and the tides are a result of this difference.

The distance from the sun to the outermost planet, Pluto, is approximately 4,000 million miles and from the sun to the nearest star, 27 million million miles.

In order more readily to appreciate the relative distances in our solar system and in the galaxy, let us reduce the scale to distances we can visualize. Place a golf ball to represent the sun on a flat surface, and at a distance of about 12 feet from the ball place a grain of sand to represent the earth. On this scale, Pluto, the farthest planet, could be represented by another grain of sand moving in an orbit 500 feet from the golf ball. All the other planets are within this orbit. If the same scale were used to project the galaxy of stars, the nearest star would be repre-

FIG. 12. Aerial photograph of Chubb Crater Lake in Ungava, the northernmost peninsula of the province of Quebec, Canada. This crater may have had an origin similar to those on the surface of the moon. (Compare with Fig. 11.) (*Photograph by Royal Canadian Air Force.*)

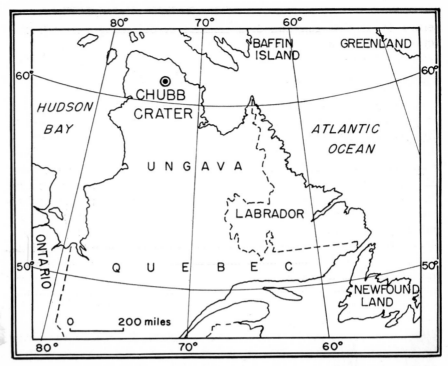

FIG. 13. Outline map of northern Quebec and Ungava, showing the location of Chubb Crater.

Facts Concerning the Solar System (*From Luyten, Moulton, and others*)

Sun and planets	Mean distance from the sun		Period of revolution, days	Diameter, miles	Density, water = 1
	Millions of miles	Earth = 1			
Sun	. . . . .	. . . . . .	. . . . . .	865,000	1.41
Moon	. . . . .	. . . . . .	. . . . . .	2,163	3.34
Mercury	36	0.387	88	3,030	3.80
Venus	67	0.723	225	7,700	4.85
Earth	93	1.000	365	7,918	5.52
Mars	142	1.524	687	4,230	4.01
Jupiter	483	5.20	4,333	86,500	1.33
Saturn	886	9.54	10,759	70,000	0.73
Uranus	1,782	19.19	30,686	31,500	1.22
Neptune	2,792	30.07	60,188	34,800	1.41
Pluto	3,666	39.50	92,611	?	?

sented by another golf ball at a distance of 600 miles from the one representing the sun.

SHAPE AND SIZE OF THE EARTH

In early youth we are taught that the earth is spherical, and most people accept this statement without giving further thought to any of the proofs of the earth's sphericity. A simple observation is to watch a ship at sea and note that as it recedes farther and farther into the distance, it appears to sink slowly beneath the water level, until eventually only the smoke from its funnels remains above the horizon. The reason for the apparent submergence of the ship is the fact that the surface of the sea is curved. This in itself does not prove that the earth is a sphere, but numerous observations in many different oceanic areas have demonstrated that the amount of curvature is everywhere nearly the same. Furthermore, modern navigation methods are based on the assumption that the earth is a sphere, and the positions of vessels have been established correctly innumerable times thereby. Hence the assumption must be correct.

Another observation which demonstrates that the earth is a sphere is the shape of the earth's shadow as seen against the face of the moon during all lunar eclipses. The edge of the shadow always appears as an arc of a circle, and it can be demonstrated geometrically that a sphere is the only body which will always cast a circular shadow upon another sphere.

Still another proof of the earth's sphericity may be demonstrated from observations on the position of the north star. Under ideal conditions, an observer at the equator should be able to see the north star on the horizon, and as he traveled northward toward the north pole, the star would rise higher and higher until the observer reached the north pole, where the star would be directly overhead. Careful measurements by the observer would show that the star rose 1 degree higher for about every 69 miles of northward travel. Since there are 360 degrees in a complete circle and each degree along a meridian equals a distance of about 69 miles, it follows that the earth's circumference is 360 times 69, or about 24,840 miles. Refined measurements have revealed that 1 degree is not exactly the same in all places and in all directions but that the true form of the earth is an oblate spheroid which bulges at the equator and is flattened slightly at the poles. In other words, it is compressed along the polar axis and distended through the equator. The amount of flattening is so slight that the difference between the polar and equatorial diameters is only about 27 miles (7,927 minus 7,900). The irregularities caused by the high mountains likewise mean a deviation from sphericity;

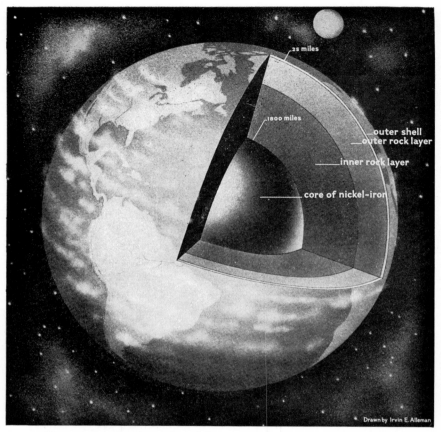

FIG. 14. Diagram showing the nature of the interior of the earth. The outer shell has a density of about 2.7; the inner layer is roughly twice that amount; and the inner metallic core has a density of at least 10.

but even the greatest of these irregularities, compared with the earth's diameter, amount to less than the roughness on the skin of an orange. The earth's polar flatness is, in fact, so insignificant that it amounts to only about ½ inch on a globe 10 feet in diameter.

The most recent proof of the earth's spherical form is shown on photographs taken at extremely high altitudes. On such photographic prints the horizon appears as a curved line.

If one ignores the slight flattening at the poles and assumes that the earth is truly spherical with a diameter of 7,900 miles, its volume is then a little more than 250 billion cubic miles [1] and its area nearly 200 million square miles.[2] Once these facts were established, it was possible

[1] Volume = $(3.14/6) \times 7,900^3$ = 250 billion cubic miles (plus).
[2] Area = $3.14 \times 7,900^2$ = 196 million square miles (plus).

$$F = \left.\begin{array}{c}g\end{array}\right. \frac{m_1 \cdot m_2}{r^2}$$

to calculate the mass or weight of the earth by the application of Newton's law of gravitation. By using a very delicate pair of scales, the Eotvos balance, physicists can compare the earth's attraction with that of a large ball of lead or quartz of known weight and thus "weigh" the earth. Its weight by this method is 6,000 million million million tons, or a 6 with 21 ciphers (6×10^{21}).

Once the volume and mass of the earth were known, its *density* was determined by dividing its *volume* into its weight, which gives a density of 5.52. Thus, the average density of the earth is about $5\frac{1}{2}$ times heavier than water. Since the superficial layers of rock of the earth's crust are known, by direct observations, to have an average density of only 2.7, it follows that the inner core must be much denser. This can be explained by a difference in composition and by the enormous pressures exerted by the outer layers on the inside (Fig. 14). The intensity of the pressure near the center can be appreciated if one realizes that at a depth of only 100 miles the pressure is already 300 tons per square inch. The inner core is thought to have a density of 10+ and to be composed mainly of metallic iron.

ROTATION AND REVOLUTION OF THE EARTH

The direction of rotation of the earth can be visualized if one imagines oneself looking down upon the north pole of the earth. From such a position the direction of rotation is counterclockwise (Fig. 15). This direction of rotation is opposite that of the apparent motion of the sun,

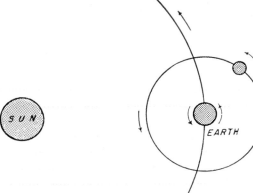

FIG. 15. Diagram showing the direction of rotation and of revolution of earth and its satellite, the moon. A, earth's orbit; B, moon's orbit.

moon, and stars, which seem to travel westward across the sky because the earth is turning in an eastward direction.

The fact that the earth rotates can be demonstrated simply by hanging a heavy weight from a long cord or wire and setting it to swinging as a pendulum. A pendulum swings along the same path until friction brings it to a stop. If the path along which the pendulum is started to swing is marked and the pendulum is allowed to swing undisturbed for several hours, the pendulum's path will be found apparently to have turned through a small angle from its original direction. After each successive hour the path will appear to have shifted farther and farther around. Since the pendulum does maintain the same path in which it started to swing, we are forced to conclude that the earth beneath it is turning. This experiment was first performed by Foucault in Paris in 1851, and in his honor the device is called the Foucault pendulum.

The velocity of rotation of the earth is such that a point on the surface at the equator travels about 1,000 miles per hour, for it completes 25,000 miles in 24 hours (cf. page 15). At the 60th parallel the rate is half this amount, or about 500 miles per hour, and at the poles it is zero. Intermediate points travel at speeds that depend on their distances north or south of the equator. The eastward velocity at a particular place may be computed easily by dividing the length of the parallel of latitude passing through the selected point by 24, which is the approximate period of rotation.

The motion of the earth in its orbit around the sun is termed revolution, and it moves through one complete revolution in 365¼ days. The earth's axis of rotation is inclined to the plane of its orbital revolution at an angle of 66.5 degrees, and it maintains this angle throughout its

FIG. 16. Sketch showing that the angle of the sun's rays at midday in June and in December differs by 47 degrees, thus indicating that the polar axis of the earth is inclined.

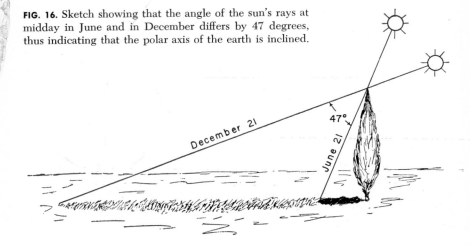

journey around the sun so that for part of the year the north pole is tilted toward the sun and for the remainder of the year it is tilted away from the sun. It is evident, then, that the vertical rays of the sun strike the area north of the equator for half of the year and south of the equator for the other half. This shifting of the maximum of solar energy from one part of the earth to another gives the earth its seasons (Figs. 16 and 17).

FIG. 17. Diagram showing why the average temperature at low latitudes is greater than that of the higher latitudes. The vertical rays of A are concentrated in the square a, whereas the same rays coming from B would be spread over the area b. Because the earth's axis is tilted, the incidence of the sun's rays at any one place changes, producing seasonal temperature variations. (*After Strahler.*)

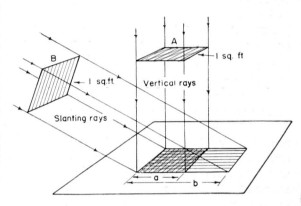

Summary of Salient Facts about the Earth

Shape	Very nearly spherical
Average circumference	Approx. 25,000 miles
Average diameter	Approx. 8,000 miles
Volume	$2,500 \times 10^8$ cubic miles
Surface area	200×10^6 square miles
Mass or weight	6×10^{21} tons
Period of rotation	24 hours
Period of revolution	365¼ days
Inclination of axis	23½ degrees

THE THREE MAJOR PARTS

The earth is regarded as consisting of three parts: (1) the atmosphere, or gaseous envelope, which surrounds the globe; (2) the hydrosphere, or water envelope, which surrounds the larger part of the solid globe and penetrates the rock sphere; (3) the lithosphere, or rock sphere, which constitutes the solid earth.

These three divisions are not independent; the atmosphere contains water and solid rock particles, or dust; the hydrosphere absorbs air and carries rock particles as sediment; and the lithosphere absorbs both air and water, which react with the rocks and change them.

Atmosphere. The atmosphere is a mixture of gases, chiefly nitrogen, oxygen, argon, carbon dioxide, and water vapor. In addition there are small amounts of helium, ozone, ammonia, sulfurous gases, etc. These substances vary somewhat in amounts, and water vapor varies considerably with the conditions of the atmosphere.

The mass of the atmosphere is about 1/1,200,000 the mass of the earth. Its pressure is about 14.7 pounds per square inch at sea level. The density of the air decreases upward, but the air is known to extend about 200 miles above the earth, and probably it extends even farther. The atmosphere is an important geologic agent. It reacts chemically with the rocks and oxidizes them, forming new compounds; it commonly breaks them up into smaller bodies and causes them to disintegrate. This disintegrated rock matter, being more finely divided, is more readily removed by wind and water. Wind—the air in motion—is an important agent of transportation. Moreover, the wind causes the movement of water to form waves and certain ocean currents. Water continually is evaporated into the atmosphere and subsequently is precipitated on the earth as rain. The atmosphere serves also as a thermal blanket which distributes the heat of the sun and tends to prevent its escape from the earth. The dust particles suspended in the atmosphere aid in the diffusion of sunlight. Furthermore, this gaseous envelope which surrounds the earth protects it from violent bombardment by meteorites. Several million meteorites fall into the earth's atmosphere daily, but most of them are disintegrated by the heat of friction which is generated as they travel through air toward the earth's surface. Their fragments settle as fine cosmic dust. Large meteorites, however, do pass through the entire thickness of the atmosphere and may penetrate the surface of the lithosphere several feet or more.

Hydrosphere. The hydrosphere includes the ocean, seas, lakes, rivers, and creeks, together with the water that has soaked into the ground and occupies the openings in the lithosphere. The greater part of the water of the hydrosphere is in the ocean. The ocean at places is about 6 miles deep, and its average depth is about 2½ miles. If the water of the ocean were evenly distributed over the entire earth, its depth would be about 2 miles. The surface of the ocean is about 143 million square miles.

Water is an important geologic agent. The rain falls upon the land and gathers into rills, which unite to form brooks and creeks. These join to form rivers, which, in general, flow to the ocean. The water carries with it rock particles, and little by little the land is worn away.

The process of degradation goes on slowly but continuously. Ultimately the continents are reduced, and their material is carried to the sea and deposited so that great beds of sediments are formed from the degraded land. The source of the energy of running water is the sun, which evaporates the water of the sea, forming clouds, from which the water is precipitated upon the earth. Thus the process of construction of new layers of rock goes on along with the destruction of the land. Air and water and vegetation working together break down the rocks and render them incoherent and therefore more readily removed by running water. Loose material that has not been removed constitutes the soil and mantle-rock.

Lithosphere. The lithosphere is the solid, or rock, portion of the earth. It is an oblate spheroid, *i.e.*, flattened at the poles, owing to rotation. About 143 million square miles lies below sea level, and 54 million square miles is land. Bordering the continents there are areas aggregating about 10 million square miles which are relatively shallow seas and which are called continental shelves (Fig. 18).

CONTINENTAL PLATFORMS AND OCEAN BASINS

When the solid lithosphere is considered without the ocean waters, the continental masses are, for the most part, plateaulike features on which most mountains and valleys form relatively minor surface irregularities. These continental platforms are outlined by comparatively steep slopes extending down to the ocean basins, whose floors are relatively flat, especially at great depths. The continental margins or shelves are flooded by the ocean, which overlaps upon the sloping, shallow edges, and therefore the continental-platform areas are in reality considerably larger than appears on conventional maps of the ocean and the continents.

Relief of Ocean Floors. The eastern margin of North America illustrates certain typical features of the ocean basins and continents (Fig. 18). There the Continental Shelf is a fairly smooth, sloping surface 75 to 100 miles wide. It descends about 10 to 20 feet per mile to a depth of 70 fathoms at its outer edge. At this seaward edge the surface descends abruptly about 350 feet per mile down the *Continental Slope* to the floor of the true ocean basin at a depth of about 2,000 fathoms below sea level. The Continental Slope is cut by numerous canyons that appear to have been eroded by streams or by currents on the ocean floor. On some slopes these so-called "submarine canyons" are as deep and precipitous as the Grand Canyon of the Colorado River. Some extend off the present-day mouths of major streams such as the Hudson and Congo, but others head near the shore line far from the mouth of any major stream. (See Chapter 13 for more details.)

FIG. 18. Photograph of relief model of Continental Shelf off the northeastern coast of the United States. (*Courtesy of Aero Service Corporation.*)

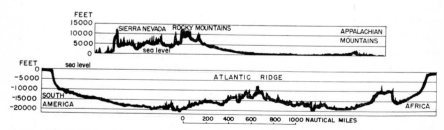

FIG. 19. Profiles across the United States and across the South Atlantic, using a similar spacing of reference points. The Mid-Atlantic Ridge is a broad, plateaulike zone on the floor of the Atlantic. (*After Shepard.*)

The broad, deep basins of the ocean such as those of the Atlantic and Pacific have remarkably smooth floors over large areas. These broad expanses may be interrupted, however, by a diversity of topographic forms such as the great submerged plateau, the *Mid-Atlantic Ridge*, which almost bisects the Atlantic Basin from north to south (Fig. 19). The depressions on the sea floor may be grouped into more or less oval or rounded basins, elongated triangles with gentle slopes, and steep-sided trenches (Fig. 20). The term *deep* is applied to any depression that is more than 6,000 meters below sea level. Such great ocean deeps generally lie along the outer side of island arcs.

Relief of Continents. The continents have an average elevation of about ½ mile above sea level. Their major surface features are mountains, plateaus, and plains. Mountains are conspicuous elevations with small summit areas and complicated internal structures, whereas plateaus rise high above their surroundings but have large summit areas and simple internal structures. Plains are broad regions of low relief commonly underlain by nearly flat-lying rocks. The continent of North America has a broad central plain lying between marginal mountain systems. The Appalachian Mountains on the east form a low series of small ranges and parallel ridges that have resulted from the erosion of folded strata. To the west of the central plain lies the great Cordilleran mountain system, which is much wider and higher than the Appalachians. The system includes the Rocky Moun-

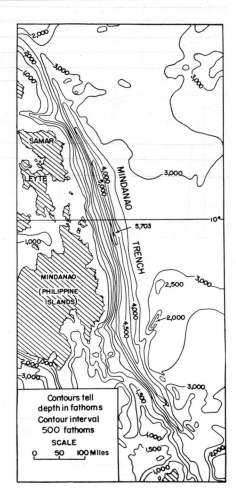

FIG. 20. The great trench on the floor of the Pacific Ocean east of the Philippine Islands. (*Redrawn from H. H. Hess, Hydrographic Office Chart 5485.*)

tains, the Sierra Nevada–Cascade chain, and, still nearer the Pacific, the Coast Ranges. High and broad plateaus lie between these mountains.

The cores of the continents are low, rolling mountains or deeply eroded oldlands composed of complexly altered ancient rocks which occur in areas that are oval or shieldlike in outline and are, therefore, known as *shields.* For South America a shield occupies much of Brazil, and in Europe the Fenno-Scandian Shield is an equivalent.

The maximum relief of the earth's lithosphere is approximately 12 miles (Fig. 21). The greatest elevation of land above sea level is Mount Everest with an altitude of 29,141 feet, or nearly 5.5 miles, and the greatest depth discovered to date is in the Mariana Trench, which descends to more than 35,600 feet, or about 6.7 miles below sea level. The continent of North America has an average elevation of 2,360 feet; Europe averages about 1,150 feet; and Asia, with its high plateaus and Himalaya, averages 3,200 feet.

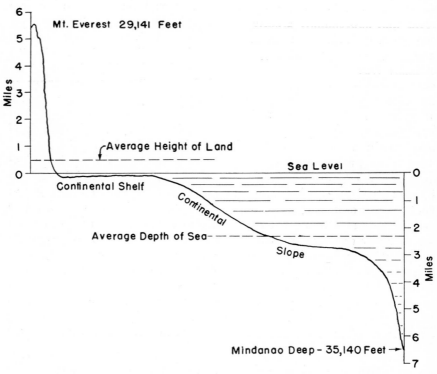

FIG. 21. Diagram showing maximum relief of continents and ocean basins.

RELATION BETWEEN CONTINENTAL MASSES AND SEA FLOORS

Permanency. Most geologists and geophysicists have long been convinced that the continental masses and the deep ocean basin have remained in the same general locations throughout all of recorded geologic time. In other words, the two have not exchanged places because of warping or folding of the earth's crust. The evidence for this conclusion lies in the observation that nearly all the sedimentary rocks of past geologic ages that are exposed on the continents are of types that were deposited in shallow epicontinental seas, whereas sample cores from the deep ocean floor are composed of fine-grained clays and oozes which accumulate so very slowly that cores a few scores of feet in length contain sediments that were deposited millions of years ago.

Isostasy. Another principle that is generally accepted by geologists and geophysicists is that the continents are composed of a lighter or less dense type of rock than that which underlies the ocean basins (Fig. 22). Careful examination and classification of rock types have shown that rocks that approximate granite [1] in composition predominate under the continent, whereas a heavier type of rock essentially similar to basalt [2] underlies the ocean basins (page 52). The specific gravity, or density, of many types of rocks has been determined with a high degree of accuracy, and it has been demonstrated that granitic rocks are about 10 per cent lighter in weight than basaltic rocks. Furthermore, even though all rocks are solid and brittle at the surface of the earth, experiments have demonstrated that they behave as a plastic material when confined under great pressures corresponding to those miles below the surface. Thus it is reasonable to assume that slow adjustments have taken place at depth and that the continental areas of lighter material have been buoyed up so as to stand higher than the heavier materials beneath the floor of the ocean basins. In other words, the continents are thought of as huge masses floating in a plastic substratum; just as an iceberg floats with seven-eighths of its mass submerged in water, the light granitic continents, floating in the heavy basaltic shell with their crests about 3 miles above the floors of the ocean basins, extend their bases, or roots, 15 to 20 miles downward into the crust.

The basaltic and somewhat plastic substratum of the continents is thought to be a continuous shell of rock that encircles the earth. This conclusion is based on the behavior of earthquake waves and on the

---

[1] Granite is a common, generally pinkish-gray, coarse-grained rock composed of orthoclase feldspar, quartz, and other minerals crystallized within the earth.

[2] Basalt is a dark gray to black, fine-grained, heavy lava rock.

fact that the most extensive lava flows on the continents are basaltic rocks. It is assumed, therefore, that volcanic conduits all over the world, on the continents as well as in the ocean basins, must have access at depth to molten rock material which upon consolidation becomes basaltic rock. Thus from direct geologic observations and from seismologic evidence which will be discussed in a later chapter, we conclude that the uppermost layer in the earth's crust is a discontinuous shell of granite overlying a continuous substratum of basaltic rock (Fig. 22). Geo-

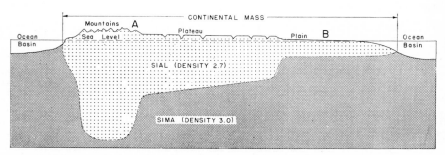

FIG. 22. Diagrammatic section through a continent, showing the light granitic sial floating in the heavier basaltic sima. Mountains which project above the general level of a continent are thought to have deep roots that project downward into the basaltic sima. The weight of a column of matter at *A* and that of one at *B* are thought to be equal.

physical investigations suggest also that the lightweight granitic rocks under the continents form a shell, or plate, not more than 20 or 30 miles thick and that they are underlain by heavy rock similar to that under the oceans.

The fact that the lighter continental blocks stand higher than the heavy oceanic segments suggests that slow movements take place below the base or roots of the continents in order to keep the two units in equilibrium. The term *isostasy* (Greek *isos*, equal + *stasis*, a standing still) is used for this condition of balance, or flotational equilibrium, between units of the earth's crust. Such a condition means that the pressures at some depth beneath large units of the crust must be substantially the same everywhere and that any local differences which develop because of processes in operation at the surface must be adjusted by slow rock flowage in the earth's plastic interior to restore or to maintain balance.

SUGGESTIONS FOR FURTHER READING

Jeffreys, Harold: The Earth, Cambridge University Press, 1953.
Menzel, Donald: Our Sun, The Blackstone Co., 1949.
Urey, H. C.: The Planets, Their Origin and Development, Yale University Press, 1952.

CHAPTER 3

Elements, Compounds, Minerals, Rocks

The Nature of Matter. Early in the history of science, matter was thought to be continuous. A copper rod was conceived of as a continuous mass of copper without spaces or particles. This idea gradually gave way to Dalton's atomic theory, which postulated that every element consists of tiny particles called atoms. According to this granular conception of matter, the atoms of any one element are tiny spheres, all exactly alike. The theory held that atoms are indestructible, that is that they cannot be divided, created, or destroyed. The discovery of radium by Pierre and Marie Curie in 1898, however, upset the theory of the indestructibility of the atom. It is now known that a number of the heavy atoms continually give off small charged particles and radiant energy, which can be shown to originate in the nucleus of the atoms. Such radioactive properties of the elements are not influenced by any external forces, temperature changes, or chemical reactions. The process is one of natural disintegration.

Soon after the discovery of radium and other radioactive elements, there evolved the electron theory, which assumes that atoms are made up of a number of smaller particles. The modern scientist, equipped with research tools of which Dalton never dreamed, can transmute the atom almost at will. In fact he has found the atom to be a veritable universe in itself. The chief units of structure in this submicroscopic universe are electrons, positrons, protons, and neutrons. The electrons are units of negative electricity; the positrons are units of positive electricity, each with approximately the same mass as an electron; protons are tiny particles with a positive charge of electricity; and neutrons are similar to protons, but they are electrically neutral. It is possible that they are formed by the union of an electron and a proton, the electrical charges of which exactly balance each other. The proton and the neutron are relatively dense, each being more than 1,800 times as heavy as the electron.

According to the theory of the orbital structure of the atom as postulated by the Danish scientist Niels Bohr, the nucleus of an atom contains all the protons and neutrons. The electrons revolve in orbits about the nucleus in much the same manner as the planets of the solar system revolve about the sun (Fig. 23). Since the mass or weight of an atom is due mainly to its protons and neutrons, it follows that the mass of an atom is largely in its nucleus. Most of the other properties, including the chemical behavior of atoms, can be ascribed to the electrons.

Behavior of Electrons. In the simple atoms such as hydrogen and helium the electrons revolve in orbits, or "shells," close to the nucleus, but in the more complex atoms, with many more electrons, additional shells are present at varying distances from the nucleus (Fig. 24). It has been found that those elements are most stable whose outermost electron shell contains eight electrons. The more active elements contain one to seven electrons in their outer shell. For example, sodium has one electron in its outer shell, and chlorine has seven. Both are highly active chemically. If sodium loses one electron and chlorine gains one, both elements attain the stable grouping of eight. The outer shell may achieve its quota of eight either by borrowing from, or lending electrons to, other elements or by atoms mutually sharing electrons.

One of the most common and widely known chemical compounds is sodium chloride, or table salt. The two elements sodium and chlorine unite and are held together by chlorine borrowing an electron from sodium. Of the 17 extranuclear electrons in the chlorine atom, 2 are in the first shell, 8 are in the next, and 7 are therefore in the outer shell. This makes the outer shell one short of being complete. Sodium has 11 extranuclear electrons, 2 of which are in the first shell and 8 in the second.

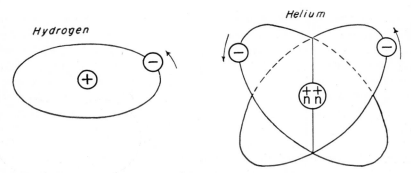

FIG. 23. The relation of electrons ($-$), protons ($+$), and neutrons (n) in atoms.

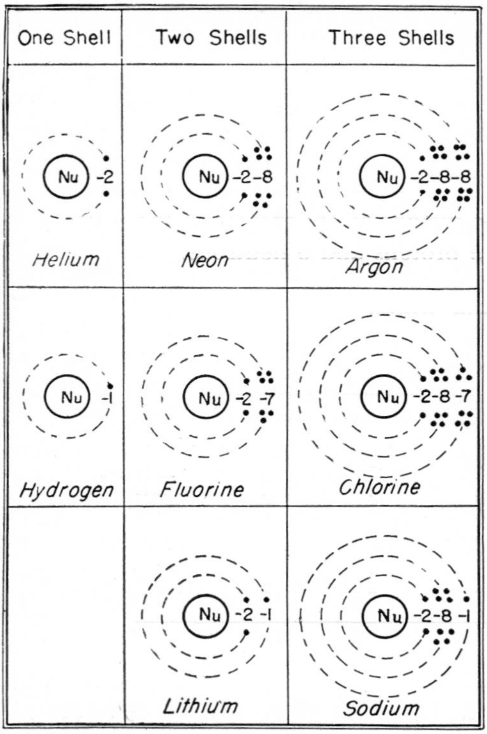

One Shell	Two Shells	Three Shells
Nu -2 *Helium*	Nu -2-8 *Neon*	Nu -2-8-8 *Argon*
Nu -1 *Hydrogen*	Nu -2-7 *Fluorine*	Nu -2-8-7 *Chlorine*
	Nu -2-1 *Lithium*	Nu -2-8-1 *Sodium*

FIG. 24. Diagrammatic sketches showing "shells" of electrons of atoms. The outer shell of helium, neon, and argon is complete, whereas the others are incomplete. *Nu* represents the nucleus of the atoms. In reality the orbits of electrons are not equally spaced, nor are they in one plane.

The remaining electron occupies a lone position in the third, or outer, shell of the atom. The two atoms will combine readily because the chlorine atom by borrowing 1 electron from the sodium completes its outer shell and the sodium by lending 1 electron also makes its outer shell complete (Fig. 25). This transfer of electrons between atoms with incomplete shells is the electrical bond that holds elements together in compounds.

Atomic Weights and Atomic Numbers. By comparing the atoms of various elements, it has been determined that each unit of atomic weight is supplied by a proton or a neutron. Furthermore, if the elements are arranged in the order of increasing atomic weights, the number of

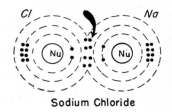

Sodium Chloride

FIG. 25. Diagrammatic sketch showing transfer of electron (indicated by arrow) from sodium to chlorine to form sodium chloride.

nuclear protons increases in the same order. Hydrogen, the lightest atom, has one; helium, the next heavier, has two; and lithium, which is next in weight, has three protons. However, helium has an approximate atomic weight of 4, and that of lithium is near 7. It appears, therefore, that the *atomic weight* is equal to the total number of protons and neutrons in the nucleus of an atom, and the term *atomic number* indicates the number of protons that are present (see accompanying table). Oxygen, for example, has an atomic weight of 16; therefore, the nucleus of an oxygen atom is composed of 8 protons and 8 neutrons.

Components of Certain Atoms

Element	Atomic number	Protons in nucleus	Neutrons in nucleus	Number of electrons	Relative atomic weights
Hydrogen	1	1	0	1	1.008
Helium	2	2	2	2	4.004
Lithium	3	3	4	3	6.940
Beryllium	4	4	5	4	9.02
Boron	5	5	6	5	10.82
Carbon	6	6	6	6	12.01

As greater accuracy was introduced in determining atomic weights, they were found to be not exactly whole numbers; for example, oxygen was in reality 15.876 times heavier than hydrogen. Since oxygen entered into more compounds than hydrogen, it was agreed among scientists, purely for convenience, to call the atomic weight of oxygen 16.000. With that value standardized, hydrogen has an atomic weight of 1.008, carbon 12.01, etc. If each proton and neutron contributes one unit of atomic mass, should not all atomic weights be whole numbers? This question was answered when it was found that many of the elements are composed of mixtures of atoms that vary slightly in atomic weight. For example, in 100 grams of chlorine of atomic weight 35.46, there are 76 grams of chlorine of atomic weight 35.00 and 24 grams of chlorine of atomic weight 37.00. The average weight of these two kinds of chlorine when mixed in this proportion is 35.46. The term *isotopes* is given to atoms of the same element which differ in atomic weights because of differences in nuclear structure.

Since the number of protons in the atoms of any one element is always the same, it follows that the weight differences are due to differences in the number of neutrons in the nuclei of the atoms. For example, each atom of uranium contains 92 protons. However, on the basis of weights, there are four isotopes of uranium weighing 234, 235,

238, and 239 units, respectively. Thus uranium 238 has 146 neutrons in its nucleus, whereas the explosive isotope, uranium 235, has three fewer neutrons:

$$Protons \quad Neutrons$$
$$92 \; + \; 146 \; = \; 238$$
$$92 \; + \; 143 \; = \; 235$$

The 20 Most Common Elements in the Earth's Crust in the Order of Their Abundance (*After Clarke and Washington*)

Element	Per cent	Element	Per cent
Oxygen, O_2	46.71	Carbon, C	0.094
Silicon, Si	27.69	Manganese, Mn	0.09
Aluminum, Al	8.07	Sulfur, S	0.08
Iron, Fe	5.05	Barium, Ba	0.05
Calcium, Ca	3.65	Chlorine, Cl	0.045
Sodium, Na	2.75	Chromium, Cr	0.035
Potassium, K	2.58	Fluorine, F	0.029
Magnesium, Mg	2.08	Zirconium, Zr	0.025
Titanium, Ti	0.62	Nickel, Ni	0.019
Hydrogen, H	0.14	All others	0.063
Phosphorus, P	0.13		
		Total	100.000

When the atom of an element loses an outer electron or gains an extra one, its electrical balance is destroyed and it becomes electrically charged. For example, when the atom of sodium loses an electron, the atom then has one excess positive charge, the positive charges being on the protons in the nucleus of the atom. Likewise, when the atom of chlorine gains an electron, the atom has one excess negative charge. Such electrically charged atoms are known as *ions*. Elements may be ionized by heating them in a gaseous state as in radio tubes and neon signs. A large number of compounds form ions of their elements when the compounds are in water solution. These charged particles become dissociated in the solution and move about in random fashion throughout the liquid. Such solutions are called *electrolytes*. Many chemical reactions of importance in geology depend upon the behavior of electrolytes.

Atoms differ in size, but their size is not determined by the number of electrons or by the number of shells in which they are distributed. The potassium atom is much larger than that of calcium even though both have four electron shells and calcium has one more electron than potassium. The importance of differences in size of atoms will be discussed later in connection with the process of replacement of atoms in various mineral crystals.

The atoms of various elements unite to form molecules. All material substances in the world are composed of these unbelievably tiny units of matter, most of which are so small that they would have to be magnified nearly 2 million times before they would be visible to the unaided eye. Some molecules contain but few atoms which are arranged in relatively simple structures. Others are much larger and contain many atoms in very complicated arrangements. A convenient scale of length used in measuring the size of molecules is the angstrom unit, which is 4/1,000,000,000 inch. Some molecules are only a few angstrom units in length, while others are much larger.

Molecules are put together to form all the ordinary materials of our everyday world (Fig. 26). Some materials like air are gases, others like water are liquids; while still others like sugar or steel are solids. In gases the molecules move rapidly to and fro in an independent existence. In liquids, however, the molecules are more closely spaced and are always in contact with one another even though their motion causes them to shift, turn, vibrate, and change partners continually. The molecules of water are always in motion, but their movement is not sufficient to cause them to break away entirely from one another. That is why at ordinary

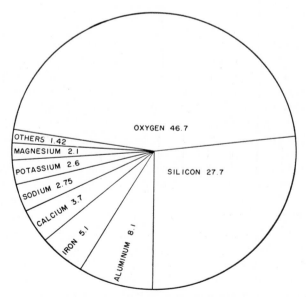

FIG. 26. The relative abundance of the most common elements of the earth's crust. All figures indicate percentages. (*After Clarke and Washington.*)

temperatures water is a liquid rather than a gas. In still other substances the mutual attractions of molecules or atoms counterbalance the effects of unorganized motion, each molecule or atom is tied to its neighbors, and a solid is formed. These three phases of matter—gaseous, liquid, and solid—are exemplified on earth as the air, the water, and the rock, respectively.

Crystals. The geometrical form of many solids suggests an arrangement of atoms or molecules in patterns of equally spaced rows and planes, like soldiers on parade (Fig. 27). Each particle is in a definite place, and the distances to its neighbors on all sides are determined by its attractive forces in various directions. The outer expressions of this inner regularity are the smooth faces and sharp angles of crystals (Figs. 28, 29). The microscope and X rays prove convincingly that many solids which do not show crystal faces have nevertheless a regular pattern in their inner structures. Solids of this sort, whether or not they recur in well-shaped crystals, are called *crystalline solids;* common salt, diamond, calcite (Fig. 30), and most metals are familiar examples. Each type of crystal has a definite internal atomic structure (Fig. 27). Solids whose particles have no regularity of arrangement and which never show crystal forms are called *amorphous solids;* rubber, opal, and glass are typical examples.

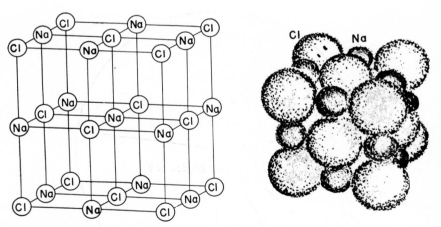

FIG. 27. Diagrams showing the arrangement of nuclei of sodium and chlorine in a crystal of common salt, NaCl, the mineral halite (*left*), and the packing arrangement of the ions (*right*).

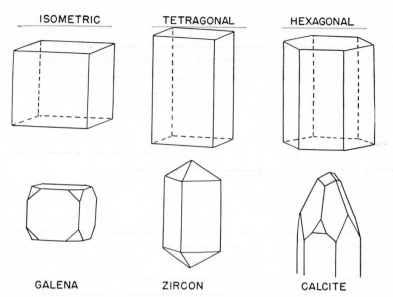

FIG. 28. Drawings of crystals in the isometric, tetragonal, and hexagonal systems, with common forms of minerals (*below*) that crystallize in each.

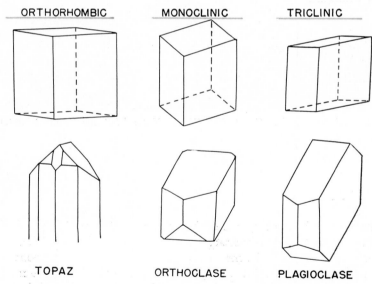

FIG. 29. Drawings of crystals in the orthorhombic, monoclinic, and triclinic systems, with common forms of minerals (*below*) that crystallize in each.

FIG. 30. Calcite crystals. (*Courtesy of Ward's Natural Science Establishment.*)

MINERALS

Definition. When we examine the rock materials which we find in the field, different kinds of particles are apparent to the eye. These particles are not mixtures; rather, each is a distinct, homogeneous substance with definite chemical and physical characteristics. Some may be dull, earthy grains, whereas others may be tiny, brilliant flakes that reflect sunlight, and still others may be dense, transparent grains that resemble bits of colored, broken glass. Each of these particles is a distinct mineral. The term *mineral*, however, is commonly used in a variety of ways. A nutritionist who suggests certain minerals for the diet or an advertiser who tries to sell water from a mineral spring does not use the term to mean a constituent of rocks. Geologists use the word to mean *a naturally occurring inorganic substance with a characteristic internal structure and with a chemical composition and physical properties that are either uniform or variable within definite limits.* Most minerals are compounds of two or more elements, but a few, such as sulfur (Fig. 31), graphite, and native gold, are single elements. Coal and petroleum are not minerals, for they are organic in origin. They are, however, called "mineral fuels" and are included under the broad term "mineral resources."

Origin of Minerals. Most minerals are formed by precipitation from various kinds of solution. Many have been formed (1) from hot liquid-rock solutions that crystallized as they cooled, or (2) from hot-water solutions that escaped from such molten masses, or (3) from volcanic vapors that came into contact with cooler rocks. At and near the surface, minerals are formed (4) by chemical reactions between the constituents of the atmosphere or ground waters of various compositions and the minerals of the rocks with which they came in contact.

FIG. 31. Crystals of sulfur. (*Courtesy of American Museum of Natural History.*)

Composition. The composition of minerals ranges from single elements to complex compounds containing 10 or more elements. Eight elements, however, make up about 98 per cent of the earth's crust (Fig. 22). Some relatively inactive elements occur in the free state (Fig. 23), whereas the active elements form compounds. Soluble compounds occur as minerals only in arid regions, and easily oxidizable compounds occur only some distance beneath the surface. Highly reactive compounds such as calcium and sodium oxides never occur as minerals. Approximately 2,000 different minerals are known, but most of these are rare. Fortunately for a beginner in geology, the number of minerals which are important constituents of ordinary rocks is surprisingly small. A group of several dozen would include all the abundant minerals in the rocks of the earth's crust.

Silicate compounds are by far the most abundant minerals; feldspars and mica (page 47) are familiar examples. *Carbonates* are another important class; its most frequent representative is the carbonate of calcium, the mineral calcite (page 48). Another fundamental combination of the abundant elements is their union with oxygen to form *oxides*. These include such common minerals as quartz, the oxide of silicon; hematite, which is ferric oxide, the chief ore of iron; and bauxite, hydrated aluminum oxide, the chief ore of aluminum. Many other metals occur as *sulfides*, such as galena (Fig. 32), the sulfide of lead, and sphalerite, the sulfide of zinc.

FIG. 32. Cubic crystals of galena. (*Courtesy of Ward's Natural Science Establishment.*)

Identification. Most minerals can be identified readily on sight if their ordinary physical properties are known. These include such properties as color, luster, crystal form, hardness, and density. To distinguish the rarer minerals, one must have recourse to a polarizing microscope and to various chemical tests. Final proof of the inner structure of mineral grains is obtained by means of X rays, which reveal the arrangement of the atoms in the crystal lattice. The physical properties of a number of common minerals are given below (pages 46 to 48).

PHYSICAL PROPERTIES OF MINERALS

Cleavage. Many crystals break readily along certain parallel planes, and thus the fragments have certain shapes determined by these planes. This tendency to break along certain planes is cleavage (Fig. 33). Some crystals, like mica, have perfect cleavage; others, like quartz and garnet, have none. Certain minerals have two or more good cleavages (Fig. 34). Many minerals that have no cleavage break, or fracture, in a characteristic way. Some minerals have a conchoidal fracture like the fracture of glass. Certain fibrous minerals, like asbestos, break in minute threads (Fig. 35).

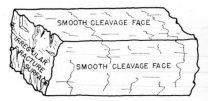

FIG. 33. Sketch showing difference between cleavage and fracture of minerals.

FIG. 34. A cleavage fragment from crystalline halite, showing perfect cubic cleavage. (*Courtesy of Ward's Natural Science Establishment.*)

Luster. The luster of a mineral is its appearance in ordinary reflected light. Those with metallic luster look like metals. Most of them are dark and opaque. Those with nonmetallic luster are usually lighter-colored and transparent on their thin edges. Vitreous luster is like that of glass or quartz; dull luster is like that of chalk; adamantine luster is brilliant like that of diamond.

Color and Streak. Color is fairly constant in some minerals but not in all. Commonly the color is due to pigments or impurities in the mineral. The streak is more nearly constant than the color. It is the color of the powder of the mineral. The streak is determined by crushing the mineral or by marking unglazed porcelain or simply by scratching it with a knife and observing the color of the powder.

Hardness. The hardness of a mineral, or its resistance to abrasion, is a fairly constant quality. The hardness generally is designated after comparing it with the Mohs' scale, in which 10 minerals are arranged in increasing hardness as follows: (1) talc, (2) gypsum, (3) calcite, (4)

FIG. 35. Asbestos, a fibrous mineral that separates into minute threads.

fluorite, (5) apatite, (6) orthoclase feldspar, (7) quartz, (8) topaz, (9) sapphire (corundum), (10) diamond.

The minerals in the part of the scale below 6 can be scratched with a knife. In the field a small-bladed penknife kept sharp at the point is found very useful, since with a little practice one may estimate closely the hardness and at the same time observe the streak. A few minerals possess magnetism, and their particles are easily picked up by a small magnet. If the knife blade is magnetized, it is more useful.

Weight. The specific gravity, or density, of a mineral is its weight compared with a volume of water equal to that of the mineral. The specific gravity of a small piece is easily determined by using a spring balance, first weighing it in air and then in a small pan suspended in a beaker of water. Pure specimens of the same mineral generally have approximately the same weight, or specific gravity, and so the determination of its specific gravity is a useful aid in the identification of a mineral.

Tenacity. Certain minerals which powder easily are brittle. Others, like gold, are malleable and can be hammered into thin sheets. Still others, like horn silver, are sectile; they cut like cheese. A mineral that bends yet does not resume its original shape when pressure is released is said to be flexible. Chlorite is an example. An elastic mineral (mica) after being bent will resume its original shape.

Other Properties. In the preceding statements emphasis is laid upon those properties of minerals which can be used to distinguish them outside the laboratory. With a blowpipe and the use of a few simple reagents, chemical tests may be made, and mineral powders or fine-grained mixtures may be investigated. The minerals differ in fusibility and in their behavior with reagents. The silicates often may be identified in the field, but exact determinations are most easily made with the microscope. The minerals or rocks are ground into thin slices, and light is passed through them. Very exact determinations can be made because the effect on light of every transparent mineral differs from that of every other one. Opaque minerals, like the sulfides of the metals, are easily studied under the microscope by reflected light.

Isomorphous Mixtures. The mineral sphalerite, zinc sulfide (ZnS), commonly contains some iron (Fe). The light yellow species is practically free from iron. If a little iron is present, its color is brown; if more iron is present, it is black. Its formula would be written (Zn,Fe)S. It is an atomic mixture of Zn and Fe. The Fe is there in place of Zn, yet the crystals of sphalerite may have the same form and essentially the same structure, and any particle of the dark sphalerite would show, on analysis, the same composition as any other part of it. This mixture, in which one atom takes the place of another without changing the structure, is known as an isomorphous mixture. An isomorphous group of compounds is one in which a series of compounds have closely related chemical composition and nearly similar structure. Thus calcite (calcium carbonate), magnesite (magnesium carbonate), and siderite (iron carbonate) all crystallize in the same crystal system. Some form isomorphous mixtures in various proportions. Many calcites contain some magnesium carbonate; others contain iron carbonate; and still others contain both. The minerals that are isomorphous mixtures constitute a large part of the earth.

COMMON MINERALS

Although many hundreds of minerals have been identified, only a few of them are of common occurrence. The earth's crust is made up chiefly of seven. The estimates given in the table on page 58 show approximately the minerals which compose the average rocks.

Feldspars. The feldspars (Fig. 29) make up almost half the rocks of the earth's crust. They are generally light-colored and are characterized by two good cleavages. In orthoclase these make angles of 90 degrees; hence the name.[1] Albite and anorthite have cleavages that make angles of about 86 degrees; hence they are termed plagioclases.[2]

Orthoclase feldspar, potassium aluminum silicate,[3] is commonly pink or flesh-colored. Albite, sodium aluminum silicate, is usually white; and anorthite, calcium aluminum silicate, is commonly gray-green.

Quartz. Quartz,[4] silicon dioxide, next to feldspar the most abundant material of the earth's crust, forms six-sided crystals and is colorless or white when pure, although it is commonly tinted. It has no cleavage, and hence it rarely presents flat surfaces when broken. In a granite in which the light-colored minerals are quartz and feldspar, the quartz may be distinguished from the feldspar by turning the rock so as to get a reflec-

---

[1] Orthoclase, Greek *orthos*, straight + *klasis*, fracture.

[2] Plagioclase, Greek *plagios*, oblique + *klasis*, fracture.

[3] The formulae of the feldspars are as follows: orthoclase, $K_2O.Al_2O_3.6SiO_2$, hardness 6; albite, $Na_2O.Al_2O_3.6SiO_2$, hardness 6.5; anorthite, $CaO.Al_2O_3.2SiO_2$, hardness 6.5. Albite and anorthite molecules form a series of isomorphous mixtures or compounds: albite, oligoclase, andesine, labradorite, bytownite, anorthite. Starting with albite, the sodium decreases, and calcium increases to anorthite. The physical properties of the isomorphous crystals vary with the composition, particularly the effect on light, as the light passes through the crystals under the microscope. The albite-anorthite series are generally striated, and with a small lens the striations often may be observed as very fine parallel lines closely set like ruled lines on a sheet of paper.

[4] The formula of quartz is SiO_2. Quartz is harder than feldspar and cannot be scratched with a knife. Its crystals scratch glass. Its hardness is 7.

tion from the cleavage planes of the feldspar. Because it has no good cleavage, the quartz breaks like glass.

Pyroxenes. The pyroxenes (Fig. 36) constitute an important group of minerals that are generally recognized by their stout crystals and their two good cleavages (Fig. 36) almost at right angles to each other (87 and

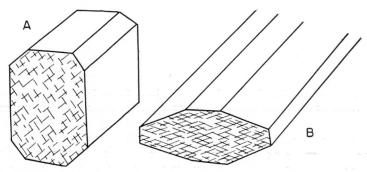

FIG. 36. Outlines showing crystal forms and directions of cleavage. A, in pyroxene; B, in hornblende.

93 degrees). Most pyroxenes are green or dark-colored, particularly those which contain much iron. Pyroxenes are calcium, magnesium, and iron silicates, and some have very complicated formulae.[1]

Hornblendes. The hornblendes, or amphiboles (Fig. 36), constitute an important group of minerals which may occur as stout crystals, but more generally they are long-bladed or fibrous ones, green to black in color. The hornblendes are calcium, magnesium, iron, and aluminum silicates and generally have complicated formulae.[2] The cleavage angles are 125 and 55 degrees.

Micas. The micas are distinguished from other minerals by their perfect cleavage, which makes it possible to separate them into extremely thin sheets. Muscovite, white mica (hydrous potassium aluminum silicate), is the variety used for stove windows. Biotite, black mica, which

---

[1] Diopside, $CaMg(SiO_3)_2$; hypersthene, $(Mg,Fe)SiO_3$; augite, like diopside but with aluminum and iron. As a rule, pyroxenes have a dull luster, and this is an aid in distinguishing them from amphiboles (hornblende), which commonly have a silky sheen.

[2] Tremolite, $Ca_2Mg_5Si_8O_{22}(OH)_2$; actinolite, $Ca_2(Mg,Fe)_5Si_8O_{22}(OH)_2$; common hornblende contains also alumina and soda. They commonly have a glittering, silky sheen, whereas pyroxenes have a duller luster.

resembles muscovite except in color, has nearly the same chemical composition but contains some iron or magnesium or both.[1]

Olivine. Olivine,[2] magnesium silicate, is found in many basic rocks and usually occurs in stout crystals. It is glassy like quartz but is generally olive-green or yellow. Its grain in a rock often resembles that of granulated sugar. Clear varieties are used for gems.

Garnet. The garnets are iron,[3] calcium, or magnesium silicates, usually red or brown with vitreous luster. They have no good cleavage and break like quartz or glass.

Chlorite. Chlorites are silicates of aluminum containing magnesium, iron, and hydrogen. They are green to dark green, and the crystals resemble mica because they have one excellent cleavage. Unlike mica the cleavage plates are not elastic, and when bent they do not resume their original shape on release. Chemically chlorite is much like biotite, but with no potassium, less silica, and more water.

Kaolinite. Kaolinite [4] (china clay), hydrous aluminum silicate, is a soft and usually light-colored mineral that occurs in minute particles. It is a constituent of many clays and shales. It feels greasy between the fingers and is plastic when wet. It is an important constituent of many soils, and it is used in making paper, china, brick, tile, and crockery.

Calcite, Dolomite, and Siderite. Calcite, calcium carbonate; dolomite, calcium magnesium carbonate; and siderite, iron carbonate,[5] are all soft minerals that are characterized by good cleavage. Calcite is the chief constituent of limestone, and dolomite is present in dolomitic limestone. Siderite is found in sedimentary rocks and is a common ore of iron.

Magnetite. Magnetite, black iron oxide, is a dark, heavy magnetic mineral that is present in small amounts in most igneous rocks. It is brittle, has no good cleavage, and is too hard to be scratched with a knife; the streak is black; it is an ore of iron.

Hematite. Hematite, red iron oxide, is the chief ore of iron. It has a red streak, like rouge or red paint.

Halite (Common Salt). Halite is the mineral name for sodium chloride. It is colorless to gray and occurs as cubic crystals that have perfect cleavage in three planes at right angles to one another (Fig. 34). Beds of

---

[1] Muscovite, $KAl_2(AlSi_3O_{10})(OH)_2$; biotite, $K(Mg,Fe)_3(AlSi_3O_{10})(OH)_2$.

[2] Olivine, $(Mg,Fe)_2SiO_4$. In many olivines the iron takes the place of part of the magnesium.

[3] Almandite, common red garnet, $Fe_3Al_2(SiO_4)_3$; pyrope garnet, $Mg_3Al_2(SiO_4)_3$; grossularite garnet, $Ca_3Al_2(SiO_4)_3$; andradite garnet, $Ca_3Fe_2(SiO_4)_3$. Garnets are about as hard as quartz.

[4] Kaolinite, $Al_2Si_2O_5(OH)_4$.

[5] Calcite, $CaCO_3$, hardness 3; dolomite, $CaMg(CO_3)_2$, hardness 3.5 to 4; siderite, $FeCO_3$, hardness 3.5 to 4.

common salt occur interstratified with sedimentary rocks. At many places, the salt is associated with gypsum.

Gypsum. Gypsum is hydrous calcium sulfate. It is usually white or colorless, has a hardness of 2, and can be scratched easily with a fingernail. Most gypsum occurs in diamond-shaped crystals or in granular masses. The crystals have one very perfect cleavage. Some having a fine fibrous structure are called satin spar. The fine-grained, massive variety is alabaster.

Reference List of Common Minerals

Mineral	Elements present
Orthoclase	Potassium, aluminum, silicon, oxygen
Albite	Sodium, aluminum, silicon, oxygen
Anorthite	Calcium, aluminum, silicon, oxygen
Quartz	Silicon, oxygen
Pyroxene	Calcium, magnesium, iron, aluminum, silicon, oxygen
Amphibole	Calcium, magnesium, iron, aluminum, silicon, oxygen, hydrogen, alkalies
Muscovite	Potassium, aluminum, silicon, oxygen, hydrogen
Biotite	Potassium, iron, magnesium, silicon, oxygen, hydrogen
Olivine	Magnesium, iron, silicon, oxygen
Chlorite	Hydrogen, magnesium, iron, silicon, oxygen, aluminum
Garnet	Calcium, magnesium, aluminum, iron, manganese, silicon, oxygen
Magnetite	Iron, oxygen
Hematite	Iron, oxygen
Limonite	Iron, oxygen, water
Ilmenite	Iron, titanium, oxygen
Apatite	Calcium, fluorine (chlorine), phosphorus, oxygen
Fluorite	Calcium, fluorine
Barite	Barium, sulfur, oxygen
Calcite	Calcium, carbon, oxygen
Dolomite	Calcium, magnesium, carbon, oxygen
Siderite	Iron, carbon, oxygen
Kaolin	Aluminum, silicon, oxygen, hydrogen
Pyrite	Iron, sulfur
Graphite	Carbon
Talc	Magnesium, silicon, oxygen, hydrogen
Serpentine	Magnesium, silicon, oxygen, hydrogen
Gypsum	Calcium, sulfur, oxygen, hydrogen
Halite (salt)	Sodium, chlorine

ROCKS

Just as elements combine in various proportions to form minerals or to form molecules that unite to form the isomorphous mixtures, so minerals are combined physically to form rocks. Rocks, on the other hand, are mixtures of various minerals in almost all proportions. Some mixtures are much more common than others, and some rocks are composed for the most part of only one mineral. A few rocks are made of organic matter or of volcanic glass instead of minerals. On the basis of their mode of formation, rocks may be classified in three general groups, namely, igneous, sedimentary, and metamorphic.

Igneous Rocks. Igneous rocks are rocks which generally have a crystalline structure and texture, indicating that they were formed by solidifi-

FIG. 37. Lava in the crater of Halemaumau, the fire pit of Kilauea. (*Photograph by T. A. Jagger, Hawaiian Volcano Observatory.*)

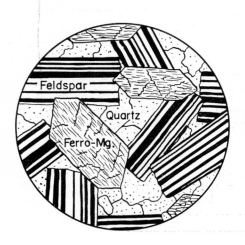

FIG. 38. Simplified sketch of a magnified thin section of an igneous rock to illustrate the sequence of crystallization and solidification of magma to form rock. The ferromagnesian minerals crystallized first, then the feldspar, and finally quartz, which fills the spaces between the grains of the other two.

cation of molten mineral matter which originated within the earth. The grains of one mineral may be large and show good crystal outlines (Fig. 38). Those of another may be smaller and exhibit few crystal outlines, whereas those of a third may be irregular and occupy the spaces between the other grains so as to indicate that they were the last to form. The rocks formed from such highly heated molten material are called *igneous*, which means "fire-made" (Fig. 37). The most common example of igneous rock is granite, which is overwhelmingly the most abundant type of rock in the foundations of the continents and in the cores of many mountains such as the Rocky Mountains and the Sierra Nevada.

The molten matter which solidifies to form the igneous rocks is termed the magma. The character of the igneous rock depends not only upon the chemical composition of the magma that formed it but also upon the conditions that prevailed when the magma cooled. If it is thrown out upon the surface, it is a lava, or extrusive rock; if it is thrust into the earth's crust and does not reach the surface, it is an intrusive rock (Fig. 39). Certain textures shown by igneous rocks depend largely on the conditions of their formation. Thus the deep-seated rocks are composed of crystals or grains and are said to be granular (Figs. 40, 41). Granular rocks were formed far below the surface, and for that reason they are exposed to the observation of man only where the surface rocks above them have been washed away (Fig. 8). Volcanoes are vents through which rocks issue, either molten rocks or fragments broken up chiefly

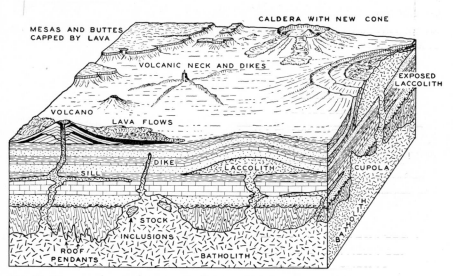

FIG. 39. Diagram showing structural relations of igneous masses. (*After F. P. Young.*)

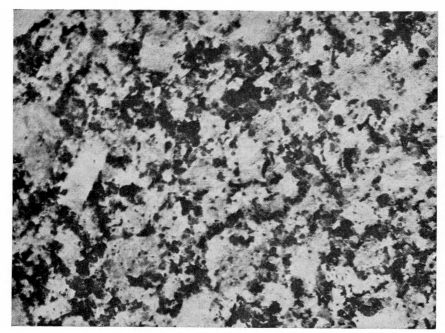

FIG. 40. Granite, an acidic igneous rock of granular texture.

FIG. 41. Gabbro, a basic igneous rock.

by the explosions of gases. Magmas contain dissolved gases; when the magma is thrown out, the gas expands, owing to release of pressure, and a bubble, or blowhole, forms. These holes are called vesicles (Fig. 42).

When a magma rising in a crack or fissure hardens, it forms a *dike* (Fig. 39). A dike is commonly tabular, that is, it is shaped like a tablet, long in two dimensions and short in the third. Magmas intruded between layers of sedimentary rocks form *sheets*, or *sills*. Many of these are nearly flat, like the sill of a doorway (from which the name is taken), but they may be tilted at high angles. Sills are similar to dikes, but they lie between beds. A thick sill that bows up the rocks above it becomes a *laccolith* (Fig. 39). A very large, irregular, deep-seated intrusion is called a *batholith* (Fig. 39), a mass that is long in each of its three dimensions.

Simplified Classification of Common Igneous Rocks

Light color / Dark color	Formed at great depths: coarse-grained; large crystals	Silicon dioxide (increases / decreases)	Formed at or near the surface: fine-grained; small crystals
	Granite (quartz, feldspar, mica)		Rhyolite (composition same as granite)
	Diorite (feldspar, hornblende)		Andesite (composition same as diorite)
	Gabbro (pyroxene, some feldspar)		Basalt (composition same as gabbro)

FIG. 42. Scoria, a form of solidified lava, showing vesicles, or cavities, formed by expansion of steam and other gases in lava before cooling. (*Photograph by Ward's Natural Science Establishment.*)

Sedimentary Rocks. Sedimentary rocks are derived from the waste products of older rocks. Under the combined effect of the atmospheric agents and processes, solid rocks constantly are being decomposed and disintegrated, and the resulting material is being transported continuously by such agents as running water, wind, or glacial ice and ultimately deposited as sediment. Most of it is in the form of solid particles, but some is dissolved mineral matter carried in solution. Every stream, whether it be a small brook, a larger creek, or a great river, carries unconsolidated debris downstream. The finer materials are carried in suspension; the coarser are rolled along the stream bed, and the dissolved mineral matter is carried in solution. Millions of tons of sediment are carried to the lakes and ocean basins every day. The Mississippi River alone is transporting and depositing on its delta more than 2 million tons every 24 hours. Much of the sand and gravel transported by a river is dropped temporarily in the form of sand bars or of beds in the slack-water parts of the stream's channel, but it is picked up again at the time of floods, when both volume and velocity of the stream are greater.

The great majority of the sedimentary rocks are of marine origin, for it is to the ocean that nature's transportation systems bring most of the products of the rock decomposition and disintegration that take place on the continents. Some deposits are laid down on land areas, but these are restricted mostly to deserts, fresh-water lakes, swamps, piedmont plains, flood plains, and river channels. The epicontinental seas of the geologic past and the shallow waters on the present continental shelves are the final sites of deposition of nearly all the rock wastage of the lands, whether the sediments had their sources in high mountain glaciers far from the sea, in deeply weathered slopes of wide valleys, or in the wave-beaten cliffs of the coast line.

The disintegrated, solid rock fragments such as gravel, sand, silt, and clay as they are transported tend to be sorted on the basis of size; where a stream discharges into a body of quieter water, the coarser material is deposited near shore as gravel and farther out as sand, still farther mud is deposited, and, farther still, calcareous matter. The belts of sediments are this rudely parallel to the shores. The orderly process of sedimentation may be modified by currents and bottom conditions that control wave action or interfere with the movement of the water shifting the sediment. Hence the different types of sediment are rarely pure, for the gravels generally contain sand, the sands generally contain mud or clay, the muds contain much fine sand and generally some calcareous matter, and calcareous rocks contain both clay and sand. Because the conditions of their formation are not uniform, muddy sands may alternate with muds. Likewise, muds are deposited with calcareous rocks. This alternation of material, or layering, is called stratification (Figs. 5, 6) and is a common feature of essentially all sedimentary rocks. When the sediments are deeply buried below younger beds, some become consolidated by pressure as water is squeezed out of them. Others become coherent by cementation. Gravels become conglomerates (Fig. 45), sands become sandstone, muds become shales, and calcareous oozes become limestones.

Sedimentary rocks or loose sediments not yet cemented or consolidated underlie approximately three-fourths of the area of the continents and most of the ocean floor. At some places they are many thousands of feet thick. Because of their wide distribution and great thickness most of the continental landscape is sculptured in such stratified rock formations. In the great chasms of the Grand Canyon and Zion Canyon they are shown to be in their original, nearly horizontal position (Fig. 43), whereas in mountainous areas they are inclined at various angles (Fig. 44). Some of these eroded areas are strikingly beautiful, but aside from possessing elements of sculptured beauty and utility sedimentary rocks are of great importance in geology in furnishing a record of past life and of the major physical events in the history of the earth. Past life is depicted by the fossils that are sealed and preserved in the strata. Some varieties of fossil are found only in beds that were formed at certain times, and such fossils serve as markers that show the relative ages of the

FIG. 43. Grand Canyon of the Colorado River as seen from the south rim. It shows the nearly horizontal sedimentary rocks in which the canyon has been eroded. (*Courtesy of Santa Fe Railway.*)

FIG. 44. Inclined stratified rocks in the mountains of the Many Glacier region, Glacier National Park, Montana. (*Courtesy of National Park Service.*)

beds containing them. Other features of the rocks, such as their composition, color, and position, furnish information concerning the climate and other geographic features of the geologic past and the many changes that have occurred in and on the earth's crust. They record the geographic extent of former seas, the advance and retreat of these seas over parts of the continents, the time and degree of uplift of continental areas, and the time of formation of mountain ranges.

Metamorphic Rocks. The term metamorphic means transformed and implies that the rocks so classed have been made by the transformation of previously formed igneous or sedimentary rocks. Many stages or degrees of intensity of metamorphism may be observed. In fact there is no sharp boundary between metamorphic rocks on the one hand and the igneous or sedimentary rocks from which they were derived on the other. Many rocks and minerals that are in stable equilibrium in one geologic environment are unstable under other environmental conditions, and consequently an adjustment to any new environment tends to take place whereby new textures and new minerals are formed to suit the new situation. The chief factors which tend to induce such a change are pressure, temperature, liquids, and a susceptible composition of the rocks on which to act. The terrific pressures and high temperatures a few miles below the earth's surface effect profound changes in the rocks, both by recrystallization of material already present and by the addition of new materials from hot liquids and vapors.

Where pressure is the dominant factor, the minerals become oriented in parallel layers, or bands. This arrangement is produced by extreme pressure in one direction, which causes the mineral grains to elongate at right angles to the direction of maximum stress, or if there is movement, the elongated minerals tend to be lined out in the direction of movement. Minerals like the micas and chlorite, which occur as thin flakes, and like hornblende and other amphiboles, in needlelike grains, commonly develop such a parallelism of structure.

A mud upon induration becomes a shale, a sedimentary rock; under strong pressure and by movement it is converted to slate (Fig. 46).

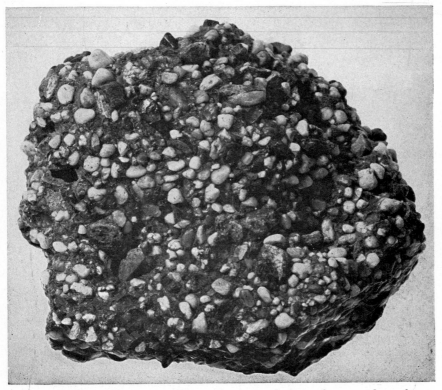

FIG. 45. Conglomerate, a sedimentary rock composed of gravel cemented together.

Similarly a granite under strong pressure and movement at depth may become a gneiss, a rudely banded, coarse-grained rock.

FIG. 46. Slate, a former shale metamorphosed by pressure. Deep Creek Canyon, Montana. (*Photograph by C. D. Walcott, U.S. Geological Survey.*)

Mineral Composition of Average Igneous and Sedimentary Rocks (*Clarke and Washington*)

Igneous rocks		Sedimentary rocks		
Minerals	Per cent	Minerals	Shale, per cent	Sandstone, per cent
Quartz	12	Quartz	22.3	66.8
Feldspars	59.5	Feldspars	30.0	11.5
Pyroxenes and amphiboles	16.8	"Clay"	25.0	6.6
Micas	3.8	Limonite	5.6	1.8
Other minerals	7.9	Carbonates	5.7	11.1
		Other minerals	11.4	2.2
Total	100.0	Total	100.0	100.0

SUGGESTIONS FOR FURTHER READING

Grout, F. F.: Petrography and Petrology, McGraw-Hill Book Company, Inc., 1932.

Kraus, E. H., W. F. Hunt, and L. S. Ramsdell: Mineralogy, 4th ed., McGraw-Hill Book Company, Inc., 1951.

Paugh, F. H.: A Field Guide to Rocks and Minerals, Houghton Mifflin Company, 1953.

Rogers, A. F.: Introduction to the Study of Minerals, 3d ed., McGraw-Hill Book Company, Inc., 1937.

Wahlstrom, E. E.: Igneous Minerals and Rocks, John Wiley & Sons, Inc., 1947.

CHAPTER 4

Atmosphere, Weather, and Climate

The atmosphere is the blanket of air that covers the rocks and the waters of the earth. Its mass is less than a millionth part of that of the earth, but its activities and influences are far-reaching. Its presence is necessary to sustain the varied life of the earth, and it acts as a blanket to equalize the temperatures of the earth's surface. It serves as a medium for the transfer of water that is evaporated from lands and seas and that is precipitated as rain upon the earth, wearing away the rocks and transporting them to the seas. It is one of the chief agents of weathering.

The weather of any one place is the temporary state of its atmospheric conditions—its temperature, air pressure, wind, humidity, cloudiness, and precipitation. Its climate is the composite of the weather over a long period of time. Climate is described in terms of mean annual temperature, temperature variations, humidity, amount and seasonal distribution of precipitation, storms, and winds. Meteorology (the study of the atmosphere) and climatology are separate branches of earth science, and so a detailed treatment of them is beyond the scope of this text, but some consideration of the atmosphere, of weather, and of climate is essential to an understanding and appreciation of the effects of the atmosphere upon geologic processes. Just as soils and vegetation are determined largely by climate, so geologic processes, especially the weathering of minerals and rocks and the erosion of the land, differ greatly from place to place in different climates.

Composition of the Air. Dry air is a mechanical mixture of gases consisting of about 78 per cent nitrogen, 21 per cent oxygen, and 0.94 per cent argon by volume. Additional constituents include carbon dioxide, hydrogen, neon, helium, krypton, xenon, oxides of nitrogen, and ozone in minute amounts and, locally, certain volatile organic substances, sulfurous gases, chlorine, etc., from volcanoes and other sources. Water vapor also is an important part of the air, probably averaging about 1.2 per cent of the total volume. Its abundance varies according to the temperature; it forms about 2.63 per cent at the equator, 0.92 per cent at Lat.

50°N., and 0.22 per cent at Lat. 70°N. Fine earthy matter, smoke, soot, pollen, spores, bacteria, volcanic dust, meteoric dust, etc., may be spread as impurities through a considerable part of the atmosphere, sufficiently at times to darken the sun and reduce visibility. The obvious evidence of the presence of dust in the atmosphere is in the occurrence of the red colors at dawn and twilight. Dust particles have an important function in that certain types of particle serve as nuclei, or centers, around which water vapor condenses to produce cloud particles.

Changes with Altitude. The air extends to great elevations above the land (Fig. 47). Mountain climbers have reached elevations of more than

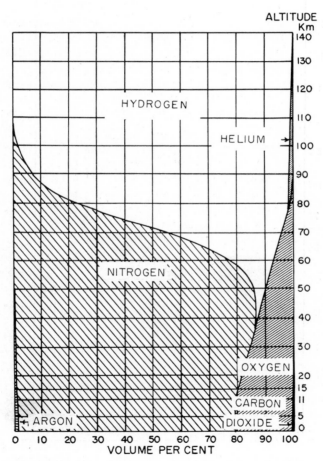

FIG. 47. Diagram showing variations in the composition of the atmosphere with altitude above sea level. (*After Humphreys.*)

29,000 feet on Mount Everest, and observers in balloons and airplanes have reached elevations of more than 17 miles. Rockets carrying meteorological instruments have reached elevations of approximately 250 miles; meteors, white-hot from friction with the atmosphere, have been observed about 125 miles high; and some auroral discharges are seen 375 miles aboveground but most of them are lower (Fig. 48).

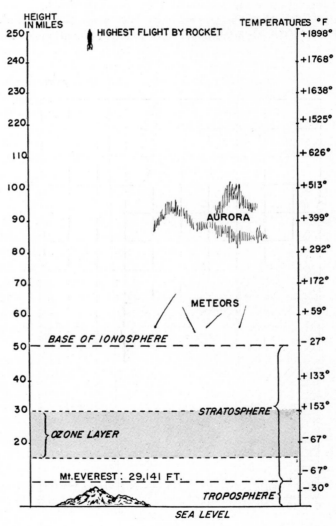

FIG. 48. Diagram showing terms used in describing the earth's atmosphere, and variations in temperature with height above sea level. (*After Lewicki.*)

Because the air is heated chiefly at the bottom, the temperature of the air decreases upward about 1°F. for every 300 feet of difference of vertical elevation to altitudes of 6 to 8 miles, above which a zone of nearly constant temperature (about −67°F.) is reached. Differences in altitude account for the pronounced differences in temperature and corresponding differences in climate, in vegetation, and in habitability of places having the same latitude. A change in altitude of 1 mile in general is about equal to a change in latitude of 800 miles.

The dust and other earthy material in the air are confined essentially to the lower layers of the atmosphere. As one ascends into the air, he leaves the smoke and coarser dust behind. The water vapor becomes less and less, until at 6 or 7 miles above sea level in the middle latitudes it is so cold that practically no moisture can remain in the air. Consequently no ordinary clouds exist. This altitude marks the lower limit of the *stratosphere,* a region of cold, clear, thin, dry air where there is a nearly constant temperature of about −67°F.

About one-half the mass of the atmosphere occurs in the lower 18,000 feet. Thus at an elevation of about 3½ miles one is above more than half the atmosphere. *Explorer II,* a United States Army balloon, reached an altitude of 72,395 feet, or 13.71 miles, above sea level. It was above 96 per cent of the mass of the atmosphere.[1]

Atmospheric Stratification. Studies of the air high above the earth have shown that the atmosphere may be divided into layers, or strata, and each layer has its own peculiar composition and physical properties. The region between the lithosphere, or solid earth, and the stratosphere is known as the *troposphere* (Fig. 48). The prefix tropo- means a turning or overturning of the air due to convection currents set up by a difference in temperature. At the level of the stratosphere there is a balance between absorbed and emitted radiation, and consequently there is no convection through it.

The height of the troposphere varies with latitude, and there are minor variations related to the seasons and to barometric pressure at the surface. The troposphere is higher in summer than in winter and higher when the surface pressure is high than when it is low. The higher the troposphere, the lower the temperature of the stratosphere. The general horizontal temperature gradient in the stratosphere is from relatively warm air at the poles to colder air at the equator, just the reverse of the gradient in the air near the earth's surface.

The temperature of −67°F. given above for the stratosphere is for its lower portion, in which actual measurements have been obtained by recording instruments. Thomas A. Blair, Senior Meteorologist, U.S.

[1] Capt. Albert W. Stevens, U.S.A., *Nat. Geog. Mag.,* vol. 69, p. 635, 1936.

Weather Bureau, states that certain phenomena studied in recent years have led to the conclusion that slightly over 10 miles above the earth's surface the temperature begins to increase slowly and continues that increase to a height of about 30 miles, where it becomes comparable with temperatures at the earth's surface.

That there is an increase in the temperature of the upper air was first suggested by a study of meteors and has been confirmed by investigations of the behavior of sound waves. A large explosion may be heard for a distance of 60 to 100 miles in all directions from its source because of the direct travel of the sound waves through the lower air. Beyond this area there is a belt about 125 miles wide in which the sound cannot be heard. Then, strangely enough, the sound again becomes audible in a zone of considerable width. This phenomenon may even be repeated, resulting in another zone of audibility beyond a second zone of silence. These outer zones of audibility can be accounted for only when it is assumed that the sound waves are refracted or reflected in the upper air and thus returned to the earth. Since sound travels faster in warm air than in cold, an assumption of increasing temperature in the upper stratosphere accounts for this bending back of the waves. The greatest height from which such refracted sound waves appear to come is about 25 miles.

Above the stratosphere at an elevation of between 15 and 30 miles is a zone in which ozone is more abundantly present than at lower or higher elevations. Some ozone occurs in the lower atmosphere, but the amount is extremely small. Ozone is similar to oxygen, except that three atoms are linked together to form the molecule, instead of two as in ordinary oxygen. The ozone layer in the atmosphere absorbs or intercepts a high percentage of the ultraviolet rays coming to the earth from interstellar space. It has been estimated that if the ozone were decreased so as to allow even half the ultraviolet rays to reach us, they would destroy our skins in a few minutes' exposure to the sun. However, if still more ozone were added to the atmosphere, it would absorb so many of the ultraviolet rays that animal life on land would suffer because of a lack of the essential "sunshine" vitamin.

At still higher elevations than that of the ozone layer is a region of high electrical conductivity. This conductivity is due to the presence of ions of gaseous atoms produced in the gases of the air by solar radiation. It is this *ionized layer* that causes radio waves to travel entirely around the earth within the atmosphere. If it were not there, the radio waves would spread out in straight lines from their source. They can only be kept within the atmosphere and made to follow a path that has the curvature of the earth by being curved back to the earth in a way similar to that by which the sound waves referred to above were curved back. Three ionized layers, or strata, at various heights have been identified: the first at about

25 to 30 miles, the second at 50 to 90 miles, and the third at about 100 to 225 miles above the surface.

The Aurora Borealis, or Northern Lights. Auroral displays are an electrical phenomenon of the atmosphere in which the gases of the upper air are made luminous by electrical discharges in a way somewhat similar to that whereby neon is made luminous in the familiar neon street lights. Auroral glows are most numerous around the magnetic poles of the earth and are closely related to magnetic disturbances on the earth. Since the greatest number of auroras occur at times of maximum sunspot activity, they are undoubtedly connected with electrical discharges from the sun. The heights of auroras above the earth correspond to the heights of the ionized layers as shown by the reflection and refraction of radio waves. The displays of rapidly changing arcs, rays, curtains, bands, and luminous patches in the Northern Hemisphere are called the *aurora borealis;* in the Southern Hemisphere they are known as the *aurora australis.*

Sources of Heat. The air is heated mainly by the sun. Additional but minor sources of heat include radiation from the interior of the earth and eruptions of steam and other hot gases from inside the earth. The amount of heat received by the earth from the sun is sufficient to melt a block of ice 1 mile square and nearly 100 feet thick every second or to melt a layer of ice about 150 feet thick over the entire earth in a year. The lower part of the atmosphere warms up more readily than the upper part on account of radiation from below and also on account of its greater density and its included water vapor. The most effective absorbents of heat in the atmosphere are water vapor and carbon dioxide. Barren rock surfaces absorb and later radiate heat more rapidly than areas covered with soil and vegetation or with snow and ice. It is noteworthy also that the land warms up and cools off faster than the sea because rocks absorb and radiate heat more readily than water; they reflect less of the sunshine than water does; they are less deeply penetrated by solar radiation; and they are less affected by cooling due to evaporation. Air temperatures over both land and sea are modified, however, by ocean currents and by prevailing winds.

Weight of the Air. The atmosphere weighs about 14.7 pounds per square inch at sea level, or enough to balance a column of water 33.9 feet high or to raise a column of mercury in a barometer to a height of 29.92 inches, or 760 millimeters. Its weight rapidly decreases upward to one-half its total weight at an elevation of about 3.4 miles. Pressures in the lowest 6 miles are variable, but above that level they are nearly uniform at all times and places for any particular elevation. The variations of pressure are caused chiefly by heating and cooling and by differences in the amount of water vapor in the lower atmosphere. Increased temperatures cause the air to expand and make it lighter. Lowered temperatures and locally mechanical crowding of the air increase its density and pressure.

Distribution of Air Pressures. Air pressures are measured by barometers which record the weight of the atmosphere above the place where the barometer is stationed. The aneroid barometer (Fig. 49) is simply a box of thin metal from which part of the air has been withdrawn and which responds to the pressure on the sides of the box. A mercury barometer is a tube filled with mercury and inverted over a bowl of it. Increased pressure on the mercury in the bowl causes the mercury to rise higher in the tube, and the tube is graduated so that the height of the mercury is easily read. Readings over the earth's surface show that there is a belt of low air pressure along the equator and that the pressure increases to the north and south of the equator and is highest approximately along the parallel 30°N. and 30°S. (Figs. 50, 51). From these

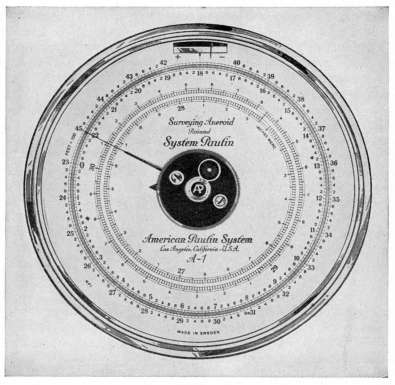

FIG. 49. Dial of an aneroid barometer. The atmospheric pressure is indicated as inches of mercury on the inner dial and as elevation above sea level on the outer dial.

belts, north and south, pressures decrease to low belts in the region of 60°N. and 60°S., and from there toward the poles there is a gradual increase in pressure.

Movements of the Atmosphere. Wind is air moving essentially along the surface of the earth. Movements of air up and down or far above the earth are "air currents." The cause of movements of the air is the heat of the sun. Hot air overflowing the equatorial belt toward the poles tends to bank up because the poleward areas are so much smaller than the equatorial areas. In latitudes of about 30° the banking up of hot air from the equator against air forced toward the equator by the earth's rotation results in high pressures, or "barometric highs." There is so much air moving northward from the equatorial zone and there is so small an area for the air to cover in the poleward regions that the equatorial air cannot readily be accommodated. It piles up in the regions about 30°N. and 30°S., causing the high barometers in these belts. In these regions areas along the longitudinal circles of the earth are appreciably smaller than along the equator.

A second reason for high pressure in these latitudes is the centrifugal force of rotation of the earth on high poleward-moving air. At high altitudes the air from the equatorial region spirals in toward the poles, just as water spirals toward the opening in a circular washbowl if the water is given a rotational motion when the drain stopper is removed. As the water in the bowl lowers, the speed of rotation increases, the rapidly rotating water piles up around the sides of the bowl, and a hollow core is formed where the water escapes through the opening. In a similar manner the air, as it spirals toward the poles, increases its velocity of rotation relative to the ground beneath it, and this action tends to keep much of the air away from the poles and thus, in the absence of other factors, to produce low-pressure polar areas. However, in spite of this effect the extremely low temperatures at the poles make the

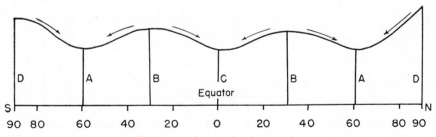

FIG. 50. An air-pressure profile from pole to pole, showing latitudes of permanent high- and low-pressure belts and direction of movement of air.

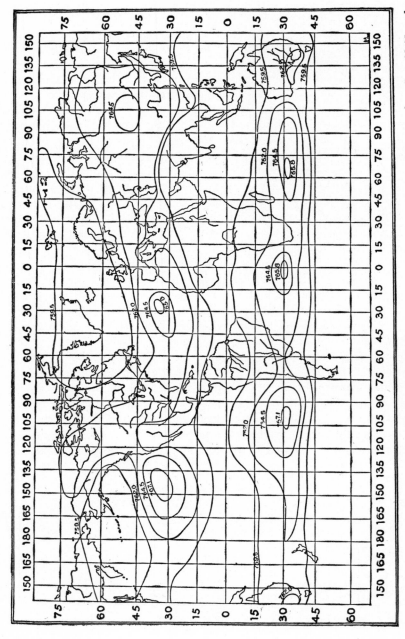

FIG. 51. Map of the world showing the average annual isobars. The belts of high barometer readings are about Lat. 32°N. and 32°S. The numbers are millimeters of mercury. (*After Buchan.*)

air there dense and heavy, and so high polar pressures result. These are surrounded by the subpolar troughs of low pressure in Lat. 60°N. and 60°S. of the equator (Figs. 50, 51). These low-pressure zones are thought to be due to an interaction between thermal and centrifugal forces in the subpolar regions. High-pressure regions are thus found at the poles and on either side of the equator (Fig. 50), while low-pressure regions occur near the equator and 60°N. and 60°S. of the equator.

The configuration of the earth greatly modifies the winds. They drag against the earth and against each other and are slowed down by the friction. The circulation of the air is thus exceedingly complicated (Fig. 52). It is modified greatly by local conditions, and it varies from day to day with temperature and precipitation and from other causes. The wind zones, trades, westerlies, and so forth, nevertheless are well-defined and are of great value to those who navigate the seas.

Cyclonic Storms. A storm is a local disturbance in the general circulation. One type of storm known as a cyclone is a region of low atmospheric pressure toward which winds blow in from all sides (Fig. 53). The earth's rotation deflects the incoming winds and causes them to curve to the right (in the Northern Hemisphere), and thus they move in a

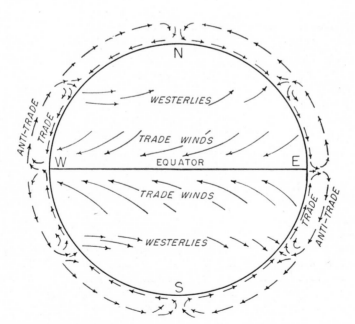

FIG. 52. Ideal diagram showing major movements of winds and high air currents. (*Based on a drawing by Ferrel.*)

counterclockwise direction around the center of the cyclonic storm. At and near the center of the cyclone the movement of air is mainly upward.

The opposite of a cyclonic storm is the anticyclone, or high-pressure area. It is a region in which descending, cool air moves spirally outward in all directions (Fig. 53A, C). In the region of westerlies, cyclones and anticyclones commonly alternate and move eastward across central North America with the general drift of the atmosphere, which moves at a rate of about 25 miles per hour (Fig. 54). Cyclones and anticyclones cover large areas and seldom have winds of destructive velocity.

In the northern two-thirds of the United States cyclones (barometric lows) commonly bring rain or snow, and the anticyclones (barometric highs) bring clear, cool weather. The precipitation in a cyclone comes mainly from its southeastern and central parts. This is due largely to the moisture-laden warm winds from the south and southeast, which are cooled and their moisture condensed as they move northward and up-

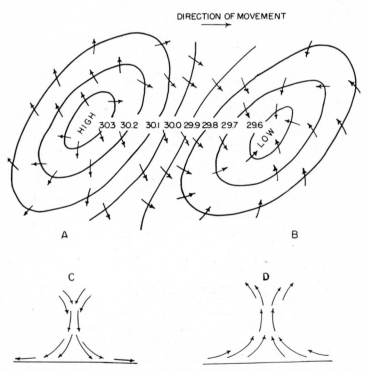

FIG. 53. Sketches of anticyclone (*A* and *C*) and cyclone (*B* and *D*). *AB*, map view; *C* and *D*, side views. Directions indicated by arrows.

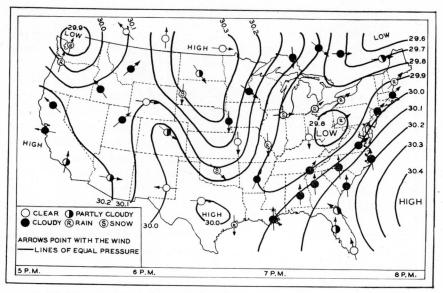

FIG. 54. Weather map for Jan. 14, 1947. The high- and low-pressure areas tend to move from the northwest toward the southeast across the continent. The pressure is recorded as inches of mercury.

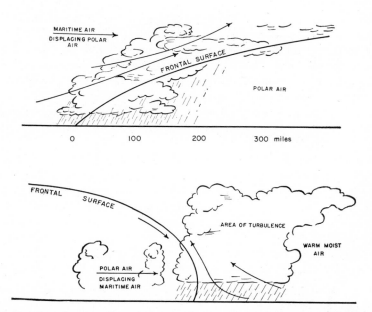

FIG. 55. Sketches showing the relations and movements of air masses that produce a warm front (*above*) and a cold front (*below*). (The frontal slopes are much exaggerated.)

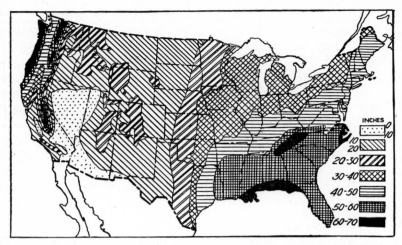

FIG. 56. Outline map of the United States, showing mean annual rainfall. (*After Fuller, U.S. Geological Survey.*)

ward (Fig. 55). Weather forecasting is based mainly on attempts to predict the direction and rate of travel of cyclones and anticyclones. By collecting data from numerous stations the Weather Bureau maps the daily positions of "highs" and "lows," the areas of rainfall and snowfall, and the temperature. From such maps even an amateur observer can predict the weather with some accuracy.

Moisture of the Air. The amount of water vapor in the air varies chiefly with the temperature. The warm air of the equatorial region may contain 3 to 4 per cent water vapor, whereas that of the cooler middle latitudes may contain only 1 per cent or less. The average for all latitudes, according to Humphreys, is about 1.2 per cent. The upper atmosphere, or stratosphere, on account of its frigid temperature contains practically no water vapor.

Condensation and Precipitation. Condensation of moisture is caused by cooling and results in precipitation of dew, rain, snow, hail, and sleet. Cooling may be caused by radiation, by contact with cold surfaces, by mixing of masses of air of different temperatures, by expansion due to movement of the air to places of lower pressure, etc. Condensation to droplets of fog or cloud is facilitated by the presence of dust particles.

Rainfall. The average rainfall of the earth is about 30 inches a year,[1] but about 20 per cent of the land receives less than 10 inches a year, and

[1] The precipitation on the earth's surface has been estimated very closely by Brückmann, who states that the annual precipitation on the entire earth's surface is 74.3 centimeters, or 29.5 inches. Of this amount 30 per cent falls on the land, which amounts to 26,679 cubic miles of water per year. Several other estimates state that the average annual precipitation is about 36 inches.

about 2 per cent receives more than 100 inches a year (Fig. 56). Rainfall on land is influenced mainly by (1) latitude; (2) nearness to the sea; (3) topography of the land, especially the presence of mountain ranges, which intercept moisture-laden winds; (4) prevailing winds; (5) seasons; and (6) the frequency of cyclonic storms, hurricanes, and typhoons. Rainfall is heaviest in the tropical belt of calm, where warm, moist air rises abundantly and where daily showers are the rule, and on the windward sides of continents and mountain ranges. By contrast, many of the great deserts of the earth lie along the high-pressure belts or in the lee of mountains.

Climates. The principal climates of the earth have been grouped as follows:

A. Tropical rainy climates
    1. Tropical rain forest (always wet), as in the Congo and Amazon Basins
    2. Tropical savanna (with wet and dry seasons), as in Burma and the veld and Sudan of Africa
B. Dry climates
    3. Low-latitude desert and steppe, as in the Sahara, Arabia, and Australia
    4. Middle-latitude desert and steppe, as in Iran, Mongolia, and the Great Basin
C. Humid mesothermal climates
    5. Mediterranean (dry-summer subtropical), as in Italy, Spain, and California
    6. Humid subtropical, as in southern China and southeastern United States
    7. Marine west coast, as in western Europe and southeastern Alaska
D. Humid microthermal climates
    8. Humid continental, as in north central United States, central Europe, and northern China
    9. Subarctic, as in Alaska, Canada, and Siberia
E. Polar climates
    10. Tundra, as on the borders of the Arctic Sea
    11. Icecap, as on Antarctica and Greenland
F. Highland climates
    12. Local climates of mountains and plateaus, varying mainly according to altitude and latitude, as in the Andes, Himalaya, Rockies, Tibet, and Mexico

These climatic types and the geographic examples listed above serve to illustrate the effects of the several climatic controls—latitude, the more or less permanent high- and low-pressure areas, prevailing winds, contesting air masses and storms, distribution of land and water, nearness to sea, mountain barriers, ocean currents, and altitude.

SUGGESTIONS FOR FURTHER READING

Blair, T. A.: Climatology, General and Regional, Prentice-Hall, Inc., 1942.

Kaplan, Joseph: The Earth's Atmosphere, *Am. Scientist*, vol. 41, pp. 49–65, 1953.

Rossby, C. G., and H. C. Willet: The Circulation of the Upper Troposphere and Lower Stratosphere, *Science*, vol. 108, pp. 643–652, 1948.

Wenstrom, W. H.: Weather and the Ocean of Air, Houghton Mifflin Company, 1942.

CHAPTER 5

Rock Weathering and Soils

Weathering. The earth's outer portion is sometimes called its crust. This is made up of various kinds of rock materials which constitute the bedrock. It is solid and resistant at depth but usually cracked and jointed toward the surface, where the whole mass may be overlain or covered by loose rock fragments of various sizes which compose the *mantle-rock*. Much of this latter may have been derived from the bedrock by the changes brought about through its contact with the moisture-laden atmosphere that has penetrated the cracks and pores. So the crust is undergoing constant change. The rocks at or near the surface are subject to alterations which finally reduce them to different physical forms and different compositions. Since the chemical and mechanical factors producing such results are associated with the weather, these processes affecting rocks are called "weathering."

This attack on rocks is produced largely by the access to the rocks of air and water, the weathering "elements." Thus weathering is related to the surface of the lithosphere, where rocks, air, and water come together. The weathering of rocks may be compared to the decay of a building. A house constructed of the strongest and most resistant stone in a few centuries will decay and fall in ruins unless it is continually repaired. Monuments (Fig. 57), gravestones, roofing slates, roads, foundations, concrete buildings, steel bridges, and all other structures are subject to weathering in the same manner. Man continually is in contest with the weather. He chooses resistant materials for buildings, and he paints exposed surfaces to delay disintegration, but ultimately all structures are destroyed by weathering and must be rebuilt.

Water soaks into the rocks, dissolves and alters minerals, expands by freezing, and enlarges joints and fractures. The process is begun on cracks or fractures (Fig. 62) and ultimately affects the entire rock. The penetration of atmospheric elements along fractures in bedrock is illustrated by Fig. 58, where weathering of the blocks produced by jointing in an igneous rock has converted them into spheroidal masses,

75

FIG. 57. Montezuma Castle built, by prehistoric tribes, into the shelter and protection of solution pits in the weathered cliffs on the Verde River bluff near Camp Verde, Arizona. (This is a national monument.) (*Photograph by Santa Fe Railway.*)

some of which have rolled out as free boulders. Ultimately these also succumb to weathering.

If rock surfaces present materials of differing chemical composition or of varying degrees of hardness, the more soluble or the softer materials are generally weathered most readily and the exposed portion becomes cellular or pitted (Fig. 59).

Weathering is partly physical and partly chemical; the two phases are disintegration and decomposition. By disintegration is meant the physical disruption of rocks to form particles of smaller size without change in composition. The particles are of the same material, and the minerals are fresh. Decomposition, on the other hand, is chemical decay by which the rocks are broken down by chemical alteration of the minerals. Normally both phases of weathering are going on at the same time, and physical disruption of rocks facilitates the access of the chemical materials involved in rock decay. In relation to erosion, weathering is but the first step—the preparation of the materials for removal.

FIG. 58. Spheroidal weathering converting jointed blocks of rock into rounded boulders. Along the American River, near Riverton, California. (*Photograph by Eliot Blackwelder.*)

FIG. 59. Solution pits due to weathering of sandstone. The softer parts of the sandstone have been washed out or blown away, leaving pits and lines of pits along the softer beds. (*Photograph by C. E. Erdmann, U.S. Geological Survey.*)

FIG. 60. Loose fragments of rock detached by weathering processes and accumulated at the foot of the cliffs as talus slopes or screes along the east side of the Sierra Nevada at Mount Whitney. (*Spence Air Photos.*)

Disintegration. *Temperature Changes.* Just as steel bridges and concrete pavements are subject to expansion when heated and to contraction when cooled, so rocks are affected by the alternate heating and cooling due to daily and seasonal changes in temperature. Repeated expansion and contraction thus tend to develop cracks in rocks. Water, entering these and other cracks, freezes and thaws. On mountaintops in the daytime the air may reach a temperature of 120°F. or more, and the rocks may become distinctly warm or even hot to the touch of a hand, but at night the temperature of the air drops below freezing. Under such conditions particularly, disintegration is effective. Hence, most high mountain peaks which are unprotected by snow are much fractured and may be covered with fields of angular blocks, many of which are on the move downslope. Some mountaintops have been reduced to domelike forms fringed by an accumulation of excess debris awaiting the opportune moment for mass movement which never fails to come.

Accumulations of rock fragments dislodged from cliffs by weathering and deposited below by gravity are *talus* (Fig. 60). The slope of the talus is approximately the angle of rest of the material, generally about 25 to 35 degrees from the horizontal, according to the size and angularity of the fragments, the amount of subsequent rainwash, and other conditions.

Smooth rocks exposed to weathering commonly spall off in thin slabs, sheets, or scales concentric with the surface. On account of the low conductivity of rocks, which tends to confine the heating and cooling to the outer part of the mass, the outer part on expanding and contracting pulls away from the inner part until finally it falls off and exposes a fresh surface to attack. Increase in volume on account of chemical changes, particularly that which is caused by the addition of water, or hydration, assists separation. The process of shelling or scaling off in such slabs, or leaves, is *exfoliation*. This process leaves smooth, rounded surfaces on most rocks regardless of their composition. Rounded granitic masses, such as Half Dome in the Yosemite Valley, California, are produced by the peeling off of slabs along curving secondary joints in the old intrusive body. In the case of Half Dome the steep, clifflike front is the result of splitting along the nearly vertical major joints. Both these processes are caused by the wedging action of water freezing in the

FIG. 61. Large slabs of rock peeling, along curving joints, under the influence of frost and gravity. These loosened pieces tumble and slide to lower levels, fracturing and breaking on the way. Half Dome, Yosemite National Park. (*Spence Air Photos.*)

FIG. 62. A live oak growing in the crack and disrupting a mass of limestone near Kerrville, Texas. (*Photograph by Dean Elting H. Comstock.*)

joints rather than by chemical change in the rock, although this latter may be a small contributing factor (Fig. 61).

As the process of disintegration continues, the exfoliated slabs and chips of rock are subjected to other stresses. This is true especially if the rock is composed of two or more minerals. In granite, for example, various minerals react differently. The dark minerals such as hornblende and biotite absorb heat more readily and also give it up more quickly than the lighter-colored feldspar and quartz. Furthermore each mineral has its own coefficient of expansion and contraction. Consequently in an intergrowth of minerals such as occurs in a granite, stresses are set up by the weathering processes which tend to separate the minerals. Finally the mineral grains fall apart and produce a sand of loose minerals. This process of *granular disintegration* is in operation over large areas where coarse-grained rocks are exposed to differential heating. Many of the slopes of Pikes Peak, Colorado, are covered with such products. The finer grains are transported by wind or water, and the coarser fragments remain until they are disintegrated more completely. At Dogtown Common, Cape Ann, Massachusetts, large granite boulders have crumbled into heaps of crystalline sand; and at Medford, Massachusetts, the exfoliated slabs of a diabase dike are disintegrated and decomposed into a soft granular mass of dark minerals.

Freezing of Water. The freezing of water in pores and cracks in rocks tends to disintegrate the rocks, for water in freezing expands about one-eleventh of its volume and exerts great pressure. Although the pressure is much less than the crushing strength of most hard rocks,[1] it is sufficient to disrupt soft rocks or rocks weakened by cracks or by partial decay. Highly porous rocks such as sandstones, whose pore space commonly ranges from 10 to 30 per cent, are disrupted in this way, and so are jointed rocks whose cracks become the loci of ice wedges. In the same manner the soils on fall-plowed lands in the north central part of the United States are made light, fluffy, and easily worked by the repeated freezing and thawing during the winter and early spring. Frost heaving also brings boulders to the surface, and it pushes up posts, stakes, foundations, and other structures.

By the combined action of frost and differential heating, unusual erosion forms may be produced. "The Old Man of the Mountain" in the White Mountains of New Hampshire is an outstanding example.

Plants and Animals. Plants and animals play a prominent part in weathering (Fig. 62). Roots grow into cracks and crevices and push the fragments up and apart, often as much as several feet. The overturning of well-rooted trees by the wind fractures the rocks and exposes them to destruction. The burrowing of animals such as earthworms, ants, and rodents and the tramping of animals, especially hoofed mammals, also contribute to the disintegration of rocks. Man likewise does his part in excavating road cuts and tunnels, in quarrying, in mining, and in the cultivation of the land. The "breaking" of the sod on the prairies, the clearing of brush and timber, and the destruction of forests by lumbering

---

[1] The crushing strengths of rocks used for construction purposes generally range as follows: sandstones 4,000 to 16,000 pounds; limestones 6,000 to 12,000 pounds; granites 15,000 to 30,000 pounds per square inch.

FIG. 63. Rock pinnacles near Crater Lake, Oregon, sculptured by differential weathering. (*Copyrighted, Sawyer Scenic Photos, Inc.*)

and by fire have upset the previous balance between weathering and erosion and indirectly have permitted rapid erosion and renewed weathering over large areas.

Decomposition. *Oxidation.* Rocks decompose or decay by chemical alteration of their component minerals by oxidation, hydration, carbonation, and solution (Figs. 63, 64). In the process of oxidation, oxygen is added to the rocks, especially to the iron compounds. The oxidation of rocks by air is aided by the presence of moisture; without water, oxidation is generally slow. Air and water break down the ferrous silicates such as pyroxenes, amphiboles, and olivine, and the ferrous iron is converted to ferric oxide (hematite) or to hydroxides (göthite, limonite) with accompanying color changes from green or black to red, yellow, or brown. Hence many soils in warm, moist climates are colored red, yellow, or brown. Locally deoxidation or reduction by organic matter may occur, and near the roots of trees and under peat bogs the bright colors may be changed to somber ones. The oxidation of pyrite, which is composed of iron and sulfur,[1] leads to the formation of sulfuric acid, which attacks the rocks and develops solution pits and accompanying stains and discolorations, so that even small amounts of iron sulfides may be injurious in building stones. The change of color of certain roofing slates from green or gray to brown is caused largely by rusting of the component iron compounds, as in normal weathering. In the oxidation of pyrite the sulfur as well as the iron is oxidized.

Hydration. Hydration involves the chemical addition of water to the minerals of a rock to form new minerals, chiefly hydrous silicates and hydrous oxides. Thus orthoclase, a mineral abundant in granite, is decomposed and converted largely to kaolin, the principal mineral in common clay. The potassium and excess silica are released at the same time.[2] Plagioclase feldspars are decomposed in the same way, and most of the alumina likewise is used in forming kaolin. Other hydrous silicates formed by hydration of the primary silicates include chlorite, serpentine, talc, zeolites, and many other minerals.

Carbonation. Another process of decomposition is carbonation, by which carbon dioxide, CO_2, is added to certain bases, particularly to oxides of calcium, magnesium, sodium, and potassium, to form carbonates or bicarbonates of these metals. All surface waters contain dissolved carbon dioxide, which is derived from the atmosphere. Carbonated water dissolves many substances more readily than pure water, and it is consequently an active agent of weathering.

It is noteworthy that the carbonated waters, although only feebly charged, are very abundant and that the carbonates of the alkalies and

---

[1] The reaction is written

$$FeS_2 + H_2O + 7O = FeSO_4 + H_2SO_4$$

pyrite   water   oxygen   ferrous   sulfuric
                          sulfate   acid

[2] $$2KAlSi_3O_8 + 2H_2O + CO_2 = Al_2Si_2O_5(OH)_4 + 4SiO_2 + K_2CO_3$$

orthoclase   water   carbon   kaolin   silica   potassium
                     dioxide   carbonate

$$2NaAlSi_3O_8 + 2H_2O + CO_2 = Al_2Si_2O_5(OH)_4 + 4SiO_2 + Na_2CO_3$$

albite   water   carbon   kaolin   silica   sodium
                 dioxide   carbonate

FIG. 64. Looking down into Bryce Canyon, Utah, showing differential weathering and erosion of sandstones. (*Photograph by George A. Grant, National Park Service.*)

alkaline earths are soluble in such waters, so that solution of these materials goes on together with carbonation and plays an important part in the decomposition of rocks by removing certain constituents. In addition to calcium, magnesium, sodium, and potassium, even the less soluble silica, alumina, and iron are taken away in part. Dissolved sulfates and chlorides are less abundant than the bicarbonates. Certain rocks particularly are subject to solution—notably limestone and marble, both composed chiefly of calcium carbonate, which is soluble in solutions that carry carbon dioxide. Gypsum and rock salt are very readily soluble in water.[1] Exposed surfaces of limestone and gypsum generally become etched or pitted by solution. Rocks that are made up of two kinds of material, one readily dissolved and another less readily dissolved, develop pitted surfaces in which the less soluble material stands out in relief.

Work of Vegetation. Vegetation assists decomposition. Lichens, which are among the first plants to grow on freshly exposed rocks, take certain chemical elements from the rocks, and the roots of other plants take up additional inorganic matter. Furthermore, the decay of the organic matter itself releases certain organic acids which increase the solvent

[1] Commercial beds of gypsum, $CaSO_4 \cdot 2H_2O$, and rock salt, $NaCl$, commonly are protected from solution in humid regions by a cover of relatively impervious beds of clay or shale.

power of the natural waters. The solubility of silica, alumina, and iron, for example, is much greater in the presence of these organic acids. The chemical activity of the small but abundant and ever-present bacteria which produce ammonia, nitric acid, carbon dioxide, and other active chemical compounds is another factor in the alteration of rocks and in the formation of soils. Indirectly vegetation serves to retain moisture and to delay erosion and hence to prolong chemical weathering.

Depth of Decomposition. Rock decomposition may proceed to great depths. Granitic rocks in the District of Columbia are decayed to a depth of 80 feet, and near Atlanta, Georgia, similar rock is decayed to approximately 100 feet. In northwestern Georgia the depth of decay of limestones is nearly 200 feet, and in Brazil shales are decayed to a depth of 400 feet.

The Influence of Climate on Weathering. The nature and extent of weathering are controlled largely by climatic conditions. For their effects on this process let us consider four climatic types: (1) the hot and moist climate of the equatorial belt, (2) the hot and dry desert climate, (3) the cool and moist climate of the temperate zones, and (4) the cold and dry arctic regions. In each of these regions, rock weathering is going on continually, but each region presents peculiarities of its own.

In a moist, warm climate, rock decay is rapid. In a dry climate, it proceeds more slowly. The effect of climate is well-illustrated by the Egyptian obelisk that was presented to New York City. It had stood without apparent injury for many centuries in the mild, dry climate of northern Egypt but began to disintegrate soon after its removal to Central Park so that special protection had to be given to it.

In the equatorial regions where the rainfall is heavy and the temperature is high, chemical processes are active, and the influences of organic agencies are pronounced. The chemical reactions are more rapid than in cooler latitudes, and consequently the decomposition of silicates is more complete, and much silica is removed in solution. The end product of such weathering is *laterite,* which consists largely of red hydrated oxides of aluminum and iron. This lateritic residue takes the place to a large extent of the clayey mantle-rock of the higher latitudes.

In desert regions peculiar conditions prevail, and therefore the character of weathering differs from that which is found elsewhere. Rainfall is sparse, so that solution by downward-percolating water is of minor importance. Some water, however, is retained by capillary action. Since the air is dry and the sun is hot, the capillary water is drawn toward the surface, where evaporation concentrates the salts that are in solution. These warm concentrated solutions react with the constituents of the rocks and tend to decompose them. The crystallization of new compounds takes place between the mineral grains, and these may cause splitting of solid rocks, in much the same manner as the freezing of water. Since waters are constantly rising toward the surface by capillary action and depositing their dissolved contents, the surface materials become ce, mented, forming "hard-pan" and irregular concretionary masses in the mantle-rock. Because of excessive evaporation, the soluble salts of sodium, calcium, and magnesium commonly occur as efflorescence on the surface. This is especially true in depressions and over flat areas, where they remain because of the inadequacy of the rainfall to wash them out. In many desert regions a brown or black shiny crust on the rocks is known as "desert varnish." It consists mainly of oxides of iron and manganese. Desert varnish has been thought generally to be the result of deposition of mineral matter from evaporated capillary water. Recent studies indicate, however, that in some instances the growth of lichens may be an important contributing factor.

In temperate regions, there are marked seasonal variations in climate, and consequently the type of weathering is to a certain extent a combination of all others. In winter, frost action is dominant, whereas in summer, spring, and autumn, percolating waters play a more important part. The elevation above sea level also is an important factor, especially if the mountains extend above the timber line. Low-altitude temperate regions generally are not subject to extreme and sudden changes of temperature. In general, solution and chemical decomposition are the dominant types of weathering in these areas.

In the subpolar regions, where a large part of the surface is covered with snow during most of the year, the underlying rocks are saturated with thaw water which is repeatedly frozen and thawed. By far the most important weathering agent in such an environment is the expansion of water when it freezes. This process shatters the rocks and leads to the accumulation of a mantle of angular fragments. Essentially similar conditions prevail in the high, snow-capped mountains of the temperate and equatorial regions.

Weathering of Limestones. The weathering of limestone is especially responsive to the climatic conditions under which it takes place. A medium to high temperature and abundant rainfall are exceptionally favorable conditions. In warm, humid regions limestones weather fairly easily and lowlands are produced, as the weathered products are carried away in solution or are transported by running water as fragments that have little resistance to wear.

In arid and semiarid regions limestones and dolomites form very resistant ridges, or uplands. Under such circumstances these rocks, already jointed, may be further broken up by mechanical weathering, and since the essential mineral matter is completely soluble, they yield as a whole to chemical weathering, which is at best a very slow process even where water is abundant. Hence bare surfaces of limestone endure long as cliffs or hill cappings in arid regions.

Exposed, flat limestone surfaces in any climate may weather somewhat irregularly, for the purer portions are more susceptible to solution; but the surface water partly charged with carbon dioxide or organic acids, running down over the limestone face of a cliff, a crack, or a cavity, may be especially effective. It dissolves the rock as it goes, the loosened insolubles drop from the surface, and eventually broad, more or less parallel furrows are developed, thus giving a fluting to the surface of the cliff or other limestone face. The fluted holes in the limestone capping of some of the hills along the Sacramento River, above the Shasta Dam, are good examples.

Through the widening of cracks or joints by chemical activity, chiefly solution, so much of the drainage of limestone areas may be transferred to underground passages as greatly to modify the weathering as well as the erosion processes on the surface. In time the surface of such a region may be covered by an impure clay soil, generally red in warm climates, composed of the insoluble residue left by the disappearing limestone. In arid regions this residue is likely to be blown away as dust.

Formation of Soils. Soils are a complex mixture of inorganic mineral matter and decomposed organic residues. They are formed from disintegrated or decayed rock which is a product of weathering. From a human point of view the formation of soil is by far the most important result of weathering. Soils differ greatly from area to area, not only in quantity, but in quality and capacity to support the growth of plants. The same agencies of weathering which produce the *mantle-rock* are continually at work breaking it up into finer and finer particles and causing its more complete decay. Soil proper is the thin upper portion of this mantle which is decomposed and altered sufficiently to support plant life. It usually contains more or less dark, carbonaceous organic matter called *humus*. The decomposed rock below the humus layer of the soil is sometimes spoken of as subsoil.

The bulk of most soil is composed of mineral grains of various sizes, but it is the presence of organisms and of organic matter, the source of soil nitrogen, that makes soils essentially different from most mantlerock. Organic matter is derived from plant and animal tissues, which are made up largely of carbon, nitrogen, and water. Nitrogen is essential to plant growth. The air contains an inexhaustible supply of it, but atmospheric nitrogen is not available to plants, which must have it in soluble form in soil solutions. Some of the bacteria in the soil are able to take nitrogen gas from the air and transform it into soluble nitrates.

A number of leguminous plants play an important role in the so-called nitrogen cycle since their roots act as hosts to various types of nitrogen-transforming bacteria.

The chief factors in soil formation are (1) parent rock material, (2) climate, (3) action of living organisms, (4) slope of the land surface, and (5) time. Any of the three principal kinds of rock—igneous, sedimentary, and metamorphic—may supply soils with the bulk of the parent rock material. However, the character of the ultimate soil derived from a given rock will depend to a considerable extent on the other factors of soil formation. Some rocks may contain the minerals which are essential to plant growth and still produce very poor soil, whereas, under favorable conditions of climate and vegetation, a fertile soil may be produced from parent material relatively low in the minerals that contain the raw materials for plant food. Partially indurated shales and sandstones are easily changed by weathering into soils, whereas the formation of soils from igneous and metamorphic rocks requires long units of time.

The influence of climate on weathering has been discussed earlier (page 85). It affects the type of weathering, the percolation of water through the soil, and the removal and redeposition of materials by such agents as wind and water. In general the soils of humid areas are more thoroughly leached than those of arid or semiarid regions. Leaching removes lime and other soluble minerals and leaves a more acid soil. High temperatures promote rapid chemical changes in the soil, both by direct chemical action and by reactions induced by living organisms. In humid regions the organic acids produced by the decay of plant tissue hasten the soil-leaching process.

The soils of steep slopes differ from those on flat surfaces because of

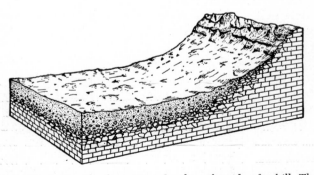

FIG. 65. Diagram illustrating the formation of soil on the side of a hill. The solid rock in the valley grades upward to partly decayed rock, which in turn grades into soil. On the steep slope no soil has accumulated because it is carried downhill.

differences in drainage, rate of runoff, and erosion. Where the slopes are considerable, solid rock may crop out at the surface, not because no mantle-rock is formed but because the loose material is removed by rainwash, wind action, or other agents of erosion as rapidly as it is formed. Figure 65 shows solid rock grading upward through subsoil to soil. On the steep slopes at the right no soil has accumulated even though the rock is disintegrating.

The texture, or size of grain, of the soil particles as well as certain other physical characteristics has much to do with the soil's ability to produce crops. The size of the mineral grains determines the amount of free surface exposed, and this, in turn, influences the quantity of water that can be retained by capillary and molecular action. Fine-textured soils have larger surface areas than do coarse-grained soils. Since it is from the surface areas of soil particles and from the film of solutions and colloids around them that plant roots obtain most of their mineral matter for plant food, the texture is an important physical property of all soils.

Residual and Transported Soils. Soils which rest upon the bedrock from which they are derived are *residual soils* (Fig. 66). Such soils show

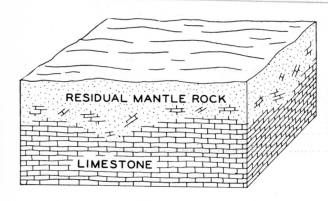

FIG. 66. Residual mantle-rock formed by weathering of underlying limestone. Fragments are found in the mantle-rock, and many of them lie horizontal like the underlying limestone.

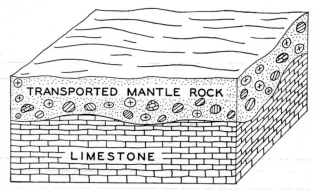

FIG. 67. Transported mantle-rock. The material of the mantle-rock is different from the flat-lying solid rock and contains different kinds of fragments, which lie in many different positions.

FIG. 68. Weathered limestone block talus near head of Twelvemile Canyon, Utah. On such a steep slope residual soil cannot accumulate because it is washed downhill. (*Photograph by U.S. Forest Service.*)

a gradual transition downward into subsoil, and this in turn grades imperceptibly into rotted rock which crumbles readily when exposed at the surface. The thickness of the subsoil varies greatly, for the depth to which rock is decayed is greater at some places than at others.

Transported soils are those which are derived from mantle-rocks that have been carried to their present positions from their places of origin (Fig. 67). Transported soils are made up largely of material that is not weathered or that is only partly weathered. They owe their present positions to some agent of transportation, such as running water, wind, moving ice sheets, or gravity (Fig. 68). Since these agents accomplish different degrees of sorting, transported soils vary in texture from fine silts to coarse gravel. They vary also in chemical composition; certain transported glacial soils are very fertile, since they are made up largely of ground-up rocks that have not been leached by water of certain valuable mineral foods that plants require.

Soil Profiles. Soil scientists have found that soils developed for a long time under a given set of climatic conditions have acquired fairly uniform characteristics over wide areas. Such well-developed soils are said to be *mature*. They exhibit a well-marked soil *profile*, consisting of three horizons, designated *A*, *B*, and *C*. These differ in color, texture, and structure and vary in thickness (Fig. 69). The *A* horizon is the topsoil, generally rich in organic matter and in soil organisms. The intermediate, or *B*, horizon, sometimes called subsoil, is more or less oxidized; it may be leached, or it may contain secondary mineral deposits such as a clay pan or iron pan. The *C* horizon is the little-altered parent rock, either loose or consolidated, from which the soil was formed. Youthful soils lack good profiles.

Classification of Soils. The mature soils are grouped into classes determined by the prevailing climate and associated vegetation (Fig. 70).

Laterite (Latin *later*, brick) soils, developed by intense weathering in hot, humid climates under the rain forest. The material is high in iron and aluminum oxides and hydroxides, is red or yellow in color, and is leached of bases and silica.

Chernozem (Russian, black earth) soils, formed in temperate, sub-humid climates, typically under tall-grass vegetation. The soil is black, granular in structure, fertile, and only moderately leached.

Podsol (Russian, salting, saltness) soils, developed in subarctic to cool, moist climates under a cover of coniferous or mixed hardwood and

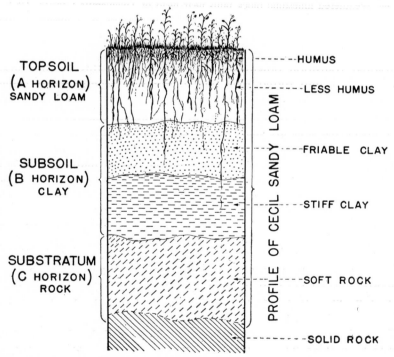

FIG. 69. *Soil profile* of a mature area. Surface water carried down through section by gravity. Deeper water rising through capillary attraction. (*Photograph by U.S. Soil Conservation Service.*)

coniferous forest. The soil is ash-gray, low in organic matter (except for surface duff), acid, leached, and underlain by a secondary clayey subsoil.

Desert soils, formed in arid regions under scanty vegetation. They are variable but are mostly low in organic matter, unleached, and light-colored.

These soil groups grade into each other through a complex series of intermediate or transitional types (see table below). In addition special types of soils occur in peat bogs, on wind-blown sand, on alluvial plains, and in other local situations where the effects of the parent rock, youthfulness of the weathering, poor drainage, or erosion on steep slopes dominate over the effects of climate and vegetation.

General Characteristics of Soils [1]

Soils	Profile	Native vegetation	Climate
Tundra	Dark-brown peaty layers over grayish horizons mottled with rust. Substrata of ever-frozen material	Lichens, moss, flowering plants, and shrubs	Frigid humid
Podsol	A few inches of leaf mat and acid humus. A very thin dark-gray A horizon, a dark-brown B horizon. Strongly acid	Coniferous or mixed coniferous and deciduous forest	Cool temperate and humid
Gray-brown	Thin leaf litter over mild humus over dark-colored surface soil 2 to 4 inches thick over grayish-brown leached horizon over heavy B horizon. Less acid than podsols	Mostly deciduous forest with mixture of conifers in places	Temperate humid
Laterites	Red-brown surface soil. Red, deep B horizon. Red parent material	Tropical savanna vegetation	Tropical wet-and-dry
Prairie	Very dark brown or grayish-brown soil grading through brown to lighter-colored parent material at depth 2 to 5 feet	Tall-grass prairie	Temperate humid
Chernozems	Black or very dark grayish-brown friable soil to a depth ranging up to 3 or 4 feet, grading through lighter color to whitish lime accumulation	Tall- and mixed-grass prairie	Temperate subhumid
Chestnut	Dark-brown friable and platy soil with lime accumulation at a depth of 1 to 4 feet	Mixed tall-and-grass prairie	Temperate to cool. Semi-arid
Sierozems	Pale grayish soil grading into calcareous material at a depth of 1 foot or less	Desert plants, scattered short grass, and brush	Temperate to cool. Arid

[1] Adapted from *Agricultural Yearbook,* 1938, pp. 996–999, U.S. Department of Agriculture.

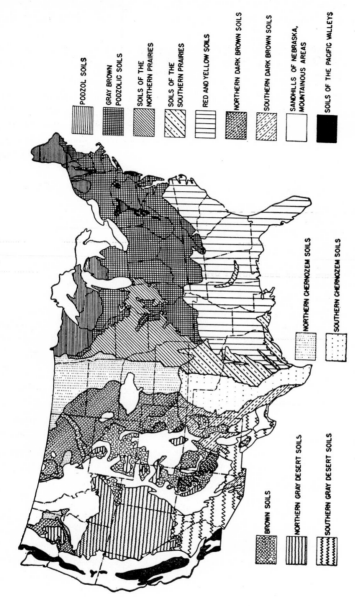

PODZOL SOILS

GRAY BROWN PODZOLIC SOILS

SOILS OF THE NORTHERN PRAIRIES

SOILS OF THE SOUTHERN PRAIRIES

RED AND YELLOW SOILS

NORTHERN DARK BROWN SOILS

SOUTHERN DARK BROWN SOILS

SANDHILLS OF NEBRASKA, MOUNTAINOUS AREAS

SOILS OF THE PACIFIC VALLEYS

NORTHERN CHERNOZEM SOILS

SOUTHERN CHERNOZEM SOILS

BROWN SOILS

NORTHERN GRAY DESERT SOILS

SOUTHERN GRAY DESERT SOILS

FIG. 70. Climatic and vegetational soil groups of the United States. (*After Marbut.*)

Replenishment of Soils. Year by year the soils are carried away by the wind or by sheet wash and by the brooks to the creeks and thence by the rivers to the sea. The farmer may observe his rich, dark soil being gradually washed away, and often he provides small dams and earthworks to prevent wash. The soil commonly is deposited over the flood plains of the rivers and over deltas and flats, and these are noted for their fertility. When the topsoil is washed away, however, new rock material is exposed to weathering to help offset the loss and this provides additional mineral substances which are necessary for plant life. Plants utilize a large number of materials for their growth. These are derived from the atmosphere and from the soil. They include carbon, hydrogen, oxygen, nitrogen, phosphorus, sulfur, potassium, calcium, and other substances. Carbon, hydrogen, and oxygen are obtained from the air and water, and nitrogen may be developed in the soil from the atmosphere by a proper rotation of crops. The clovers, beans, peas, and similar crops add nitrogen compounds to the soil. In general, phosphorus is present in igneous rocks as the mineral apatite (calcium phosphate) and in sedimentary rocks as a nearly similar substance, and these supply soils. Potassium is present in orthoclase and in many shales and other sedimentary rocks. When soils are cultivated continually for many years, however, and particularly when grain is harvested and removed from the land, there is a steady decrease in fertility.

When soil has been exposed to weathering for ages with very little erosion and very little removal of rock matter to expose new minerals to decay, the mineral fertilizers are essential. The chief mineral fertilizers are nitrates, phosphates, potash salts, and calcium salts. All these are added to certain soils in large amounts. Nitrates are obtained from the desert regions of Chile, where they have formed by the drying up of waters containing sodium nitrates and other salts. In recent years much nitrate has been made artificially from nitrogen of the air. Potash salts have been imported largely from Germany, where they are found with salt and gypsum in beds that have resulted from the drying up of ancient seas. Recently large amounts of potash salts have been found in West Texas and in New Mexico. The calcium phosphate of commerce is obtained chiefly from "rock phosphate," which is found in sedimentary beds. The phosphate is made more readily available by treatment with sulfuric acid. Calcium is added to the soil as calcium sulfate (gypsum) and calcium carbonate (powdered limestone). Often these substances are mixed together as a fine powder and worked into the soil as the crop is planted so that only a small amount may be required annually. In an agricultural region the distribution and prosperity of its people are directly related to the fertility of the soil. Government agencies have been formed to give assistance by furnishing soil analyses and suggesting means of improving local soils by proper cultivation and by use of the type of fertilizer indicated. The Bureau of Soils in the United States recognizes more than 1,500 different soil types. In many cases the differences are slight.

SUGGESTIONS FOR FURTHER READING

Baver, Leonard David: Soil Physics, John Wiley & Sons, Inc., 1940.

Bennett, Hugh Hammond: Soil Conservation, McGraw-Hill Book Company, Inc., 1939.

Blackwelder, Eliot: Exfoliation as a Phase of Rock Weathering, *Jour. Geology,* vol. 33, pp. 793–806, 1925.

Jenny, Hans: Factors of Soil Formation, McGraw-Hill Book Company, Inc., 1941.

Reiche, Parry: A Survey of Weathering Processes and Products, The University of New Mexico Press, 1950.

Robinson, G. W.: Soils, Their Origin, Constitution and Classification, 2d ed., Thomas Murby and Company, London, 1936.

CHAPTER 6

Wind as an Agent of Gradation

Nature of Wind Work. The earth's atmosphere is made of air, and wind is air in motion. Winds are likely to be regarded as currents of air moving more or less parallel to the earth's surface; but their flow often is turbulent—moving upward or downward, twisting and turning with momentary conditions—even within the atmosphere itself. Winds are essentially density currents generally moving from high- to low-pressure areas although their load of moisture, or even of dust, may modify their flow. They react to resistances of any kind, and anomalies are numerous. The energy which causes wind is derived from the heat of the sun, and part of this energy is expended in moving water vapor in over the land to fall as rain and in shifting the finer rock particles, such as dust, sand, and small pebbles, on the earth's surface. It is with the movement and deposition of these rock particles that gradation, as caused directly by the wind, is concerned. Since these materials are land-derived, such wind work is more important over the land than over the sea; nevertheless wind-borne dust and silt may be carried far out to sea and ultimately may be dropped into ocean waters.

As compared with streams of water, winds do not have the concentrated thrust and the steadiness of great rivers, so that the work of wind on the whole is less important than the work of streams. Its great field of activity, however, is in arid regions, which are more or less devoid of vegetation and are plentifully supplied with fine rock waste, and where stream work is at its minimum. For this reason the wind tends to compensate for the reduction of the work of streams in arid regions and to supplement their activity. Wind work, however, is not confined to arid regions, for even the most humid regions have dry seasons favorable to wind activity, and wind-borne dust may be carried to them notwithstanding their prevailingly humid climate.

Methods of Wind Erosion. In loose, dry materials the impact of the wind itself is sufficient to remove vast quantities of earthy matter by the process of *deflation* (Latin *deflare*, to blow away). Eddies, whirlwinds, and updrafts help the wind to lift and remove its load in this way. Thus many exposed uplands are swept free of loose material, which is carried away as fast as weathering produces it (Fig. 71). The remaining loose particles themselves may be but the heavy residuals discarded by the wind, which has blown away (deflated) the fine clay particles produced by the weathering of a rock such as granite. A more spectacular but perhaps less important method of wind erosion is that of *corrasion* and *abrasion* (Latin *abradere*, to scrape off or rub away), that is, the use of a natural sandblast whereby the wind employs its load of sand as a cutting tool in the same manner as man cleans stone or brick buildings or cuts figures on stone with the aid of air-driven sand as an abrasive. By means of the sand swept along by the wind, rock surfaces are scoured and grooved. In arid regions such grooves are very conspicuous, and where the winds have slight variation of direction, the grooves show a parallel alignment and their sides are often strongly fluted. Many odd-shaped land forms are developed. These include undercut hills, with accompanying broad, shallow caves, mushroom rocks, table rocks, pedestals, and similar sculpturings (Fig. 72).

Deep hollows may be developed by wind erosion in loose or easily deflated rock material. In the Gobi Desert these hollows range from

FIG. 71. Cave rocks near Sierra La Sal, Dry Valley, Utah. Wind-swept plain and wind-scoured mesa in a region where the wind is a powerful eroding and transporting agent. Note the absence of accumulated weathered rock material; also the scoured and grooved bedrock.

FIG. 72. Medicine Rocks near Baker, Montana. A semiarid region where wind abrasion and wind scour are important factors in rapidly removing the products of rock disintegration. (*U.S. Forest Service.*)

about 300 yards to 30 miles or more in length and from 50 to 400 feet in depth. The depths are limited by the position of the regional groundwater level. Hence in some regions such hollowed-out areas may extend below sea level.

The sand grains used as tools in the natural sandblast are themselves subjected to wear, so that they are chipped, pitted, and generally reduced in size. Examined with a lens, the battered grains may show a "frosted" surface like that shown by ground glass and concentric cracks like the familiar "moon" texture in marbles.

Special Effects of Wind Erosion. Occasionally one may see fields of young wheat or corn ruined by the removal of soil by deflation to such an extent that the tender roots are exposed to a withering sun. Fallow land in dry-farming areas especially is subject to damage in this way. An inch or two of soil thus may be taken away by the wind in the course of a few days. Many examples of wind abrasion which have been recorded by man may be given. These include the "frosting" and ultimate destruction of glass windows exposed along sandy seashores, the cutting down of telephone poles just above the ground in deserts, the marring of the Sphinx and of certain pyramids in Egypt, the undercutting of stone foundations of buildings, and many others. From these examples it is only a short step to a similar interpretation of many oddities of wind-swept arid regions. These include beveled stones—*einkanter* or *dreikanter* (meaning one- or three-edged) (Fig. 73).

Einkanter apparently are formed by the cutting of pebbles under conditions of a constant direction of the wind; dreikanter, shaped like brazil nuts, suggest that the pebbles were overturned, perhaps as a result of undermining, so that several facets are developed in succession. The polish developed on rocks by the sandblast is generally somewhat dull, but on certain fine-grained hard rocks such as quartzite it may be highly lustrous.

Transportation by Wind. *Methods of Transportation.* The method by which rock particles are carried by the wind varies according to size, shape, and density of the particles and with the velocity of the wind. In

FIG. 73. Wind-polished and faceted pebbles, or ventifacts from the Big Horn Basin, Wyoming.

(a)	(b)	(c)	(d)

FIG. 74. Tornado which occurred near Gothenburg, Nebraska, in the autumn of 1930. (a) The tornado cone forming in the clouds; (b) the fully developed cone approaching the earth; (c) the cone as it reached the earth; (d) the cone striking a farmhouse, which appeared to explode. (*Courtesy of U.S. Weather Bureau.*)

general, dust particles are carried in suspension and sand grains by traction, chiefly by rolling or creep. Small, angular grains of dust, with relatively large surface areas as compared with their volumes, remain suspended in air better than larger grains or grains with smooth surfaces which approach the spherical form, and light materials are suspended in air more readily than heavy ones. In ordinary winds sand grains are too heavy to be carried in suspension so that normally they are moved by rolling along the surface of the ground or in part by bouncing, skipping, and gliding. A light zephyr can carry dust in suspension, a gentle breeze can roll fine sand, whereas a strong breeze, with a velocity of about 25 miles per hour, can move sand grains a millimeter in diameter, and gales and hurricanes can carry sand in suspension to heights of hundreds of feet and can roll along the ground pebbles 2 or 3 inches in diameter.

Uncomfortable reminders of distant sources are the blasts of fine sand, carried by desert winds, that may be encountered by ships passing up and down the Red Sea to and from the Suez Canal. These are more or less horizontal winds of varying strength, and the type of load carried is a function of the velocity. There are, however, upward-moving currents of air that may lift fine particles high above the surface. The *whirlwind* "dust devil," or "devil wind," is a minor spinning wind of surface origin that builds upward and is characteristic of hot, sunny days. It raises dust and other light materials that may drift some distance from the origin, but the surface effects of such a wind are trivial even over regions where they are common.

The *tornado* (Fig. 74) is a much more violent whirling mass of air with much greater lifting power but of slight gradational effect, partly because tornadoes are infrequent and affect the surface for short distances only. It originates as a column of whirling air in the storm clouds, hanging down and traveling with them. It builds up a very high speed of rising air rotating around an axis that may dip down to the surface. Tornadoes with their great spiral, chimneylike updrafts (Fig. 74) have been known to lift heavy objects and to transport them several miles, but they, too, are of slight geologic importance.

Although upward currents of air in the center of a whirl, such as a tornado, may lift and transport objects even heavier than sand grains, such storms are relatively rare and the gradational effect is slight. It is the ordinary winds, more or less parallel to the surface of the earth, that are involved in large-scale sand movements. These movements of sand are at or near the surface, generally within inches of it, and rarely rising more than 3 or 4 feet, although fine sand has been known to rise higher and to have been carried in suspension for unusual distances. Under the motive power of the wind loose grains of sand may be picked up from the surface, carried for some distance forward, and dropped, only to be picked up and dropped again in a series of bounding movements known as *saltation* (Fig. 78). The impact of the falling grains as they strike urges others forward also. This impulse, together with the drag of the wind on the surface over which it is blowing, causes a forward motion, or *creep*, of the loose sand. Saltation and creep are among the most important factors producing the movements of drifting sand. The buffeted grains are rounded by wear, and the surfaces are frosted by the numerous impacts suffered in transit.

Sources of Load. The sources of the wind's load of dust and sand are varied. Probably the principal source is the rock waste formed by weathering and corrasion. Disintegrating sandstones, flood-plain and sand-bar deposits of rivers, glacial moraines, beach sands (Fig. 75), deposits of dried-up lakes, and the like, commonly serve as immediate sources. In addition, volcanic explosions supply tremendous quantities of light, highly angular rock dust which is well-suited to the capacity of the wind, but such explosions are infrequent, though temporarily they may be of great importance.

Extent of Wind Transportation. Dust and fine sand (Fig. 76) may be carried to great distances by the wind. Volcanic dust from the explosive eruption of Katmai Volcano in Alaska in 1912 was spread to such an extent that the material upon settling formed a deposit 1 foot thick at a distance of 100 miles to the leeward from the source, and appreciable quantities were carried as far as Seattle, Washington, about 1,600 miles away. When the volcano Krakatao in 1883 blew more than 1 cubic mile of its top off and greatly reduced the island on which it stood, dust was

FIG. 75. Beach sand carried inland by wind along coast of California south of Point Sal. (*Spence Air Photos.*)

FIG. 76. An approaching dust storm, western Oklahoma. (*Copyright photograph by Pictures, Inc.*)

carried into the upper atmosphere so as to cause brilliant sunsets for a period of several months, at first nearby and about 2 weeks later entirely around the globe. Certain ancient deposits of volcanic ash, now consolidated into rock, likewise testify to the power of wind transportation. Many examples of dust falls and dust-laden rain- or snowstorms are on record. Thus snow which fell in Minnesota and Wisconsin in the early spring of 1925 carried reddish silt apparently derived from the southwestern states.

Near the sources of the dust great quantities are transported. Thus in the drier parts of the prairies and plains of North America, sometimes called the "dust bowl," there may be periods during which the air is so filled with dust that one can see but a short distance and even breathing is difficult. Driving an automobile is almost impossible, and lights are required in houses. The dust piles up at fences, even obliterating them, while around the buildings great dunelike heaps of dust are formed (Fig. 77). In this region the deflation of topsoil is chiefly the consequence of introducing farming in a climate little suited to it. Under natural conditions very little of the soil was blown away although it is quite probable that frequent successions of dry years occurred far back in the climatic history of the area. This condition has been so discouraging to the inhabitants that during the dry 1930's much farm land was abandoned. After one such dust storm, observations on the quantity of dust

FIG. 77. A semiarid area in the Southwest. Prolonged drought has converted topsoil into dust, which has been deposited, partially covering buildings and fences. (*Copyright photograph by Pictures, Inc.*)

left over the surface indicated that 125 tons had fallen on every square mile at a distance of approximately 500 miles from the probable source of the dust.

Dust storms originating in the Sahara Desert have been observed to drop silt in Italy on the following day and in France, England, and Germany, 200 to 2,500 miles from the source, a day or two later. Such a dust storm from Mar. 9 to 12, 1901, is estimated to have deposited about 1,960,420 tons of dust in a sheet about 0.25 millimeter thick over Europe and 1,650,000 tons in northern Africa. Likewise ships in the middle and south Atlantic Ocean have experienced falls of silt and fine sand, apparently derived from the Sahara Desert, and ships off the coast of Japan have received falls of dust from the interior of China, 1,000 miles away. New Zealand has received dust from Australia, 1,400 miles away.

Mineral fragments of dustlike size may rise to great heights, be carried long distances by the wind, and the finest of them may remain in suspension for a long period of time. Such, however, is not the usual history of mineral particles classified as sand.

The transportation of sand rolled on the ground is much more limited —generally to distances of a few miles or less. In France, however, sand has been blown inland from the seashore fully 5 miles, and great sand deposits of the Sahara Desert lie on a limestone plateau 100 miles from the outcrops of sandstone whose disintegration apparently has supplied the sand.

Sorting and Rounding during Transportation. The wind's power to transport by suspension is notably different from its capacity for rolling, so that a separation of rock particles occurs depending on the method of

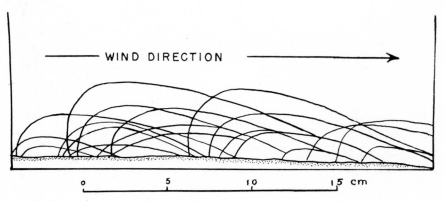

FIG. 78. Lines showing paths of sand grains in saltation over a loose sand surface. (*Sketched from Bagnold photograph.*)

transportation. In general, the separation removes clay dust and silt from the larger and heavier sand. The rolling sands themselves may be further sorted on the ground according to the effective velocities of the wind and shape of sand grains. Pebbles generally are too big to move. Sand particles rolled along the ground are subject to considerable wear so that they become well-rounded, even those of very fine sizes (0.3 to 0.1 millimeter or less), whereas suspended dust particles are little changed.

Deposition by Wind. *Dust Deposits.* Slackening of the wind allows its suspended load to settle slowly out of the air. Rain and snow are even more effective in rapidly clearing the air. The general haziness of the atmosphere in the Pacific Northwest in late summer is due to dust and smoke from forest fires. It disappears when the fall rains begin. Occurrences of "mud rains" and dust-colored snows are referred to elsewhere. Normally the rate of deposition of dust is very slow, except in connection with volcanic outbursts. At Kodiak, Alaska, in 1912, 5 inches of volcanic dust from Katmai fell during a single night.

Dust deposits in general are widespread and without special form and hence escape much notice, but their total bulk is undoubtedly large. Ancient cities of the Near East were partly buried under such a mantle of dust, apparently on account of a change of climate in the region. Wind-blown deposits in general are called *aeolian* deposits. Some deposits of wind-laid dust are of such magnitude as to deserve a special name. Dust that is composed of volcanic materials is volcanic ash. It is derived

FIG. 79. Fifty feet of loess showing a nearly vertical face at Missouri Valley, Iowa. (*Photograph by Alden, U.S. Geological Survey.*)

from explosive volcanic eruptions, and many of its particles are glassy, often sharp. Surface dust, originating chiefly from desiccated glacial outwash or from desert areas, has given rise to deposits called *loess* (Fig. 79).

Prominent loess deposits occur in the Mississippi Valley, in the Palouse hills of eastern Washington, in the plains of Germany, in the interior of China, in the pampas of Argentina, and elsewhere.

The typical loess of the Mississippi Valley is nonstratified yellowish silt, intermediate in texture between clay and sand, and is composed of a variety of minerals, including quartz, feldspar, hornblende, calcite, and many others, all very slightly weathered. It has the physical composition and general appearance of ground-up rather than chemically weathered rock. The deposits range in thickness from a few feet or less to at least 100 feet. When exposed in the banks of gullies or excavations, the loess reveals the curious property of standing in vertical cliffs even though the material is not cemented together. This is well shown at Council Bluffs, Iowa. Apparently the grains are sufficiently angular to interlock rather than roll or slide over each other as most sand grains do. In general the thickness of the loess decreases with distance from the source. That lying farther out may have accumulated slowly over grasslands, and the traces of former roots receding upward as the dust thickened probably gave rise to the vaguely defined vertical tubelets, partially filled with calcareous deposit, commonly found in the loess and contributing to the property of standing as vertical faces just mentioned. Many exposures, however, show a prominent vertical jointing that appears to be independent of these depositional features.

On account of its texture and the freshness of the component minerals, loess makes fertile, easily worked soil, as it does in the "corn belt" of Iowa and Illinois. The loess of the Mississippi Valley lies principally just beyond or on the outer rim of the glacial deposits of the recent ice age, from which deposits the materials of the loess presumably were derived before vegetation had become reestablished (Fig. 80). It is surmised that at the height of the melting season much of the fine rock material, or "rock flour," was carried to the outer margin of the outwash from the glacier. As the cooler season came, the melting diminished and these marginal muds dried out, forming dust. This, together with any other fine rock material available, probably was the dust that blew out over adjacent areas to be deposited as loess. Some of the dust deposits appear to be related to the marginal and outward-flowing streams discharging the melt waters, such as the Missouri and Mississippi Rivers. The dust along these rivers may have had the same origin as that suggested above but have been carried farther out first by these major streams. From the periodically dried-up flood plains of these rivers at the present time strong westerly winds whip up the dust and carry it to the adjacent uplands.

The loess deposits of China are said to reach the enormous thickness of 1,000 feet in Shensi and adjoining provinces. This loess is believed to have accumulated from silt blown in from the deserts of Central Asia by the prevailing westerly winds. It is so easily eroded by wind and rainwash that certain roadways in it, through the wear of centuries of travel, have become depressed into deep, narrow, canyonlike defiles. To restrain soil erosion, the loess-covered valley slopes are terraced by the Chinese farmers. Many of the farmers in the loess district inhabit caves excavated in bluffs of the loess.

Dunes. Wind-blown rock material, such as sand or soil, tends to lodge at places where there is interference with the winds which bear them. Mounds or piles of wind-blown sand heaped up in this manner are called sand dunes (Fig. 81). They are common along sandy sea coasts,

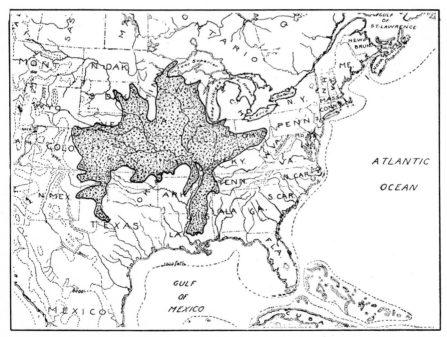

FIG. 80. Outline map showing the general distribution of loess deposits in the central portion of the United States. In some of the indicated region the loess coverage does not exceed 33 per cent of the surface, and it may be absent adjacent to the major streams. Other limited parts of the area have surface deposits of wind-blown sand. (See map, Pleistocene Eolian Deposits of the United States, Alaska and Parts of Canada, Geological Society of America, 1952.)

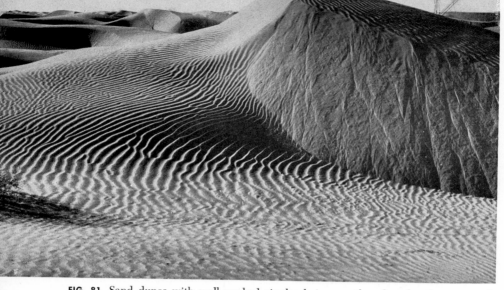

FIG. 81. Sand dunes with well-marked ripples being smothered under the steep, advancing front of the slip face (*upper right*). East side of the Imperial Valley, California. (*Photograph by Frashers.*)

the sandy shores of lakes, the flood plains of aggrading streams flowing through sandy areas, some of the drift-covered areas adjacent to the margin of the late Pleistocene glacier, the easily eroded, lately formed sandstones of parts of the Great Plains, and especially in sandy desert areas. In fact, wherever loose sand is available in abundance on land, dunes are likely to be formed, especially if there is a persistent wind direction.

Dunes are commonly formed of sand composed mostly of quartz, but in Otero County, New Mexico, the dunes are composed of grains of snowy white gypsum, those in the Keys off the southeast coast of Florida of calcareous algae and foraminifera, in Bermuda of coral sand, and in Italy of olivine sand. During the dry years of the thirties, the cultivated topsoil of the "dust bowl" was blown into dunelike deposits over highways, barnyards (Fig. 77), and gardens. In fact any loose, dry material of sand size exposed to the wind may be blown into dunes. Thus in the polar regions, and to a less extent at lower latitudes, fine, loose, dry crystals of ice are often drifted into banks of dunelike form, and this also is approached, but not quite duplicated, by dry snowflakes or pellets in the more common snowdrift.

Dune Formation. In its very early stages a dune is an oval sand pile with the wind flowing swiftly and freely over it (Fig. 82). But almost immediately a lag in wind velocity develops on the leeward side because of air swirls and funnel winds set up in the protected zone, or *wind shadow.* As the height of sand increases and the summit of the pile advances faster than the leeward foot, a crest is formed and a steep slope, or *slip face* (Fig. 83), develops down which the sand grains, dropping out of the retarded wind behind the crest, slide or roll. The lateral margins of the developing dune also may be dragged forward with the wind to produce winglike extensions, or horns, in that direction.

On the windward side of a typical dune (Fig. 82) the mid-profile normally shows a long, gentle slope of about 5 to 15 degrees from the horizontal, and on the leeward side a steeper slope, or slip face, with an angle of 20 to 30 degrees, or up to the limiting angle of sand repose at about 34 degrees. Since most of this moving sand, sliding down the slip face, previously was taken from the front margin of the windward side, swept up the slope, and dropped at the crest, the continual transfer

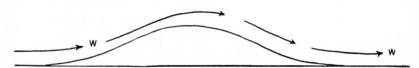

FIG. 82a. Outline sketch showing longitudinal section of the early sand-pile stage of a dune, streamlined in the direction of the wind (w) but with little or no distinctive plan.

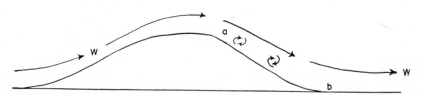

FIG. 82b. Outline sketch showing longitudinal section of a sand dune with crest (a) forming and advancing with the wind (w) but with the dune as a whole not migrating. The curving arrows in the lee of the crest indicate the type of wind movement in the wind shadow and a-b is the developing slip face.

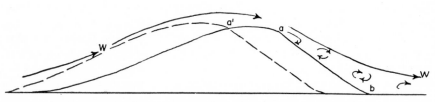

FIG. 82c. Outline sketch showing longitudinal section of a sand dune with crest (a) completed, slip face (a-b) developed, active, and the dune migrating with the wind (w) from a' to a. The whirls in the wind shadow are indicated by the curving arrows.

FIG. 83. Sand dunes, mostly crowded barchans, showing the ripple-marked, gentle windward side and the steep slip face of the leeward side. East side of the Imperial Valley, California. (*Photograph by Frashers.*)

produces a slow migration of the dune in the direction of the wind movement. The rate of dune migration varies with local conditions. Usually it does not exceed a few feet per year but may be as much as 100 feet or more per year. As a dune migrates, it gradually loses part of its sand and thus shrinks in size. Unless there is a supply of new material, dunes are eventually dissipated but during their growth and migration they may cover valuable forests (Fig. 84) and farm lands. Responding to controlling factors, such as topography, restriction by vegetation, sand supply, and a prevailing wind, dunes may travel, often in groups or colonies, miles from the original source of the sand and far beyond the obstruction that may have caused them to develop. Dunes are commonly of moderate height and over large areas may not greatly exceed 20 to 60 feet; but some may run into hundreds of feet. In the Great Dunes National Monument, Colorado, some dunes are more than 500 feet high. In the Sahara some of the largest dunes may approach 1,000 feet.

Dune Types. There are two somewhat different kinds of sand accumulation that have been included under the general name of dune.

These are (1) the heaps of sand piled up in sandy areas because some extraneous object has interfered with the free movement of the wind and (2) the desert sand piles that form where nothing but wind and sand are involved. No clear line of distinction or of separation can be drawn between the two.

Wherever loose sand is available and is being shifted by the wind, any obstruction, such as a boulder, a tuft of grass, or a shrub, interferes with the wind's transporting power and causes it to lose part of its sand load and form a dune. If the wind has a constant or prevailing direction, the dune assumes the normal plan and profile. But variable winds tend to produce the characteristic profile with each change in wind direction, and so the typical form is lost in the confused sand pile that results.

On a grass-covered dune or other area of sand, a break in the sod may become the location of a *blowout,* with the sand moved out by the wind formed into a dune around the margin of the hollowed-out area. Such dunes may be horseshoe-shaped, with the concavity, or open end, to windward and the dune embracing the blowout. The cavity excavated may be quite irregular, but the slope out of it often is somewhat continuous with the windward slope of the dune, and the rounded front is the slip face. Blowouts also occur in and among crowded dunes wherever sag in the sand surface allows a funneling of air currents through it. By this process the complexity of transverse sand ridges and other closely grouped dunes may be increased (Fig. 83).

FIG. 84. Sand dunes, on the Oregon coast, encroaching upon a forest; Woahink Lake in the distance. (*National Park Service.*)

FIG. 85. Crag-and-tail sand dune, Valencia County, New Mexico. (*U.S. Soil Conservation.*)

Wind, laden with sand and blowing through gaps or over rocky ledges, may deposit long, narrow sand ridges outlining the shape of the wind shadow, or sand may tail out from a crag against which it has been abandoned by the wind so as to form a *crag-and-tail dune* (Fig. 85) or *sand drift*. Such deposits of sand are fixed in position and are not always classified as dunes, but they are formed by the same general type of

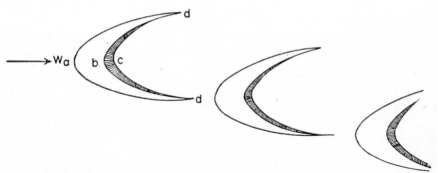

FIG. 86. Outline sketch of barchans such as are found in the Arabian Desert, showing wind direction and echelon arrangement of dunes.

a	Windward margin		*b-c*	Slip face
b	Crest		*d*	Horns, or points of wings
a-b	Windward slope		*W*	Wind direction

gradational process. In fact, with additional sand, typical dunes may develop and migrate away from the outer tip of the sand drift.

In regions, such as deserts or semideserts, where dunes have the best opportunity for free development, two general types are recognized. These are the transverse dune, or *barchan* (Fig. 86), and the longitudinal dune, or *seif* (Fig. 87). In its simplest form the barchan is crescent-shaped with the gentle slope of the windward side on the outer curve and having the points or wings of the crescent drawn out with the wind on the leeward side. It is a streamlined dune (Fig. 88) produced by wind blowing from one direction only, and any variation in wind direction tends to destroy its typical form. The barchan is best-developed in a

FIG. 87. Outline sketch of seifs such as are found in the Libyan Desert, showing prevailing and strong secondary (dotted arrow) winds, with the tendency of small dunes to unite into a longitudinal ridge. W, prevailing wind; W′, strong secondary wind.

FIG. 88. Sand dunes, mostly crowded barchans but showing a tendency to pass into seifs. Along the All-American Irrigation Canal, in the eastern part of Imperial County, California. (*Spence Air Photos.*)

FIG. 89. Cross-bedded aeolian sandstone near Zion Canyon, southern Utah. (*Courtesy of National Park Service.*)

region where the supply of sand is limited. An abundance of wind-blown sand produces crowded and overlapping barchans, or compound transverse dunes, with all the resultant complexities common to them. The seif is a sand dune resembling in plan the outline of an Arabian sword. It is developed by several winds having set but somewhat different directions. The strong wind, or modifying element, blows occasionally and from a direction different from that of the gentler prevailing wind. The resulting seif has a form that might develop if the more distant part of a crescent-shaped dune were blown away by the stronger wind, leaving only the near half of the barchan, to which more sand had been added. In reality, conversion from barchans to seifs, or vice versa, does take place and thus suggests that the latter may be but modifications of the simpler type of dune, that is, of the barchan (Fig. 88). Seifs are especially well-developed in Arabia, the Libyan Desert, the French Sahara, and the Australian desert. They commonly occur in linear chains, whereas the barchan is usually found in echelon or in colonies and is somewhat more widespread in distribution.

Dune Structure. A section of an active dune shows the bedding of the gentle windward side cutting sharply across the steeper beds of the slip face. As the dune is sheared off again in the process of migration or by variable winds and the sand redeposited, the complexity of the cross-bedded internal structure may be much increased. Beds of rounded grains of fairly uniform size, usually of frosted quartz, and the truncation of layers with many changes in direction of bedding inclination are tell-tale wind-drift characteristics that are common in sand dunes of all ages. They are as readily recognized in the ancient Navaho sandstone (Fig. 89) of Jurassic age as in the active sand dunes on the south shore of Lake Michigan.

Ripple marks are common on sand dunes (Fig. 83) and on the sand surfaces associated with them. They are formed by friction at the interface of wind and sand under the sorting action of surface creep, the coarsest grains collecting at the crests and the finest in the troughs. Variations in wind intensity produce removal or deposition of sand so as continually to modify the sand ripples, adjusting and readjusting their crests. Strong winds tend to produce asymmetrical ripples, and very strong winds may obliterate them entirely.

Deserts. In arid and desert regions (Fig. 90) wind is a dominant gradational factor. Often it is seasonal and may blow for days from a single direction. In desert (Fig. 91) areas the sky is usually clear, the

FIG. 90. Barren gullied hills showing erosion pattern in a dry area. Gower's Gulch, eastern Inyo County, California, a desert. (*Photograph by Frashers.*)

FIG. 91. Edge of the Mojave Desert, near Thorn, California. The sparse vegetation is cactus, joshua trees, creosote bush, and burro bush.

atmosphere persistently dry, and the daily range in temperature great. There is little or no soil, and vegetation is sparse or lacking, for the annual rainfall is less than 6 inches. Life is adapted to taking advantage of moisture when it comes and conserving it over a very long period of time. Some desert regions may have no rainfall for several years and then be subjected to a veritable deluge of water which dashes down slopes in floods or torrents. These sweep with them everything loose and rip off that which is not strongly attached or anchored. Many of the deserts are closed drainage basins, and the gullies, or canyons, down which this deluge pours end abruptly at the base of the slope and never unite into complete drainage systems. Instead the water from each canyon, or gully, spreads out over the gentler surface and drops its load of sediment in great, apronlike fans (Fig. 92). These unite laterally to form a compound alluvial fan, or piedmont alluvial plain (bajada), that continues basinward and gradually buries hills or any other irregularity encountered. The turbulent water ends its journey in the temporary or playa lakes at the foot of the slopes, where desiccation then takes place. There is thus turned over to atmospheric processes a new lot of rock waste with each such storm period.

But there are other important features of running water impressed on the desert and left to the winds for their modifying effects. The dry ravines, or *wadies*, become channels through which the wind is funneled, and their walls are worn and polished by wind-driven sand. Eventually the sand may be blown into dunes, but the fine rock particles

116

FIG. 92. The desert. Alluvial fans on the left and in the distance; seiflike sand dunes in the foreground. Death Valley, looking south near Stove Pipe Wells, California. (*Spence Air Photos.*)

FIG. 93. Deflation of lake beds near Fossil Lake, Lake County, Oregon. The highest of the remnants, protected by hard layers or shrubs, is about 6 feet high. In the foreground fragments of hard rock, too heavy to be blown away, remain as "lag" stones, or residuals.

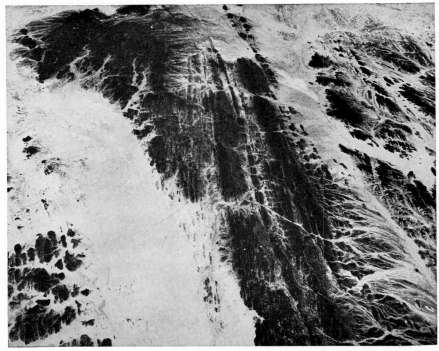

FIG. 94. Drifting sand (white) spreading over the eroded upturned edges of sedimentary rocks in central Arabia. (*United States Air Force.*)

and the dust from the dry playas are caught up by the wind and blown beyond the confines of the basin, leaving behind only the larger fragments such as coarse-grained sand and pebbles, or *lag stones* (Fig. 93). Accumulating over a long period of time and with the sand grains gradually moved out from around them, these lag stones may become so abundant over the surface that they form *lag gravels,* and finally the pebbles may even touch each other to produce a *desert pavement.* Lag stones often show a shiny black or brown iron-manganese crust known as *desert varnish.* Many are well-polished and -beveled to form the faceted pebbles known as *einkanter* or *dreikanter* as previously mentioned. The surfaces of so-called stony deserts are made by wind removal of all the fine products of disintegration so as to leave only the coarser lag gravels and boulders strewn over a rocky surface.

Contrary to popular conception, only small parts of deserts are covered with drifting sands. The Sahara Desert covers 3,500,000 square miles. Less than ½ million square miles is dune-covered; the remainder has a boulder-strewn rocky floor. In the Arabian Desert wind-blown sand covers about 35 per cent of the area; in the Gobi Desert a much smaller per cent is sand-dune and sand-drift surface; and the sun-parched sand dunes in the arid portions of the United States cover even less than 10 per cent of the total desert area. Thus it is apparent that expanses of relatively barren rock (Fig. 94) are more characteristic of deserts than are dunes. As running water dwindles, and fails at the edge of the desert, the wind takes over the work and thus becomes the most important agent of desert gradation, although mass movement may still be active. In the Peruvian portion of the Atacama Desert precipitation occurs so seldom that the natives say it never rains. Here the effects of water are almost nil, the erosional work being left largely to wind and gravity.

The interiors of continental glaciers exhibit many of the characteristics of true deserts, and some geologists are inclined to regard them as such. On an ice-covered area, however, the wind expends its energy chiefly on snow and ice and so produces little that resembles its effect on other types of rock surface and loose rock materials. But during certain seasons at

FIG. 95. Barchans near Fort St. John, Peace River District, British Columbia. These dunes are pinned down by vegetation. They were formed by strong winds blowing from the right, probably off a former continental glacier. The present prevailing wind is from the left. (*Royal Canadian Air Force.*)

least the strong winds blowing off a glacier may be dry and at the edge of the ice may pick up fine, dry rock material and later drop it elsewhere as the dust deposits called loess. The sand of these dried-up marginal outwash areas, added to the basal part of the wind, becomes an effective sandblast which cuts or carves exposed rocks and cobbles on the surface of the drift, producing the familiar dreikanter, while the sand is carried on and formed into dunes over the borderlands just beyond the source of the wind load. Some of these areas (Fig. 95) still show the barchans, now pinned down by vegetation, so arranged in relation to the North American area recently glaciated that they could have been formed only by a wind blowing off the edge of the ice and in a direction opposite to that of the present prevailing wind in the region where they are found.

SUGGESTIONS FOR FURTHER READING

Bagnold, R. A.: The Physics of Blown Sand and Desert Dunes, William Morrow and Co., 1942.

Berkey, C. P., and F. K. Morris: Geology of Mongolia, American Museum of Natural History, 1927.

Cressey, George B.: The Indiana Sand Dunes and Shore Lines of the Lake Michigan Basin, *Geog. Soc. Chicago Bull.* 8, 1928.

Gautier, E. F.: Sahara, the Great Desert, Columbia University Press, 1935.

Sears, Paul B.: Deserts on the March, University of Oklahoma Press, 1935.

CHAPTER 7

Ground Water

The water that is contained in the pores and cracks of the soil and rocks beneath the surface is called underground water, or simply ground water. Along with the waters of the oceans, lakes, rivers, and the air, it completes the sphere of the earth known as the hydrosphere. It is that portion of the hydrosphere which occupies voids in the lithosphere. This water is of great importance to human beings, for the inhabitants of many regions are totally dependent upon it for domestic and industrial uses. Man obtains most of the ground water he uses by digging, boring, or drilling wells.

Sources. There are several sources of ground water, but the most important is the *meteoric* water that falls from the atmosphere as rain or snow (Fig. 96). Of the water that is precipitated, a part is carried by small streams and rivers to the sea, another part is evaporated, and still another part soaks into the ground and is stored in the openings in the soil and rocks. The total annual rainfall upon the land areas of the earth is estimated to be approximately 26,000 cubic miles. About one-fifth of this amount is carried off directly by streams, whereas most of the remainder, which is more than 20,000 cubic miles, enters the soil and rocks before being discharged as seepage or springs that feed the streams. The distribution of rainfall is very irregular, and consequently the ratio of rainfall to immediate runoff is likewise variable. In general, in areas with an annual rainfall of 50 inches, only about half of it becomes ground water, whereas, with a rainfall of only 20 inches, nearly 85 per cent soaks into the earth. In the vast desert regions of northern Africa, Central Asia, Arabia, Australia, and the coast of Peru where very little water is precipitated, fully 95 per cent enters openings in unconsolidated mantle-rock before it is again evaporated or discharged to the sea.

A second source of ground water is the water that occupied the spaces between grains of sand, silt, and other materials as the sediments accumulated on the floors of the oceans or lakes to form the sedimentary rocks that now underlie large areas of the continents. Such trapped

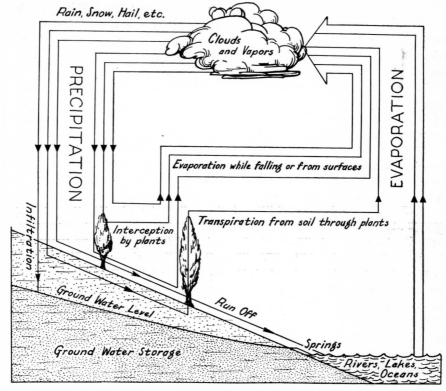

FIG. 96. The hydrologic cycle.

water is called *connate* water and is commonly found along with oil in the productive beds of many oil fields. As a general rule, connate water is more mineralized than sea water because, during the long periods of geologic time that it has been in the rocks, it has dissolved much additional mineral matter.

A third possible source of ground water is that derived from steam from deep-seated magmas. Such *magmatic,* or juvenile, water is added to the regional ground water wherever large masses of magma are thrust from below into the crust of the earth. It seems probable that waters of certain hot springs are in part of magmatic origin, especially in such areas as Yellowstone Park and the region of active geysers in New Zealand (page 134). Magmatic waters are thought to be the sources of certain ores and of unusual mineral deposits.

Descent of Ground Water. The amount of rain water that penetrates the earth is determined by several factors, the chief of which are stated below.

1. Amount and kind of precipitation. Within certain limits the amount of water that soaks into the ground is determined by the amount of precipitation as rain. In desert areas ground water generally lies deep, and little water occurs near the surface because there is little rain.

2. Rate of precipitation. The more rapid the fall, the less water sinks into the ground, for the surface soon becomes saturated. The same is true of the melting of snow—the more rapid the rate of melting, the less water sinks into the ground, especially into frozen ground.

3. Slope of the surface. The steeper the slope of the ground, the greater the percentage of the runoff. The flatter the ground is, the more water will sink below the surface because the runoff is retarded and the water has a longer time to soak into the ground.

4. Porosity and permeability of the soil and rock. Weathered and stratified rocks are usually more favorable for the entrance of water than massive, igneous rock. The part of a rock which is occupied by voids determines its porosity (Fig. 97). Thus if 1 gallon of sand will hold 0.3 gallon of water when saturated, the porosity is said to be 30 per cent, for three-tenths of its volume is made up of pores between the grains. The porosity of different types of rock varies from less than 1 per cent in massive granite to more than 40 per cent in poorly cemented sandstones. The granite selected for the tomb of Gen. U. S. Grant was considered the strongest granite in the United States. Porosity tests showed that it possessed about one-fourth of 1 per cent pore space. Thus even the strongest and most massive rocks contain measurable pores.

The porosity of sedimentary materials depends on the following factors:

a. The shape and arrangement of the constituent particles.

b. The degree of sorting of the particles (Fig. 98).

c. The degree of compaction and cementation.

d. The amount of mineral matter removed through solution by percolating waters.

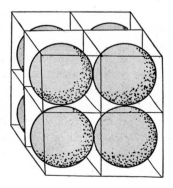

FIG. 97. Spherical particles in circumscribed cubes, showing the method of packing of mineral grains of uniform size that would produce maximum porosity in a rock. The spheres occupy only slightly more than half the volume of the cubes.

FIG. 98. Photographs of sand and gravel, illustrating the effect of size of grain and degree of sorting on the size of pores, which in turn influences the permeability. *Upper right*, all coarse with large pores. *Lower right*, all fine with very small pores. *Upper left*, all intermediate. *Lower left*, mixture of the other three; here the fine grains fill the pores between the larger grains and thus decrease the permeability.

Permeability is a term used to express the ability of a rock formation to transmit water. It is a measure of the velocity of percolation and may be said to be the rate at which a formation will allow water to flow through it under a given amount of pressure. A rock with high porosity is not necessarily highly permeable. The permeability varies with the degree of sorting or with the arrangement of grains of coarse and fine material. Coarse-grained sand and clean gravels without fine-grained particles in the spaces between grains are the most permeable and allow water to move readily through them.

5. Structure of the rock formations. Inclined strata will allow more water to penetrate the earth than flat-lying beds. Water passing down inclined beds will follow the most porous layers. If the rocks are horizontal, the water passing downward must cross also the least porous beds.

6. Amount and kind of vegetation on the surface. Plants and organic matter derived from plants check the flow of surface water, and more

water sinks below the surface. Forests and meadows hold back the runoff and also retard evaporation.

7. Amount of moisture in the atmosphere. If the humidity is low immediately after a shower, more of the rainfall evaporates before it can sink into the earth. This is especially true in arid regions, where even after heavy rains the bulk of the water dries up or by evaporation passes again into the atmosphere.

Level of Ground Water. The terms "ground-water level," "water table," and "plane of saturation" are commonly used to describe the upper surface of the zone within the earth below which the openings in rocks are filled with water (Fig. 98). The upper limit of this zone of saturation is not a plane but is undulating. It tends to follow the undulations of the topography of a region, but it is more regular. It generally lies lower below a valley than below a hilltop, but it lies deeper below a hilltop than below a valley.

The level of the plane of saturation is controlled by several factors, such as the amount of rainfall, the amount of evaporation, and the porosity of the rocks. The general level does not respond at once following each period of rainfall because of the time required for the water to percolate downward through the unsaturated materials above the water table. In fact during a heavy rainfall a saturated zone may be formed near the surface, constituting a temporary "perched" water table at some distance above the plane of general saturation.

The rise of the water table following a period of rainfall never corresponds in amount to the number of inches of precipitation, owing to run-

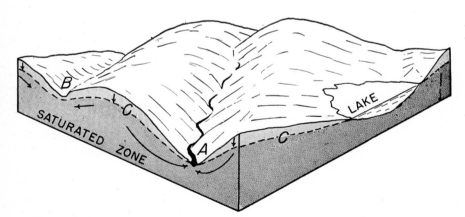

FIG. 99. Generalized diagram showing the relation of the water table to lakes, streams, and the surface of the ground. For the sake of simplicity, the region is drawn as if underlain by a rock formation of uniform porosity. A, permanent stream; B, a temporary stream gully; C, the regional water table.

off, losses through evaporation, absorption by vegetation, and absorption by decomposed rock materials in the unsaturated zone above. The difference of elevation between the top of this zone in a wet year and in a dry year is normally greater under the hilltops than on the slopes and in the valleys. Since the water table oscillates with climatic changes (Fig. 99), there is a zone within the earth that is above ground-water level in dry periods but below it during wet periods. In moist, hilly regions this zone may be of considerable vertical extent.

A moist fringe is drawn upward a few inches to a few feet above the water table by capillary openings, and some water also is held in the soil in spite of the pull of gravity (Fig. 100). Between is the intermittently wet and dry *vadose* zone, or zone of aeration, a zone favorable to leaching and oxidation (Fig. 101). The saturated zone sometimes is called the *phreatic* zone (Greek *phrear,* a well).

The water table on either side of a river usually slopes toward the stream; contrary to the common belief that ground-water supplies are replenished by rivers, the reverse is more often true. Rivers are essentially surface streams receiving ground water from springs and seepage. They generally do not contribute to the zone of saturation or ground water, except in arid regions where the local conditions are such that the zone of saturation lies below the river and the stream actually loses water into the earth. Such a river is known as an *influent stream.* The reverse condition, where gound water furnishes water through springs to streams, more generally prevails (Fig. 102). Such a river is known as an *effluent stream.* It lies in a trough on the water table, and the ground-water flow is toward it. Influent streams, on the other hand, lie on ridges in the water table.

Perched Water Table. Under certain conditions a body of water in porous or pervious material may be perched or suspended within the zone of aeration above the main water table. These bodies of water are generally above an irregularly shaped mass of impermeable rock, above basin-shaped beds of clay, or in lenses

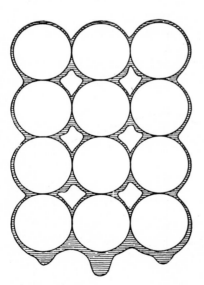

FIG. 100. Diagram showing how a liquid clings to solid particles against the pull of gravity as in the soil zone. (*Drawn from photograph by L. J. Briggs.*)

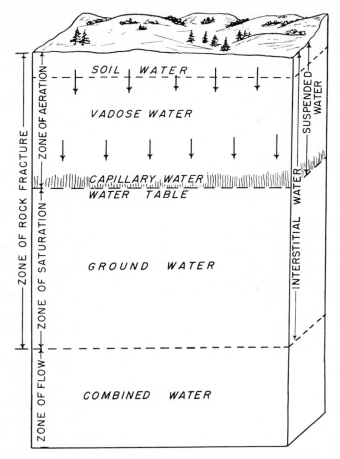

FIG. 101. Diagram showing distribution of subsurface water.

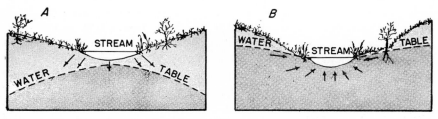

FIG. 102. Diagrams showing the relation of streams to ground water. *A*, an influent stream which lies above the water table; *B*, an effluent stream which lies in a trough on the water table.

or wedge-shaped masses of sand and gravel, which catch and hold the downward-percolating water. They are called perched because they are higher than the main water table. Such occurrences are common in arid and semiarid regions and may be important sources of water.

In parts of the glaciated region of northeastern North America where large areas are covered by a thick mantle of clayey glacial drift, many of the lakes are in basins the floors of which do not extend down to the regional water table. The perched water in such lakes is prevented from percolating downward to the main water table by impermeable clay layers between the floors of the lakes and the normal regional water level.

Movements of Ground Water. Above the water table, ground water moves downward and generally not far laterally. In the zone of saturation it is not stationary. Its movements are slow, but it tends to migrate along the paths of least resistance through the rocks; and if there is a lower outlet along the bottom of a valley, lake, or other basin, it will move to it even though it may follow a very crooked route before it finds a point where it can issue again at the surface. If the paths of least resistance are downward, the water may sink to great depths before it rises through some porous formation or fracture which crops out at a point lower than that at which the water first entered the saturated zone. The cause of movement is gravity.

The downward movement of water toward the zone of saturation is termed the "vadose," or shallow, circulation. The thickness of this zone is variable, since its lower limit is determined by the position of the ground-water level. Near permanent streams or lakes or other bodies of water it lies near the surface. In hilly regions with average rainfall, however, its depth from the surface varies from a few to several hundred feet. In arid regions, where the amount of rainfall is small and evaporation rapid, this zone may extend to much greater depths.

Below the water table the circulation of water depends on (1) the relief of the region, or potential head; (2) the number, continuity, spacing, and size of the openings in the rocks; (3) the inclination of the layers of sediments or lava; and (4) possible barriers of clay, shale, or other relatively impervious rocks. As a rule, the flow of water in this deeper zone is much slower than in the vadose zone because the openings are less numerous and smaller. For this reason friction on their walls is greater. In fine-grained rocks the underground circulation becomes exceedingly sluggish, the water moving perhaps not more than a few feet per year.

The depth to which the surface waters penetrate varies with the character of the rocks. In some rocks, surface waters reach a depth of several thousand feet, whereas in others very little water is collected at depths of more than a few hundred feet. In the copper-bearing rocks at Keweenaw

Point, Michigan, shafts have been sunk over a mile below the surface, and at a number of places the rocks are dry and dusty near the lower ends of the shafts. Many holes bored deep into the earth in search of oil have penetrated dry rocks at depths of 2,000 or 3,000 feet. A study of the movement of underground water indicates that there is an indefinite division between a sluggish deep circulation and a zone of essentially stagnant waters at still greater depths.

Springs. Springs are formed wherever underground waters flow to the surface through natural openings in the ground. The rate and manner of flow are regulated by the geological structure of the mantle-rock and of underlying formations (Fig. 103). Ground water always flows along planes or channels of least resistance. At first it percolates and seeps slowly through the rocks, but in time it wears well-defined courses. Springs usually issue upon a hillside or in a valley. An ordinary hillside spring is formed where sand, gravel, sandstone, or other porous strata rest upon impervious beds. Where the water comes to the surface along an escarpment, it "weeps" out in the form of hundreds of small seepage springs. If the strata are inclined, deep-seated fissure springs or artesian springs may issue through points along fault planes that cut the impervious strata. Such fissure springs may discharge fresh water on the floor of the sea, where it will rise through the heavier salt water before the two become

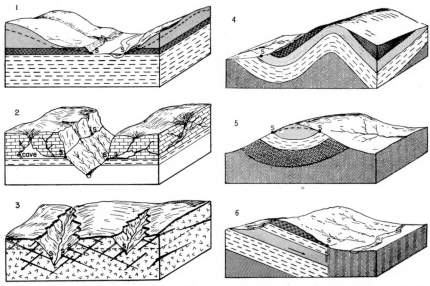

FIG. 103. Diagrams showing various kinds of subsurface rock structures favorable for the formation of springs. Locations of springs are marked by S.

mixed. Such springs are found along the coast of the Mediterranean Sea. In the Gulf of Argos, Greece, a body of fresh water, estimated to extend over an area 50 feet in diameter, probably represents the exit of a fissure spring, for it discharges fresh water with such force that it forms a convex surface on the sea.

Hot Springs. Hot springs are vents in the earth's crust from which hot water issues. Some hot springs and a considerable number of warm ones are found in areas remote from igneous centers, and it is believed that the water of such springs is normal rain water that has penetrated the ground and moved downward to great depths. The temperature of the earth's crust increases downward at a rate of about 1°C. for every 30 meters (about 100 feet). Ground waters at a depth of 1 mile would be about 50°C. hotter than the average surface temperature; and if such water were to rise without much dilution, it would be noticeably warmer than surface waters. Many hot springs and the hottest ones are found in volcanic areas. This suggests a connection between certain hot springs and cooling igneous rocks.

Gases like those which issue from the surface in volcanic areas are present also in many hot springs, and certain vents from which gases issue in dry seasons become hot springs in wet seasons. In some the gases issue vigorously and agitate the water. Such are known as boiling springs. Some that contain rock fragments, particularly oxidized particles of iron, color the water yellow or red and are called "paint pots," "ink bowls," etc. Algae, which are simple forms of vegetable life, thrive in the warm waters of certain springs. Some of them are brightly colored, and they color the walls of the springs.

Waters and Deposits of Hot Springs. The waters that issue from hot springs contain many salts, chiefly alkalies and alkaline earths, which are present as carbonates, chlorides, and sulfates. Certain warm springs in areas remote from volcanic activity carry abundant mineral salts, but alkalies and chlorides are much less prominent in such waters than in those of volcanic areas. *Tufa* is material deposited by springs around their vents. It is generally deposited more abundantly by hot springs because their waters before issuing can carry more mineral matter in solution than colder water. Much tufa consists chiefly of calcium carbonate. Deposits so formed of nearly pure calcium carbonate are called "travertine." If the calcium carbonate forms crystalline bands and takes a good polish, it is "Mexican onyx." When the tufa contains fragments cemented by calcium carbonate, it is a "breccia"; some of it is highly prized as an ornamental stone. Spring deposits are called "sinter" and, if of calcium carbonate, "calcareous sinter." *Geyserite,* or "siliceous sinter," is a term applied to siliceous hot-spring deposits, particularly to deposits made by geysers. Where deposits are abundant, a spring or geyser may build a mound or terrace (Fig. 104) or a bowllike structure around the orifice of the spring or geyser and the water that issues may pour over the top of the bowl. Deposition of long-continued overflow builds up the terrace. Calcium carbonate is the salt most abundantly deposited by both hot and cold springs. It frequently forms great beds near the outlets, and at resorts it clogs the pipes that lead the hot water to bathing pools. Silica also occurs abundantly in many hot waters, and it is the chief material deposited by some of the famous hot springs of Yellowstone National Park.

Geysers.   Geysers are hot springs from which the water is expelled vigorously at intervals. They are much less numerous than ordinary hot springs. Groups of geysers are situated in Yellowstone Park in the United States (Fig. 105), in Iceland, and in New Zealand. These areas are regions of recent volcanic activity. Certain geysers, when they erupt, throw hot water several hundred feet into the air. In others the water reaches only a few feet above the surface. Most geysers are active at irregular intervals. In some the eruptions occur many days apart; in others the intervals are weeks or months. In general, the water of the geysers does not differ from that of other hot springs. In certain geysers, after the activity ceases, some of the water flows away from the vent, but in others practically all of it

FIG. 104. Travertine deposits named Opal Terraces at Mammoth Hot Springs, Yellowstone National Park. (*Courtesy of Northern Pacific Railway.*)

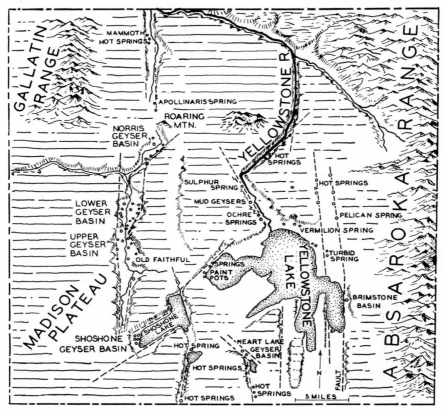

FIG. 105. The Yellowstone Basin, showing the distribution of geysers and hot springs. (*After Lobeck, from Atlas of American Geology.*)

flows back into it again. One of the best known geysers is Old Faithful of Yellowstone Park (Fig. 106), which for many years erupted regularly at intervals of less than 60 minutes. In recent years this interval has changed somewhat, yet the geyser is still comparatively regular in its eruptions. An eruption of Wairoa Geyser, New Zealand, is shown in Fig. 107.

The eruption of a geyser is preceded by rumblings and by violent boilings. The water flows over the top of the vent, and soon low columns of spouting water appear. These are followed by strong jets, which are thrown scores of feet into the air.

Eruptions of Geysers. The theory of eruption generally accepted is that of Bunsen, who studied the geysers of Iceland. It is based on the fact that the temperature at which water boils increases with pressure. This temperature is 212°F. at sea level on the surface of the earth, where the pressure above the water is 1 atmosphere, or about 14.7 pounds per square inch. At 2 atmospheres water boils at 248°F. and at 10 atmospheres at 357°F. A column of water 33 feet high has a pressure of about 1 atmosphere, that is, a column 1 square inch in cross section and 33 feet

FIG. 106. Old Faithful Geyser in eruption, Yellowstone National Park. (*Courtesy of Northern Pacific Railway.*)

Approximate Pressure Necessary to Hold Water in the Liquid State at Certain Depths

1	2	3
Pressure, atmospheres	Depth, feet, to produce pressures of Column 1	Temperature, degrees Fahrenheit
1	0	212
2	33	248
10	295	357
25	787	437

Column 1 shows approximately the pressures at which water boils at the temperatures of Column 3.
Column 2 shows depths in a water column where these pressures exist.
Column 3 shows temperatures at which water will boil under pressures of Column 1.

long weighs about 14.7 pounds. The temperatures at which water will boil at various pressures are shown in the accompanying table.

The water thrown from geysers is mainly rain water that has soaked into the ground, and the heat is supplied by hot lavas or other igneous rocks. Steam (later condensed to water) and other gases probably have originated in the magma that formed the cooling igneous rocks. If water flows into a fissure or tube (Fig. 108) and becomes warm with depth by absorbing hot gases or by contact with hot rocks, it may remain as water, although it is much hotter than 212°F., which is the boiling point of water at the surface. It does not become steam because of the water pressure above it. If water continues to enter the tube, ultimately it will flow over at the surface and that from the greater depth will rise to take the place of the overflow; but the water at great depth is so hot that it would become steam if it were not for the great pressure of the water column above it. Finally the temperature rises to such a point that steam is formed, even under the great pressure. This steam pushes up the column of water

FIG. 107. Wairoa Geyser in eruption, New Zealand. (*Photograph courtesy of New Zealand Government Publicity.*)

and, mixing with that above, makes it lighter; soon some of the water spills over at the top and reduces the pressure. Then part of the super-heated water flashes into steam, and an eruption follows. It is probable that the superheating of water at great depths causes the eruption of some geysers and that the collection of steam and other gases in the high parts of crooked tubes of geysers operates to cause the eruption of others. The crookedness of tubes prevents the convection of heat, thereby hastens boiling, and prohibits continuous overflow as simple hot springs.

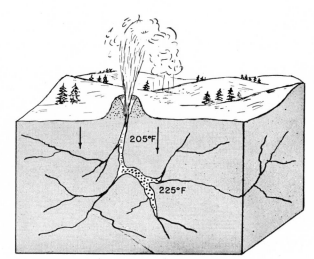

FIG. 108. Diagrammatic section illustrating geyser eruption according to the theory of Bunsen. Ground water in fractures and vents below the surface is heated to the boiling point at depth, nearer the source of heat, before it reaches the boiling point in the upper part of the vent (see table, page 134). For simplicity only a few fractures are shown.

GRADATIONAL WORK OF GROUND WATER

Chemical Activity of Ground Water. The various processes of rock decomposition, such as oxidation, carbonation, and hydration, which have already been described as phases of weathering, are active in the zone of circulating ground waters. Not only do they produce reactions within the earth that are analogous to those at the surface, but at many places the waters are more active because of the greater heat and pressure that exist below the earth's surface. The various phases of the chemical work of ground water may be divided into two main groups, namely, *solution* and *deposition*. These two processes may be going on simultaneously, for ground water may be dissolving one mineral at the same time that it is depositing another.

Ground Water as a Solvent. Ground water continually is dissolving material from the rocks below the surface of the earth. All spring water contains dissolved mineral matter. The formation of subterranean caves

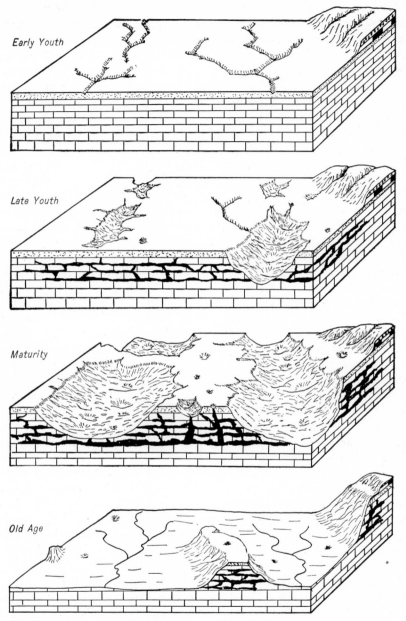

FIG. 109. Four stages of erosion of an area with flat-lying limestone in which underground drainage is developed. The caves are shown black. (*After A. K. Lobeck, Kentucky Geological Survey.*)

and channels is evidence of this process. If ground water were chemically pure, relatively little mineral matter would be dissolved; but since most ground water is of meteoric origin, carbon dioxide, oxygen, and other gases were added to it as it fell through the atmosphere. Furthermore, decomposing organic matter in the soil near the surface adds organic acids to the percolating water, and these greatly increase its solvent power. As it penetrates to greater depths, it is heated and its solvent action is increased. Since some minerals are more soluble than others, it carries away first those constituents of the rocks which are dissolved most readily and thus makes the rock more porous.

Because of the greater resistance to solution of certain minerals extensive deposits of economic value have been concentrated at or near the surface by the solution and removal of the valueless minerals associated with them. The extensive residual iron ores of Cuba, of the Appalachian region, and of the Lake Superior region in the United States, together with great deposits of manganese and aluminum in various parts of the world, owe their concentration to the solvent action of ground water.

Underground Channels and Caves. Ground water sinks readily in regions where there are cracks or joints in the rocks. These are gradually enlarged by the corrosive work of the descending water and at certain places become greatly extended parallel to the bedding where the rock has layers that are easily dissolved (Fig. 109). In time these channels become large so that considerable surface water drains into them. Where the openings to the channels form conspicuous holes at the surface of the earth, they are termed *sinkholes,* or swallow holes. Such sinks are most commonly formed in limestone, gypsum, and salt. In other rocks the insoluble parts left as a residue are far larger than the percentage dissolved. In such rocks, therefore, the soil or rock waste fills the space originally occupied by the rock, and no such cavities result. Where pure limestone is attacked, the whole rock is soluble and therefore nothing remains to fill the spaces where percolating waters dissolve the strata. Thus in the course of time an elaborate system of spacious tunnels and chambers may be dissolved out of solid rock below the water table. The vast labyrinth of the Mammoth Cave of Kentucky and the intricate grottoes of Carlsbad Caverns in New Mexico, Luray Cave in Virginia, Wyandotte Cave in Indiana, and many other famous caves on this and other continents owe their origin to the solvent action of ground water.

In regions where caves and sinkholes abound, some of the roofs of the caverns collapse, and a very irregular type of topography is developed. Similarly, portions of the roofs of underground channels and galleries may collapse so as to leave natural bridges over solution valleys. The

FIG. 110. Stalactites, stalagmites, and pillars in the caverns of Luray, Virginia. (*Courtesy of Luray Caverns Corp.*)

slopes to the sinkholes and also the slopes of the elevations between them become steep and clifflike. The surface is etched out in a network of numerous short gullies and ravines, which terminate abruptly where they discharge their waters into subterranean channels, and consequently the surface is rough. Such topography is characteristically developed in the Karst Mountains, northeast of the head of the Adriatic Sea in an area composed of limestone. In the United States similar topography is developed in limestone areas in central Tennessee and Kentucky and is referred to as *karst topography*.

Occasionally the bottoms of sinkholes become choked with debris, and small lakes or ponds are formed. Alachua Lake, Florida, is an example. Prior to 1871 the surface drainage of Alachua prairie emptied into a large sinkhole. That year the outlet of the sink was clogged, and a lake nearly 8 miles long and 4 miles wide was formed. About 20 years later the outlet was again opened, and the lake was drained underground.

Deposits in Caves. When a region is dissected by streams and the water table is lowered thereby below cave level, deposition in the cave may set in by water entering the cave from above. Thus caves opened by solution may tend to be filled later. Most of the mineral matter deposited in caves is calcium carbonate. It assumes various forms, among them the *stalactites,* which are attached to the roof of the cavern or to some projecting edge, and the *stalagmites,* which form on the floor of the cavern and build upward, forming mounds and cones on the limestone floor (Figs. 110, 111).

Stalactites assume many shapes, determined by the manner in which the water trickles over them and by the amount of water present. Beau-

FIG. 111. Stalactites and stalagmites, some of them joined to form pillars in the Dome Room of Carlsbad Caverns, New Mexico. (*Courtesy of Santa Fe Railway.*)

tiful forms fringed with crystals of calcite, curtainlike draperies hanging from the roofs, grotesque shapes that rise from the floors, and pillars ornamented with many varieties of sculpture may be observed in the same cavern. An iciclelike stalactite broken across shows a radial structure, with fibrous crystals passing across concentric zones of growth. The growing stalactite is kept moist by calcium-bearing water trickling over its surface and is lengthened at the lower end and thickened from the center of the structure.

Stalactites have their beginning on the damp roof of the cave, where drops of water gather and begin to evaporate and thus lose carbon dioxide. The drops then become saturated with carbonate and deposit the excess as a ring at their margins. Drop after drop lengthens the ring into a long pendant with a pipestemlike hole in the middle. Those which reach the floor of the cave become solid stalks which may thicken into massive pillars. Many pillars are formed also by the union of stalagmites that grow upward from the floor with stalactites that hang from the roof. Some of the deposits in Carlsbad Caverns, New Mexico, are extensive; Giant Dome, for example, is an enormous stalagmite, about 16 feet in diameter and 62 feet high. Twin Domes is another stalagmite mass more than 200 feet wide at the base and over 100 feet high.

Famous Caves. One of the largest cave systems in the world is that of the Carlsbad Caverns in New Mexico, located in a region of limestone and gypsum in the Guadalupe Mountains. Because of its fantastic display of ornamental stalactites, stalagmites, pillars, curtains, and frescoes of onyx, it was made a national park in 1930. One gallery, the Big Room, is about 4,000 feet long and has a maximum width of 625 feet and a maximum ceiling height of about 300 feet.

Perhaps the best-known of American caverns is Mammoth Cave in Kentucky. Some of its caverns have been studied and mapped in detail, but there are many others that have never been fully explored. There are several hundred miles of connected galleries with lakes, rivers, and waterfalls in the Mammoth Cave system. These galleries vary in height from a foot or two to more than 100 feet. In some parts of the cave one gallery is located above another. Mammoth Dome, which is an expanded portion of the cavern, is about 400 feet long, 150 feet wide, and 80 to 250 feet high.

Luray Cave in the Shenandoah valley, Virginia (Fig. 110), is famous for its brilliantly colored stalactites, of which there are as many as 40,000 visible from a single point. One celebrated group is that of the Swords of the Titans composed of eight staffs, 50 feet long, 3 to 8 feet wide, and as much as 2 feet thick.

Other noted limestone caverns in the United States are the Wyandotte and Marengo caves in Indiana, Wind Cave in South Dakota, and Marble

Cave in Missouri. One of the best-known foreign caverns is at Adelsberg in Italy. Its four great chambers are visited frequently, and festivals are conducted in its grottoes.

Replacement or Substitution. Where solution and deposition are in progress simultaneously, one mineral may be dissolved and other mineral matter deposited in its place. This process is *replacement.* If the material replaced is of organic origin, it becomes *petrified* by the mineral matter that replaces it. Thus if a log or stump is buried in a bed of sand or volcanic ash that later becomes saturated with ground water, the replacement of the wood by silica is accomplished slowly as the wood is removed (Fig. 112). Eventually, a large tree trunk may be converted into a solid mass of silica. The famous petrified logs and forests of Arizona owe their origin to this process. Erosion has again exposed them, so that, at present, silicified stumps and logs occur at the earth's surface (Fig. 113).

A crystal of iron sulfide is replaced by iron oxide and yet retains the shape of the sulfide crystal. These replacements are *pseudomorphs* (false forms), and by studying them it is possible often to trace the changes through which a mineral or rock has passed. In some regions it is possible

FIG. 112. Cross section of a petrified tree trunk that is completely replaced by opal (silica and water). The structure of the original woody tissue is preserved. (*Courtesy of American Museum of Natural History.*)

FIG. 113. A large petrified log in Petrified Forest National Monument, Holbrook, Arizona. (*Courtesy of National Park Service.*)

to trace the altered sedimentary rock into the unaltered sedimentary rock and to follow the changes step by step, for the grain, bedding, and other textures of the original rock are preserved in the altered rock after metamorphism.

Igneous rocks also are profoundly changed by replacement. Much material is removed, and other material takes its place. Commonly, however, the texture or pattern of the rock is preserved, because the outlines of the original crystals form the outlines of the replacing crystals or of groups of the replacing crystals. By comparing the textures of the fresh and altered rocks, often it becomes evident that they were once alike and parts of the same body.

Deposition by Ground Water. A considerable portion of the mineral matter taken into solution by ground water is again deposited before it is carried far. Subsurface waters in large measure are acidic solvents in the zone of leaching above the ground-water table, but beneath this surface the water may move so slowly that it remains in contact with the rock walls of the fractures and pores for so long a time that its acidity is neutralized, and precipitation ensues. The precipitated minerals tend to fill the spaces and to cement the rocks more thoroughly for some distance below the ground-water level. The zone throughout which such deposition takes place is known as the *zone of cementation.*

At places mineral-bearing waters deposit their loads upon the walls of cracks or joints to form *veins.* This type of deposition takes place also when hot magmatic waters or vapors penetrate the rocks. The precipitation is brought about by the cooling effect produced by the fissure walls, by surface waters, or by chemical reactions with the minerals lining the fracture. Thus an acid solution flowing through a fissure in limestone may become neutralized in contact with the calcium carbonate, and the mineral matter in solution may be deposited to fill the fissure and thus form a mineral vein.

Many of the veins formed by the precipitation of minerals from hot magmatic waters which are charged with sulfur compounds contain sulfides of metals such as copper, lead, zinc, silver, and many others. Where such ore minerals are present in sufficient quantities, the veins are mined and the metals extracted. Most veins formed from cold meteoric ground waters are filled with quartz and calcite. Some pyrite also may be present.

Under certain conditions chemical precipitation takes place about some nucleus, such as a leaf or animal remains or even a pebble. Deposition once started seems to lead to further precipitation on the same surface, and concentric layers of mineral matter are deposited (Fig. 114). Rounded, irregular bodies called *concretions* are formed in this manner. They are most commonly formed in rather porous sedimentary rocks. Many coal beds contain concretionary masses of iron sulfide in the form of the mineral marcasite. Other concretions are made of calcite, quartz, gypsum, barium sulfate, calcium phosphate, or other compounds.

FIG. 114. Calcareous concretions from clay beds.

Cavities in rocks may become lined with crystals by precipitation from ground water. Those which are round or egg-shaped are called *geodes*. In certain semiarid regions capillary action draws lime-bearing waters to the surface, where, by evaporation, a lime-rich deposit called *caliche* is formed.

Mineral Matter in Spring Water. Even the clearest and most sparkling spring water contains some dissolved mineral matter. As a rule this consists principally of carbonates of calcium, magnesium, and sodium and sulfates of calcium and sodium, with smaller amounts of silicates, phosphates, and chlorides. Some of these materials are taken into solution through the action of gases absorbed by rain from the atmosphere. Other materials are derived from decomposing rock and organic matter in the soil. The gases are mainly carbon dioxide, hydrogen sulfide, and marsh gas. In areas covered with a mantle of humus, organic acids also are abstracted from the soil and aid in decomposing minerals and in forming soluble salts.

A spring in which the amount of mineral matter in solution is relatively great is a mineral spring. One in which lime predominates is a calcareous spring; and where the water carries a large proportion of iron, the spring is a ferruginous, or chalybeate, spring. Iron-bearing springs are readily recognized by the yellow or brown ochre deposits around or near their vents. Springs high in sodium chloride are brine springs. They occur where beds of rock salt exist beneath the surface, where the rocks have chloride minerals disseminated through them, or where salt water issues from some deep-seated reservoir. The term *medicinal spring* is applied to mineral springs which are supposed to have curative effects in certain types of disease. Such springs may contain sulfurous waters, alkaline waters, or bitter waters, each of which derives its name from the soluble salt that predominates.

The amount of dissolved mineral matter brought to the surface by spring waters is enormous. Thousands of tons of gypsum issue annually at the springs of Leuk, in Switzerland, and it has been estimated that the famous springs of Bath, in England, bring up so much mineral matter in solution yearly that if it were taken out of the water and made into a monument it would make a column 9 feet in diameter and 140 feet high. In central Florida, Silver Springs carry about 600 tons of mineral matter daily, and Falls Creek, in Oklahoma, receives water from springs that carry so much lime that a series of travertine dams have been deposited across the stream valley.

Wells. Prehistoric man used the water from springs, brooks, rivers, and lakes. His villages were built where water was readily obtained at the surface. However, with the growth of civilization, large quantities of water were required in regions where surface water was not available or where it was too polluted for domestic use. Digging or boring for water dates back to very early historic times, especially in China and India. In Babylonia irrigation works were constructed as early as 2000 B.C. In India today more land is irrigated from wells than from streams.

Most wells are holes dug or bored into the earth to a point below the water table. They serve as reservoirs into which the ground water percolates. If the water level is near the surface, the wells are shallow, whereas on high plateaus where the water level is as much as several hundred feet below the surface, correspondingly deep wells are required in order to obtain water. Most wells are sunk until they penetrate a permeable rock below the water table. This often necessitates boring through hundreds of feet of impervious clays or shales that are saturated with water, but the pore spaces in such rocks are so minute that water cannot flow through them rapidly enough to supply the well adequately.

Even in highly permeable rocks, the removal of water through a well draws the water table down adjacent to the well and produces a slope, or gradient, toward the well on the water table (Fig. 115). Such a *cone of depression* is steep in materials of low permeability and may not have a radius of more than a few hundred feet. In uniformly permeable sands and gravels, however, a measurable lowering in observation wells may

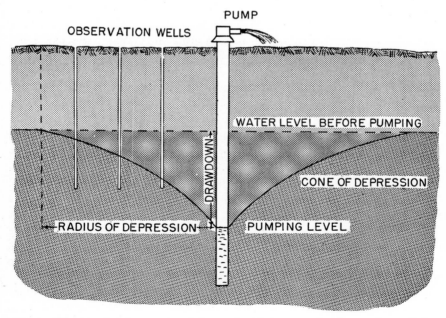

FIG. 115. Diagram showing a cone of depression of the water level around a well that is being pumped.

FIG. 116. Diagram showing subsurface conditions favorable for artesian circulation.

extend several thousand feet from the pumping well and produce "interference" with neighboring wells.

Artesian Wells. Artesian wells received their name from Artois, a province in France, where the water in many wells rises above the surface of the earth, as it does in fountains. Today the term artesian well is applied to any deep well from which ground water under pressure is obtained, even though the water does not rise completely to the surface. All flowing wells are artesian, but not all artesian wells overflow. Artesian flow takes place because of differences in the pressure under which ground water exists in different parts of a water-bearing stratum. The principle involved is that expressed in the maxim, "Water seeks its own level." The force causing it to seek that level is gravity. The pressure produced by gravity acting on water is hydrostatic pressure. Technically, hydrostatic pressure is that property of water by means of which pressure is transmitted equally throughout it in all directions almost instantly. If an object is placed in a body of clear water at rest, hydrostatic pressure may be thought of as the force causing the space occupied by the object to fill up when the object is removed.

In an artesian system the water-bearing bed may be compared to a tube filled with water where the intake is higher than the outlet. The conditions essential for a flowing artesian well (see Fig. 116) are summarized below:

1. There must be a pervious stratum, the aquifer, which water enters and passes through.

2. There must be an impervious bed above the permeable one to prevent the water from escaping to the surface as springs.

3. There must be an impervious stratum below or else a tightening of the rocks with depth to prevent the water from escaping downward.

4. There must be an inclination from the horizontal of the permeable bed so that the place at which the water enters it will stand at a higher

elevation than the surface of the earth at the well. The force of gravity will then cause the water to flow downward. This condition is commonly called "head."

5. The porous stratum must crop out so that water may enter it, or if covered it must be covered by permeable material at the intake.

6. There must be adequate rainfall to supply water.

These required conditions apply only to sedimentary strata. Artesian flows may be obtained from other kinds of rock, even from unconsolidated sediments, but the structural and textural relations must be such that they contain water under hydrostatic pressure. Artesian flows may be obtained from bedding, cleavage, or shearing planes, from solution passages, from joint and fault fractures, and from contacts of sedimentary with igneous or metamorphic rocks.

At many places the sources of the water in the intake areas are scores or even hundreds of miles distant from the wells. In parts of Arkansas, Alabama, California, and Arizona the principal water supplies for irrigation projects are drawn from artesian wells that derive their water from the foothills of the mountainous areas scores of miles away.

Depths of Artesian Wells. The depth to the porous stratum is determined by the geological structural relations. The Grenelle Artesian in the Paris Basin is 2,000 feet deep; a well near Leipzig, Germany, is 5,735 feet; one near Pittsburgh, Pennsylvania, is 4,625 feet deep. Most of the wells in the famous Dakota sandstone basin are 1,000 feet deep or more. Many flowing wells in the glacial drift are less than 100 feet deep.

Water Supplies. Ground water is a natural resource upon which a large part of our population depends. It supplies many municipalities and is widely used in agriculture and industry. Wells and springs are estimated currently to furnish an average of 25 to 30 billion gallons per day, or about one-sixth of the total water used for irrigational, industrial, and public purposes.

The most abundant yields of ground water come from unconsolidated mantle-rock, from permeable sedimentary rocks, and from some lava flows. The most copious yields from unconsolidated sediments come from (1) alluvial sands and gravels, (2) glacial outwash (page 260), (3) stream terraces and flood plains (page 200), and (4) sandy coastal plain deposits (page 346). Among the consolidated rocks the greatest yield may be expected from (1) permeable sandstones, (2) cavernous limestones, (3) closely jointed rocks such as quartzite and granite, and (4) jointed vesicular or cavernous lavas and basalt. Shattering of solid rocks by faulting or folding or artificially by explosives is helpful.

Most persons in the United States, except those living in arid regions, have never had to think much about water supply. A fairly high average rainfall throughout most of our continent and the presence of many large inland rivers and lakes have deluded us into believing that water is one resource about which we need have little concern. During the past few decades, however, we have been forced to recognize that we depend heavily upon water as an essential resource and that difficulties with water supply are increasing. The time already has come when we must abolish wasteful practices, especially in critical areas. Undoubtedly the over-all supply is adequate, provided the problem is recognized and practices modified to conserve this vital resource.

SUGGESTIONS FOR FURTHER READING

Allen, E. T., and A. L. Day: Hot Springs of the Yellowstone National Park, Carnegie Institution of Washington, 1935.

Baker, D. M., and H. Conkling: Water Supply and Utilization, John Wiley & Sons, Inc., 1930.

Tolman, C. F.: Ground Water, McGraw-Hill Book Company, Inc., 1937.

CHAPTER 8

Gradation by Mass Movement of Surface Materials

The products of weathering, where accumulated over a mass of bedrock, form a protecting blanket which retards change in the underlying mass and, if thick enough, may prevent it entirely. The removal of weathered debris by the wind, running water, and glaciation is readily recognized at the earth's surface everywhere. But in other regions where these agents are least effective, the products of rock disintegration and decomposition may be on the move, also. In such places one of the most active forces at work is gravity, which, in conjunction with many other factors, may produce results of marked effect on the landscape (Fig. 117).

On sloping surfaces, where part of the force of gravity may be translated into motion, there are types of transportation of rock waste in which the debris load becomes progressively greater as the volume of water available diminishes. On such surfaces water acts as a lubricant and as excess weight, and so the rock material, creeping slowly under the force of gravity, may move suddenly as a massive landslide. The rate of such mass movements may be exceedingly slow, or it may be very rapid. In either case this movement accounts for a large and essential part of erosion.

Classification of the various types of mass movement is difficult for the obvious reason that they tend to merge into each other. Some grade into other, quite different forms of movement of rock waste. Thus a mudflow with slight addition of water may become a heavily loaded stream of water, and similarly frost action is closely related to glaciation.

C. F. S. Sharpe has divided mass movement of rock waste into three major groups:

1. Slow flowage—rock creep, talus creep, soil creep, rock-glacier creep, and solifluction.

2. Rapid flowage—earth flow, mudflow, and debris avalanche.

149

FIG. 117. Rock waste moving down slope under the influence of ice, water, mud, and other similar factors, along the mountainside at Avalanche Lake. Glacier National Park, Montana. (*National Park Service.*)

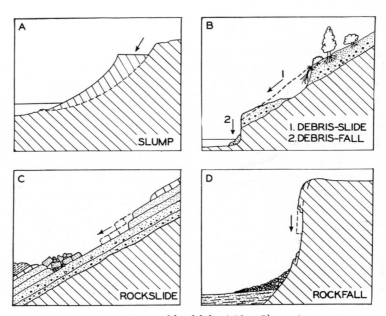

FIG. 118. Types of landslide. (*After Sharpe.*)

3. Sliding—slump, debris slide, debris fall, rockslide, rockfall (Fig. 118).

1. Creep, or Slow Flowage. Slow but continuous downward migration of soil and mantle-rock under the force of gravity is known as *creep*. Evidences of such creep are to be found on almost every soil-covered slope. It expresses itself in such signs as tilted fence posts and telegraph poles, broken or displaced retaining walls, and curved trees which when tilted down slope by creep tend to return to a vertical position during growth. Even roadbeds and railroad grades may be moved out of alignment.

Degradation by creep down a slope may be going on even though a continuous covering of tough sod may be present at the surface. In the headward portions of the drainage channels of western Kansas a slow creeping of the clays and soils takes place under the sod. Where boulders are present in the soil, turf or sod rolls may be observed down slope from the creeping boulders. On some sodded slopes crescentic scarps and cracks a few feet to 100 feet long or more have the horns of the crescents pointing down slope. Such features are due to unequal rates of movements on the sloping surface.

The rate of creep, usually imperceptible except to observations of long duration, depends upon factors such as temperature changes, amount

FIG. 119. Soil formed from limestone on hillside slope near Trail Ridge, Utah. Much of this weathered material was formed higher up the mountainside but was transported to lower levels by creep and frost action. (*Photograph by U.S. Forest Service.*)

of rainfall, angle of slope, type of soil, and nature of parent material (Fig. 119). In aeolian soil, such as loess, which has a tendency to stand nearly vertical, creep is exceedingly slow, whereas in loosely consolidated, sandy soils with a high proportion of rounded grains the response to the force of gravity and creep is more pronounced. Rates of 5 to 10 feet in 50 years have been measured. On forested slopes the root mat tends to retard the movement, especially that of the coarser particles. However, clay and other fine soil minerals pass through the network of roots quite easily.

In areas where there is alternate freezing and thawing the rate of creep is increased by the wedging and heaving action of ice. The power of frost heaving has been measured experimentally and found to reach pressures as high as 14 tons per square foot. The lifting action of frost acts at right angles to the slope of a hillside and may thrust surface materials upward as much as several feet. Subsequently, when the frost melts, the boulders and other rock particles settle back vertically under the influence of gravity. Thus the new position of rest is down slope from the original, and, with repeated freezing and thawing, frost-heaved rock materials move down a sloping surface far more rapidly than they would if the temperature never fell below the freezing point.

Other agencies that assist creep are active in warmer climates. Clayey slopes may contract and crack during dry seasons, and when such desiccation fissures are closed or filled, there is a greater movement down slope than up. In hot, semiarid regions, where rocks and mineral grains crumble as a result of weathering processes, most of the products of weathering fall or roll down slope. Other things being equal, creep is more rapid in saturated mantle-rock, but movement takes place even under the most arid conditions.

"Rock creep" refers to the slow downhill slipping of large joint blocks wherever well-jointed massive formations crop out along a slope. By this process a joint block gradually widens the gap between itself and the parent outcrop and eventually tilts to the angle of slope of the surface. In bedded sedimentary strata or in slaty rocks, a downhill bending of the strata may be observed. In some hillside outcrops the bedding planes not only sag but may even show a reversal of the true direction of dip.

The term "talus creep" refers to the slow downslope movement of moderately coarse irregular blocks of a talus or scree which fall from receding cliffs where they are loosened by various agents of weathering. Such creep is found wherever a steep talus slope exists, and its rate of movement is determined by the climatic conditions of the region. Where thermal changes are great, the rate is higher than at low altitudes in the tropics, where the daily temperature changes are slight. The most rapid movement occurs in cold regions, where the expansive force of the alternate freeze and thaw of ice in the spaces between the fragments of rock waste or within the fragments themselves tends to thrust the material down a sloping surface. In some parts of the Mountain states and areas farther north (Fig. 120) many such accumulations of moving rock debris occur on steep slopes and in gullies, there giving rise to rock masses of such suggestive shape and action that they have been termed *rock glaciers*. Frost action and an icy matrix have important parts in their movement, but gravity appears to be the chief motive factor.

The growth of vegetation, especially tree roots forcing their way into cracks and other available spaces, may tip or wedge rock fragments into an unstable position and thus cause them to come under such direct gravitative action that they move down the slope. Burrowing animals or even the tread of the feet of passing animals may throw rock fragments and particles into an unbalanced position from which downslope movement is inevitable. These may seem insignificant factors among processes leading to reduction of the land, but they contribute to the slow transfer of rock waste to lower levels, as do all the other gravity mass movements.

Solifluction, or soil flowage, is the term applied to a type of creep

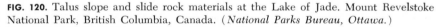

FIG. 120. Talus slope and slide rock materials at the Lake of Jade. Mount Revelstoke National Park, British Columbia, Canada. (*National Parks Bureau, Ottawa.*)

FIG. 121. Stone stripes, St. Elias Range, Alaska. (*Photograph by Robert P. Sharp.*)

that takes place in regions where the ground freezes to considerable depth and, as it thaws during warm seasons, the upper thawed portion creeps downhill over the frozen material at greater depth. As thawing continues from the surface downward, the melt waters cannot drain downward and eventually the upper, unfrozen layer of soil becomes saturated. In this condition it will move as a viscous liquid down slopes of as little as 2 or 3 degrees. Such slowly moving masses of fine debris may carry in suspension blocks of rock of considerable size.

Solifluction is a process particularly effective above the timber line in mountain areas, and in the subarctic and arctic regions, where permafrost, or perennially frozen ground, is present at depth and the superficial layers are softened by summer melting of their contained frost.

In these regions above or beyond the timber line, where frost action is a major factor in breaking up rock and displacing the fragments, there are unique arrangements of the rock waste. Large areas are covered by loose rocks, many of them angular, that have been rived from outcrops or from large boulders. Terracelike accumulations of the outward-moving angular blocks may result, but where the source masses are large boulders, the angular fragments that have split from them fall, many on edge, around the parent mass, or core, to form a somewhat circular or polygonal arrangement, hence called a *stone ring* or *stone polygon.* Under strong frost action such an arrangement may have been caused by heave from centers even below surface and the rings developed by frost-ejected fragments. Such rings or polygons are found on nearly level ground and on slightly sloping surfaces.

If the source boulders under frost riving, or splitting, are somewhat evenly spaced, the resultant stone rings may give rise to a rather uniform pattern, each unit enclosed by a ridge or wall of rock material fragmented by the process. The diameter of such rings or polygons, in regions of permafrost, may range from 6 to 30 feet, but miniature polygons composed of smaller fragmental material have been reported from less rigorous climatic areas.

On side hills or mountain slopes, where gravity becomes the major motive force, the developing rings creep down the hillside and elongate into ellipses and loops to form a mesh or net of garlandlike stony borders or walls that are the margins and ends of long tongues of finer material on the move. These garland tongues may be 2 to 6 feet or more across and have a flattened convex surface. The stony border may be several feet wide and contain rock fragments up to 2 feet in diameter, and possibly larger.

Garland loops and tongues may continue to elongate on steeper slopes or where mobility is great and pass into *stone stripes*, which may be traced down slope, as nearly parallel stony ridges (Figs. 121, 122), for several hundred feet before losing their identity. On still greater slopes garland loops and tongues may not be able to form, and the stone stripes develop directly from frost heave. Even the stone stripes fail to form on increased slopes where the frost-heaved rock fragments slide or roll down to a lodgment area below. Many of these features of frost action are excellently developed, and still under the active agent, from British Columbia northward through the Mackenzie District, the Yukon, and Alaska.

Present-day land surfaces show relics of ancient stone rings and stone stripes beyond the borders of permafrost even as far distant as Nova Scotia, New England, and Pennsylvania. These may have been formed during the time when a subarctic climate extended far south of its present limit and when frost action controlled the physiographic processes beyond the edge of the ice front as it then existed. Other features characteristic of permafrost are general about the borders of the Wisconsin drift-covered area and even far down along the Appalachian Mountains, where a subarctic or alpine climate may have extended.

Many mountaintops undergo active mass movement of rock waste by frost even though permafrost does not exist. Thus in such regions fields (felsenmeer) of rock fragments, many of them angular blocks, may be produced from bedrock by frost action, and these loose masses start moving down slope, becoming subangular to rounded as they travel,

FIG. 122. Close-up view of a stone stripe, St. Elias Range, Alaska. (*Photograph by Robert P. Sharp.*)

still under frost action. Solifluction aids in this movement and eventually may be the major cause of movement throughout the balance of their journey. All these mass movements of rock in which frost is the dominant motive force tend to produce a rounded landscape characteristic of *cryoplanation*, or the leveling process dominant under subarctic and arctic climates.

2. Rapid Flowage, or Debris Flow. The more rapid movements, earth flow, mudflow, debris avalanche, etc., originate and move under much the same influences as those of slow flowage except that the conditions favorable to movement are accentuated. Hence there is no sharp line to be drawn between slow and rapid flowage. The simplest of these latter are the earth flows. They are the least obvious in their movements although so continuous that their results eventually may be striking. Earth flows are in the nature of landslides in which the movement is so slow that much time is necessary for the earth mass to attain stability at the new and lower position. The movement is usually on gentle slopes and may require months or years to complete. Few slopes are free from them.

Mudflows resemble solifluction except that they move much faster and they usually follow former stream channels. In steep mountain areas where large amounts of suitable rock material are available and where great quantities of water may be supplied by heavy rains of "cloudburst" type or by rapid melting of a heavy accumulation of winter snow, an impressive type of mudflow, the Alpine mudflow, occurs frequently.

An excellent example [1] of Alpine mudflow occurred in southern California in May, 1941, when during unseasonably warm days the rapid melting of the heavy accumulation of winter snow supplied water to start the movement. The source of the rock material was largely the weathered micaceous schists in the shatter zone of the San Andreas fault high up on the north side of the San Gabriel Range. Here at the head of Heath Canyon the loosened debris started sliding down, then broke into a rushing and roaring mass, and left behind a steep, fan-shaped scar face rising 1,000 feet and a nearly vertical, arcuate scarp 100 to 150 feet high at the top. Being unable to funnel rapidly through a narrow, converging bottleneck into the narrow canyon below, the debris piled up to a thickness of 20 to 30 feet, and the more liquid portion cascaded over the retarded coarser material. The pent-up pressure, behind the temporary obstruction thus formed, caused the mud to break through at intervals, producing a periodic series of wavelike surges of liquid mud that plunged and raced down its course with rumbling and grating flow. occasionally splashing mud 20 feet into the air and splattering trees, shrubs, buildings, and spectators alike. The supply of material continued

---

[1] Robert P. Sharp and Laurence H. Nobles, Mudflow of 1941 at Wrightwood, Southern California, *Geol. Soc. America Bull.*, vol. 64, pp. 547–560, 1953.

FIG. 123. An earth flow streaming through a steep, narrow mountain valley near the north end of Stikine Mountains, Yukon Territory, Canada. (*Royal Canadian Air Force.*)

about 1 week, rising to a maximum during midday, then decreasing gradually, and ceasing at night. In the more fluid portion the mud mass was about 25 to 30 per cent water (by weight), and the rock debris, making up the balance, consisted of a mixture of fine, medium, and coarse materials, including large boulders. Fragments 2 to 3 feet in diameter were common 1½ miles below the origin of the flow.

In the upper part of the course the mud velocity was high but decreased with distance because of a decreasing gradient of the path it followed. Midway down an average speed of about 9 to 10 feet per second was maintained by the surge fronts, the tops of which tended to move ahead of or outrun the base, but near the lower end of the flow the velocity did not exceed 1 or 2 feet per second. The material in motion was rather thoroughly jumbled and resembled newly mixed concrete. Boulders were borne along as submerged masses where the energy available was sufficient to move them, but the coarser material was gradually nudged to the sides or shoved ahead at the front as a coarse aggregate where the mud became more viscous or the velocity decreased on a lower slope. At some places the mud spilled over the edge of its channel, during passage of a forward surge, and mud levees were built up by deposition of part of the load.

This mudflow was generally confined to a narrow strip 20 to 150 feet wide, although a width of 300 to 1,000 feet was attained at a few places. Its course is evident for a distance of 15 miles down the valley, some 5,000 feet below the source. It was estimated that nearly $1\frac{1}{4}$ million cubic yards of debris was involved in the mass movement. In the lower reaches the movement of the mudflow was maintained on a slope of about 75 feet per mile.

Alpine mudflows have been reported, not only in the United States and Canada (Fig. 123), but in the Andes, Alps, Himalaya, and elsewhere. They constitute one of the more spectacular types of mass movement occurring in the higher altitudes of the temperate zones.

Mudflows of the more common type are produced in arid or semiarid regions when water is suddenly supplied by heavy rainfall to an area in which there is much fine rock debris on moderately steep slopes. This is especially true of areas where deeply weathered material contains enough clay or silt to aid in lubrication of the mass. As a mudflow moves down a high-gradient valley, it acquires more and more load and eventually the amount of debris in the frontal portion is so great that it acts as a temporary dam across the valley. The pressure of water, however, pushes the whole viscous frontal dam forward, carrying with it huge boulders suspended in the muddy matrix.

In some parts of the United States mudflows are of common occurrence, and in some regions they have caused considerable damage. Most damage is done when the frontal dam bursts as the flow passes from the confining walls of a narrow valley onto the wide surface of an alluvial fan or cone. At that point the suspension of water and mud breaks through the frontal dam and rushes forward with tremendous force, carrying with it huge boulders and smaller rock debris. Along the Wasatch Range front from Salt Lake City northward, almost every canyon has a mudflow fan, and many of the flows have blocked highways, weakened or destroyed buildings, and ruined many acres of good farm land. Similar conditions exist in the rugged parts of Arizona, Nevada, and California, where immense quantities of rock waste have been transported from the mountainous areas and deposited on the piedmont slopes (Fig. 124).

Mudflows are also common on the steep slopes of active volcanoes newly strewn with thick accumulations of volcanic dust and cinders unstably poised in the event of heavy rains.

In humid regions mudflows are rare, but a movement of rock debris somewhat similar to the rapidly moving snow avalanches in mountainous topography takes place on steep hillside slopes. Such a rapidly flowing slide is termed a debris avalanche. Debris avalanches occur along rela-

FIG. 124. Margin of a recent mudflow now dry and sun-cracked, on an alluvial fan along the east side of the Stillwater Range, Churchill County, Nevada. (*Photograph by Eliot Blackwelder.*)

tively narrow zones, following heavy rains, which increase the weight of the loose surface material on the steep slopes. Slippage generally occurs on the smooth underlying rock surface. Numerous debris avalanches have been reported from the Appalachian Mountains, the White and Green Mountains of New England, and the Pacific Northwest. They are common wherever steep slopes occur with easily detached rock material lying in unstable positions. There may be much snow and ice mingled with the rock waste, and such rock avalanches grade into the avalanches of snow on snowy slopes. They leave a bare scarp from which the debris originates and a disturbed path down to the place where the mass comes to rest.

3. Slide, or Sliding. Free fall, rolling, sliding, gliding, slumping, and the like, are common and characteristic movements of rock and rock waste wherever such materials are affected by an unbalanced factor of gravity (Fig. 118). Although they usually supplement other phases of mass movement, these in themselves may lead to slow or rapid movement. As the mass becomes free, it moves onward with such speed as is possible against the resistance it may meet. Thus in free fall the speed is the accelerating velocity of gravity. Masses falling in this manner are fractured and broken by impact when they strike the surface below, and from that point they may roll, slide, or glide forward until the energy of motion is spent.

Free fall, or rockfall, is the chief factor supplying the talus material at the foot of the cliffs common in rugged regions. This rock waste may accumulate as a cone-shaped mass until the slope thus formed is at the angle of rest (maximum about 30 degrees) for such loose materials. When that angle is attained, there is little remaining obstruction to the movement of the fragments of later rockfalls; so when these strike the talus, they may set in motion other loose pieces of rock with which they come into contact. Parts or all of this disturbed rock debris may tumble or slide on down the slope to the point where movement is temporarily checked.

Large blocks and boulders that have rolled or slidden into mountain streams and tend to block them may resume their journey downgrade after currents have slowly removed the gravel and rock fragments underneath them. This undermining process, repeated many times, brings mass movement into play with each unbalanced position the boulders attain and thus moves them to ever-lower levels. By these mass-moving processes larger quantities of fallen rock are subjected to weathering.

Where large masses of earth and rock slide bodily down steep slopes, the movement is called a landslide (Fig. 125). A common type is a large slump block. In mountainous regions a series of landslides may give rise to a larger train of rock debris that continues to move gradually down the mountain valley. Such creeping masses are referred to as rock streams. These grade into the rock glaciers mentioned earlier, whose progress is

FIG. 125. Landslide of the slump-block type at Point Firmin on the coast of California. (*Spence Air Photos.*)

FIG. 126. The Lower Gros Ventre landslide, northwestern Wyoming.

accelerated by the expansive force of freezing, thawing, and refreezing of water in the spaces between the rock fragments.

Many destructive landslides have taken place during the past few centuries. In 1855 a mass of rock debris 3,500 feet long, 1,000 feet wide, and 600 feet high descended in the valley of the Tiber River. It formed a dam across the valley so that the village of San Stefano was flooded to a depth of 50 feet. Many lives were lost, and buildings were destroyed. Along the Lievre River, north of Buckingham, Quebec, an area of about 100 acres slid into the river. A clay terrace was resting on gneissic rock, and after several days of rain the clay had become saturated with water and slid under the additional weight. The momentum developed was so great that large masses of the clay were thrust up the opposite bank of the stream to a height of 25 feet. Another destructive slide occurred in Canada in 1903 at Frank, Alberta, where the entire face of Turtle Mountain, estimated at 40 million cubic yards, broke loose and was dashed to the base of the mountain and hurled across a valley and 400 feet up the opposite side. The length of the slide was about 2½ miles. The entire period of movement was less than 2 minutes. In the Columbia River Gorge near Stevenson, Washington, numerous slides are continually creeping toward the valley.

In the Gros Ventre valley, Wyoming, south of Yellowstone Park, a huge rockslide occurred in 1925 (Fig. 126). The slide mass, some 50 million cubic yards, descended about 2,000 feet, probably sliding down dip on a layer of saturated clay. The front of the mass plunged across the valley, rose 350 feet up the steep opposite side, and settled back. The dam thus formed across the valley was nearly 250 feet high and ½ mile long.

Mass movement may take place even beneath the sea.[1] Thus bottom studies suggest that sediments perched precariously, as near the top of the Continental Slope, may be dislodged by an earthquake or by any other trigger action and rush down the slope or through one of the submarine canyons in a manner very similar to the action of an ordinary landslide or mudflow. As these travel down the canyons, they may change from slides to mudflows and then to turbidity currents and thus carry rock materials long distances from the starting point of movement. Possibly these canyons, common along the Continental Slope, are maintained or kept from filling up largely by flows of mud and by density currents originating in the sudden movement of rock waste lodged temporarily at or near their upper ends. Submarine slides or mudflows, such as those which broke the Atlantic cable off the Grand Banks in 1929, may attain a very high velocity and produce results on the ocean bottom comparable with those on land.

SUGGESTIONS FOR FURTHER READING

Anderson, J. A.: Solifluction, a Component of Subaerial Denudation, *Jour. Geology*, vol. 14, pp. 91–114, 1906.

Blackwelder, Eliot: Mudflow as a Geologic Agent in Semi-arid Mountains, *Geol. Soc. America Bull.*, vol. 39, pp, 465–480, 1928.

Boyd, Louise A.: Weathering and Soil Flow in Mackenzie Valley, *Am. Geog. Soc. Spec. Pub.* 18, pp. 171–177, 1935.

Bryan, Kirk: Cryopedology, *Am. Jour. Sci.*, 5th ser., vol. 244, pp. 622–642, 1946.

Howe, E.: Landslides in the San Juan Mountains, Colorado, *U.S. Geol. Survey Prof. Paper* 67, 1909.

Legget, Robert F.: Geology and Engineering, pp. 211–246, McGraw-Hill Book Company, Inc., 1939.

Sharpe, C. F. S.: Landslides and Related Phenomena, Columbia University Press, 1938.

Woolley, Rolf R.: Cloudburst Floods in Utah, 1850–1938, *U.S. Geol. Survey Water Supply Paper* 994, 1946.

[1] Maurice Ewing, *Pacific Petroleum Geologist*, vol. 7, no. 3, p. 1, 1953.

CHAPTER 9

Rivers and Valleys

Introduction. Of the various agencies which have fashioned the face of the land areas of the earth, running water is by far the most effective. Its gradational work includes the degrading, or wearing down, of elevated land surfaces by streams and the deposition of the rock materials thus obtained to aggrade, or build up, areas at lower levels, where the velocities of the streams have decreased and their transporting power has diminished. These rock materials or sediments may be picked up again at a later time and carried still farther on their journey to the ocean, toward which they have been moving, or they may make the full trip in one journey with little or no interruption.

Water falls upon the earth mainly as rain, sleet, hail, and snow. Some of this water is evaporated, some penetrates the ground to become part of the ground water, some is retained on the surface for long periods as ice in glaciers, and another portion is carried off as streams to find its way to the sea. The total annual rainfall on all the land areas of the earth has been estimated to be about 26,679 cubic miles. About 22 per cent of the precipitation is carried off by streams and constitutes the *runoff*. This runoff is the chief degrading agent on the land surface and is, therefore, the most important factor in the process of erosion (Fig 127), or the reduction of land areas to lower levels. Since the average elevation of the continents is about ½ mile and the amount of water carried by streams is about 5,800 cubic miles per year, the energy available for eroding land areas is great.

Distribution of Rainfall. The work of running water begins with the raindrop. Drops run together to form rills, and these join to form brooks, creeks, and rivers; there are no sharp dividing lines between them. The amount of rainfall which a given area receives has a direct bearing on the rate at which erosion will proceed. The distribution of rainfall is influenced by the winds, which carry water vapor from places where it evaporated to regions where the temperature favors its condensation and precipitation. Therefore to understand the rainfall of any given region, it

164

is necessary to know (1) the prevailing and periodical winds, (2) the topography of the surface over which the winds have previously passed, and (3) the altitude and physiography of the region itself, as well as (4) its latitude and (5) its nearness to the sea.

The amount of rainfall is very unequally distributed over the earth as a whole. At certain places, as in parts of India, it is over 500 inches a year, whereas in the Sahara Desert it is less than 10 inches. On the Atlantic Coastal Plain of North America it is approximately 40 inches a year. Farther west in the northern portion of the interior basin it is 30 inches, and on the Great Plains it is 20 inches or less. In parts of the Great Basin province of the Southwest, between the southern Rockies and the Sierras, in the region known as the American Desert, less than 10 inches of moisture falls per year. In some desert regions several years may elapse between showers, and then they may be torrential and so flush out the loose materials from the gullies and canyons in a deluge of water, mud, and rock.

Runoff. That portion of the rainfall which flows off the surface of the land in the form of visible streams is the runoff. Its amount is not uniform, even in areas with equal amounts of precipitation. In regions of marked relief the runoff will exceed that of the plains or prairies, and unconsolidated sediments or soils will absorb more rain than indurated

FIG. 127. The Grand Canyon of the Colorado River, looking east toward the Painted Desert. (*Photograph by Spence Air Photos.*)

FIG. 128. Sheet erosion and gullying by rainwash in a beanfield near Torrance, New Mexico. (*Photograph by Soil Conservation Service.*)

rocks. Porous formations, however, when saturated with water and frozen ground water, allow a high percentage of water to run off. The character and amount of vegetation also influence the runoff. A heavy sod on a slope may shed water like a thatched roof. Most vegetation, however, holds water and delays the runoff. This is true especially of decaying plant tissue, for it acts like a sponge and absorbs large quantities of water. Weeds, brush, and logs also delay runoff by damming the surface water that otherwise would be free to flow away. The removal of forests, therefore, tends to increase the variability of the streams' volume and to increase the size and frequency of floods.

Dry, hot winds evaporate much of the water which remains on or near the surface. In arid regions, where the humidity is low, the winds are so dry that evaporation goes on rapidly. In the moist tropics, however, the humidity is high, and exposed surfaces remain damp. Under such conditions a smaller part of the rainfall is evaporated.

Ratio of Runoff to Rainfall. The percentage of the rainfall discharged by rivers cannot be measured precisely, for no rule can be made to apply to all parts of a continent. In general, in areas with an annual rainfall of 50 inches about one-half is discharged by rivers, whereas with a rainfall of 20 inches only 15 per cent is discharged. The Ohio River discharges about 30 per cent of the rainfall of its basin, while the Missouri River carries away only 15 per cent. In southwestern North America a number of the streams do not discharge more than 5 per cent of the rainfall. On some of the parched and porous soils the percentage of runoff may approach zero.

RAINWASH

Sheet Flow and Sheet Erosion. On smooth slopes the runoff takes the form of a thin film of water which moves downhill more or less uniformly as *sheet flow*. Although the erosional effects of such a sheet of water may appear offhand to be negligible, careful studies of losses of topsoil from cultivated fields have shown that sheet flow is responsible for the movement down slope of tremendous tonnages of soil materials. This removal of topsoil affects especially the finer ingredients and usually leaves behind the coarser, less effective materials, thus greatly decreasing the fertility of the fields involved. Sheet erosion may be inconspicuous but is nonetheless real.

Gullying. On uneven slopes the runoff seeks out and follows the initial depressions and thus collects into rills. These rills then modify the original slopes by enlarging their runways into miniature valleys called *gullies*. Even where sheet flow prevails at the outset, in the absence of initial irregularities of slope, a concentration of runoff may develop by the differential erosion of the soft or weak materials ahead of the more resistant areas. Thus sheet erosion may give way to gullying.

Rainwash, whether by sheet erosion or by gullying, is an important, though somewhat neglected, phase of the work of running water (see Fig. 128).

DEGRADATIONAL WORK OF STREAMS

Methods of Stream Erosion. Water which falls on the land and is not evaporated aids in transporting to the sea the products of weathering. The processes of weathering and erosion frequently act jointly and are so intimately related that distinction is difficult. Certainly without the removal of the accumulated debris by the agents of erosion the weathering processes would soon be much diminished or even cease entirely. In most places running water is the agent chiefly responsible for this removal. The erosive work is accomplished by a number of subprocesses which act in cooperation with each other. These are:

1. Corrasion, or the mechanical wear of the bed due to the impact and friction of silt, sand, gravel, and boulders carried by the stream (Fig. 129). Attrition, or abrasive wearing of the rock fragments in transit by

rubbing, by grinding, or by impact of rock upon rock, commonly accompanies this process.

2. Corrosion, or the solvent action of water on the rock minerals.

3. Hydraulicking, or the quarrying effect of the impact of water itself thrown against loose debris, into concavities and recesses, or into joint cracks, as in the undercutting of stream banks. Much of the loose debris consists of the products of rock weathering.

Of course all erosion, whether by corrasion, corrosion, or hydraulicking, implies removal or transportation.

Corrasion. The corrasive or abrasive action of clear water is slight. This is well-shown in clear streams like the Niagara River, a stream of clear water from which most of the sediment has settled in Lake Erie. Delicate plants such as algae grow at the very brink of the falls and form a green coating on the rocks. The current is very swift, but the force of the torrent is unable to tear the tiny plants from the rocky bed. But when the running water transports grains or pebbles of mineral matter, it becomes a powerful agent of erosion and the results of its work are seen in the excavation of deep canyons and gorges carved in solid rock. The downcutting of a stream is accomplished chiefly by means of the bottom load, or sand, pebbles, and silt which it sweeps along near the bottom of the stream. With these as tools it grinds and rasps the rocks of its bed as sandpaper or as a file abrades.

The corrasive power of river water varies as the square of the velocity of the stream. This relation is appreciated when it is recalled that, if the speed of the current is doubled, it will hurl twice as many sand grains as before in the same period, and it will throw each grain against an exposed

FIG. 129. Stream sediments on the bottom of a valley in Nevada. When carried by the stream, the rock fragments aid in abrading the valley. (*Photograph by Erdmann, U.S. Geological Survey.*)

rock in the stream bed with twice the force at its former speed. Thus the rock surface will be eroded four times as fast as it was before the speed was doubled. There are other factors also to be considered, such as the character and amount of the transported material and the character and structure of the rocks through which the channel is excavated.

Corrosion. Chemically pure water does not exist under natural conditions. Because of its solvent power, it is ever charging itself with impurities, many of which greatly increase its efficiency as a solvent. The water of many streams, especially after flowing through bogs and marshes where decaying vegetation abounds, is charged with carbonic acid in solution. With the aid of this acid, together with atmospheric oxygen, stream water acts on the rock surfaces with which it comes in contact. The rate of dissolution of the rocks is almost imperceptible, except where calcareous sediments are corroded along joints and fissures. The amount taken in solution by any one stream may seem small, but in the aggregate, the amount of material thus dissolved from the land and carried into the sea is great. It is estimated that about 5 billion metric tons of solid material goes into solution on the continents annually, but the greater part of this is contributed to the streams by ground water.

Hydraulicking. All mechanical methods of erosion by stream water itself that do not involve the use of tools are included under the term hydraulicking. These are the scour of loose material by the stream current passing over it, the effect of the impact of flowing water against a stream bank, and the wedging loose and quarrying of joint blocks by hydraulic pressure.

TRANSPORTATION

Sources of Materials. The materials carried by a stream are its load. The load is derived from a number of sources. (1) The larger part is supplied by the weathering and removal of rock from the slopes of its tributaries. During a rain the immediate runoff is muddy with waste as it rushes along gullies or washes down the hillsides. This is true of cultivated regions, especially where plowed fields lie on the slopes and numerous rills and minor tributaries carry the unconsolidated material to the larger streams. (2) Some of the load that a stream carries is obtained by wearing it from its banks or bed, and (3) some of it may fall into the river from steep banks where it has been dislodged by the pull of gravity upon weathered debris. (4) In regions with sparse vegetation, earth particles are moved by the wind, and sand or dust may be dropped into the stream to increase its load. (5) Great numbers of streams that owe their origin to the melting of glacial ice are turbid and loaded with silt.

The ice and water from its melting carry "rock flour" produced by the grinding of the boulders held in the ice. (6) In regions of volcanic activity vast quantities of dust and ash are discharged into the atmosphere, and some of it falls into streams or is carried into them by rills during subsequent rainfall. During the eruption in the Katmai region of Alaska in 1912 some streams were completely clogged with ash, and small boats were filled and buried under the debris. (7) Minor methods by which streams are supplied with material include the impact of driftwood or of floating blocks of ice on the walls of the stream channels, disturbances produced by the uprooting of trees, and those produced by the work of animals and plants.

Along valleys with steep slopes where heavy rainfall soaks the loose products of rock waste that have accumulated on a clayey surface or on consolidated rock, landslides frequently take place, and these may form temporary dams across river channels. When the ponded water overflows or breaks through the dam, it carries everything before it. In this way even small brooks become powerful erosive agents and displace hundreds of tons of material from the walls of their valleys in a few hours.

Methods of Transportation of Load. A body immersed in water loses weight equal to that of the water displaced. Most of the mineral and rock fragments carried by a stream weigh about $2\frac{1}{2}$ times as much as water. Immersed in water they therefore lose two-fifths of their weight. Water films, moreover, are attached to small particles, rendering these lighter and facilitating their transportation by running water.

Streams move their loads (1) by pushing and dragging many of the angular pieces; (2) by rolling the rounded and subangular pebbles along their floors; (3) by carrying in suspension the fine grains of sand, clay, and silt; and (4) by dissolving and carrying in solution the more soluble compounds. Because of the irregularities of the stream bed, the velocity of the current varies at different places along the stream; and since there is greater energy where the velocity is increased, the movement of the sediment is not uniform. The turbulence of eddies and crosscurrents produced by the deflection of the water from the irregularities of the stream bed tend to keep in suspension particles which would otherwise settle to the bottom of the stream. Many particles fall to the bottom many times during their journey and remain lodged on the floor of the channel until they are lifted up by deflection currents to near the surface, where the velocity is greater. Most of the material carried a short distance above the floor of the stream proceeds by a series of short leaps or jumps. This type of progress is "saltation," a term also applied to the similar transportation of sand grains by the wind. *Stream traction* is that process by which rock material is forced downstream by pushing, rolling, and saltation.

Relation of Velocity to Transportation. The velocity of a stream is determined by (1) the slope, or gradient, of the stream bed, (2) the shape and configuration of the valley walls, (3) the volume of water in the stream, and (4) the amount of sediment the stream is carrying.

Since the flow of water is due to gravity, it is obvious that in general, the greater the fall per mile, the faster the water will flow. The slope commonly decreases from headwaters toward the mouth of a stream, and consequently the velocity diminishes also. The average slope of the large rivers of all continents is approximately 2 feet per mile. For many of the navigable streams it is less than 1 foot per mile. Irregularities of the channel walls and bottom cause the water to be checked by friction, and it follows that, the smoother and narrower a channel, the lower will be the loss of energy because of friction. A stream bed studded with boulders or one running at right angles to rough, rocky ridges on its floor has obstacles that check the velocity of the stream.

An increase in volume accelerates the rate of flow of a stream by bringing about increased depth of water without greatly increasing the amount of friction. The rate of flow varies from time to time as the source of supply of its water varies. In many regions this variation is a periodic one, as, for example, in rivers whose sources are in snow-covered mountains, like the headwaters of the Colorado River, where the flow is faster when the volume is increased by the melting of the snow in the spring.

The spectacular effects of floods in transporting both large sizes of particles and large total loads of debris are convincing proofs of the great increase in the transporting power of streams even from only moderate increases in velocity. In general, for coarse loads, the size of a particle transported by traction varies directly with the 2.6 power of the velocity.

The following table shows the velocities of bottom currents in a river that are necessary for the currents to move materials of different sizes.

A similar relation between the progressive decrease in the velocity and the accompanying decrease in grain size of the sediments on the bed of the Mississippi River between Cairo, Illinois, and the Gulf of Mexico is shown by the following table. The figures are based on 600 samples taken at low-water stage of the river by the U.S. Waterways Experiment Station, Vicksburg, Mississippi. The bed load of gravel and sand near Cairo gradually gives way downstream to fine sand, silt, and clay.

Competency of Streams

Nature of material carried	Velocity of current, meters per second
Fine sand	0.2
Medium sand	0.3
Coarse sand	0.4
Granule gravel	0.6
Pebble gravel	1.6
Boulders	11.7

Mississippi River Sediments between Cairo and the Gulf of Mexico, Per Cent (After Nevin)

Miles below Cairo	100	300	500	700	900	1,000
Large gravel	8	3	6	2	Trace	
Medium gravel	10	2	6	2	Trace	
Fine gravel	11	3	2	1	Trace	
Coarse sand	30	22	9	8	1	
Medium sand	32	50	46	44	26	9
Fine sand	8	18	26	40	68	65
Very fine sand	Trace	1	2	1	2	4
Silt	Trace	Trace	2	1	2	10
Clay	Trace	Trace	1	Trace	1	10

Amount of Load. The quantity of material transported by a river is not constant, owing to the varying volume and accompanying varying velocity and also to the variable amounts of rock waste supplied by tributaries. In order to ascertain the total load, the average annual discharge of water must be determined, and the average amount of solid sediments transported and of salts carried in solution. The amount of water discharged may be ascertained by multiplying the number of square feet in the average cross section of the stream by its velocity per second, giving the discharge per second in cubic feet. The amount of silt to a cubic foot of water is found by filtering samples of the water taken from different parts of the stream during different seasons. The amount of salts in solution is obtained by evaporating filtered samples, and the composition of the salts is found by chemical analyses.

The Mississippi River annually carries to the Gulf of Mexico about 22,000,000,000,000 cubic feet of water, containing in suspension 340,500,000 tons, rolling on the bottom 40,000,000 tons, and carrying in solution 136,400,000 tons, or a total load of 516,900,000 tons of rock waste. According to recent estimates more than 800,000,000 tons of material in all are carried by the rivers of the United States each year. Miller states that a train of ordinary freight cars long enough to carry this load would reach around the earth six times in the region of the equator. The total load carried in solution per year by all the rivers is the equivalent of about 100 tons for every square mile of land surface on all the continents.

Abrasion of Load in Transit. Dragging and rolling rock fragments over one another and over the surface of the stream bed results in wearing of the transported pebbles themselves. Such wearing is *attrition*. Partly because of this action, the load is finer near the mouth of large rivers, and as one goes upstream, an increase in the size of rock fragments carried by streams is noted. A further reason for such distribution is that the velocity of the stream decreases toward the mouth, and hence the stream is unable to move coarse material. A high percentage of the fine silt in the lower courses of a stream, however, is derived from the attrition of the coarser material gathered by its headwaters. The progressive increase in degree of rounding of pebbles at increasing distances downstream along many rivers eloquently emphasizes the wear such pebbles undergo en route.

Rate of Denudation. A river system with its numerous tributaries covers the land with a network of watercourses, which carry their loads toward the trunk stream. With a uniform amount of rainfall the rate of denudation will be greatest in the region of the headwaters of the stream, somewhat less over the more gentle slopes of the intermediate zone, and least in the level areas near the coast line. In a large drainage basin the rate of stream erosion is influenced by many factors such as (1) the velocity of the stream, (2) its volume of water, (3) the nature and amount of its load, and (4) the character of the rocks or soils over which it flows.

In the headwaters the gradient of the stream bed is steeper, the velocity is greater, and the transporting power is higher than near its mouth. If the fragments collected by the headwaters of a river are composed mainly of resistant minerals such as quartz, while the floors and walls of the valley farther down its course are composed of softer rocks, the valley will be eroded much more rapidly than if the load of the stream is mostly clay or silt. To cut rapidly, the stream must carry some resistant sediment as tools, but not so much as to decrease its velocity, for then the force of its tools is diminished. Sedimentary rocks, especially those cemented with calcium carbonate, are much more easily eroded than massive igneous rocks. Thin-bedded sediments or the presence of joints and fissures favors rapid erosion.

Estimates of the rate at which certain rivers are eroding the areas that they drain have been made by various groups of investigators. The Mississippi River and its tributaries, draining an area of approximately 1,265,000 square miles, are now lowering the basin of that river at the average rate of about 1 foot in 9,000 years.

DEVELOPMENT AND ALTERATION OF VALLEYS

A large part of the water that falls as rain runs off the surface of the region where it falls. If the surface has a smooth, uniform slope like a gently pitching roof, it flows off as a sheet and no channels are developed. Such smooth surfaces, however, are rare. Slight irregularities lead to the formation of rills, which erode small furrows. The rills unite to form rivulets, and the uniting rivulets form torrents, which cut deep gorges and canyons, which are eventually transformed into wide valleys with gentle slopes. Some of the details of this transformation are discussed on the pages that follow.

FIG. 130. Head erosion in a young valley, of canyon type, invading the forest slope on the south side of Mount Pinos in Kern County, California. Elevation slightly above 8,000 feet. (*Spence Air Photos.*)

Valley Growth. The lengthening of a valley is accomplished for the most part by head erosion, that is, many streams start at or near the places of their outlets and grow in length by cutting backward into the slopes, thus increasing the area drained by the stream (Figs. 130, 131). This process continues until the gully reaches an obstacle, such as a resistant rock formation, or until it reaches a point where lack of slope or the tributaries from the opposite side of a slope stop its progress. This interstream area, or line of separation, constitutes the *divide*, or interfluve. If the erosion on the two sides of the divide is about equal, a *fixed divide* is established, for even though continued rainfall may tend to lower it, its geographic position remains unchanged. Where erosion on one side is more rapid than on the other, however, the divide shifts slowly toward the side of less rapid denudation.

If, in its migration headward, a stream reaches a lake, the lake basin becomes a part of the stream system and the streams flowing into the lake become tributaries of the same system. Its retreat is retarded at the lake until the stream cuts downward to the level of the lake basin and drains it.

Deepening of a Valley. The deepening of a valley accompanies its growth in length, for while cutting backward the stream wears its bed downward. During each successive downpour the gully acquires more surface water and is washed out deeper. Side gullies develop and grow

FIG. 131. Aerial photograph of fields gullied by headward erosion. The lined areas are cultivated fields which are being reduced in size by the gullies (dark, tree-covered) that are encroaching on the fields from all sides. (*Photograph by Mark Hurd Air Mapping Company.*)

FIG. 132. Canyon de Chelly, Arizona. The valley of a creek along the east side of Chinle Valley cutting downward in sedimentary rocks with very little lateral erosion. (*Spence Air Photos.*)

into tributaries, the tributaries also acquire side gullies, and the surface water of a large area is directed through the one main channel. It follows that the erosion of the main channel will be increased, for increased volume means increased velocity with its greater eroding power. As long as the valley is shallow, its supply of water is limited to the immediate runoff at the time of rainfall. Streams that flow only during a rainy season or during a downpour of rain are *intermittent* streams. As a valley is deepened, the floor of its channel approaches the level below which the pore spaces of the rocks are full of water, or the ground-water table, and after the bottom of a valley penetrates this level, its reserve of water is sufficiently increased so that it supports a stream even during the dry seasons. Streams that have their valleys cut to the ground-water level are *permanent* streams.

In regions where the gradients are steep, the downcutting by the streams will proceed much more rapidly than where the slopes are low and the streams sluggish. In fact, many slow streams make their valleys shallower, for they deposit more than they take away. Where the gradient is such that there is approximately a balance between the amount a stream erodes and the amount it aggrades, the stream is said to be *at grade,* or it is commonly referred to as a *graded* stream. In a long valley, like the Mississippi, deepening may be in progress toward its upper end, whereas the same valley may be becoming shallower because of deposition in its lower course. Where the rate of deepening exceeds that of the erosion of the banks, deep canyons with clifflike walls are developed (Fig. 132). The depth to which a valley may lower its bed depends on the elevation of the land in which it has been cut. High plateaus such as the Colorado Plateau or high mountains such as the Himalayan Range commonly have valleys of great depth.

The depth limit of a valley is determined by the level of the body of water into which its river flows. The channel of a large river, such as the Mississippi, near its mouth may be cut somewhat lower than sea level, but in general the level of the lake or ocean is approximately the depth limit of the valley of the river that discharges into it. Only the lower end of a valley ever attains this limit, for the stream bed must have a gradient, or the river will not flow. The lowest possible level to which a stream can erode its drainage basin by mechanical wear is called *base level* of stream erosion.

Widening of a Valley. The widening of a valley, or lateral erosion, goes on in conjunction with its deepening. If this were not the case, all valleys would be canyons with steep walls. In some regions, conditions for downcutting are more favorable than for lateral erosion, as along the Gunnison River in Colorado and along the upper portion of Zion Canyon, Utah, where nearly vertical walls over 2,000 feet high are only a few hundred feet apart at the brink of the canyon. Most valleys are much wider than their streams, however, although the character of the rock over which the stream flows may produce local variations in the width, so that narrow portions alternate with wider ones. If a stream crosses a tilted bed of hard, resistant rock lying between softer ones, the valley will widen faster both above and below the hard bed than it does where the stream crosses it. A *narrows* will be formed where the stream cuts across the resistant rock.

Valley widening is accomplished in many ways, the most important of which are (1) by creeping or slumping, (2) by rain wash, (3) by the activities of animals and plants, (4) by glacial abrasion, (5) by undercutting, and (6) by tributaries.

1. While the slopes are steep, the loose products of rock weathering creep slowly downward under the action of gravity. If clayey material becomes thoroughly saturated with water during a rainy season, large masses of it may slide or slump toward the valley floor and carry debris

with it to lower levels. This process is in progress on a large scale along parts of the valley of the Columbia River, where huge landslides are moving toward the valley, carrying forests and buildings with them. Although this is a matter largely controlled by mass movement, the presence of water not only increases the weight of the rock waste precariously perched but also may lubricate the surface over which the slide takes place and help cascade the debris into the low land, where it lodges.

2. Rain falling on the slopes of a valley washes loose material with it; and where the valley is in unconsolidated sediments, furrows and gullies are excavated in its walls. The debris is carried toward the stream channel, and the valley is widened.

3. Many land animals visit streams to obtain water or to graze along the banks; and as they walk along the valley slopes, loose debris is dislodged. Burrowing animals bring sand and clay to the surface that is

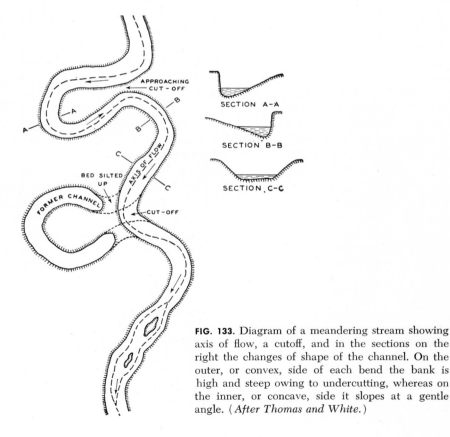

FIG. 133. Diagram of a meandering stream showing axis of flow, a cutoff, and in the sections on the right the changes of shape of the channel. On the outer, or convex, side of each bend the bank is high and steep owing to undercutting, whereas on the inner, or concave, side it slopes at a gentle angle. (*After Thomas and White.*)

readily washed down the slopes. Roots of trees aid in the disruption of the rocks along the valley; and when the trees are overturned, more material is loosened and eventually carried downward.

4. At high altitudes where glaciers partially fill the valleys, ice widens the bottom as rapidly as the walls are eroded back and wide, flat-bottomed valleys result.

5. The course of a stream is rarely straight, and at each curve it tends to cut more on one bank than on the other (Figs. 133, 134). This is due to the fact that the water tends to pile up on the bend and the outside of the

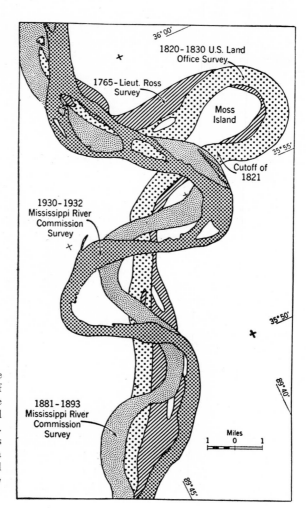

FIG. 134. Progressive changes in the channel of the Mississippi River above Memphis, during a period of more than 150 years. The sketch shows meanders and the meander belt of a major stream on its flood plain. (*United States Army Engineers.*)

FIG. 135. Meanders and oxbow lakes along Mudjatik River in northern Saskatchewan. (*Royal Canadian Air Force.*)

curve receives a greater volume of water. In this way the velocity is increased, and the bank is undermined and moved back. As a valley approaches base level, its gradient is decreased and the flow of its stream becomes more gentle. In such a slow stream the currents easily are deflected (1) by some obstacle on the floor of the channel or (2) by a projection of more resistant rock along its bank or (3) by the entrance of swifter currents from a tributary stream. The deflected current strikes the opposite bank and as it moves downstream tends to be thrown back again to the side from which it first issued. Thus the stream develops a series of winding curves, or meanders (Fig. 135). In a sluggish stream the successive meanders tend to be of about the same size, and the strip within which these are confined is the *meander belt*. According to M. S. W. Jefferson [1] this belt is about eighteen times the width of the stream; but on flood plains of very low relief the meander belt itself meanders, thus complicating any attempt to define it, although the general concept seems to hold true. Once started, the meanders become more and more pronounced, and finally a series of loops separated by narrow necks of land are developed. Eventually the stream cuts through the narrowed neck of land between two loops and leaves the meander as a long, curved *oxbow lake* (Fig. 135). Where this happens, the river shortens its course and the current is modified so that a new meander is likely to be formed because of the shifting of the currents. The old deserted loops with their

[1] *Nat. Geog. Mag.*, vol. 13, pp. 373–384, 1902.

shallow lakes are converted gradually into stagnant pools and bogs characteristic of flood plains in the later stages of their development.

Level or flattened areas commonly accompany the widening of a valley, especially where the stream has cut its channel down to a low gradient. Such flats are temporary base levels established by the local conditions that govern the stream's gradient. Later, when conditions of velocity, volume, and load are altered, the stream may cut deeper into the flats and leave them as terraces along the valley. The Mississippi River has developed flats along its upper course where the floor of the valley is more than 600 feet above sea level (Fig. 136). A short distance south of St. Paul it has such a flat over 1 mile wide that is cut about 250 feet below the general level of the region. In the neighborhood of St. Louis the flats are about 400 feet above sea level and about 150 feet below the regional upland. Still farther downstream in Tennessee and Arkansas the flats are 35 miles wide and lie 220 feet above the sea.

The width limit of a valley depends on the distance between neighboring streams. Parallel valleys may be widened until the divide between them becomes a sharp, narrow ridge that is gradually lowered as the region approaches base level.

FIG. 136. Flats of the Mississippi River Valley near Dubuque, Iowa, with numerous abandoned channels, and partly filled lakes. The topography of the uplands is still in early maturity. (Lancaster quadrangle, Wisconsin, Iowa, Illinois.) (*U.S. Geological Survey.*)

STAGES IN VALLEY DEVELOPMENT

Cycle of Erosion. A newly uplifted land area marks the starting point of the history of a river-drainage system. It is evident that the topography produced by stream erosion, as such an area is drained, will change as erosion continues. Changes are determined in part by the altitude of the uplifted area and the character and structural relations of its subsurface rock formations. The first effect of erosion is to roughen the surface of the area by excavating gullies and valleys and by leaving ridges and hills as divides. Eventually, the divides are lowered, and the result is a plain or comparatively level surface. Hence, erosion tends eventually to produce a plain. The time involved in the development of the various stages of topographic expression through which a region passes as it is transformed into a featureless plain comprises a *cycle of erosion*. For purposes of comparison and study of land surfaces this cycle is divided into three stages—youthful, mature, and old. The topography of a valley is youthful when most of the work of the stream is not yet done; it is mature when the erosive agents have accomplished so much work that most of the area consists of slopes; and it is old when erosion has nearly finished its work. Maturity is the most rugged, but the cycle is a continuous one, and obviously there is no clear line of demarcation between any two stages. The use of these terms is intended to convey the idea of stages rather than periods of time expressed in years; for one valley may reach maturity in a much shorter period than an adjoining one, especially if the former is in softer rocks and the latter in a region of more resistant rocks. A distinction

FIG. 137. Maturely dissected mountains in Japan. Streams are numerous, the land is all in slope, and the divides are narrow. (*Photograph by United States Air Force.*)

should be made also between the age of the stream in the cycle of erosion and the stage in the erosion cycle to which the area it drains has progressed, for certain streams with youthful characteristics may traverse regions that are typically mature.

Youthful Streams and Valleys. Most youthful streams are rapid streams that flow in V-shaped canyons or gorgelike valleys with steep sides. The slopes are steep because sufficient time has not yet elapsed for the valleys to be widened. If the area is a recent uplift, the streams are not numerous and they have few tributaries. Since they have not had time to erode extensively, they still may have rapids and waterfalls along their courses. The divides are wide and are poorly drained, as is shown by the presence of upland lakes and swamps. This condition is illustrated in the valley of the Red River of the North or in portions of the coastal plain areas of southeastern United States. The gorge of the Niagara River, the canyon of the Yellowstone, and the valley of the Rhine are all youthful valleys. The Grand Canyon of the Colorado, which also is a young valley, is the grandest of all examples.

Maturity. As erosion continues, the topography changes until the features characteristic of youth are chiseled into different forms and the sharp, straight lines of the landscape give place to valleys with flaring sides and gently rounded upper slopes. By the gnawing back of the headward tributaries the divides are narrowed, and the region becomes thoroughly dissected by a complex network of valleys, resulting in very rugged topography (Fig. 137). The number of tributaries is to some extent determined by the amount of rainfall. In southeastern United States with a heavy annual precipitation, tributaries and streams are more numerous than in the semiarid or arid plains of the Southwest. As the tributaries are deepened, the lakes and swamps are drained or filled and the escarpments that produced waterfalls and rapids are lowered, so that the rivers attain gradients that are near the lowest slopes over which their loads of sediment can be transported. Toward the close of this stage the lower courses of the streams become graded, and then they swing from side to side, thus widening their valleys and developing flood plains along the valleys.

From the standpoint of human activities, rugged mature topography offers many obstacles; and it is the least desirable for many enterprises. Because of the network of deep valleys, roads cannot follow the straight survey lines but follow the crests of the main divides or the winding valleys of the major streams. Railroad grades cross areas of mature topography by using high trestles over the valleys and by penetrating the hills with long tunnels. Typical mature topography now exists in the region of the Allegheny and Cumberland Plateaus to the west of the Appalachian Mountains.

Old Age. By continued erosion the rugged relief of the mature stage of topography gradually is reduced, and the deep channels are transformed into broad valleys with gentle slopes and low divides. The gradient is lowered until the streams lose their vigor and deposit rather than erode. The valleys become shallower, owing to deposition, and the sluggish streams swing from side to side in long, looplike meanders over the deposits of their own flood plains. A land area thus worn down to nearly a plain with the gentle slopes of old-age topography is a *peneplane*. Frequently, isolated hills or mountains of more resistant rocks rise to greater heights above the general level of the peneplane. These are called *monadnocks* after the type example of Mount Monadnock in New Hampshire.

Relation of Peneplane to Base Level. Theoretically, the ultimate base level of all stream valleys is sea level. Since the flow of a stream is influenced by gravity, however, it is evident that erosion can proceed only as long as a stream retains sufficient gradient to transport its load. As a land surface approaches a peneplane, it approaches also base level (Fig. 138). In many regions a peneplane condition is produced while the region still is several hundred feet above sea level.

Summary of Changes during a Cycle of Stream Development

Characteristics	Youthful stage	Mature stage	Old-age stage
Trends of channels	Straight	Meanders common	Meanders numerous
Gradient and velocity	High	Moderate	Low
Waterfalls and rapids	Many	Few	None
Nature of erosion	Downcutting predominates	Lateral planation prominent	Lateral planation predominant
Width of valleys	Narrow, V-shaped	Broad and well-defined	Very broad with low boundaries
Depth of valleys	Moderately deep	Deepest	Shallow
Number of tributaries	Few, small	Maximum number	Few, large
Nature of divides	High and wide	High and narrow	Low and narrow
Relief	Maximum for entire drainage system	Maximum for region of headwaters	Low
Number of lakes	Many on uplands	Very few	Many on lowlands
Adjustment to structure	Not adjusted	Well-adjusted	Roughly adjusted
Material transported	Coarse and fine	Sands and silts prominent	Sands and silts predominant
Deposition by streams	Minimum deposition	Deposition at insides of curves	Deposition in channels and on levees
General drainage	Poorly developed	Well-drained, most efficient	Drainage sluggish

The Arid Cycle. To accomplish its work in arid and semiarid regions, the erosion cycle is much more dependent on minor base-leveling processes to supplement those of running water, the latter, however, still remaining an important factor even though long periods of no precipitation may affect the dry area. Most of the deserts and semideserts of the United States are internal or closed drainage basins separated by mountain ranges from regions with outlets to the ocean. This is also the condition in some other desert regions, such as the Sahara, the Libyan, or the Kara Kum. Some of these basins may extend below sea level, and from them the only escape of sediment is by solution or by wind activity, only the latter being of much importance. It is evident, therefore, that over a long time interval surfaces below sea level are built up to reach the common base level toward which the present general erosion of the continent is tending.

Desert regions developed in areas of soft or slightly consolidated bedrock may show only retardation of the base-leveling processes commonly found elsewhere, but if the bedrock is of varying degrees of resistance to erosion, cliffs and ridges of the more durable beds soon develop over the surface, especially if folded or faulted, and these features tend to perpetuate themselves throughout the greater part of the erosion cycle. Although this same feature may be present as part of the erosion history in a humid climate, it is much more pronounced and conspicuous in a dry region (Fig. 139), where these cliffs of resistant beds finally become the conspicuous steep-sided monadnocks (inselbergs), or remnants of the receding cliffs.

FIG. 138. The even sky line of the Laurentian peneplane eastward at Long Lake, upper portion of Manigotagan River, southeastern Manitoba near the Ontario border. (*Geological Survey of Canada.*)

FIG. 139. Retreating escarpment under erosional attack on a valley wall in east central Utah, in a semiarid climate. (*Photograph by U.S. Geological Survey.*)

Such rains as may fall on the higher lands above the cliffs or scarps separating the outer from the inner and lower part of the desert basin form the usual pattern of rills and minor streams that join and produce a few canyonlike gullies, or wadies. Since the amount of rock debris swept down through these steep gullies by the occasional torrent is small, the stream may still be eroding when it arrives at the abrupt end of the canyonlike part of its course. The result is the undercutting and collapse of the cliffs bordering the higher ground, their gradual recession or retreat, and the formation of a gradually sloping surface where the cliffs formerly stood. This truncated rock surface has been called a *rock fan*, or *pediment*. It is essentially a surface of bare rock, but it bears scattered rock fragments fallen from the crumbling cliffs or even a thin mantle of rock waste brought down the wadies from the higher areas. Adjacent pediments may unite laterally to form a compound pediment resembling an alluviated piedmont area.

Weathering, although slowed down by the scarcity of water, still continues and ultimately may be remarkably complete because of the long interval during which the surfaces remain exposed. Thus when the jointed and disintegrated masses topple from the face of a cliff, they fall into innumerable fragments, which are still further broken as they strike the hard rock surface of the pediment below; over this the shattered materials move under every impetus, slight though it may be, the net result being always downward. Bare cliffs (Fig. 140) are thus left rising sharply above the pediment, with a conspicuous lack of talus slope or other accummulation of loose rock at the cliff base.

The near absence of vegetation and the lack of the binding effect of roots in such loose surface materials as occur in the desert favor movement of the rock debris. The receding cliffs thus leave a slightly concave and sloping rock surface, or pediment, which passes gradually downslope into the rock-strewn and thinly covered portion of the rock fan (bajada), which in turn may give place basinward to a salt or playa lake or its desiccated remnants.

A pediment may be invaded and regraded by a lower one adjacent, or the whole area may be captured and converted into the usual valley by the tributaries of a stream flowing to the sea. Bajadas in desert regions may pass so imperceptibly into the alluvial fans of nearby semiarid plains that it is not always certain where the former end and the latter begin, just as it may be difficult to delimit the desert itself.

Disturbed Erosion Cycles. As the drainage basin of a river system passes through the successive stages of a normal cycle of erosion, it may be interrupted at any stage by various geological processes. Among them

FIG. 140. Receding cliffs and detached remnants rising above the pediment in an arid region. Monument Valley, Arizona-Utah. (*Courtesy of Santa Fe Railway.*)

the following are perhaps the most important: (1) glaciation and other interferences by gradational agents; (2) volcanic action; (3) diastrophism.

1. A glacier may fill a stream valley with ice or cover its basin with a snow field that protects the surface from weathering and stream erosion. During the Great Ice Age, when most of northeastern North America was subjected to continental glaciation, many areas within that region were in the mature stage of topography. As the glacier receded, however, enormous amounts of glacial debris were deposited irregularly, forming hills, ridges, knobs, and depressions over the preglacial topography, with the result that youthful features again were developed and superimposed on large areas which had been eroded far beyond the youthful stage. This is true especially of the region to the south and east of the Great Lakes in the United States.

The encroachment of sand dunes, the deposition of sheets of loess, the escape of the surface runoff into limestone sinks and caverns, and the blocking and lateral shifting of the mouth of a stream by waves and shore currents along a seacoast also delay the progress of a stream's work.

2. Lava may flow down the slopes of a valley and completely fill its stream channel, or the volume of lava may be so great that the entire area is deeply buried and the drainage system profoundly modified. In such areas the erosion cycle is interrupted, and a new cycle is initiated on the surface of the lava field. The Columbia Plateau, covering an area of over 200,000 square miles in Washington and Oregon, is a lava field where the streams and valleys of the old erosion surface were at many places almost completely buried.

3. Diastrophism may bring about interruptions that are varied both in character and in the results produced. They may modify the cycle of erosion only locally and temporarily, or they may cause the streams to start their work anew. Changes in level may be produced by elevation or by depression.

Drowning. Depression of the land or rise of sea level hastens the development of old age by bringing the depressed area nearer base level and by decreasing the amount of material the streams must remove before a featureless plain is developed. When such rise in sea level occurs along the coast line, the sea occupies the lower ends of the valleys and converts them into bays and estuaries. The valleys then are *drowned*. Thus the Hudson River is drowned as far north as Albany, and the St. Lawrence River appears as an arm of the sea as far as Montreal. Narragansett, Delaware, Chesapeake, and other bays along the coast of the United States are drowned valleys resulting from a sinking of the seaboard areas, or a rise of sea level. Before submergence took place, many of the streams which now flow into Chesapeake Bay discharged their waters into the lower course of the Susquehanna River, to which they were tributaries (Fig. 141). Such tributaries, isolated from their trunk streams by drowning, are called *dismembered* streams. With subsequent emergence they would extend their courses and again become parts of the major stream system.

Rejuvenation. If a peneplaned area is elevated, the gradients of the streams are increased and they set to work cutting gorges and canyons in the bottoms of their old valleys, with the result that the region again takes on the characteristics of youth. Such a region is said to be rejuvenated; the infusion of new vigor through an increased gradient quickens the velocity of the streams, and they become rejuvenated streams.

After such an uplift a river sinks its valley within the new upland; and if the old streams had meandering courses before rejuvenation, the winding channel is deepened and the old meanders become entrenched (Figs. 142, 143). Eventually, during renewed maturity, the wide lobes of the individual meanders become separated by mountains formed by the dissection of a slowly elevated plain. If, during the elevation, a stream is able to hold its course notwithstanding change of level in the earth's crust, the stream is *antecedent*, that is, it antedates the diastrophic events that influence the present topography.

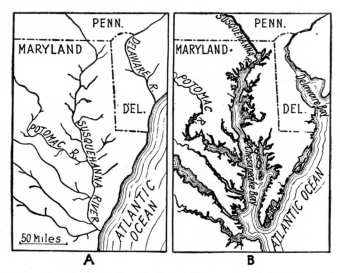

FIG. 141. Drowned and dismembered rivers. Delaware and Chesapeake Bays (*B*) were formed by sinking of the Coastal Plain, which permitted the Atlantic Ocean to drown the lower parts of the valleys. The tributary rivers (*A*), which formerly emptied into the main streams, are *dismembered* streams. A, probable conditions before subsidence; B, present conditions. (*Based on a drawing by Salisbury.*)

FIG. 142. Entrenched meanders of San Juan River, Utah, showing cutoff with erosional mountains within the cutoff loop (*left of center*). The present river lies 75 feet lower than the floor of the loop. The creeks that flow along each side of the loop have cut a gorge through which they enter the river. (*Photograph by Fairchild Aerial Surveys, Los Angeles.*)

Antecedent streams with entrenched meanders are common in the Appalachian region. The Susquehanna River of southern New York and northern Pennsylvania and the New River of the Cumberland Plateau are examples. The Yakima River of central Washington and the San Juan River of southeastern Utah are both deeply entrenched. Some of the natural bridges of Utah owe their origin to the perforation of necks between entrenched meanders. The famous Rainbow Bridge, carved out of sandstone, has a height of 305 feet and a span 270 feet long across the neck between old meanders (Fig. 144).

Uniform slow emergence, or elevation, affecting extensive areas may revive the streams without greatly altering the major features of the topography. In this way an old peneplane may be lifted up to an altitude

FIG. 143. Entrenched meanders in San Juan Canyon, Utah. The meandering course was developed during a former erosion cycle, when the river was flowing over a graded plain. The meanders became entrenched when the stream was rejuvenated by the uplift of the area. (*Spence Air Photos.*)

FIG. 144. Rainbow Natural Bridge, southern Utah. A bridge formed by the stream undercutting the narrow neck of one of its meanders and leaving a resistant layer of rock spanning the gap. (*National Park Service.*)

FIG. 145. Soil erosion near Lumpkin, Georgia. (*Photograph by United States Air Force.*)

of several thousand feet above sea level without warping the old erosion surface.

Faulting may produce tilting; and where the movement is upward, the streams are revived, and the cycle of erosion is interrupted. If the movement is downward, the gradient is decreased and the velocity of the stream is checked. Notable depression or elevation along a fault line across a valley may so impede the flowing streams that the waters become *ponded* and the rate of erosion is changed.

GEOGRAPHIC ASPECTS

General. Certain aspects of stream work affect man quite intimately, even disastrously. As between degradation and aggradation, perhaps the former poses the more serious problems. Heavy rains and the resulting floodwaters from streams not only carry away the soil from cultivated fields but also ruin buildings, dams, and power installations, flood highways, wash out railway embankments and bridges, and may cover valuable agricultural bottom lands with heavy deposits of sand, gravel, and boulders and render them useless for farming.

Soil Erosion. One of the principal problems arising from the gradational work of running water is that of soil erosion. Soil is the surficial layer of disintegrated mantle-rock that normally shows a profile of weathering and is capable of supporting plant growth. Generally it is colored dark by decaying organic matter, and it contains the many substances that promote plant growth, these being derived from the rocks, from the air, and from water. Each year parts of the soil are washed away, and each year additions are made by weathering. If the additions are less than the losses, the land deteriorates.

Of about 600 million acres of agricultural land in the United States, about 100 million acres of once-productive land already has been essentially ruined for practical crop use, and about twice as much more has lost much of the topsoil or is in serious danger of doing so. About 100,000 acres is being lost each year. The total losses in value of the land and in its productivity are estimated to be about 400 million dollars a year.

Causes of Soil Erosion. The most severe erosion takes place on slopes, and particularly on slopes where cleanly tilled crops such as cotton, corn, and tobacco are grown. Soil erosion is much less severe where the grasses, alfalfa, and the small grains are grown. Forests protect the soil from erosion, and where these are cut down and particularly where the slash and undergrowth are removed or burned, erosion is greatly increased (Figs. 145 to 147).

Experiments at Bethany, Missouri, with a mean precipitation of 33.5 inches, on an 8 per cent slope that was cropped continuously to corn showed a loss of 67.4 tons of soil per year per acre. Where corn was rotated with wheat and clover, less than half that was lost; and where alfalfa was grown, the loss under the same conditions was only 0.2 ton of soil per acre. The water lost by runoff was greatly increased as soil loss increased; it was 26 per cent where corn was grown and only 3.4 per cent where alfalfa was grown. Grass crops are almost as effective as alfalfa in conserving soil and decreasing runoff.

Other contributing factors include single cropping, overcropping, destruction of soil structure by improper tillage, breaking of the prairie sod, careless logging, burning of grass and stubble, dry farming of submarginal lands, exposure of fallow land, overgrazing, concentrated rainfall, and up- and downslope plowing and cultivation.

Methods of Prevention and Control. Various methods are in use to decrease soil erosion and land destruction. Dams of earth, rock, or logs are built in gullies to check their growth, and vegetation is planted on the bare surfaces to hold the soils (Figs. 148, 149). Where slopes are farmed, strips of tilled crops are planted along contours to alternate with strips of

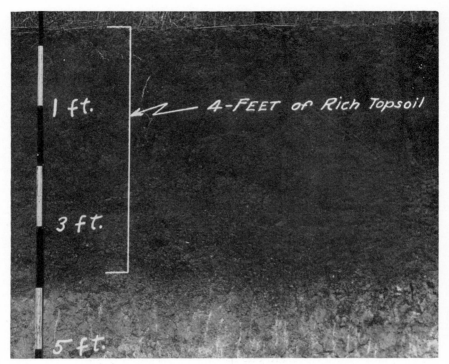

FIG. 146. Soil profile with thick humus layer in *A* horizon, on flat topography in eastern Texas. (*Courtesy of Soil Conservation Service.*)

FIG. 147. Soil profile on gently sloping surface near area shown in Fig. 146. Soil erosion has removed the humus layer of the *A* horizon. (*Courtesy of Soil Conservation Service.*)

194

FIG. 148. Before planting—gullies on an upper Tennessee Valley farm. Photographed Dec. 5, 1933, just before treatment. (*Courtesy of Tennessee Valley Authority.*)

FIG. 149. After planting—same gullies as shown in Fig. 148 on upper Tennessee Valley farm after treatment. Photograph taken July 24, 1935. Treatment consisted chiefly in planting of black locust seedlings. Some stone check dams were built. (*Courtesy of Tennessee Valley Authority.*)

small grain, grass, or other nontilled crops. These catch the rain water flowing down the slopes, spread it out, and protect the tilled ground from erosion. They greatly increase the water absorbed by the ground and decrease the runoff.

Terracing, trenching, ridging, and furrowing along contours also are at places effective. These are preventive measures. Where lands already are deeply trenched with many gullies, the problems are those of reclamation. Small dams and terraces are built to catch the soil in transit, and small, rich garden and orchard plots thus are provided. Certain areas have been reforested and others put to grass. Notwithstanding all these methods of conservation, land destruction by erosion steadily gains in the United States where rainstorms are violent and tilled crops are cultivated over vast areas.

Other desirable practices in soil management include the selective use of the land, use of cover crops, crop rotation, contour plowing and cultivation, proper tillage, use of fertilizers, use of trashy fallow, protection of stream banks, prevention and control of floods, and return of submarginal lands to forest or permanent pasture.

Other Problems. Streams affect man's activities in several other ways. The shifting of stream channels complicates political boundaries. Rivers in flood undermine bridge footings, destroy property, devastate lowlands, and do other damage. Hence the prevention and control of floods and the protection of riverbanks and levees deeply concern man. Man is interested also in the maintenance of steady flow for maximum power development, in the silting of reservoirs, in the recovery of gold and other valuable materials from stream gravels, and in the use of streams for water supply, navigation, fishing, recreation, and the disposal of sewage and industrial wastes. Engineers, foresters, geologists, and others contribute toward the solution of these manifold and far-reaching problems.

STREAM DEPOSITION

Stream transportation is attended by stream deposition. Anything that decreases the transporting power of a stream promotes deposition. Along the course of every river the current frequently is checked, and at such places sediments are deposited. Even the bed of a stream having a relatively high velocity will have part of its surface covered with rock fragments, which the stream was forced to drop because of decreases in the transporting power of its currents. Since conditions favoring transportation vary from time to time and from place to place, sediments derived from the land generally are not all carried directly to the sea: some may be deposited to form definite features in the topography as a region passes through a cycle of erosion.

Factors Causing Deposition. 1. *Diminished Velocity.* A slight diminution of the rate of flow of a loaded stream will initiate deposition. A loss of velocity may be brought about (*a*) by a decrease of slope or gradient of the stream bed; (*b*) by a decrease in volume of the stream; (*c*) by a change in the configuration of the valley; (*d*) by encountering obstructions such as heaps of residual boulders formed from more resistant dikes or beds that cross the valley or by temporary dams formed by floating trees or rafts of logs; (*e*) by freezing; (*f*) by flowing into a body of quiet water such as a lake, estuary, or bay.

2. *Diminished Volume.* Since the volume of water affects the carrying power of a stream directly, variations in volume cause streams alternately to aggrade and degrade their beds. Many streams have seasonal high-water stages, during which more and coarser sediments are carried; later these are deposited when the amount of rainfall decreases. Diminished volume may result also in other ways. Some of the water of the stream may sink into the earth where the stream flows through a dry region. In such regions the bottom of the valley does not reach the ground-water level, and some of the water of the stream is absorbed by the soil and

FIG. 150. Alluvial fan at the mouth of Hanaupah Canyon on the west side of Death Valley, California. Since the fan was deposited, it has been partly dissected, thus showing an increase in water supply or a decrease in available load upstream. (*Spence Air Photos.*)

FIG. 151. Dissected piedmont alluvial plain. Huntington Palisades, near Santa Monica, California. (*Spence Air Photos.*)

rocks over which it flows. Such absorption is common in areas underlain by permeable gravel and sand. Further loss of volume may be caused by evaporation in arid regions and by diversion of the water for irrigation or for other purposes. Over long periods of time a progressive drying of the climate of an area may change the regimen of the streams and leave only dry washes in a region that was formerly moist. Conversely, an increase in precipitation may increase both volume and transportation. Such variations may be seasonal and periodic, or the shift to dry may even be permanent.

3. *Increase of Cross Section.* Where a stream breaks up into a number of distributaries, the volume of each branch is less than that of the original stream but the total cross-sectional area of the stream becomes greater. Any such division, or even the mere widening or flattening of a stream channel, increases the bottom friction, slows the velocity, and reduces the efficiency of the stream as an agent of transportation. If, as a result of division, a stream drops much of its load in its own channel, it then flows as small distributary streamlets through and over its own sediments.

Places of Deposition. Stream deposits, or alluvium, may accumulate in a number of different places, such as (1) at the foot of steep slopes, (2) in stream channels, (3) on flood plains, and (4) at débouchures.

Forms of Stream Deposits. The principal forms of stream deposits include (1) alluvial fans and cones, (2) piedmont alluvial plains, (3) bars and channel fill, (4) flood plains, (5) alluvial terraces, and (6) deltas.

Alluvial Fans and Cones. Where a stream descending a steep slope issues from the mountains on a plain or in a wide valley, its velocity suddenly is diminished and a large part of its load is deposited and spread out in the form of a fan-shaped heap at the opening of the ravine or gully through which the stream flows (Fig. 150). As the deposit thickens, its thickness becomes greatest at the mouth of the steep valley and a cone-shaped structure is developed. The slope of the cone's surface varies with the size and velocity of the stream and the character of the transported sediment. In general, coarse materials tend to pile up as cones and finer ones to flatten out as fans, but there are all gradations between these.

Conditions favorable to the formation of fans or cones are not entirely topographic. Climatic variations also may be a factor. An abrupt change of slope was the chief factor in the formation of the fans at the western base of the Sierra Nevada in California and at the eastern base of the Front Range of the Rocky Mountains. Huge fans have been built up also at the base of The Himalaya in India and at the base of the Andes in Argentina and at many other places.

Piedmont Alluvial Plains. Where streams discharge on a plain near each other, their fans may coalesce and form a continuous sheet of aggraded sediments along the base of the mountain range and eventually build up a piedmont alluvial plain (Fig. 151), sometimes called a compound alluvial fan, a bajada, or an alluvial apron.

Bars and Channel Fill. Deposits made in a stream's channel show a great diversity of form, but as a group they are called *bars* or simply *channel fill*. Some bars are mounds of gravel and sand that form submerged shoals in the stream, some are islands (at least at low-water stages), some are accumulations before or behind obstructions, and others are deposits left at the edges of the channel. A very characteristic type forms at the inner side of each sharp bend of a stream's course. The main current makes a rapid sweep along the outer bank, and undercurrents pass across to the inner side of the curve and deposit parts of their loads. Deposits so formed, when exposed during the low-water stage of a stream, are the familiar sandbanks or pebble beaches of streams.

At high-water stages bars are subject to a shift in position or an alteration in form; some may be destroyed entirely, and new ones may appear elsewhere.

Braided Streams. In streams that are heavily loaded (Fig. 152), especially in those subject to loss of volume in semiarid regions, sediment is being deposited continually, and the bed is steadily rising until eventually numerous sand bars deflect the currents and the river flows not in a single channel but in many anastomosing streamlets which together with the sand bars that separate them are continually shifting. A river which, owing to deposition, is split into many branching and reuniting channels is a *braided stream*. The Platte River in Nebraska is a braided stream

FIG. 152. An overloaded, or braided, stream, Matanuska River, Alaska. (*Sketched from photograph by Mendenhall, U.S. Geological Survey.*)

flowing in a broad alluvial valley nearly 1 mile wide. During most of the year a small volume of water finds its way in a tortuous course through a series of interlacing streamlets whose positions shift at every flood.

Scour and Fill. When the volume and velocity of an aggrading stream are suddenly increased, as in time of flood, the stream digs new channels in the sediments on its floor; and when the flood subsides, they are again filled. Such alternate filling and excavating is referred to as *scour and fill.* One of the most striking examples of a stream that transports its sediment in this manner is the lower portion of the Missouri River. During periods of high velocity, scouring reaches a depth of about 80 feet in the vicinity of Nebraska City, and 25 miles upstream from Omaha a fill of about 40 feet is cut to bedrock during seasons of flood. The products of such excavation are moved downstream and eventually, after many periods of rest, reach the sea.

Flood-plain Deposits. In times of flood, when the volume of a stream is high, fine silt, mud, and sand are laid down on the level tract, or flood plain, over which the river spreads. During each high-water stage, the bed of alluvium becomes thicker, and the height of the flood plain is increased until the deepening of the main channel by erosion makes the height of the flood plain above the normal stream so great that the plain is no longer overspread by the river, except in times of very high floods. The part of the flood plain of the Mississippi River from Cairo, Illinois, at the junction of the Ohio River, to the Gulf of Mexico varies from 30 to 60 miles in width and is approximately 600 miles long. Most flood plains are bounded on either side by relatively steep slopes. These slopes may be sufficiently steep to form bluffs, especially if the valley has been widened by lateral cutting in resistant rocks. In some cases where the rocks bordering a valley are weak and easily eroded, the slopes are so gentle that it is difficult to detect where the flood plain ends and the valley sides begin.

Wide flood plains commonly are sheet plains interrupted by sloughs, whereas narrow flood plains on steeper slopes have a characteristic channel-and-bar topography. The surfaces of other flood plains exhibit a combination of broad, shallow pans and low mounds.

Natural Levees. During floods the whole flood plain may be covered with waters flowing seaward. In this wide expanse of water the current is most rapid along the axis of the river channel, where the water is the deepest. Along the margin of the channel, where the rapid currents come in contact with the slowly moving water of the flood plain, the velocity suddenly is checked, and the currents drop all but fine sediments carried in suspension. In this way the flood-plain deposits are built up highest on the immediate border of the channel and slope gradually toward the valley sides. These embankments of aggraded material resemble the levees constructed by man in his attempt to confine a stream to a narrow channel, and they are known as *natural levees* (Figs. 153, 154).

The levees are low ridges seldom more than a few feet higher than

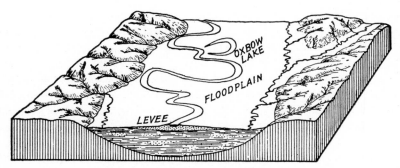

FIG. 153. Diagram of the flood plain and natural levees of a large river. Note the oxbow lake and Yazoo effect on the marginal streams.

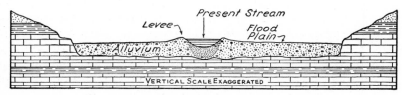

FIG. 154. Diagram showing flood plain of a river with levees. If a city is built on such a plain, frequent inundation is to be expected.

the backland toward which they descend with a slope so slight that the region appears flat. Some levees, however, are so high that during flood-time they stand out as long, low islands with the main channel of the river on one side and the floodwaters of the backland and uplands on the other side. During moderately high water, natural levees serve as a protection to the river flats, as they retain the waters in a definite channel. However, during unusually high floods, a river may break through its embankments and flood the lowlands beyond with numerous streams.

Along many rivers the levees are so high that tributaries flow parallel to the main stream for considerable distances before they find a place to join the main stream. The Yazoo River parallels the main channel of the Mississippi River for about 200 miles and serves as the typical example of this *Yazoo effect*.

Many cities are built on flood plains because they offer flat ground for buildings near water transportation. Such cities are almost certain to be inundated during high water. Disastrous floods occur nearly every year along the Mississippi River and its tributaries. Since certain cities are built on plains formed at floodtimes of the streams (Fig. 154), frequent inundation should be expected.

Alluvial Terraces. A stream that has aggraded its valley to a considerable depth may excavate part of the deposits previously laid down. The alluvial sediments are carved into one or more terraces or narrow plains and flats that fringe the sides of the valley. Such flat-topped stream terraces are the remnants of former flood plains, below which the streams that made them have cut their channels to develop new flood plains at lower levels.

The chief factors that aid the development of stream terraces are (1) uplift, or rejuvenation, of the stream, (2) partial loss of load and renewed ability to erode farther downstream, (3) failure of supply of sediments in the upper stream course, (4) exchange of a small amount of coarse for a large amount of fine sediment, (5) elimination of meanders and consequent increase of velocity, and (6) increase in volume of the stream due to piracy or to other causes.

Terraces are a normal feature of the history of any stream. They appear first in the lower, or older, part of the valley and are gradually extended upstream. Where traced upstream or downstream, they are found to pass into the flood plain. It is rare that terraces of the same age are equally developed along both sides of a stream at the same time, for the new, or lowered, channel is likely to lie near one side of the old flood plain. Even if terraces are formed on both sides, erosion is constantly attacking them and may destroy them; and the older the terrace, the smaller the remnants become until finally the terrace disappears.

Alluvial terraces protected by spurs of hard rock underneath them or on the upstream side are said to be *rock-perched* or *rock-defended* terraces.

Deltas. Where rivers laden with sediments flow into a body of quiet water such as a lake or a bay or into the sea, the velocity suddenly is checked, and rapid deposition of sediments follows. Where the shore currents are of insufficient strength to transport the load brought in by the river or where coastal configuration protects the mouth of the stream from rapid tidal currents, the debris which the river brings settles near its mouth and builds up a delta, named from the Greek letter Δ, the shape of which it somewhat resembles. Where a river discharges into a sea, the silty fresh water tends to float on the heavier salt water until the fresh and the saline waters mix. Where fresh water, with fine silt in suspension, mixes with sea water, the salts of sea water cause the silt to be deposited.

Since waves, tides, and currents are weaker in lakes than in the sea, deltas are more common in lakes. However, the larger deltas are built in the sea, for there the largest rivers discharge. Some streams build no deltas because of the lack of sediments. The Niagara River as it flows into Lake Ontario is so free from silt that no sediments are being deposited.

Growth of Deltas. A delta consists of successive layers of debris brought down from the land and spread out over a fan-shaped area on

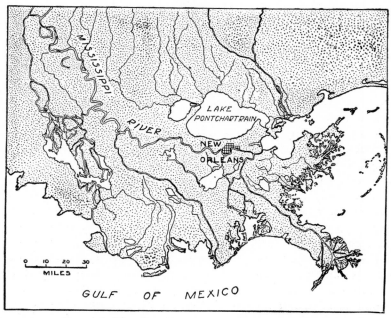

FIG. 155. Map of part of the delta of the Mississippi River. (*Drawn from maps and aerial photographs.*)

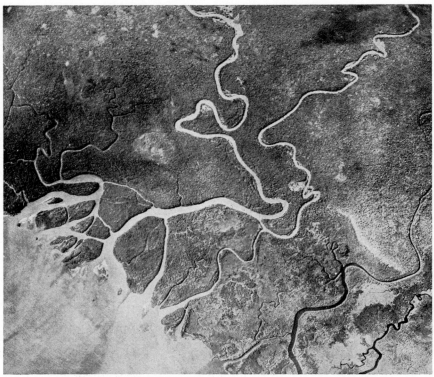

FIG. 156. Distributaries and delta building in Dutch East Indies. (*Photograph by United States Air Force.*)

the bottom of the basin at the mouth of the river. Where the stream current reaches quiet water, the bulk of its coarser load is dropped and the finer material is carried farther out. The accumulating sediments tend to reduce the gradient of the stream so that it aggrades rapidly, and soon it begins to break up into distributaries which wind to and fro over the newly formed alluvial land (Fig. 155). Deposition continues in these currents until many of the channels are completely choked and others are opened; later these also are choked and abandoned. In this way many partially filled areas remain as lakes in the delta, and coalescing distributaries enclose islands. The main channels build their accumulations of coarse debris farther and farther out into the sea, and the minor distributaries assist by adding their products of aggradation until the deposits are built up to and above sea level (Fig. 156).

The *rate of growth* of deltas varies with the size and velocity of the rivers and the geologic nature of the drainage basins. The Mississippi River is pushing the embankments of its chief distributaries into the Gulf at a rate of about 1 mile in 16 years. The northern portion of the Adriatic Sea is being filled so rapidly by the Po and other streams that cities originally built on the coast line are now far from the sea. Adria, formerly a port, is now 14 miles inland; on other parts of the coast line, zones 20 miles wide have been built up within the past 1,800 years. The Tiber River, yellow in color because of the abundance of sediment which it carries, is adding to the coast line around its mouth at the rate of about 1 mile a century. At the mouth of the Danube a great delta is growing into the Black Sea. At the major outlets the water is shallowing so fast that the lines of soundings of 6 and 36 feet deep are advancing into the sea nearly 400 feet per year.

The Ganges-Brahmaputra Delta has an area of approximately 60,000 square miles with an apex 200 miles inland. The Mississippi Delta began to form north of Cairo, Illinois, and deltalike deposits are found southward for 600 miles. Its width varies from 30 to 60 miles. The total area including its northerly extension is over 30,000 square miles. Only about one-third of this area has been formed during recent geologic time. Most of Holland represents the combined deltas of the Rhine, the Maas, and the Scheldt Rivers.

Structure of Deltas. The structure of a delta deposit is essentially the same at the mouth of every large river. A section shows nearly horizontal beds of fine silt at the bottom. Because of their position these beds are termed the *bottomset* beds. Above them is found a series of more steeply inclined strata of coarser sand and gravel which represents the heavier load dropped by the river currents as they encountered the quiet waters of the coast. The slopes of these beds, called the *foreset* beds, approach the angle of repose of the material of which they are composed but on large deltas usually are only a few hundred feet per mile. They, in turn,

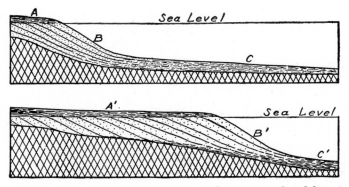

FIG. 157. Diagram illustrating the development and structure of a delta: *A* and *A'*, topset beds; *B* and *B'*, foreset beds; *C* and *C'*, bottomset beds.

are capped by nearly horizontal strata, the *topset* beds, which represent the last deposits of the river as the distributaries aggrade the alluvial flats of the growing delta (Fig. 157).

A delta consists of two parts: (1) a seaward margin, or submerged part, resting upon the marine Continental Shelf; and (2) a landward part that is not submerged but is covered with the subaerial and fresh-water sediments. The land portion gradually is built out over the submerged portion, which in turn steadily is built out into the deeper water. Because of these relations, oceanic deltas have marine beds that grade upward and landward into fresh-water sediments.

Subsidence of Deltas. Subsidence of large deltas has been noted at the mouths of many rivers. In general, aggradation has kept pace with the sinking, but in some delta deposits marine limestones and shales are interbedded with fresh-water sediments and old soils. From the structural relations of the sediments it is evident that at times subsidence gained on upbuilding and the delta surface again was covered by the sea. Deep borings in various deltas reveal similar successions. At New Orleans drift-wood was penetrated at 1,042 feet. Depths of 500 to 800 feet are not uncommon in many deltas now being formed. During earlier geologic times some deltas subsided to depths of more than 10,000 feet as the river-borne sediments accumulated on the surface. In the region that is now the northern Appalachian Mountains area an ancient delta was once deposited, and the Susquehanna River has since excavated its channel through the delta beds, which show a thickness of 13,000 feet.

Stream Deposition in Arid Regions. In arid regions the rainfall is so slight that the runoff is not able to transport all the sediments brought into the larger valleys by the rainwash. For this reason a large proportion of the material derived from the erosion of the bordering hills or mountains, where the rainfall may be considerable, is deposited in the valleys, where rainfall is much less, with the result that sediments accumulate

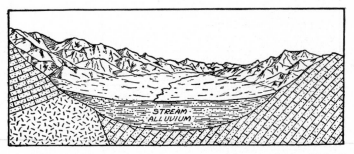

FIG. 158. An aggraded structural valley in a semiarid region. (*After U.S. Geological Survey.*)

to a depth of many hundred feet (Fig. 158). Desert-valley filling characteristically is shown in the smaller intermontane valleys of Arizona and California (Fig. 159). There many of the valley walls are angular mountain slopes with narrow, gorgelike tributary valleys leading back into the mountains. A huge alluvial fan or cone is formed at the mouth of each tributary, and where the gradients are high, many of the fans are composed of boulders and large stones, transported by the torrents produced by cloudbursts of only a few minutes' duration that sweep over such areas at rare intervals.

In regions where the major valleys are wider the outer margins of the fans are composed of fine sand and silt, and here wind work becomes active, and sand-dune areas are developed. In many of the valley bottoms the wind is a more effective agent of transportation than running water. Occasionally, however, when the rainfall is heavy in the mountains at the headwaters, a desert valley may have a river that floods the aeolian sediments of its plains for hundreds of miles along its course, so that fluvial and aeolian sediments become interbedded.

Chemical Precipitation from Stream Waters. In arid regions the solids dissolved in a stream may become concentrated enough to be precipitated as a coating on pebbles at low-water stages. Under exceptional circumstances in a humid region a stream fed by cold springs highly charged

FIG. 159. Alluvial deposits, Death Valley, Inyo County, California. (*Spence Air Photos.*)

with dissolved calcium bicarbonate may deposit calcium carbonate along its course, as carbon dioxide is released by warming, by agitation over rapids, or by organisms. Most stream waters are too dilute to make chemical deposits en route to the sea.

SUGGESTIONS FOR FURTHER READING

Cotton, C. A.: Classification and Correlation of River Terraces, *Jour. Geomorphology,* vol. 3, pp. 27–37, 1940.

Davis, W. M.: Base Level, Grade, and Peneplain, *Jour. Geology,* vol. 10, pp. 77–111, 1902.

Eardley, A. J.: Yukon River Channel Shifting, *Geol. Soc., America Bull.,* vol. 49, pp. 343, 358, 1938.

Gilbert, G. K.: The Transportation of Debris by Running Water, *U.S. Geol. Survey Prof. Paper* 86, 1914.

King, Lester C.: South African Scenery, A Textbook of Geomorphology, 2d ed., rev., Edinburgh, 1951.

Lobeck, A. K.: Geomorphology, McGraw-Hill Book Company, Inc., 1939.

Russell, I. C.: Rivers of North America, G. P. Putnam's Sons, 1898.

Russell, R. J.: Lower Mississippi River Delta, *Louisiana Dept. Cons. Geol. Bull.* 8, 1936.

Thornburg, W. D.: Principles of Geomorphology, John Wiley & Sons, Inc., 1954.

CHAPTER 10

Snow, Ice, and Valley Glaciers

Freezing of Ground Water. Fresh water under ordinary surface conditions forms ice when the temperature reaches 32°F., and as it passes from the liquid to the solid state (Fig. 160), there is a 9 per cent increase in volume. Since all soils are porous and since nearly all solid rocks near the surface have innumerable joints and fissures that contain moisture, the expansion of water as it freezes is an important factor in rock disintegration (Fig. 161). In high mountainous districts and in the arctic or subarctic regions, where there is a marked daily fluctuation of temperature, small angular fragments are wedged from the surface of exposed cliffs and accumulate as heaps of talus at the base of steep slopes and crags. Along the coast of Greenland and in Alpine regions the amount of rock disruption caused by frost is enormous. There some of the snow of the long winters is melted during the summer months, and water fills the joints and fissures of the rocks. The summer nights are sufficiently cold to freeze water, and the resulting ice splits off large blocks from the cliffs. In mountain valleys with high gradients talus material creeps under its own weight and frequently forms "rock streams," or "rock glaciers," that move slowly down the valley.

This is part of the mass movement of surface materials that has been discussed on a previous page, but the point here is that the freezing of the water in or added to the talus accelerates the downslope movement and may initiate it.

In soils the frozen water forms an icy cement which binds together the fragments of the mantle-rock, fills the pore spaces, and hinders the downward penetration of water as the snow melts in the spring. On hillsides and mountain slopes such a frozen surface may become a gliding plane in the rock waste, and huge masses of water-soaked rock debris slump toward the valley as landslides. In agricultural districts where the soil is composed of bouldery clay, each season's frost carries boulders nearer the surface. The stones are moved by the expansive force of freezing water-soaked clay that yields in the direction of least resistance, and in

FIG. 160. Snowflakes, showing some of the crystal patterns assumed by water as it solidifies from the atmosphere. (*Photograph by Prof. U. Nakaya, Hokkaido University.*)

general such frost heaving is toward the surface of the earth. When the frost leaves in the spring, the particles of soil sink back to their original positions but the boulders are prevented from settling by pebbles or clay which falls into cavities that lie below them. In time much of the bouldery material of the mantle-rock may come to lie at or near the surface. Farmers have cleared these boulders from their fields in some regions and built them into stone fences.

Permafrost. In regions adjacent to existing icecaps or continental glaciers, and in some high mountainous areas, the rocks are filled with perennial frost. This is called *permafrost* in reference to its persistence.

It is very extensive in northern Eurasia and North America. While Antarctica and the lower end of South America have areas where the ground remains permanently frozen, the Southern Hemisphere has a relatively small amount of land properly situated in high latitudes for that condition to develop. Permafrost is a reservoir of cold which may accumulate or waste with climatic variation. It probably precedes and lingers on after every glacial period, or it may occur independently.

A mean annual air temperature of 30 to 24°F. is generally given as that required to produce permafrost, but other factors may also be effective in producing that result. These are given by Robert F. Black as follows:

1. Long, cold winters and short, cool summers.
2. Low precipitation the year round and especially low snowfall.
3. Clear winters and cloudy summers.
4. Rapid evaporation the year round.
5. Strong, cold winds in summer and winter.
6. Low insolation.

Permafrost is more than frozen ground water, although of course that is included. Besides acting as a cement between fragments and thus completely sealing the pore spaces in mantle-rock, these ice crystals increase in size and add to their number to form films, veins, wedges, irregular bodies, and continuous lenslike layers of relatively clear ice that may be of large size. Poorly drained areas underlain by clay or very fine silt or by peat offer especially favorable conditions for the development of these extensive masses of clear ice. Not only does frost form a subsurface mass impervious to the downward movement of water, but this cementing

FIG. 161. Blocks of rock loosened by frost and the expansive force of ice. Yosemite National Park, California. (*After Matthes, U.S. Geological Survey.*)

FIG. 162. In the immediate foreground are frost polygons near Churchill, Manitoba. (*Royal Canadian Air Force.*)

material is easily activated by temperature changes. Freezing increases the volume of soil partly because of the expansion of water changing to ice and additionally, in the regions of permafrost, because of the formation of masses of clear ice within it. Since water will move readily toward growing crystals of ice, the additional moisture necessary to produce the volume increase is drawn by capillarity from any adjacent source. In silts this volume increase may result in more than doubling the size of the bed affected.

The frost causes a thorough stirring or kneading of the materials during alternate melting and freezing. Although areas of bare soil are more intensely affected, the heave and thrust also tear the tough mat of peat commonly covering the soil of sodded areas and thus form *peat rings*, or *polygons* (Fig. 162), and leave bare scars or naked soil where parting takes place. These rings, or chunks, of sod creep downslope or move under a viscous flow to lower level. Wherever the frost is unduly confined, pressure increases and the upward expansion may become explosive and toss aside the surface materials and fragments of rock as the strain is relieved. Freezing and thawing may cause the surface to move laterally and produce tension on slopes and buckling on flats. The removal of much of the ice or water from boggy soil or inflated silts and peat may cause the surface to cave in.

The various processes of *cryoplanation* attributable to permafrost in the Arctic reduce the landscape to characteristic long, smooth slopes and gently rounded forms.

The depth to which this perennially frozen ground extends varies from place to place. In Alaska, on the Seward Peninsula, it ranges from zero near lakes, large streams, and warm springs, to 300 feet or more; south of Barrow it is 1,000 feet. On the Kezhevinkov Bay, in northern Siberia, it is 1,700 feet, and at Nordvik permanently frozen ground occurs to a depth of 2,000 feet.

In the Northern Hemisphere the outer, or southern, border of perennially frozen ground is fringed by a wide area under which it is discontinuous and sporadic for a distance of 500 miles or more. Permafrost underlies the tundra region of the north and continues out under the conifer forests. These trees spread their roots horizontally into the loose soil over the frozen ground. To them the frost is an asset since it supplies plenty of moisture even where the annual rainfall is limited. In Canada permafrost extends as far south as the southern shores of Hudson Bay. In Siberia it reaches as far south as the Amur Valley. Some of the northern Siberian rivers flow on a bed of ice the year round.

Permafrost is thin or absent under some glaciers, and certain areas from which glaciers recently have receded do not contain it. The Pleistocene continental glaciers, now largely melted, were very thick so that the ground or rock surface beneath them may not have been frozen. However, permanently frozen ground, or permafrost, must have been present at the outer margin of the ice sheet and have extended as far outward as conditions favored its development.

Cumulative data in Europe show that during the height of Pleistocene glaciation permafrost occurred in southern England, northern France, Germany, and Poland. The remnants of surface features, similar to those developed over areas now affected by permafrost, have been recognized at various places in the drift of the upper Mississippi Valley and from Maine through New York, Pennsylvania, and farther south. Even the sweeping slopes and gently rounded forms characteristic of much of the drift topography in North America suggest cryoplanation and lingering permafrost before the present vegetation took over.

Freezing of River Water. When river water freezes, it exerts a disruptive effect at the sides and bottom of its channel like that which results from the freezing of ground water. Mud, gravel, and boulders become incased in the ice and are pushed downstream or are floated by thick cakes of ice to the banks of the stream or halted by an ice jam across the valley. If a large amount of ice accumulates at a narrow place in the valley, the water is ponded and deposition of the stream's sediment follows. When the jam eventually breaks, the volume of the stream is greatly increased and the acceleration of velocity that accompanies this raises the transporting power of the stream immensely. Many of the Canadian rivers flowing into Hudson Bay are dammed at their rapids in this manner. As the ice breaks in early summer, many of the incased boulders are stranded on the shores, where they remain until they are pushed or floated farther during the next season.

Ice on Lakes and Seas. A body of quiet water, such as a lake or inland sea, does not commonly freeze at the surface until all the water from top to bottom is near the freezing temperature. Fresh water is densest at 39°F., and when the surface water reaches this temperature, it sinks and is replaced by warmer water from below until the whole body of water reaches its greatest density (39°F.), when this vertical circulation ceases. As the temperature of the lake surface continues to approach the freezing point (32°F.), this colder water remains afloat and finally forms a crust of ice. Thus the lakes of average depth freeze over at the surface completely when the temperature is below the freezing point for an extended period. Deep lakes, such as the Great Lakes, freeze near shore lines but do not completely freeze over, even in the coldest winters. Since the cold surface water sinks and is replaced by warmer and lighter water from the depths, all the water in such deep basins does not reach the temperature of greatest density, and hence above freezing.

If a lake is shallow for some distance from shore, the ice anchors itself to the bottom; and by freezing the water in the sediments on the floor of the basin the ice covering of the basin becomes continuous with the frozen land at the level of the lake. With fluctuations of temperature the ice expands and contracts, and in contracting during a period of low temperature it forms cracks which are filled with water that congeals to cement the fractures. In this way a continuous sheet of ice is formed again to fit the outlines of the basin. If later the temperature is raised, the ice expands, making the ice cover too large to fit the basin, and it crowds the shore line, exerting an enormous horizontal thrust in all directions. In this way much loose material is crowded ashore, forming, after melting of the ice, walls of sand, gravel, and larger stones that parallel the shore lines. They differ from beaches or bars in that the material is often unsorted, and it slopes steeply toward the basin. Hundreds of glacial lakes in the upper Mississippi Valley region have conspicuous *ice ramparts* (Fig. 163) formed in this way.

On many lakes under the vegetation of a floating bog, ice is continuous laterally with the ice of the surrounding soil. At such places the expanding ice arches up the soil in a series of ridges parallel to the shore. Many small lakes in the glaciated region of the northern part of the United States are entirely surrounded by wire grass bogs underlain by thick beds of peat that are saturated with water. The shove of shore ice on such lakes pushes the ice of the surrounding bogs into huge domes and ridges.

Should strong winds arise when the ice on a lake is breaking, large cakes of ice with enclosed pebbles and boulders are driven ashore and pushed out on the beach. If the drift of ice rafts parallels the shore line, erosion of the banks takes place by the ice, which tears away the beach materials or smooths them into terracelike structures.

Sea water does not freeze until it reaches a temperature of 26 to 28°F. The freezing temperature is not so nearly uniform as that of fresh water, because of the varying salinity of the sea. In high latitudes the sea water is all near the freezing point, but after the ice attains a thickness of 6 to 10 feet, it protects the water below from the intense cold of the polar winters. Where ice forms alongshore in the high latitudes, it is at many places over 50 feet thick. Such masses are the result not of the direct freezing of the ocean water but of the conversion of snow into ice by the spray from waves and of the heaping up of ice alongshore by storms. Such ice, commonly referred to as the *ice foot of the shore*, is an important factor in shore-line erosion. It protects the shore from wave action and

FIG. 163. Ice rampart, 8 to 10 feet high, along the shore of Lake Mendota at Picnic Point, Madison, Wisconsin. This wall of bouldery drift was produced by ice shove from the lake during the ice-expansion stage brought about by temperature changes in February. (*Courtesy of Wisconsin Geological and Natural History Survey.*)

serves as a raft on which debris, broken from the cliffs by the action of frost during the winter, may gather and be carried out to sea when the ice breaks.

Broken sea ice floats in large cakes known as *floes*. This floe ice frequently is jammed together into ice packs that have very irregular surfaces and stand high above the water, owing to the crowding of the ice cakes. Along the coast of Labrador and in many arctic bays ice forms on the sea bottom and is spoken of as *ground ice*, or *anchor ice*.

Snow. Not all bodies of ice are formed from the freezing of water on the surface or within the water-soaked mantle-rock. They may result from the compacting of snow. Pond or lake ice is heavier per unit of volume. Hence it is slightly different from ice formed from snow because in the pond ice the axes of the crystals are parallel and perpendicular to the freezing surface, resulting in a compact form of solid ice. In ice formed from snow the arrangement of the crystals is controlled by the flakes, in each of which the axial direction is fixed before the haphazard fall to the earth's surface. Further development of such crystals results in interlocking axes devoid of systematic arrangement. This produces a loose, more or less porous solid.

Snow is of common occurrence during the colder season on many portions of the earth's surface and may occur even at the equator on elevated areas such as mountains. It is encountered at all seasons by high-flying aircraft, on which icing was a problem that required special attention and a definite solution. When the atmosphere becomes saturated with moisture, a slight drop in temperature produces condensation. If the temperature is above freezing, this excess moisture is eliminated in the form of rain; but when the temperature is less than 32°F., commonly it takes the form of snow-flakes (Fig. 160). A large portion of the moisture that is precipitated as rain runs off as surface water, but snow generally accumulates in the region where it falls and generally remains as long as the temperature of the air in contact with it is below the freezing point.

Snow Fields. In regions where the mean annual temperature is near the freezing point of water, much of the snow remains unmelted from one year to the next and consequently accumulates to great depths. The elevation of the lower limit of this accumulating snow is called the *snow line*, but usually it is a very irregular line. The regions where such low temperatures com-

Approximate Position of Snow Line with Respect to Elevations above Sea Level

	Feet
Greenland	2,200
Lapland	3,000
Norway	5,000
Pyrenees	6,000
Alps	9,000
The Himalaya:	
South side	13,000
North side	16,000
Mexico	14,000
Andes, in Bolivia:	
East side	16,000
West side	18,000

monly prevail are chiefly in high latitudes or at high elevations. The location of the snow line is also influenced by the regional topography, the wind, the variation in minimum temperature from year to year, and similar local conditions. Apart from the temperature, the amount of snowfall is pehaps the most important factor.

Where the amount of snow that accumulates during the cold season is greater than the amount removed by melting during the warmer season, a *snow field* is formed. Snow fields are widely distributed. They may occur in any latitude at high altitudes and at all altitudes in high latitudes. Snow fields are common in the high mountains of South America and Mexico and in the Rocky Mountain system of the United States, Canada (Fig. 164), and Alaska. They become progressively more widespread toward the north. In Eurasia snow fields exist in The Himalaya, the Caucasus, the Pyrenees, and the Alps, in the ranges of the Scandinavian peninsula, and on such islands as Iceland, Spitzbergen, Nova Zembla, and others along the arctic borders of Siberia and North America. In Africa snow fields and valley glaciers occur on Kilimanjaro and Ruwenzori near

FIG. 164. A portion of the Columbia ice field, reported to be the largest existing remnant of the cordilleran ice sheet. Its melt water gives rise to the Saskatchewan River, running to Hudson Bay and thence to the Atlantic, the Athabaska, reaching the Arctic through the Mackenzie, and the Fraser and Columbia, flowing into the Pacific Ocean. (*Canadian National Railways.*)

the equator. Certain of the high mountains of New Zealand also have snow fields. The snow grades downward into solid ice and thus becomes an *ice field,* with no very marked distinction to be made between it and the snow field from which it originates. As accumulation continues, the mass of ice may begin to move downslope or be squeezed out from the area of greatest thickness with very little definite indication of the point where motion begins. The two largest areas of snow and ice on the surface of the earth are those of Greenland and Antarctica, and of these Antarctica is by far the larger and contains more ice and snow than all the glaciers and snow fields of the rest of the world combined (Fig. 165). These two regions alone have more than 5,700,000 square miles of ice-covered territory. Sonic, or echo, sounding in Greenland shows the ice to be as much as 8,000 feet thick, and sounding in Antarctica gives similar results. It has been estimated that the ice of these two great icecaps, if it were all melted, would raise the level of the sea more than 200 feet.

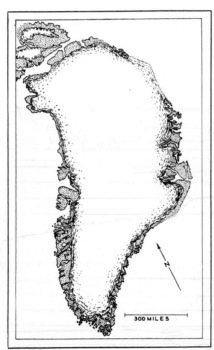

FIG. 165. The continental ice sheet on the surface of Greenland. The main part of the island is covered by glacial ice, and there is only a narrow fringe of land along the coast.

Compacting of Snow. The snow as it falls on the snow fields is commonly flaky and dry, but as it accumulates, it is compacted, partially melted, and in refreezing acquires a granular texture much like that of the snow in old snowbanks during the latter part of a northern winter. Unless wet, a handful of such snow runs through the fingers like a similar amount of wheat grains, pellets of shot, or dry sand grains. It bears little resemblance to the soft, feathery flakes as they fall gently from wintry clouds. Such granular snow is the *névé,* or *firn,* of the snow field or of the surface of the glacier (Fig. 166).

The icy pellets composing a snowbank that has lain through the greater part of a winter season are the same thing, although seldom so called. The transformation from snow to névé and this, in turn, into ice is very slow and is brought about by the interaction of a number of factors that result in the larger granules growing at the expense of the smaller ones. Although granular, the névé is in reality a haphazard heap of ice crystals, each of which has its edges and faces obliterated because of the ease with which ice changes to liquid and back to solid again. The face of the crystal and the thin edge between faces are most exposed to this change. Deeper down in the névé the granules are continually changing, assuming new form, moving into closer contact, filling in vacant spaces, and reorienting themselves with reference to adjacent granules. This is the process referred to as the growth of crystal granules. Not only does it produce a solid mass of ice with interlocking crystals, but it is a powerful factor in glacial motion. Accumulated masses of compacted snow, perched high in the mountains, may be released by changing weather conditions and slide down the slope as avalanches (Fig. 167). In the snow fields the weight of the upper layers of snow, aided by successive storms and drifts or by avalanches from neighboring peaks, squeezes the lower layers, and they are recrystallized into solid ice.

During the summer months the surface of a snow field frequently

FIG. 166. Crevasses and coarse granular snow, or névé, on the surface of the Columbia ice field, Jasper National Park, Alberta, Canada. (*Government Travel Bureau, Ottawa, Canada.*)

FIG. 167. Unstable snow masses above ice fields in Alaska. The melting and freezing, sliding and avalanching of such masses of snow are partly responsible for the steep, blunt upper ends of cirques. (*Photograph by United States Air Force.*)

reaches a temperature sufficiently warm to melt most of the flaky snow above the névé bed, and a thin crust of ice is formed when the temperature is again lowered. This crust separates the névé below from the snow of the next winter and remains in the névé field as a thin layer of ice; such layers give the whole deposit a stratified structure. Stratification is still more marked where wind-blown dust and coarser debris accumulate on the surface and are covered by subsequent snowfalls. In some Himalayan snow fields the separate strata of névé between successive layers, or crusts, of ice indicate an enormous amount of precipitation annually. In others, such as the firn fields of the Alps, each yearly deposit forms a thin layer 2 to 5 feet thick. In some Alpine snow fields the total thickness of the névé beds is over 1,500 feet.

Glaciers. When granular snow or the massive ice resulting from its recrystallization accumulates to a great thickness, it begins to move, or flow, from its place of accumulation and forms a glacier. These ice masses in mountain ranges vary in size from short but wide tongues of ice or snow on the narrow benches of a cliff, such as the snowbank glaciers of the Bighorn Mountains of Wyoming, to the tongues of ice extending down the valleys from the mountains of Alaska or from The Himalaya in Asia.

The Seward Glacier in Alaska is 50 miles long and 3 to 5 miles wide. The Hubbard Glacier of Alaska is somewhat longer but not so wide. The Asiatic glaciers, in the vicinity of Mount Everest, are more than 30 miles long. Those in the Alps are numerous but usually not more than a few miles in length. The thickness of the ice in mountain glaciers is difficult to determine, but it is doubtful whether in many of them it exceeds 2,000 feet. Still greater glaciers are found in the arctic and antarctic regions, where extensive névé and ice fields have accumulated and spread out in all directions.

Types of Glacier. As glacial ice spreads or flows from the place where it formed, it assumes various shapes that are molded to a considerable extent by the surface over which the ice flows. On the basis of their mode of occurrence all glaciers may be classed as follows: (1) the mountain,

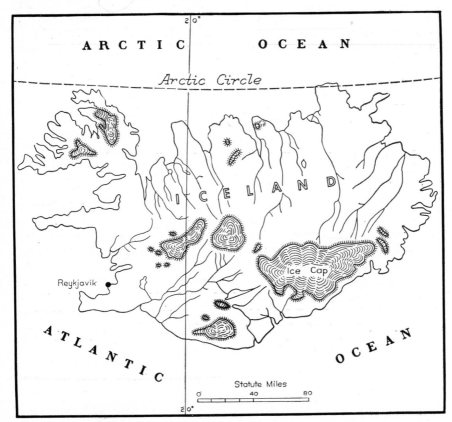

FIG. 168. Iceland, showing small icecaps which are the remnants of a former more extensive glaciation covering the whole island.

FIG. 169. Sharp, jagged peaks and ridges above effective glaciation in the Alps. Here the snow blows and slides off into the lodgment basins of glacial accumulation, leaving the tops of mountains bare.

or valley, type; (2) the confluent, or piedmont, type; (3) the continental, or ice-sheet, type. The latter is also called an icecap (Fig. 168).

Mountain, or *valley, glaciers* descend from high peaks (Fig. 169) and occur along the flanks of mountain ranges in nearly all latitudes. They represent the discharge or solid drainage from an ice field through valleys which were originally formed by streams. At many places it is difficult to draw a definite distinction between a true glacier and a snow field, since they merge into each other and one mountain glacier is formed by the union of a number of smaller tributary ice tongues, each of which is in turn fed by the snow field. Obviously there is some motion in the snow or ice field since it discharges its excess into the mountain, or valley, glacier.

If a mountain glacier descends to the lower end of a valley, it expands and spreads laterally as a broad, flat lobe, or ice apron. Many Alaskan ice streams show such expansion; and when several glaciers from the same range coalesce in their expanded portions, a *piedmont glacier* is formed. The Malaspina Glacier in Alaska, a magnificent example of this type, is formed by the union of the lower ends of many valley glaciers descending from the ice fields near the summit of Mount St. Elias and the neighboring mountains.

Continental glaciers, or ice sheets, cover vast areas and move over the lower ridges, hills, and valleys with but little regard for them. Usually the ice is thicker than the height of the ridges and the depths of the valleys combined. Most of Antarctica is now buried under a vast continental glacier, or ice sheet, and in the interior all the irregularities except the mountain peaks are concealed.

Although all glaciers may be included conveniently within these types, several subtypes are often recognized. Some of these are probably special cases of the alpine, or valley, type but have certain peculiarities that have suggested their names. Thus a glacier may cascade down a steep slope or project from a hanging valley, break off, and fall as blocks, or chunks, which pressure and freezing reunite at the base of the plunge to form a *reconstructed glacier*. Perched on the upper part of a cliff, often at the head of a steep, blunt-ended valley, there may be a broad, snow-capped mass of clear ice, often crescent-shaped, forming a *cliff glacier*, or *hanging glacier* (Fig. 170). The *polar*, or *high-latitude, glacier* of northern Greenland is a steep-sided, blunt-ended tongue of ice extending down a valley from the plateau on which the ice sheet is located. The

FIG. 170. Cirque lakes—Lake Ellen Wilson and Lake Lincoln—with Mount Jackson in the background. Several cliff glaciers are shown on the mountainside with an excellent one above the lake in the lower right. Glacier National Park, Montana. (*Great Northern Railway photograph.*)

tidewater, or *tidal, glacier* is also of the valley type but extends out into the sea, where its outer end, usually rising and falling with the tide, periodically breaks off in great chunks, or blocks, that float away as *icebergs* (Fig. 171). The term icecap may be regarded as synonymous with continental glacier, or ice sheet, but the term has been used also in a more limited way to designate the smaller patches or remnants of ice that spread or move out from a center. Those still present on Iceland (Fig. 168) are excellent examples.

MOUNTAIN, VALLEY, OR ALPINE GLACIERS

Distribution. The most typical mountain glaciers are formed in well-defined valleys upon the mountainsides, and for this reason they are referred to commonly as valley glaciers. Their form is, in general, similar to the shape of the valley, and their size is dependent upon the extent of the snow field, the amount of precipitation, and the temperature. Mountain glaciers are not present in all mountains which rise above the snow line, for on many isolated peaks the topography is unfavorable to the accumulation of snow. Extinct or dormant volcanoes may have great masses of snow and ice within their craters but few, if any, alpine glaciers on their slopes. However, many ancient volcanic cones that were deeply dissected by streams before the last glacial epoch are now harboring hundreds of ice streams in their steeply sloping valleys. Such lofty peaks as Mount Shasta, Mount Rainier, and Mount Hood send down large glaciers in all directions. On Mount Shasta some are 2 miles long, and on Mount Rainier several glaciers are nearly 7 miles long.

Valley glaciers occur in most of the high mountain ranges of the world. The Alps alone have approximately 2,000 in the depressions on the sides of their lofty peaks. In northern Scandinavia several large plateaus have glaciers moving into their marginal valleys. The Himalaya in Asia are famous for their wonderful valley glaciers, some of which extend far

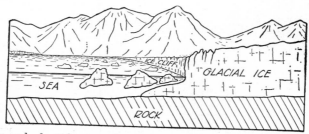

FIG. 171. The end of a tidewater glacier. Huge blocks of ice break from the ice cliff and float away as icebergs. (*After Russell.*)

down from their sources. In the United States the valley glaciers are confined to the isolated mountain peaks, but in the Selkirks of British
Columbia and farther north in Alaska (Fig. 172), hundreds of glaciers of
this type fill mountain valleys.

Limits of Glaciers. The position of the upper end, or head, of a valley
glacier in general is determined by the place where the more rapidly
moving ice breaks away from the sluggish snow or ice field. It is commonly marked by one or more large gaping cracks, or *crevasses,* known
as the *bergschrund.* Usually it is a region of change in declivity of the
base over which the ice passes. Here begins the gradational work of the
glacier itself. As the glacial ice moves away from the snow field, it carries
with it large masses of rock plucked from the mountainside and as this
process is repeated, a broad depression may be developed and give rise
to a steep, blunt-ended valley. In such a case the amphitheaterlike valley
head is called a *cirque* and may have precipitous walls hundreds of feet
high. Its basin serves as the collecting ground for the snow of successive
storms and for that swept into it by winds or carried into it by avalanches
from the snow fields above. The cirque wall, therefore, becomes the
upper limit of the glacier, and its basin serves as the feeding ground for
its ice.

Not all valley glaciers, however, begin with a cirque. In fact many may
be found, particularly in the Alps, where it is exceedingly difficult to distinguish the glacier from the ice field, and if a limiting line is drawn, it will

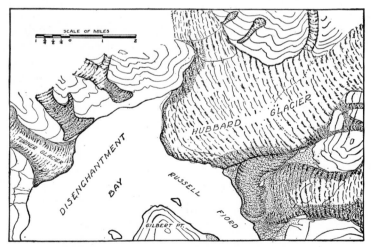

FIG. 172. A group of glaciers in the region of Yakutat Bay, Alaska. These glaciers were
once tributaries of a larger ice stream that filled Disenchantment Bay. (*After Tarr
and Martin, National Geographical Society.*)

be more or less arbitrary. The above-mentioned series of crevasses (the bergschrund), even though but slightly developed, may still serve as the most satisfactory mark of separation between the definitely moving glacier and the relatively motionless ice field.

The lower limit, or terminus, of the valley glacier generally is in the mountain valley, where the amount of ice waste, or melting, is about equal to the forward movement, or flow, of the ice. In most latitudes this position is some distance below the general snow line of the area; but as one proceeds toward high latitudes, the glaciers extend progressively to lower and lower altitudes, until near the polar regions they push downward to the sea, where large blocks are broken off and floated as icebergs (Fig. 171). The seaward end of a glaciated valley that is partly submerged is a *fiord*. Fiords are typically developed along the coast of Norway. The end of a glacier is rarely stationary. When the temperature becomes such that melting exceeds the forward movement, the edge of the glacier retreats; and when more ice moves down than is melted, the edge of the glacier advances. The ice moves forward at all times, but the position of the edge depends on the rate of advance and the rate of melting. The amount of advance or retreat is dependent upon temperature and snowfall; and since both usually show annual variations, the lower ends of glaciers fluctuate. The most marked variations seem to appear with climatic cycles. The Swiss glaciers showed a steady advance during the Middle Ages and reached a maximum about 1820. This advance was followed by a progressive retreat until about 1840, when they again advanced until 1860, and since that time many have shown a marked retreat. However, during the past few years the glaciers of the

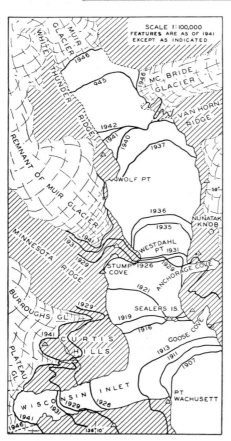

FIG. 173. Map showing the recession of Muir Glacier, Alaska, from 1907 to 1946. (*After W. O. Field, Jr.*)

French Alps have been advancing from 70 to 150 feet per year. Monthly observations on the Bossons Glacier on Mount Blanc show that this glacier advances with an oscillating movement—first on one side, then on the other, then in the middle. A recession of the edges of glaciers in Glacier Bay, Alaska, is now in progress on a large scale, and it has been estimated that the edges of the Muir Glacier have retreated 7 miles in the past 20 years (Fig. 173).

Movements of Glaciers. A glacier moves so slowly that to a casual observer it appears to be at rest, but closer inspection shows that it does move, as the evidence of movement is very positive. The first determinations as to the amount of movement were made by noting the changes that took place in the debris on their surfaces. Conspicuous boulders on the surface of the ice were observed to change their positions slowly from year to year. Later such crude observations led to careful measurements of the rate of change, which was found to vary considerably, not only in different glaciers but in different parts of the same glacier.

The rapidity of glacial flowage is influenced by several factors, the chief of which are the gradient of the valley, the thickness of the ice, and the temperature. To these may be added the smoothness of the surface over which the ice moves, the amount of water in the ice—both that which falls on it and that produced by melting—and finally the amount of debris in the ice. If a glacier is loaded with boulders, sand, and finely ground rock waste, it moves more slowly than clean ice.

Alpine glaciers move 1 to 3 feet a day. The Bossons Glacier carried the bodies of three guides, who perished in a fissure, a distance of nearly 8,000 feet in 41 years, or an average of about 1 foot in 2 days. It has been calculated that a particle of ice would require approximately 500 years to move from the summit of the Jungfrau to the end of the Aletsch Glacier, an ice stream about 10 miles long. Many of the large Alaskan glaciers move at a more rapid rate. The Muir Glacier commonly moves as much as 7 feet a day, and the Child Glacier flows nearly 30 feet per day during the summer months. Extraordinary velocities have been recorded for the ice tongues which descend to the fiords along the coast of Greenland, where rates of nearly 100 feet a day have been observed, but in the same region the inland ice at some distance back from the narrow fiords moves only a fraction of an inch per day.

The movement of a glacier resembles that of a river in many ways; the center moves more rapidly than the margins, where it meets resistance along the walls of the valley; the surface moves more rapidly than the deeper portions of the ice, where its load of debris is greater and irregularities are encountered on the valley floor. At curves in its course the convex portion moves more rapidly than the concave, in much the same way that the velocity of a stream is accelerated on a long limb of a curve and checked on the opposite side. Since some parts of the ice move faster than other parts, the movement of a glacier is spoken of as "differential movement" (Fig. 174). The amount of differential movement has been determined in many glaciers by placing stakes in a straight line over the surface of the ice in alignment with fixed points on the walls of the valley. After a few days the line of pegs curves downstream, indicating that the central part moves more rapidly than the sides.

At many places near the center of a glacier the ice moves four times as fast as it does near the sides. Similarly, by driving a vertical line of pegs where a wall of ice is exposed at the side of a glacier, it is found that the top moves faster than the bottom.

Causes of Glacial Motion. Some of the factors that may be involved in the movement of glaciers have been suggested in preceding paragraphs. Glaciers move downslope under the influence of gravity. They squeeze out from great accumulations of snow and ice. They may slide forward under the expansion of absorbed heat (below the melting point). They move under a kind of slow flowage. But these are merely preliminary observations on what is actually happening in glacial motion. Glaciers are composed of ice, and ice is a rock formed of a single mineral that always occurs in the crystalline form. Glacial motion, then, is movement by rock flowage.

A large number of experimental and microscopic data on ice from glaciers has accumulated through work done on the spot and in the laboratory. From this it is apparent that the main causes of glacial motion lie within the ice of the glacier itself as it reacts to the changing conditions under which it exists. The ice particles or molecules cannot have the freedom of movement accredited to those in a liquid, even a viscous liquid, and any flowage observed must be solid flowage. Melting of the ice at points of greatest compression, the forward and downward movement of the water thus produced, and its refreezing are of great importance. When ice refreezes, it expands and the surrounding ice mass is subjected to the thrust of its expansive force. It is evident that the thrust in the direction toward the lower end of a valley is augmented by the force of gravity, whereas movement toward the head of the glacier is retarded by the

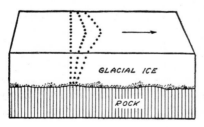

FIG. 174. Diagram illustrating the differential movement of a valley glacier. Stakes driven in a straight row across the top of a glacier in a short time show a curve downstream. Pegs placed on the side of the glacier demonstrate that the top moves faster than the bottom.

same force. Ice changes its form through the growth of its crystal granules and during this process molds itself into the available space, thus moving in the direction of least pressure. In the case of a glacier this is always from its source. Furthermore, as glacial ice moves, it recrystallizes and develops a structure somewhat similar to that of a schist such as is produced by the recrystallization of a shale. The ice crystals become arranged in a more definite order, with their axes tending to become parallel. As this process continues, gliding planes are developed in the crystals and along the crystal faces and movement takes place along such planes. Where the lower portion of a glacier carries the most debris, it is greatly retarded by its load and the clean ice above moves so much faster that it is sheared over the portion near the bottom. Such shearing planes are conspicuous in the glaciers of high latitudes, where vertical or overhanging ice cliffs hundreds of feet high allow the structure of the ice to be seen. As the temperature of ice rises, it expands, giving a forward thrust to the glacier. When cooling takes place, there is no corresponding contraction of the whole body of ice but instead cracks, or crevasses, form which later may be healed or closed in various ways and thus obliterated, but always by added snow, ice, or debris. This expansion and filling in of the cracks formed by subsequent contraction contributes its bit to the forward movement. The sum of all these factors, and perhaps others, is glacial motion.

Surface Features. *Crevasses.* Where glacial ice passes over irregularities in the bottom of the valley, a change from a lesser to a greater gradient is encountered and tension is produced in the upper surface so that the rigid ice cracks. The resulting fissures are called *crevasses* (Fig. 175). Their direction on the surface of the glacier generally is roughly transverse to the long axis of the ice stream. When first formed, they extend downward nearly vertically; but since the upper surface of the glacier moves more rapidly than the lower portion, they assume an inclination which dips up the valley. They also curve downstream because of the more rapid movement of the ice in the center of the valley. Such fissures are widest in the central portion of the glacier and taper gradually to narrow cracks at their extremities. They vary in depth from a few to several hundred feet and in width from a fraction of an inch to great chasms. In some it is safe to descend to the bottom, and in those near the upper end of the glacier, where englacial debris is not abundant, the wall ice is perfectly clear with a greenish-blue transparency. The sides of the crevasses are frequently hung with icicles and embossed with wreaths of snow.

Along with the transverse crevasses most glaciers are fissured also on the sides or margins (Figs. 176, 177). The marginal crevasses do not extend in the direction of the long axis of the glacier but point up the valley about 45 degrees. They are due to the more rapid movement of the central

FIG. 175. The surface of Athabaska Glacier in the Canadian Rockies, Alberta. (*Courtesy of Canadian Film Board.*)

portion of the glacier. Longitudinal crevasses occur also, especially wherever a glacier issues from a narrow portion of a valley into a wider one. There it has room to spread and in so doing has a tendency to fall apart, forming longitudinal fissures. Similar structures are common also on terminal lobes.

Bergschrund. At the upper end of a mountain glacier where the ice breaks away from the névé fields, there is a great crevasse or a series of open fissures that is known as the bergschrund (Fig. 178). The névé and ice forming the upper margin of the bergschrund stand higher than the

FIG. 176. Tumbling Glacier as it enters Berg Lake. This is the much crevassed outer end of one of the glaciers that discharge the surplus ice from Mount Robson British Columbia. (*Canadian National Railways.*)

portion that has moved away. The displaced block has been subjected to a downward and to a horizontal movement as well, thus forming a huge crack in the ice. Such movement is greatest during the summer months. During the winter the process is halted, and the bergschrund fills with snow and ice that enter the irregularities and joints of the rock wall. The following spring it opens again and carries big blocks of rocks with it.

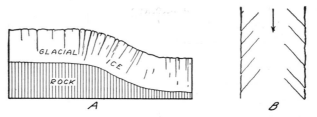

FIG. 177. Diagrams illustrating the origin of crevasses. *A*, crevasses produced by cracking due to a change in the gradient of the bed of the glacier; *B*, marginal oblique crevasses produced by the more rapid movement of the central part of the glacier, which tends to pull the ice from the more slowly moving marginal portions.

FIG. 178. A crevasse developing along the side of the Jungfrau, where the glacier is moving away from the stagnant ice, as viewed from the Jungfraujoch Plateau, Switzerland.

In this way huge amphitheaters are formed at the upper ends of glacial valleys.

Moraines. The rock debris carried by glacial ice is morainic material, and from its position with respect to the ice mass it is classified as super-glacial, englacial, or subglacial morainic debris. Its distribution on and in a glacier is dependent upon the topography of the mountain valley. If the valley is deep, the mountainsides are undermined by the moving ice and heaps of rock fragments or immense blocks of rock gather on the ice at the sides of the valley, forming a lateral moraine; and when two tributary glaciers meet, a medial moraine (Figs. 179, 180) is formed by the union of the lateral moraines. As a rule the medial moraine loses its identity toward the terminus of the glacier. Often, however, the moraines remain distinct and may be seen for miles, stretching up the glacier side by side.

The debris carried to the terminus of the glacier is deposited about its end as the ice melts and at many places forms a crescent-shaped ridge known as a terminal moraine. Such ridges are more pronounced in continental and piedmont glaciers, where the glacier-fed streams have lower gradients and, therefore, do not so readily carry away the glacial debris. Mountain streams have high velocities, and they therefore carry the mate-

FIG. 179. Unteraar, an Alpine glacier showing lateral and medial moraines well-developed. Switzerland.

FIG. 180. An Alaskan glacier with numerous tributaries forming a series of cirques, or blunt steep-headed valleys. (*Photograph by United States Air Force.*)

rial of the terminal moraine for some distance beyond the glacier and distribute it along the valleys as they aggrade their beds.

Huge heaps of ice blocks often are found where a tributary glacier unites with the main ice stream by descending a precipice. Large masses

FIG. 181. Vegetation growing on the debris-covered surface of Variegated Glacier, Yakutat Bay, Alaska. (*Photograph by E. S. Moore.*)

of ice are detached at the end of the tributary and are dropped to the glacier below, forming *icefalls* and *-cascades*. Later the shattered blocks are recemented at the base of the cliff and become incorporated into the mass of the main glacier.

Features Due to Ablation. The surface of a glacier is exposed to the heat of the sun and the action of dry winds, both of which produce irregularities by melting and evaporation (Fig. 181). Morainic material on the glacier protects the ice from the sun's rays so that at places the moraines, or belts of debris, lie on ice walls that project upward 100 feet above the general surface of the ice. Such ridges are especially conspicuous on the Aar Glacier in Switzerland, and in Greenland some have been found that are nearly 400 feet high. In the same way flat blocks of rock shelter the ice beneath and remain on pillars or pedestals as the surrounding surface is lowered. Such structures are spoken of as *ice tables*, or *glacier tables* (Fig. 182). The tables are rarely horizontal but are inclined to the side that is most exposed to the rays of the sun. As melting continues, the blocks of stone perched on the columns of ice are dislodged and the pinnacles that formerly supported them remain on the surface of the glacier as irregularities called *ice pyramids*.

Small heaps of dust and thin slabs of rock absorb the sun's heat and so become sufficiently warm to melt the underlying ice. They sink below its surface, forming depressions, or *dust wells*. For the same reason thin, bouldery moraines sometimes are found sunk below the surface of the

feature due to ablation

FIG. 182. A glacial table, or rock-capped ice pillar, on the surface of Gornergrat Glacier, Switzerland. (*Photograph by E. S. Moore.*)

FIG. 183. The amount of ablation, or surface melting, in 12 days, midsummer, 1950, on Emmons Glacier, northeast side of Mount Rainier, Washington, is shown by the point the man indicates on the rod and the ice surface on which he stands. The vertical rods had been set in holes drilled 6 feet into the ice and were further supported by sand piled around them. (*Courtesy of George P. Rigsby.*)

FIG. 184. Opening into a cavern, or subglacial tunnel, at the margin of Hidden Glacier, Alaska. (*Photograph by E. S. Moore.*)

glacier, or scattered pebbles are found at the bottom of water-filled pits. Leaves are blown on the surface of some mountain glaciers, and during the summer months they are warmed by the sun and sink below the surface.

Ablation may reduce the thickness of a glacier several inches per day and thus produce marked effects in the course of a few weeks (Fig. 183) during the melting season.

On warm days the surface of a glacier has innumerable rills and pools of water, which unite to form small streams that rush and tumble as waterfalls into the crevasses and are lost in the depths of the ice. The water carries with it mud, sand, and boulders from the surface moraines. These erode the crevasses and produce vertical shafts that are referred to as *glacier mills,* or *moulins.* A moulin once formed moves down the valley with the glacier, but since the irregularity in the floor of the valley that produced the crevasse in which the moulin formed remains stationary, the process is repeated many times near the same place and a long row of deep shafts is developed in the ice. Some of these streams erode subglacial channels that form large tunnels in the basal part of the ice (Fig. 184).

Erosion by Valley Glaciers. Valley, or alpine, glaciers usually move down valleys formed by the erosion of running water prior to the appearance of the ice. But a glacier immediately begins to modify the region it occupies. The results of erosion by valley glaciers are so characteristic and differ so widely from those produced by other gradational agents that a glaciated valley is readily recognized even though the glacier itself has entirely disappeared. The erosion may be accomplished (1) by cleaning off the residual, loose debris; (2) by breaking or wearing off the surface of the bedrock over which it passes; and (3) by a process known as plucking, whereby joint blocks are pulled out and carried along with the ice. Such erosion is accomplished not merely by the pressure of the ice but by means of the sharp sand, angular pebbles, and boulders and other rock debris that serve as the abrasives with which the glacier grinds and polishes. The intensity of this action can perhaps be appreciated more fully by considering the force exerted when a thick mass of ice passes over a rock surface. Since 1 cubic foot of ice weighs about 57 pounds, a glacier 1,000 feet thick would exert a pressure of approximately 28 tons per square foot.

The boulders and pebbles left in a glaciated valley are polished and striated in such a manner as to indicate that ice is sufficiently rigid to hold the debris firmly. The embedded rocks act as the teeth on a gigantic file. Many glaciated valleys appear as if such a file had been pressed down heavily and dragged along the valley. The irregularities on the floor and walls of the valley are rounded, grooved, and smoothed on the upstream side and show sharp, angular projections on the leeward side, where

u-shaped glaciated valley.

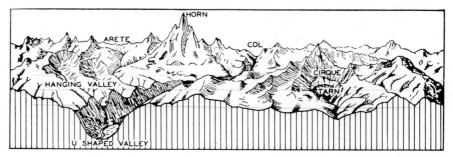

FIG. 185. Yosemite Valley in California. A deep, flat-bottomed valley carved from massive igneous rock by a stream and modified by a glacier. (*Spence Air Photos.*)

plucking rather than abrasion was most active. Much of the waste of such glacial abrasion is carried away in suspension as finely ground *rock flour* that gives a milky appearance to the streams that issue from the end of a glacier.

Changes Produced in Topography. Where glacial erosion is active for an extended period, ice-sculptured topographic features replace those produced by ordinary atmospheric weathering and corrasion. A youthful river valley is usually V-shaped in section; but when such a valley is

FIG. 186. Diagram showing the relations of land forms produced by mountain glaciation.

glaciated, its sides are eroded as well as the bottom and a broad, flat-bottomed, U-shaped valley results (Figs. 185, 186). The projecting and overlapping spurs that are characteristic of youthful topography are truncated, and the walls of the valley are made smooth and straight. In Alaska many of the glaciated valleys are straight and are referred to as "canals."

The floor of a glaciated valley often shows irregularities rounded into dome-shaped bosses that are sloping and smooth on the side from which the glacier moved but rough and jagged on the leeward side as a result of glacial plucking. Such rock structures are known as *roches moutonnées* (sheep-shaped rocks).

In a normal river system the tributary streams enter the main valley at the level of the main stream. If such a system is glaciated, the main valley, because of its greater volume of ice, is deepened more rapidly than the smaller tributary, and when the ice disappears, the elevation of the tributary at the junction is higher than that of the main channel. In many mountain streams the difference amounts to hundreds of feet, and in some of them to more than 2,000 feet. Valleys that discharge high above the floor of the main stream are called *hanging valleys* (Figs. 187, 188), and their streams leap in a series of cascades into the major channel or discharge as waterfalls such as the famous waterfalls of the Yosemite.

FIG. 187. Citadel Mountain, an arête, or knife-edge ridge, separating the hanging valley of Virginia Creek from the next valley to the right. In the foreground is St. Mary Lake. Glacier National Park, Montana.

hanging valleys

FIG. 188. Mount Athabaska and hanging valleys containing glaciers. Athabaska Glacier in the foreground is a tongue of ice extending down from the Columbia ice field. Jasper National Park in the Canadian Rockies, Alberta. (*Courtesy of British Photo Laboratories.*)

Mountain glaciers develop *cirques,* or amphitheaterlike depressions with steeply rising walls, at the upper ends of glaciated valleys (Fig. 189). These gigantic semicircular bowls carved out of the mountainsides are among the most striking features in the mountain topography of such regions as the Selkirks in Canada, the Rocky Mountains of the United States (Fig. 190), or the magnificent mountain scenery of the Alps in Switzerland. Their precipitous walls are produced by the plucking and sapping action of the ice, which adheres to the rocks by filling the joints and fractures near the base of the cliffs. During the warmer season, as the ice moves down the valley, it pulls away from the walls of the cirque and plucks out the blocks of rock so that they move with it. With the coming of winter the process is halted, and the crevasse, or bergschrund, between the moving ice and the rock wall fills with snow; but the following spring it again opens, and more rock is quarried from the cirque wall. In this way cirques are progressively enlarged, deepened, and caused to extend headward, until eventually those on one side of a mountain range recede into the area of others on the opposite side of the divide, and the space between them is narrowed, producing sharp, serrated, comblike ridges (Fig. 191), or *horns*, such as the lofty Matterhorn of the Swiss Alps. Most of the deep, clear lakes that lend beauty to the mountains rest in rock basins that are parts of glacial cirques.

Features of Deposition. Since mountain glaciers are surrounded by large areas of exposed rock that are constantly subjected to denudation, they collect a great deal of rock waste that is carried by the ice toward the terminus of the glacier. This debris, called moraine, is supplied chiefly by the mechanically weathered material which falls from the walls of the valley and by rock abraded from the bed, and it is classified with reference to its position as lateral or medial moraine or as superglacial, englacial

FIG. 189. Glaciated mountain valleys. View southward from the northern border of the Canyon Ranges, Mackenzie Mountains. The glacial sculpturing increases toward the interior, where some excellent cirques are developed. Northwest Territories. (*Royal Canadian Air Force.*)

cirques

FIG. 190. Cirques, with their small, crescentlike glaciers, in the High Sierra near Mount Sill, California. (*Spence Air Photos.*)

horn

FIG. 191. Apache Peak, Colorado. Part of a knife-edge ridge, or arête, produced by the headward erosion of the glaciers that form cirques. (*Photograph by H. E. Kellogg.*)

(Fig. 192), or subglacial debris. When the ice eventually is melted, both ice and water play a part in the deposition of the sediments. The heaps of debris dropped directly by the ice are called *glacial deposits,* and those made by glacial streams are called *glaciofluviatile deposits.* The term *glacial drift* is commonly applied to all the material transported and deposited by glacial ice. *Till* is unstratified glacial drift.

Ground Moraine. The basal portion of a valley glacier may become so filled with debris that the ice cannot transport it all, and then part of it remains upon the bottom and is overridden as the ice moves onward. It is most likely to become overloaded for some distance beyond a place where an irregularity at the lower surface of the ice favors the gathering of debris or near the end, where the ice mass is thinner. All the material deposited beneath the advancing ice, together with that deposited from the base as an irregular sheet during melting, constitutes the ground

englacial moraines or debris

FIG. 192. The terminus of Windermere Glacier, British Columbia, where it discharges into a lake. Note the crumpled structure as outlined by the englacial debris. (*Courtesy of Canada Department of the Interior.*)

moraine. It consists of a heterogeneous mass of fine clay or sand, striated pebbles, and boulders that show neither assortment nor stratification. The material of such ice-deposited wastes sometimes is called boulder clay, because it is made up of fine to coarse sandy clay through which are dispersed boulders of all sizes and up to many tons in weight.

Terminal Moraines. At the terminus of a glacier where the amount of ice waste due to melting equals or nearly equals the advance due to glacial movement, debris is dropped as a *terminal moraine.* The end of the glacier, hence the location of the terminal moraine, will advance or retreat whenever the factors determining its location have been thrown out of balance. In many regions where the glaciers at one time pushed out upon the piedmont areas and halted there for a number of years, the moraines are still present as well-defined topographic features. They are usually crescent- or horseshoe-shaped in outline, with their concave sides toward the head of the valley. The height of such a moraine is dependent to a considerable extent upon the length of time during which the front of the glacier remained stationary, for it is obvious that rapid retreat would not allow much material to be piled up at the same place. If a glacier advanced 1,000 feet a year for a period of 50 years and melted as fast as the ice moved, the end would remain stationary and all its moraine debris would be deposited at approximately the same place in the valley during the whole period of time. However, if the end of the glacier receded 1,000 feet a year, even though its ice moved forward at the rate of 500 feet a year, very little debris would be piled up at any spot and consequently no pronounced morainic ridge would be formed. The rock debris of the whole 1,500 feet melted would be distributed over the 1,000 feet of recession as part of the ground moraine.

Lateral Moraines. The debris that accumulates on the borders of a valley glacier forms the lateral moraines of the moving ice stream. When the glacier melts, the lateral moraines are left as ridges, or terracelike structures, bordering the steep-sided mountain valleys. In most glaciated valleys they are more conspicuous than either the ground moraines or the terminal moraines. Where the gradient of the mountain valley is not too great, the glacial streams leave most of the material of the terminal moraine at the place where it was deposited, and at such places the lateral and terminal moraines unite as a continuous ridge, or dam, across the valley, and the enclosed basin becomes occupied by a lake, swamp, or meadow.

Glaciofluviatile Deposits. In the region where the melting of glacial ice is in progress, innumerable streams are formed on the surface, at the margins, and at the bottom of the glacier. During the summer months great torrents issue from ice caves or tunnels and carry boulders, pebbles, sand, and fine rock flour; but as the streams emerge from the restricted channels on or in the ice, they spread out over a greater area or divide into many distributaries and consequently become overloaded and drop a large part of their sediments. Since the streams issue from the ice in the region where the terminal moraine is being deposited, most of the glacio-fluviatile sediments are carried beyond the terminal moraine. The shape of the water-laid deposit where the glacier ends on a plain area is similar to that of an elongated alluvial fan. Where the end of the glacier is confined by the walls of the valley, the fluviatile deposits are confined to the width of the valley and build a *valley train*. Its sediments are sorted and stratified with coarse gravel and boulders near the glacier, grading horizontally through fine sand to silt and rock flour at a distance of a few miles below the terminus of the glacier.

SUGGESTIONS FOR FURTHER READING

Black, Robert F.: Permafrost, *Smithsonian Inst. Ann. Rept. for* 1950, pp. 273–301, 1951.

Gould, L. M.: Cold, Brewer, Warren & Putman, Inc., 1931.

Matthes, F. E.: Geologic History of Yosemite Valley, *U.S. Geol. Survey Prof. Paper* 160, 1930.

Muller, Siemon W.: Permafrost or Permanently Frozen Ground and Related Engineering Problems, *U.S. Geol. Survey Spec. Rept., Strategic Eng. Study* 62, 2d ed., 1945.

CHAPTER 11

Piedmont and Continental Glaciers

Piedmont Glaciers. Piedmont glaciers are found only in subpolar regions having mountains of strong relief and valleys extending to plains of low altitude where several adjacent mountain glaciers spread out or deploy and become confluent. The sloping ice surface formed in this way is like a piedmont alluvial plain, from which this type of glacier takes its name. Because of the marked change in gradient of the valleys as they reach the piedmont area, the movement of the ice is greatly retarded, and in many piedmont glaciers it becomes almost imperceptible. The Malispina Glacier on the western side of Yakutat Bay in Alaska is a classic example of this type of glacier (Figs. 193, 194). It consists of three principal lobes, and each lobe represents the expanded lower portion of one or more large valley glaciers that move down the slopes of Mount St. Elias. These lobes are fed by the Seward, Agassiz, Tyndall, and Guyot Glaciers, and the piedmont glacier formed by their coalescence is a vast, nearly horizontal plateau of ice that is 70 miles wide along the Alaskan coast. Where the individual valley glaciers emerge from their mountain valleys, differential movement is initiated in the ice plateau and its surface becomes broken by thousands of crevasses. Toward the margins, where ice movement decreases and melting and freezing increase, these crevasses are gradually healed, and the surface shows but minor irregularities. The outer margin for a width of 5 miles or more is covered with moraine. At certain places this marginal ice has reached such a stage of stagnation that forests grow upon the moraine, even though ice hundreds of feet thick is still present below the morainic soil.

Continental Glaciers. The great sheets of ice that cover large land areas are known as *continental glaciers*. They are snow field, ice field, and glacier all in one. Usually continental glaciers are very thick and spread outward in all directions over highland and lowland alike, with little regard for the topography of the surface over which they move. These differ from valley glaciers in that their movements are not confined within valley walls; but they differ from the small icecaps, such as those

246

on Iceland (Fig. 168), only in size. Continental glaciers are in fact large icecaps.

There are two areas now covered by continental glaciers. These are Greenland and Antarctica. Greenland is an island that is reported to contain 839,782 square miles. On its high central plateau area somewhat more than 600,000 square miles is ice-covered (Fig. 165); only the mountainous margin is comparatively bare. Even in this rugged border the valleys are usually filled by tongues of ice extending downward to the sea from the great ice mass of the interior. The adjacent large islands of Canada, such as Ellsmere, have icecaps that are related to the Greenland glacier although not now continuous with it.

Antarctica is a continent of about 6 million square miles, most of which is covered by a continental glacier (Fig. 195) that reaches from the interior to the sea. At many places the glacier even joins the *shelf ice,* or frozen sea water (Figs. 196, 197), that extends out into the ocean from the coast line. Through the passes in the mountains that border parts of the Antarctic continent great tongues of ice, such as the Beardmore Glacier, descend to the coast and push out into the sea beyond,

FIG. 193. View of model of region including Yakutat Bay and Malaspina Glacier (*Model by Lawrence Martin. Copyright, 1909, by University of Wisconsin.*)

FIG. 194. Map of Alaska, showing the location of the Malaspina Glacier, a typical piedmont glacier formed by the union of a group of valley glaciers that descend from the slopes of Mount St. Elias.

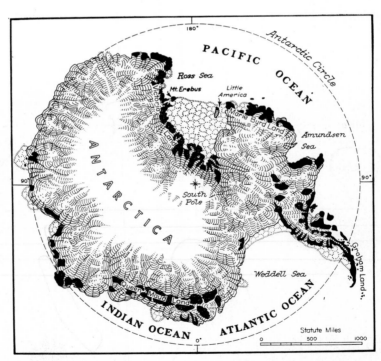

FIG. 195. Antarctica. A continent of about 6 million square miles still largely covered by an icecap. Parts of the coast are fringed by shelf ice, and tongues of ice, extending down from the interior through mountain gaps, descend to the sea, where great masses are broken from the end and float away as icebergs.

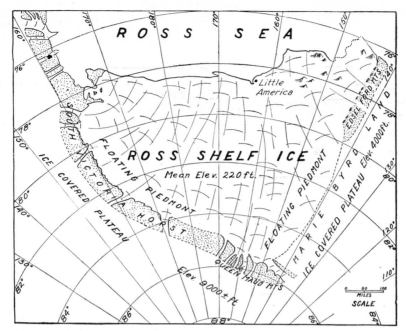

FIG. 196. Map of the Ross shelf ice, Antarctica (see Fig. 195). A floating mass of ice approximately 1,000 feet thick and covering more than ¼ million square miles. (*Redrawn from a map by L. M. Gould.*)

FIG. 197. Folds in the Ross shelf ice over the Bay of Whales near Little America, Antarctica. (*Photograph courtesy of L. M. Gould, Geologist, Byrd Antarctic Expedition.*)

249

even overriding shelf ice. Here and there great blocks of ice break off and float away as icebergs on the three oceans that border its coast line.

In the continental glaciers the whole ice sheet presents a featureless and very gently sloping surface, except here and there where a bare hill, or peak, known as a *nunatak*, rises above the general level of the ice surface. The continental ice sheets are not fed by small tributaries with marginal belts of ice and rock. There are no medial moraines on the continental glaciers corresponding to the medial moraines of the valley glaciers, but above the zone of melting the ice is clear and white.

Such widespread glaciation, covering large portions of continents, gives rise to the term *ice age*. During the known history of the earth there have been three and possibly four or more great ice ages. The present glaciation is regarded as the dwindling stages of the last, or Pleistocene, ice age. Ice still covers one-third or more of the area over which continental glaciers spread during their greatest advance some 10,000 or more years ago. The nearness to glacial conditions at present, even within the interior of continental North America, may be appreciated by the fact that in northern Ontario, just south and west of Hudson and James Bays, snowbanks linger long into the spring, many of the small lakes are slow to thaw out completely, and perpetual frost occurs within the soil only a few feet below the surface. Even in some of the valleys of the New England mountains the last snowbank is melted scarcely more than 1 month before the first fall of winter snow, and occasionally, in some favored

FIG. 198. A glaciated rock surface showing striae and the smooth, rounded contour produced by abrasion. (*Photograph by B. Willis.*)

ravines, snow lingers through the year. The water well drilled on top of Mount Washington penetrated cold rock and froze at 260 feet. It would appear that the White Mountain region of New Hampshire is just emerging from the chilling effects of the glacial invasion that so recently covered a large portion of North America. A drop of only a few degrees in the average annual temperature or an increase in the amount of winter snowfall might restore continental glaciation over a vast area.

Erosion by Continental Glaciers. The efficiency of a continental ice sheet as an instrument of erosion is particularly well-shown by the effects of the vast icecap that covered northeastern North America during the geologically recent ice age. From a study of the features developed during that period, it is evident that corrasion is by far the most important erosion process and that it is accomplished primarily by the scouring and grinding action of rock fragments either frozen into the bottom of the glacier or pushed along beneath it. Glacial plucking is limited in its action to areas of steeply dipping or highly jointed rock formations.

A feature peculiar to extensive lowlands that have been glaciated by ice sheets is the almost total absence of residual soils or mantle-rock waste. Such loose soils and rotten rock are scoured off and dragged along by the passage of the ice, and bare, rounded, and striated surfaces of fresh rocks remain (Figs. 198 to 200). Similar features are formed also by mountain glaciation. In some regions, like the plains of the upper Mississippi Basin, the glaciers moved over large areas of residual

FIG. 199. Glacial striae on bedrock and boulders of glacial origin at Lucerne, Switzerland.

soils with little disturbance of them, but such soils are now covered with a thick bed of glacial drift or till.

The effect of a continental ice sheet on the regional topography and relief is less obvious than that of a mountain or valley glacier. An ice sheet erodes the region between the valleys nearly as intensely as in the stream channels. Where the direction of movement of the glacier parallels that of the major streams of the region, however, some of the valleys are gouged and deepened and the regional relief is markedly increased. The relief is decreased where the ice moves across the valleys and partially or completely fills them with glacial drift.

FIG. 200. Outline map of New England, showing the direction of movement of glacial ice as indicated by striae on the bedrock surface. (*After Goldthwait.*)

Depositional Features. *General Characteristics of Drift.* Because of its origin the most characteristic feature of the drift deposited by a continental glacier is its heterogeneity. In a small area may be found both stratified drift and unstratified till, with variations in size from fine clay and sand through coarse gravel (Fig. 201) to huge boulders. The size and shape of the particles are dependent to a considerable degree upon the resistance of the rock to abrasion (Fig. 202). Rocks such as schists, clayey limestones, and shales are readily broken by the ice and are converted into glacial clay, silt, or small pebbles, whereas massive igneous rock, hard limestones, and quartzites are more resistant, and these constitute most of the larger boulders. Glacial drift generally contains rocks of many different kinds, depending upon those that are present in the areas over which the ice moved.

The large glacial boulders that are foreign to the underlying rock are

FIG. 201. Interbedded sorted and unsorted drift.

FIG. 202. Scratched and striated opposite sides of a cobblestone from the drift.

erratic

FIG. 203. A glacial erratic. A huge granitic boulder weighing many tons. It is wholly unlike the underlying rock and far from its source. No natural agent other than glacial ice could have transported it to its present location.

erratics (Figs. 203, 204). Some immense masses of rock have traveled hundreds of miles from their sources. One of the largest erratics known in the United States is a mass of granite at Madison, New Hampshire, that measures 90 by 40 by 30 feet. Likewise on Mount Tom, near Northampton, Massachusetts, large, angular granite boulders are perched on the top of a high ridge of basic igneous rock. Such boulders are found in positions where no agent of transportation other than ice could have placed them.

The thickness of the drift varies greatly owing to (1) the irregularities of the surface upon which it was deposited, (2) the variations in the

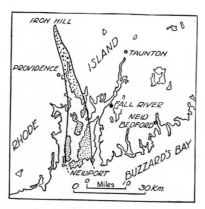
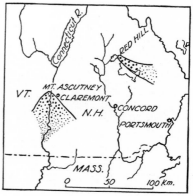

FIG. 204. Maps showing glacial-boulder trains in New England. The black iron-bearing rock of Iron Hill was distributed over a progressively wider area southward toward Newport. The rocks of Red Hill and Mount Ascutney were spread in a similar manner.

amount of debris carried by the ice, (3) the rate of advance or retreat of the glacier, and (4) the amount of erosion subsequent to its deposition. As a general rule, high, rugged regions have very thin coats of drift, and extensive low, smooth areas, like those of central Iowa and south central Minnesota, have 100 to 600 feet of drift and very few rock outcrops.

Terminal Moraines. The terminal moraines of a continental glacier are more conspicuous and more complex than those developed by a valley glacier. This is due in part to the absence of streams of high gradient, such as those which issue from mountain glaciers and transport much of the debris to the valley trains. Where the terminus of a continental glacier is in a partially peneplaned area, most of the morainic material remains where it was dropped at the margin of the melting ice. If the ice front is nearly stationary or fluctuates for an extended period in a zone not more than a few miles wide, series of morainal ridges are developed coinciding with the outline of the marginal lobes of the glacier. These constitute the terminal moraines. Such moraines are characterized by many small, rounded hills of drift with adjacent depressions distributed in a disorderly fashion in a relatively long, narrow zone that paralleled the ice front at the time of deposition (Fig. 205). In many regions one side of the system of hills has a steeper slope than the opposite side, and the steep slopes lie in the direction from which the ice came. Many of the larger ridges have superimposed upon them smaller hills and conical mounds, which make the depressions seem still deeper. Because of its irregularity such topography is commonly referred to as "knob-and-kettle," or "hummocky," topography.

Where a retreating glacier halts in its retreat and its edge remains in

FIG. 205. Glacial moraine topography near St. Paul, Minnesota.

nearly a constant position for a considerable period of time, a moraine may develop. Such a deposit is a *recessional moraine* (Fig. 206).

Ground Moraines. The ground moraine is the most important and the most widespread depositional feature of a continental ice sheet. It is the

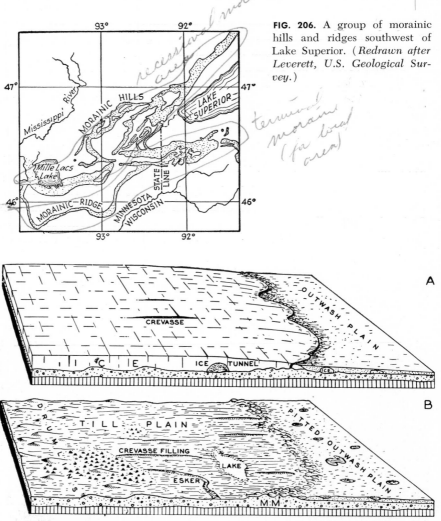

FIG. 206. A group of morainic hills and ridges southwest of Lake Superior. (*Redrawn after Leverett, U.S. Geological Survey.*)

FIG. 207. Diagrams to illustrate the field relations of various types of glacial deposit and their relation to the part of the glacier by which they were formed. *A*, the margin of a retreating continental ice sheet. *B*, the same area after the ice has melted. Note the rugged topography of the marginal moraine (*MM*), the swamps and lake of the poorly drained till plain, and the esker that was deposited in the ice tunnel. (*After Trewartha.*)

drift that was deposited below the ice during the period of recession. Instead of being concentrated in high knobs and ridges, as in the terminal moraine, it is scattered over the surface where the ice melted. Youthful ground-moraine topography commonly is characterized by numerous large depressions occupied by bogs, swamps, and lakes with no apparent relation between major streams and higher land. Such areas are usually poorly drained because of the damming of the preglacial streams and the unequal distribution of glacial till (Fig. 207).

Certain areas of the ground moraine have small, smooth, oval hills of till that are lenticular in horizontal section and have their longer axes parallel to the movement of the ice which formerly covered them. Such hills are called *drumlins* (Figs. 208, 209). They are commonly 25 to 150 feet high. Many of them are 1,000 to 3,000 feet long and about 500 feet wide. In some regions they show many variations in size and shape from mammillary, or dome-shaped, hills to slender, or linear, ridges (Figs. 210, 211). They are conspicuously developed in Nova Scotia, Massachusetts near Boston, western New York, the northern part of the Lower Peninsula of Michigan, eastern Wisconsin, north central Minnesota, parts of Saskatchewan, Alberta, British Columbia, and the Northwest Territories of Canada. They also occur in various parts of Europe. Most drumlins are composed of unsorted till that exhibits very little lamination due to water action. The gentle slope of the drumlin lies in the direction toward which the ice moved. This is the opposite of the relation of the gentle slope to direction of movement where the ice erodes.

FIG. 208. Drumlin islands at Peninsula Point, Mahone Bay, Chester, Nova Scotia. (*Geological Survey of Canada.*)

The mechanics of drumlin formation have not been fully explained; but the wide distribution of these streamlined hills indicates that conditions suitable to their formation were commonly met during the deposi-

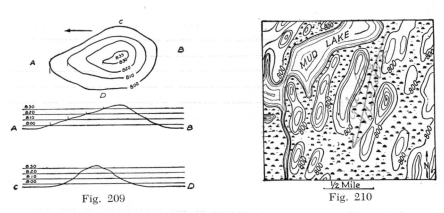

Fig. 209   Fig. 210

FIG. 209. Plan and profile views of a drumlin. The arrow indicates direction of movement of the ice. The gentle slope commonly lies in the direction toward which the ice moved.

FIG. 210. Drumlins near Waterloo, Wisconsin. (*Courtesy of U.S. Geological Survey.*)

FIG. 211. Rock drumlins, or crag-and-tail drumloids, near Carp Lake in northern British Columbia. (*Geological Survey of Canada.*)

tional stage of the glacier. Their composition of mixed glacial debris, often of the clayey rather than the gravelly type, their location on the glacier side behind a terminal or recessional moraine, their parallel orientation and streamlined shape, and their usual grouping adjacent to an abundant supply of the suitable materials have suggested that drumlins may have been formed either by overloading of the basal portion of the glacier from locally abundant loose material near its outer edge or by the overriding of an end moraine by a slight advance of the ice. In any case the shape probably was formed by forward movement of the ice sheet. This is indicated near Carp Lake, in northern British Columbia, where the stoss ends of the drumloids, or "rock drumlins," are rock outcrops followed by a crag-and-tail effect (Fig. 211).

Glaciofluviatile Deposits. *Eskers.* Eskers are winding ridges (serpent ridges) (Fig. 212) of irregularly stratified sand and gravel that are found within the area of the ground moraine. Many of them are several miles long, and they are rarely more than a few rods wide. Their courses are roughly parallel to the direction of the movement of the glacier. Some are so nearly symmetrical in outline that they resemble railroad grades. The ridges are evidently the beds of streams which flowed in tun-

FIG. 212. An esker, or "serpent ridge," near Fort Ripley, Minnesota, as seen from the air. (*Courtesy of W. S. Cooper.*)

nels or ice-walled gorges in or beneath the ice and aggraded their beds before the stream issued from the ice front. Some undoubtedly are crevasse fillings. They are seldom continuous for long distances, and some of them serve as ridges, or divides, between shallow lakes and bogs in the ground moraine.

Kames. Some of the hills of gravel deposited by heavily laden glacial streams flowing in and on the ice near the terminus are conical in outline and are referred to as *kames* (Figs. 213, 214). Some of them may be short ridges formed in the reentrant angles of the ice front where subglacial water under pressure is escaping and depositing its overload. Kames are likely to be associated with the terminal-moraine belt and with the numerous kettle lakes common to that environment. The eskers and kames that are preserved as part of the characteristic drift topography were formed during the recessional or stagnant stage of the last ice sheet. Any later active advance of the ice sheet would destroy all such surface features previously formed.

Outwash Plains. The water from the melting ice at the edge of an ice sheet flows through the terminal-moraine debris as a great number of streams rather than as a continuous sheet of water. Each of these streams builds a low alluvial fan, and the fans coalesce into a plain that slopes gently away from the terminal-moraine area. Such a plain is composed of material washed out beyond the terminal moraine, and it is called an

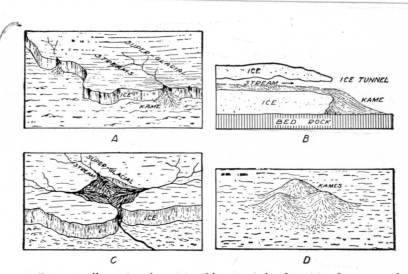

FIG. 213. Diagrams illustrating the origin of kames. *A*, by deposition from superglacial streams at the margin of the ice; *B*, by englacial streams discharging at the margin of the glacier; *C*, by deposition from superglacial streams in deep reentrants between lobes; *D*, a group of kames after the ice has melted.

FIG. 214. Kames in Ninemile Valley, New York. (*Photograph by Gilbert, U.S. Geological Survey.*)

outwash plain. The heaviest load is deposited near the terminal moraine, and there the deposits often are composed of gravel and coarse sand, whereas farther away the slopes are more gentle and the deposits are fine sands and silt. Many of the outwash plains of the northeastern part of the United States are so nearly flat that often they are referred to as prairies.

Small, kettlelike depressions with no outlets are formed in outwash plains by the melting of great masses of ice left during the recession of the ice front. Where such depressions are numerous, the outwash areas are *pitted plains.*

Temporary Glacial Lakes. Since a continental glacier covers all the land, it follows that divides between drainage basins also are buried under the ice. If a land surface in front of the glacier slopes toward the ice edge, water derived from the melting of the glacier will accumulate against the high land or divide and the margin of the ice which serves as a dam will prevent the water from following its former course (Fig. 215). In this way

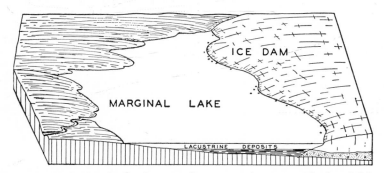

FIG. 215. Diagrammatic sketch showing the origin of a marginal glacial lake. The normal preglacial drainage was to the right. The ice sheet served as a dam, blocking the flow of water in that direction.

large areas of land may be flooded, forming marginal glacial lakes. Such lakes will exist until an outlet is cut across the lowest point in the divide. Numerous lakes were so formed along the margins of the continental ice sheets that covered parts of Europe and North America during the recent ice age. The outlets of many of these lakes cut broad and deep channels through the divides of drainage systems and at a number of places excavated valleys across continental divides where no streams exist at the present time. Most of these lakes were small and were soon filled with sediments derived from the glacier. Some, however, covered hundreds of square miles and existed for sufficiently long periods to form important depositional features.

The former presence of temporary glacial lakes is shown by shore-line features such as beaches, beach ridges, bars, deltas, and the finer sediments deposited over the lake bottom. At many places a series of shore lines are found at different elevations, due to fluctuating levels of the water.

Glacial Lake Agassiz. The receding ice sheet southwest of Hudson Bay made the largest temporary glacial lake that was formed on the North American continent. Its development was due to the northward slope of the valley of the Red River of the North. After the glacier receded over the divide between the Minnesota River and the Red River, the water accumulated along the south and west margins of the ice and, with a continued retreat of the ice, the lake increased in size and depth until

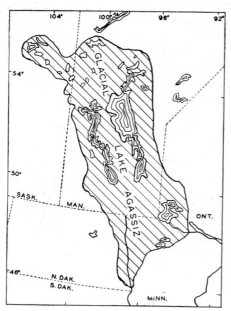

eventually the water stood at a sufficiently high level to flow over the crest of the Continental Divide and into the Minnesota River at Browns Valley, Minnesota. When at its maximum extent, Lake Agassiz was about 700 miles long and 250 miles wide. It covered over 100,000 square miles, more than the combined area of all the present Great Lakes. Lake Winnipeg in Canada and Lake of the Woods on the international boundary occupy depressions in the bed of this ancient lake (Fig. 216).

FIG. 216. Map showing the extent of glacial Lake Agassiz during its highest water stage. (*After Upham, U.S. Geological Survey.*)

While the glacier continued to block the northward drainage and Lake Agassiz received the melt water, the overflow into the Minnesota River produced a broad, turbulent stream, sometimes referred to as glacial River Warren, that cut its channel 50 to 90 feet below the present level of the Minnesota River and discharged into the Mississippi at Fort Snelling. Later when a northward escape for this melt water was uncovered, Lake Agassiz disappeared, River Warren dwindled, and its valley became clogged with the sediments over which the present river finds its way.

The Great Lakes. These North American lakes owe much of their size and importance to the erosional and depositional effects of glaciation on the middle and upper portions of the St. Lawrence River system. Their present basins were scooped out, and the rock materials thus obtained were added to the glacial load and then deposited as part of the drift farther to the south and west. During the recessional stages of the continental glacier, while the St. Lawrence outlet to the Atlantic was still blocked by ice, marginal lakes, formed in the uncovered southwestern extremities of these basins, spilled over the divides and discharged the melt water through streams draining southward. These outlets, especially to the St. Croix from Duluth and to the Illinois from Chicago, are conspicuous features of the present-day topography. Adjacent to the lakes, particularly Lake Superior in Minnesota and Lake Erie in Ohio, the old shore lines, beaches, and lake-shore cliffs of these marginal lakes are still plainly to be seen. The early pioneers of Ohio used these old lake beaches as roads, and parts of them still serve that purpose. These beaches indicate the various levels assumed by the lakes as melting of the ice sheet uncovered successively lower outlets which dropped the water level until finally the channel and mouth of the St. Lawrence itself were freed from ice and the drainage was established in its present course. The intricate history of these changes has been worked out in detail and forms a remarkable chapter in the glacial history of the region.

Glacial Lake Sediments. The cold waters of marginal glacial lakes have a higher density than water at moderate temperatures. For this reason the settling of silts and clays is retarded, and thus the fine sediments in suspension become diffused throughout the lake waters and are deposited over the floor of the entire basin. The fine-grained sediments are laid down in plainly separated annual layers called *varves* (Fig. 217). Varve is a Swedish word that means the deposits of a season, whether of winter and summer or wet and dry seasons. Glacial-lake varves commonly consist of two laminae, one of which was laid down during the summer and the other during the winter. The summer band consists of a light-colored, coarse silt, whereas the winter band is darker in color, finer-grained, and thinner. The winter band is sharply separated from the sum-

FIG. 217. Varved clays 3½ miles south of Kazabazua, Gatineau County, Quebec. These banded, or varved, clays were deposited in a lake of the glacial period, and each pair of light and dark bands represents a year's accumulation of very fine sediment. (*Geological Survey of Canada.*)

mer band above but grades into the summer band below. Thus each varve represents a year. The varves vary in thickness and in other characteristics, and accordingly it is possible to match, or correlate, the top sets in one lake with the bottom sets in the next lake in the direction of recession of the ice and thus count the years consecutively. In this way the rate of recession of the last ice sheet has been calculated. It has been shown, for example, that 4,300 years elapsed while the ice was retreating 185 miles up the Connecticut River Valley from Hartford, Connecticut, to St. Johnsbury, Vermont. Varved clays are well exposed along Mink Brook at Hanover, New Hampshire.

Deposition from Stagnant Ice. During the period of retreat of the last continental ice sheet, large areas of ice lost their forward motion and became great masses of stagnant ice. Their loss of motion may have been due to climatic changes or to the nature of the topography over which they stood. As the stagnant ice melted, no recessional or marginal moraines were formed, since such moraines can form only where there is forward movement of the ice accompanied by melting at the ice front. Where wastage takes place without movement, stratified drift is more abundant than glacial till. The preponderance of stratified drift is due to the fact that melting took place over a large area instead of being confined for the most part to the marginal zone of the glacier. Under such conditions, melt-water streams on and under the ice do not have their channels disturbed by the movement of the ice. Consequently the water flowing through crevasses and tunnels in the stagnant ice builds up long, narrow strings or trains of sand and gravel which stand as ridges of stratified drift after the ice has wasted away. Many eskers were built in this way. Where the ice had an intersecting network of cracks and crevasses that became partially filled with sediments, the *crevasse fillings* formed ridges or hummocks that enclosed depressions, or *kettles*, when the blocks of ice between the crevasses melted away. Many of the kettles now contain ponds, lakes, or swamps. Where lakes fed by melt water existed at the margin or on the surface of the stagnant ice, streams deposited deltas and lake sediments on the floors of the lakes. When the ice was melted and the water level lowered, such lake sediments remained as flat-topped terraces along the channels through which the waters drained.

Stream Diversion through Glacial Deposition. The unequal deposition of glacial drift had a profound effect upon the preglacial topography of the areas that were glaciated. Numerous valleys were completely filled with glacial till, and as the ice receded, many old channels were so obstructed that new surface-drainage courses were established. Even such major streams as the St. Lawrence, the Mississippi, the Ohio, and the Missouri Rivers locally were turned from their preexisting channels by the work of the glaciers. In regions of rugged and mountainous topography the channels have not been so greatly diverted, but in a number of regions drift accumulations in a valley buried projecting spurs of bedrock, and postglacial streams eroding new channels through such deposits have become superimposed on the old buried ledges that formerly were parts of old valley walls.

Ancient Glacial Deposits. A geologically ancient glacial till which has been cemented into a firm rock is called *tillite*. Such ancient tillites have been recognized at many places, and they are supposed to be the deposits of ice sheets which covered the regions in former geological periods. Near Kimberley, South Africa, a bed of hard tillite occurs over glaciated bedrock surfaces that are striated and polished. In Australia thick tillite beds occur at several geological horizons. Similar and even more ancient deposits have been reported from central Canada and from northern Norway. In eastern Massachusetts a Permian conglomerate is regarded as tillite or glacial conglomerate. The formation is exposed at many places in the Boston Basin, where it contains striated and faceted pebbles and other indications of its glacial origin. Like the recent, or Pleistocene, glaciation, some of these ancient ice ages show evidence of several advances of the ice with prolonged warm periods intervening. These fluctuations in climatic conditions, from warm to cold and back again, appear to be characteristic of an ice age. Widespread glaciation on a continental scale is not a thing of recent development but one that has affected the earth's surface at intervals over a very long period of time and may be expected to occur again.

Causes of Glaciation. Many hypotheses have been offered to account for the climate which resulted in continental glaciation, but none is generally accepted. One possible contributing cause is a variation in total solar energy or variations due to the eccentricity of the earth's orbit. Another theory postulates great elevation of the land in the areas that were glaciated. A more recent atmospheric hypothesis, developed by T. C. Chamberlin, is based upon possible variations in the amount of carbon dioxide and water vapor in the atmosphere. Experimental evidence indicates that both carbon dioxide and water prevent the radiation of much of the heat derived from the sun. When these substances are less abundant, the amount of radiation increases and a colder climate ensues. The enlarging of the land areas may have decreased the amount of water vapor in the atmosphere and thereby decreased its ability to retain the heat derived from the sun.

SUGGESTIONS FOR FURTHER READING

Coleman, A. P.: Ice Ages, Recent and Ancient, The Macmillan Company, 1926.
Daly, R. A.: The Changing World of the Ice Age, Yale University Press, 1934.
Flint, R. F.: Glacial Geology and the Pleistocene Epoch, John Wiley & Sons, Inc., 1947.
Sharp, Robert P.: Glacier Flow, *Geol. Soc. America Bull.*, vol. 65, pp. 821–838, 1954.

CHAPTER 12

Lakes and Swamps, or Marshes

General Features of Lakes. A lake is a natural inland depression or reservoir containing an appreciable amount of water (Fig. 218). Usually it is regarded as a body of quiet or standing water although some, such as Lake Erie, have definite currents flowing through them. Lakes are due to obstructed surface drainage and are a temporary feature in the erosional history of a land surface. They are more likely to occur in regions where the permanent ground-water level is at or near the surface, but ponds and small lakes may be associated with perched water tables quite above the regional water table or ground-water level. Some lakes may occur over vadose zones or where the subsoil is only partially filled with water. These depend chiefly, for their water supply, on rainfall or the water from melting snows running into a basin of sufficient size and depth to conserve water from one precipitation period to another.

Lakes vary in size from small ponds to great inland seas covering many thousands of square miles, such as the Caspian Sea or the Great Lakes. They are widely distributed over the earth's surface, occurring in mountain areas, on plateaus and plains, along valleys and seacoasts. They vary in depth from shallow water covering low, boggy depressions to rocky basins over 5,000 feet deep. Soundings in Lake Baikal in Siberia have recorded a depth of 5,618 feet. Lake waters vary in chemical composition from the soft, fresh water of a mountain lake fed by glaciers to the bitter, concentrated waters of the Great Salt Lake or the Dead Sea. Their composition depends largely upon the composition of the rocks over which and through which the waters that feed them have passed and the extent to which they have been concentrated.

Functions of Lakes. Most lakes have outlet streams that feed rivers. Such lake basins act as safety valves for the rivers they feed, for they tend to regulate the volume of discharge and thereby to prevent floods. The floodwaters of inflowing streams spread out over the wide basin of a lake and raise the water level so slowly as to cause but slight damage along the valley of the main outlet. In like manner, during seasons of

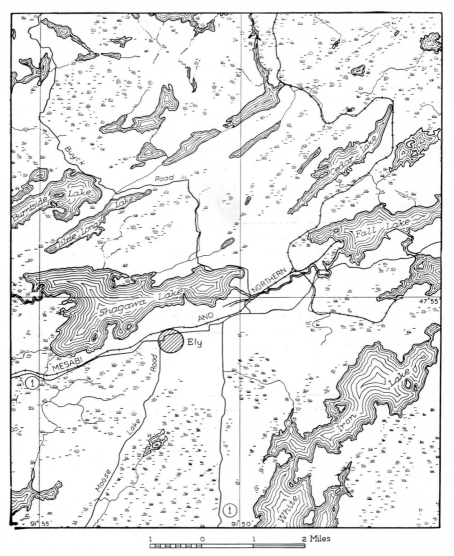

FIG. 218. Lakes on the ground moraine of northeastern Minnesota, showing elongation of lakes and swamps in the direction of glacial movement during the late ice age.

drought, the water from lakes flows out more slowly, and thus the lakes aid in preserving the permanent streams. This regulatory effect of lakes on rivers and creeks has been one of the prime reasons for developing artificial lakes or reservoirs to contain the excess rainfall, where no such natural ponding occurs, and thus to prevent the disastrous floods that might be caused by too rapid runoff farther downstream. Artificial lakes also conserve water for irrigation and power generation.

Lakes exert an influence upon local climatic conditions by increasing the rainfall. They tend to temper both the cold of winter and the heat of summer.

They serve likewise as settling basins in the drainage systems of the land. The load of sediment brought by inflowing streams is sorted and gradually dropped on the lake bottom as the velocity of the water is slowed and finally checked. In favorable localities this process develops deltas as well as other shore and shallow-water features similar to those along the seashore.

ORIGIN OF LAKE BASINS

Any geologic process which may produce a depression upon the surface of the earth or obstruct drainage channels may produce a lake. Most lake basins are the results of gradational processes, but some are due to diastrophic movements, and others are due to volcanic activity.

Basins Due to Glaciation. Lakes generally are numerous in areas recently covered with glacial ice (Fig. 219). Some glacial lakes are due to erosion, others to deposition, and still others to a combination of these two processes. Numerous basins in mountain valleys were excavated by

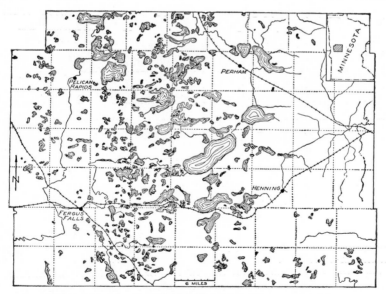

FIG. 219. Irregular lakes in glacial-drift basins. West central Minnesota.

FIG. 220. Chasm Lake, a cirque lake, or tarn, high in the Rocky Mountains. Longs Peak rises as a 2,000-foot cliff, forming part of the cirque wall. (*Photograph by Denver Tourist Bureau.*)

glacial abrasion on the high slopes. As recession of the ice took place, rain water and snow melt filled these basins to form cirque lakes, or tarns (Fig. 220). The rock basins, occupied by such lakes, are either smoothed and striated by the abrasion of the rock-shod bottom of the glacier or are walled by jagged cliffs formed by glacial plucking or quarrying out of angular blocks. These cirque lakes, or tarns, are perhaps the most common type of lake in high mountain regions. Valley glaciers, in their retreat from advanced positions, frequently leave crescent-shaped ridges of rock debris, convex downstream, which serve as dams in the valleys and retain lakes behind them. Many valleys of the Cordilleras contain lakes that were so formed. Numerous examples may be seen in the Wasatch Mountains of Utah. Glaciers also may obstruct the drainage of lateral valleys so as to cause lakes to form in them.

Continental glaciation is even more prolific in its production of basins. Over the surface of the drift sheets that cover large areas in northeastern North America and northwestern Europe lakes occur by the thousand. Finland alone has more than 60,000 glacial lakes, while Norway and Sweden are just about as thickly set with them. Maine, Minnesota, Ontario, Manitoba, and the Northwest Territories are North American rivals of this European region in abundance of such lakes. In the unusually rugged drift surface of parts of Minnesota small kettle lakes may exceed a score to the square mile. Some occur in shallow basins on the outwash plains; others are surrounded by extensive marshes on the ground moraine; and the deepest and most irregular basins are found in the terminal-moraine zones (Fig. 219).

A preglacial valley partially blocked by deposition of drift may give rise to a chain of lakes. The deepening of narrow valleys and the deposition of drift across their lower ends have given rise to the famous "Finger Lakes" of western New York (Fig. 221). Glacial abrasion deepened some of these valleys below sea level, and the present lakes in them are deep as well as narrow.

It seems probable that the basins of the Great Lakes of North America are due largely to glacial erosion, drift deposition, and the modification of an older drainage system much of which was doubtless the ancestral St. Lawrence River. The Great Lakes had an intricate history as marginal lakes along the ice front during the later stages of the great continental glacier of North America. The evidence of this history is preserved

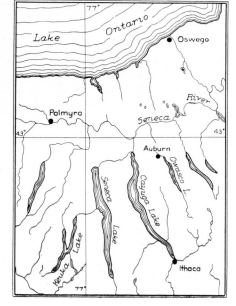

FIG. 221. Map showing the shape and orientation of the Finger Lakes of western New York. These lakes lie in preglacial valleys that have been overdeepened by glaciation.

in the old shore lines high above the levels of the present Great Lakes and the old abandoned channels through which the excess water was discharged southward from these higher levels.

Lakes resulting from glaciation vary in size from small ponds to basins that cover more than 30,000 square miles. Although some have basins extending several hundred feet below sea level, many of them are shallow and of short duration as lakes but may persist as swamps, or marshes.

Basins Formed by Streams. Lake basins are formed by both the degradational and the aggradational work of streams. At certain places the two processes have been active in the formation of a single depression. Many shallow lakes are formed upon flood plains by streams that wander in meandering loops over the valley flats. Where the stream cuts off a meander, the abandoned part of the channel remains as a crescent-shaped *oxbow lake* (Fig. 135). Numerous irregular lake basins are formed also in the depressions between the natural levees and the outer edges of the flood plains or by rapid sedimentation on the flood plain of the main stream, thus ponding the lower ends of the tributaries. These commonly are referred to as *lateral lakes.* Still farther down the valley, on the delta surface, the water in the main channel breaks through the levees and forms branching channels, which in turn form still other distributaries. In this way shallow depressions are completely surrounded by delta sediments, and the basins are converted into *delta lakes* (Fig. 222). The deltas of the Nile, Danube, Ganges, and Mississippi Rivers show such basins now in the process of construction. Lake Borgne in Louisiana is not yet completed. The low delta lands of Holland also contain many lakes of this type. Many of the bayous, associated with the lower Mississippi

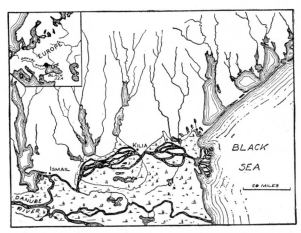

FIG. 222. Lakes formed by delta sediments damming the outlets of tributary streams. (*After Reclus.*)

River, are little more than a succession of small, elongate lakes which contain water all the time but become a continuous stream only during the rainy season. Deadman's Lake, about 8 miles southeast of Carlisle, Arkansas, is a good example. During the winter rains, it joins others to form a continuous stream and becomes Bayou Two-Prairie, an intermittent tributary to Bayou Meto.

Where a tributary stream brings to the main stream an excess of sediment, it is deposited as an obstruction, or dam, in the channel of the main stream and the water is ponded, forming a *river lake*. This is illustrated strikingly in the Mississippi River above the mouth of the Chippewa River of Wisconsin, where the Mississippi expands over its flood plain and forms Lake Pepin (Fig. 223). In the great valley of California the high-gradient Kings River that flows from the Sierra Nevada range has built an alluvial fan that obstructs the drainage to such an extent that Tulare Lake is formed above the fan. Lake San Cristobal in Colorado owes its origin to the Slumgullion mudflow, the lower part of which has built a dam across a valley.

The lodgment of driftwood in the bed of a low-gradient stream may pond the water and form a lake in the stream valley. These rafts, or jams, of trees and logs are formed of timber that caves into the stream from forested banks that are undercut. A remarkable series of irregular lakes has been formed by this process along the Red River in Louisiana (Fig. 224), where timber rafts several square miles in area, covered with living vegetation, formed floating islands and jams that dammed the streams so as to cause the development of shallow lakes 20 to 30 miles long. A number of the jams have been removed, and the main stream has deepened its channel as much as 15 feet. As a result of this

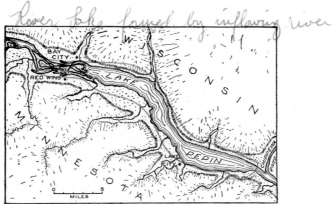

FIG. 223. Lake Pepin, part of the Mississippi River where it has spread out over its former flood plain. The widening of the river is due to the deposition of an excess of sediment brought to the valley by the Chippewa River.

deepening the tributaries have lowered their valleys, and the lakes are being drained.

Streams may excavate depressions in their beds that later form lake basins, particularly at the bases of rapids and waterfalls, where corrasion is accelerated. Many examples occur in the channels of mountain streams, where nearly every waterfall has its plunge pool at the base. An impressively deep pool of this sort is known to occur at the foot of Niagara Falls. Where stream courses with deep plunge basins are abandoned, the depressions may become lakes. Fall Lake at Grand Coulee, in the state of Washington and Jamesville Lake, near Syracuse, New York, are examples.

Basins Formed by Ground Water. Subsurface waters also may lead to the formation of lake basins at the surface. It has been pointed out that the solution and removal by underground water of large quantities of carbonates of lime and magnesia from regions underlain by limestone lead to the formation of underground cavities and channels. As such cavities increase in size, their roofs may collapse and depressions, or sinks, are formed at the surface. If the regional ground-water level later is brought near to the surface, the basins are occupied by lakes. A number of lake basins in Florida were formed in this way, and other examples

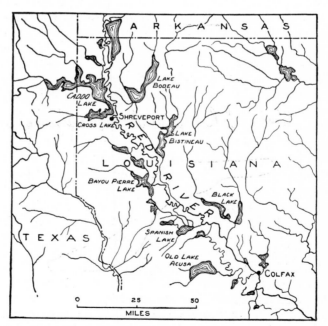

FIG. 224. Valley lakes along the Red River in Louisiana. Some of the lakes were formed by log rafts acting as dams. (*After Veatch, U.S. Geological Survey.*)

are found in the limestone-sink, or "karst," regions of Tennessee and Kentucky.

Basins Formed by Waves and Shore Currents. The combined action of wind and waves along the shores of the oceans, seas, and large lakes leads to the formation of sand- and gravel bars, forming lakes and lagoons that are landlocked. They are most numerous where bars have been built across the entrances of bays or where they extend from a headland and cut off a curve of the original shore line. Many such lakes occur along the shore of Lake Ontario and along the Atlantic Coast from New York southwest to Panama. Wind-blown sand may aid in completing the barrier between the newly formed lake and the ocean. Lakes thus formed along the seacoast are salty or brackish when they originate, but over a long period of time they may become fresh if the inflow of fresh water is great enough to displace the other water. Some of these coastal lakes discharge excess water only through the sand barrier blocking their normal drainage outlet.

Basins Due to Wind Activity. Winds transport rock particles of sand and dust size in any region where this type of rock material is available. Such activity, however, is likely to be most obvious in arid and semiarid regions, where it is little interrupted by the effects of running water. Winds are not limited in their gradational work by a base level, nor do they tend to produce a plain. Their downcutting is limited only by the presence of ground water. The fine sand and dust particles picked up at one place may be carried an appreciable distance and deposited in mounds at a higher level than that from which they were removed. The result may be hills or ridges associated with deflation basins. In dry regions these basins are likely to contain water only during wet seasons, and in deserts they may remain dry. But sand dunes and dune topography may occur in humid regions, and the basins among the dunes may be filled with water to form lakes or ponds. Some excellent examples occur in northwestern Indiana near the south end of Lake Michigan. Wind-blown sand may be a material aid in or the main cause of the formation of either river or coastal lakes where the migration of dunes cuts off portions of an estuary or blocks part of a channel.

Basins Produced by Mass Movement. The movement of large masses of rock debris, such as mudflows and landslides, may dam a stream course, pond the water, and produce a lake. Lakes of this origin are known to have been formed in various mountainous localities in Europe, Asia, and North America. It is probably a common occurrence wherever suitable conditions for mass movement exist. Lake San Cristobal in Colorado, formed by the Slumgullion mudflow, and the small lakes produced by the Gros Ventre landslide (Fig. 126) in northwestern Wyoming are good examples. The loose slide or flow materials of these dams are seldom more than temporary blocks to a stream, unless they are piled high enough to divert the overflow to some other possible outlet and thus to spare the dam from the rapid erosion likely to occur in such easily eroded material when water spills directly over it.

Basins Due to Diastrophism. The crust of the earth is unstable, and movements of land areas have resulted in the formation of depressions that retain water. Folding and faulting produced an enormous troughlike basin that contributed to the formation of Lake Superior, whose bed later was gouged out by glaciation of the nonresistant rock in the trough. The warping of a river valley may likewise produce a lake basin. This is true especially if the warping elevates one part of the valley so that it is higher than the part of the valley toward the source of the stream. In such a basin the water is ponded and forms a lake. Some large lake basins have been formed by the uplift of mountains around them. This is shown on a large scale in the Great Basin area of Utah and adjoining states.

Warping and folding often are accompanied by the breaking and displacement of rock strata along faults. Differential movement along fault blocks may cause part of a valley to sink, thus giving rise to a lake basin. A chain of valleys due to downfaulting of narrow blocks of the earth's crust have formed the Great Rift Valley in Asia and Africa. This rift includes the Jordan River, the Dead Sea (Fig. 225), part of the Red Sea, the Upper Nile, and the chain of African lakes including Tanganyika, Leopold, and Nyasa. The basin of Lake Tanganyika extends 1,700 feet below sea level. In the western part of the United States a number of basins have been formed by the same process. Lake Tahoe on the California-Nevada state boundary is one of the deepest lakes in North America. There an earth block settled several thousand feet to form a lake basin 22 miles long and 12 miles wide. The basins of Warner Lakes and of Abert Lake in Oregon also are due to faulting. The basin of Donald Lake in the Mackenzie District of Canada is chiefly due to several parallel faults, one of which is of major importance.

Displacements or undulations in the earth's surface developed during earthquakes may produce depressions that later become filled with water and form lakes. Reelfoot Lake in western Tennessee was formed during the earthquakes of 1811–1812, when there was sinking of numerous adjacent areas in Arkansas, Tennessee, and Missouri.

FIG. 225. Section across the Dead Sea, showing the outline of its basin, which was produced by the depression of a block of the earth's crust along fractures, or faults. (*After Blanckenhorn.*)

Where diastrophism causes a recession of the sea, the newly emerged portions of the sea bottom may include depressions that continue to hold water and these soon become fresh-water lakes from the inflow of land-derived runoff. The Arctic Coastal Plain of the Yukon district shows an abundance of such lakes on the lowland adjacent to the south shore of Beaufort Sea (Fig. 226). Some of the lakes of Florida also are in basins that were recently a part of the Atlantic Continental Shelf. These lakes are surrounded by marine sediments of recent origin, all of which are but a few feet above sea level. Such lakes are in regions of extreme topographic youth, and when drainage channels are established, the shallow basins soon are emptied.

Basins Produced by Volcanic Activity. Lava, rising from the earth's interior through vents in the surface, may so fill or obstruct a river valley that a lake is formed. Such basins once existed on the west slope of the Sierra Nevada, but the lakes have been drained by the erosion of the lava dams.

Lakes also occupy the hollows of extinct volcanic craters (Fig. 227), some of which are at considerable altitudes above the surrounding country. In the western part of the United States examples are found in Arizona, Nevada, California, and Oregon. Of this group Crater Lake in Oregon (Fig. 228) is the most renowned. This lake shows such extraor-

FIG. 226. The Arctic Coastal Plain, Yukon, showing numerous lakes filling the basins of an undulating surface recently part of the sea bottom. To the north, beyond the coast line, the Beaufort Sea is partly covered by ice floes. (*Courtesy of Royal Canadian Air Force.*)

FIG. 227. Crater Lakes on Paoha Island in Mono Lake, Leevining, California. (*Photograph by Frashers.*)

Crater Lakes.

FIG. 228. Crater Lake, Oregon. Wizard Island near the opposite shore is a small volcanic cone within the crater. (*Courtesy of Sawyer Scenic Photos, Inc.*)

dinary geological features that the region it occupies has been declared a national park. Crater Lake is situated in the Cascade Mountains in southwestern Oregon, at an elevation of 6,239 feet above the sea. It is nearly circular, without bays or promontories, and is about 5 miles in diameter. The cliffs of dark andesite encircling it rise precipitously to heights varying from 900 to 2,200 feet and nowhere offer an easy means of access to the basin within. There are no streams tributary to the lake, and no visible outlet. The waters probably escape by seeping through the walls and floor, as precipitation in this region is in excess of evaporation.

The basin of Crater Lake presumably was formed by the collapse and subsidence of the core of the volcanic mountain, carrying the summit downward as it sank. This was perhaps due to the withdrawal of lava from the mass of the magma deep in the earth beneath the volcano. After the removal of the summit of the mountain, the volcano again became active and built a small volcanic cone within the ancient crater. This cone is Wizard Island in the present lake.

Basins of Unusual Origin. Large meteorites striking the earth produce scars, some of which are now filled with water. Chubb Crater, in northern Quebec, is a circular scar of that sort which now contains a lake two miles across. Others of comparable size are reported to occur in northern Siberia. These, too, are filled with water and are now lakes.

SPECIAL TYPES OF LAKE

Saline Lakes. The waters of lakes vary much as to their mineral content. Those which have outlets generally are fresh. The incoming water that feeds most lakes is largely the runoff supplied by recent rains or melting snows and the ground water that has its chief source in the same meteoric water. Having had a more deliberate journey over and through the weathered rock material and even through the bedrock itself, ground water may carry much dissolved mineral matter and thus contribute it to the lake by way of springs and seepage. But in most regions the water supply that comes to lakes has a low content of dissolved mineral matter. The salinity is increased somewhat by evaporation, but there is no great concentration of salts because the water flowing out of the lake is renewed by fresh water flowing in. Lakes that are in undrained basins also are continually receiving fresh water. Evaporation takes place from the surface of such lakes; and although the water entering the lake may carry only small amounts of mineral matter, this is concentrated in the lakes. Since there is no outlet, the water steadily becomes more salty and may reach the point of saturation and deposit salt (Fig. 229). The kind of salt that predominates depends upon the chemical composition of the rocks in the region of the lake basin and subordinately upon the springs

FIG. 229. "Bad Water." Elevation −280 feet below sea level. A remnant of the ancient lake in the lowest part of Death Valley. The rough, flat area in the middle ground consists of various salts precipitated from the saturated water. Telescope Mountain in background. (*Photo by Frashers.*)

that rise in the basin. In some it is near the salinity of sea water; in others alkaline salts predominate; and in several localities borax salts are abundant.

Some salt lakes are of oceanic origin. The Caspian Sea, which is the largest body of inland salt water known, was cut off from the ocean by the elevation of the intervening land. The most favorable conditions for the formation of terrestrial saline lakes are in regions where mountain streams discharge into interior drainage basins where the climate is arid. Such conditions are prevalent over parts of nearly every continent and especially over a large area in the southwestern part of the United States, where Great Salt Lake of Utah is the most notable example. Great Salt Lake is but a shrunken remnant (Fig. 230) that contains the residue of a vast fresh-water lake that once covered an area of 20,000 square miles, mainly to the west and south of its present lake shores. The fresh-water predecessor, known as Lake Bonneville, overflowed to the north through the Snake and Columbia Rivers into the Pacific Ocean (Fig. 231). It left a record of its boundaries in the form of hundreds of miles of shore beaches, terraces, and wave-cut cliffs which it formed along its mountainous shores at the different levels at which it stood (Fig. 232). Lake Bonneville once had a maximum depth of over 1,000 feet. Where the famous Mormon temple now stands in Salt Lake City, the water of this lake was once so deep that the temple would be under 850 feet of water

FIG. 230. Map of Great Salt Lake, showing its relation to the vast ancestral lake known as Lake Bonneville (*shaded*). (*After Gilbert, U.S. Geological Survey.*)

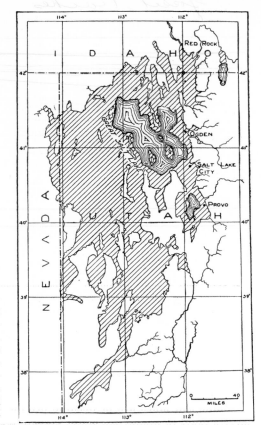

FIG. 231. (*Below*) Red Rock Pass in southeastern Idaho, looking southward along the outlet of ancient Lake Bonneville. The railroad and U.S. Highway No. 91 take advantage of the easy grade to escape from the bottom of a northeast extension of the basin, shown in the distance, several hundred feet below the surrounding territory. (*Spence Air Photos.*)

FIG. 232. Ancient shore-line terraces of Lake Bonneville. (*After Gilbert, U.S. Geological Survey.*)

if the lake again attained its former level. As the level of Lake Bonneville sank below its outlet, because of diminished rainfall in that region, its waters became more and more salty, until the present Great Salt Lake is nearly five times as salty as the ocean. It has been estimated that the lake water contains 400 million tons of common salt and also millions of tons of salts of calcium, magnesium, and potash. In marginal pools, where the water is only a few inches deep, it becomes so concentrated by evaporation that common salt crystals are formed and accumulate as a brilliant white sediment. The lakes in the region of Great Salt Lake are surrounded by marine sedimentary rocks that supply sodium chloride. Hot springs are numerous in the southwestern part of the United States and contribute large amounts of salts to certain lakes.

Alkaline Lakes. Lakes containing excessive amounts of alkaline carbonates are commonly called alkaline lakes. They occur at many places in Egypt, Hungary, Venezuela, etc., and are merely a special kind of saline lake. Some have thinolitic and dendritic tufa deposits on their shores. They are found along the western part of the Great Basin in the United States. Mono Lake in east central California is an example. Its basin lies at the eastern base of the Sierra Nevada, where it covers an area of about 90 square miles. Its size varies with the seasons and, to some extent, from year to year. This lake also, like many in the Great Basin country, had a much larger ancestor, as is shown by numerous shore features carved on the slopes of its basin (Fig. 233). The highest beach line is nearly 700 feet above the present water level. When filled to that beach, it covered an area of about 320 square miles.

Playa Lakes. Shallow, flat-bottomed depressions are formed by weathering and wind action in desert areas. During the wet seasons they are flooded by waters from intermittent streams; and when the water supply ceases, they shrink and finally disappear by evaporation, leaving in their beds deposits of alkali salts that often are as white as freshly fallen snow.

Such ephemeral lakes are characteristic features in the deserts of the Great Basin. In the Black Rock Desert in the northwestern part of Nevada during the winter months a lake forms that covers an area of 450 to 500 square miles and is seldom more than a few inches deep. Following heavy storms it appears as a vast sheet of liquid mud. In a few days all the water may evaporate, leaving a hard, dry, barren surface showing a reticulate pattern of mud cracks. Similar lakes exist in the deserts of Arizona, New Mexico, and Sonora. They are found also in the desert areas of other continents.

Artificial Lakes. Although these are exceedingly temporary or transitory bodies of water, some artificial lakes are quite large and important factors in the geological history of their region while they last. Such water bodies are similar to natural lakes in their shore-line development and sedimentation history, except that these processes may be modified by artificial withdrawal of water from the reservoir, thus causing unusual fluctuation in the level of the ponded water. When the water level is low, the immediate runoff tends to destroy the normal shore line along the artificial lake, whereas during high water a new shore line may be developed at a higher level and at places farther up the valley affected. Turbidity currents, entering the upper end of the reservoir or its sides at the ends of tributaries, spread along the bottom and may carry their exceedingly fine detritus its full length, to be stopped only by the dam, where it accumulates.

FIG. 233. Mono Lake, California. Looking down over the baylike west end of the lake from one of the old beaches above Leevining. (*Photograph by Frashers.*)

Artificial lakes are built by man and by beavers. Both use the same method of obstructing, or damming, the natural drainage and using the eroded area upstream as the basin for ponding the water. Some of the chief reasons for building dams that form artificial lakes are for water power, water supply for domestic use, irrigation, flood control, etc. Many of these artificial obstructions to drainage merely raise the water level in

Some High Dams and Important Artificial Lakes of the World [1]

Name	Location	Height of dam, feet	Capacity, millions of acre-feet	Date of completion
Aswan	Nile R., Egypt	174	4.06	1934
Chelsea	Canada	100	1.98	1927
Cherokee	Holston R., Tenn.	212	1.56	1942
Coolidge	Gila R., Ariz.	249	1.20	1928
Denison	Red R., Okla.-Tex.	165	5.82	1944
Douglas	French Broad R., Tenn.	160	1.54	1943
Dnieprostroy	Dnieper R., Russia	200	0.89	1932
El Azucar	San Juan R., Mexico	142	1.70	1943
Elephant Butte	Rio Grande, N. Mex.	301	2.21	1916
Fontana	Lower Tennessee R., N.C.	470	1.45	1944
Fort Peck	Missouri R., Mont.	250	19.41	1940
Gatun	Chagres R., Panama	115	4.40	1912
Grand Coulee	Columbia R., Wash.	550	9.51	1942
Hartebeestpoort	Union of South Africa	198	1.25	1923
Hoover	Colorado R., Ariz.-Nev.	726	31.14	1936
Hume	Murray R., Australia	180	2.00	1936
Kentucky	Tennessee R., Ky.	160	6.10	1944
Kingsley	North Platte R., Neb.	162	2.00	1941
Krishnarajah Sagara	India	146	1.11	1932
La Angostura	Bavispe R., Mexico	291	1.02	1941
Lazaro Cardenas	Nazas R., Mexico	295	3.26	1948
Mansfield	Colorado R., Tex.	270	1.93	1941
Mettur	Cauvery R., India	214	2.15	1934
Norfolk	North Fork R., Ark.	230	1.93	1944
Norris	Clinch R., Tenn.	265	2.56	1936
Osage	Osage R., Mo.	148	1.99	1931
Owyhee	Owyhee R., Oreg.	417	1.12	1932
Pathfinder	North Platte R., Wyo.	214	1.07	1909
Pensacola	Grand R., Okla.	152	1.97	1940
Quabbin	Swift R., Mass.	170	1.27	1939
Ricobaya	Spain	326	0.96	1935
Roosevelt	Salt R., Ariz.	280	1.40	1911
Saluda	Saluda R., S.C.	208	2.30	1930
Sardis	Little Tallahatchee R., Miss.	117	1.56	1940
Seminole	North Platte R., Wyo.	295	1.02	1938
Shasta	Sacramento R., Calif.	602	4.50	1945
Watts Bar	Tennessee R., Tenn.	97	1.13	1942
Wheeler	Tennessee R., Ala.	72	1.15	1936

[1] For these and other data on artificial lakes see Geographical Comparisons, Britannia World Atlas, C. F. Hammond Company, New York, 1945, pp 6–7.

the river channels above the dam; hence the outline of the quiet water takes on somewhat the dendritic pattern of the stream system, the backwater filling the tributaries to or slightly above dam level. In some cases man has diverted the water from one drainage system to another and so changed the erosional history of both systems. This change may become permanent.

Formerly the beaver was an abundant inhabitant of the streams and valleys in many parts of North America. Their habit of building dams across streams to produce ponds or lakes, in which to construct their homes, is well-known. After being nearly extinct, beavers are now increasing in numbers, and once more their dams are producing ponds that assume somewhat the role of former days. Beaver-made ponds or lakes form important lodgment areas for sediments. The dams may be 10 to 20 feet high and extend 50 to 100 feet or more across a valley. The quiet water, ponded behind the dam, is gradually shallowed by deposition of silt. Eventually the basin is filled and the area covered by vegetation to form the "beaver meadows," or "wet meadows," abundantly developed in some regions. The extent of the area affected is increased by successive dams built farther and farther upstream until the strip may be miles in length. The surface, on which sedimentation is taking place, thus rises toward the source of the stream, but the dam or series of dams may be lost under cover of later sediments and its true character discovered only by careful exploration. The long, narrow *wet meadows*, common along the Continental Divide near the headwaters of the Colorado and the Platte Rivers, are the remnants of such beaver work [1] rather than detritus-filled glacial lakes, for which they have been mistaken.

MOVEMENTS OF LAKE WATER

Lakes are definitely part of the disposal system of meteoric water and as such are usually connected in humid areas with streams of various sorts. Some lakes, such as Kioga and Albert in central Africa, or Erie and Ontario of North America, are integral parts of the main line of great river systems and have definite currents flowing through them. Many smaller lakes are similarly situated but have less conspicuous inlets and outlets. In them the flow may not be so obvious but is there nevertheless. In fact in all lakes that have an outlet there is drift, or gradual movement, of the water towards the outflowing stream, and in every lake there is movement of adjustment to any inflowing water. This may be movement on the surface, within the water mass, or along the bottom of the lake,

---

[1] Donald L. Ives, *Jour. Geomorphology*, vol. 5, pp. 191–203, 1945.

depending on differences in density of the incoming water and of that standing in the lake. The two main causes of this difference are turbidity of the river water and temperature inequalities between river and lake, although salinity may also be a factor.

Of course circulation takes place between different parts of a lake, due to heating and cooling, to which the surface is especially responsive. Large lakes may show definite currents set up by other causes but mostly traceable to the wind. The warm surface water drifts with the wind to the opposite shore, and the cooler water rises to replace it along the shore from which the warm water has drifted. This is in addition to the bottom-to-top movement, or circulation set up by surface heating, although the two movements operate together. Strong winds blowing from one direction for a long period produce currents that may become effective gradational agents along the shore line. In large lakes these are very important both constructively and destructively.

PROCESSES MODIFYING LAKE BASINS

Destruction of Lakes. The shape and capacity of a lake basin depend largely upon the forces that operate at the time of its formation. But whatever the original outline or depth of the basin may be, it does not long remain the same, for gradation begins immediately and is constantly at work modifying the lake shores, filling the basin with sediment, or draining it by erosion lowering its outlet. Sooner or later most lakes are destroyed by the completion of these processes. In some cases the extinction of lakes is due to evaporation or to the diversion of streams and the failure of their water supply. Whatever fills or destroys the basin terminates the lake, just as surely as does the cutting off of its water supply.

Shore-line Changes. The shore-line development of lakes, except on a smaller scale, is similar to that along the seacoast. There is, however, the lack of an appreciable tide in lakes, and longshore currents are seldom strong. Waves produced by high winds may be of destructive violence and expend their energy on the materials forming the shores. Where these shores are rocky the loose and broken pieces are hurled by the waves back against the projecting bedrock and act as tools to cut or wear away the rocky mass of the shore as high up as the waves can reach. The rock above topples as it is undercut and adds to the effective tools of the waves, while the pieces themselves are ground to fine material and washed basinward by the returning water. The deposition of these loose materials forms a *wave-built terrace* that is a continuation of the thinly veneered *rock terrace* left where the cliff formerly stood.

Currents moving along the shore may deposit detritus to build spits and bars, cutting off indentations which then become ponds or secondary lakes, which pass into marginal swamps as filling takes place. Islands near shore may become land-tied through the development of bars, or tombolos, extending out to them. All these features are especially well-shown at several places along the shores of the Great Lakes of North America. The processes affecting shore lines are given in greater detail in the discussion of oceans, where the results differ but slightly from those along lake shores.

Delta Building. Lakes are well-suited to the development of deltas, and many lake basins are partially filled by deposits of that sort. Deltas are built by sediment-laden streams discharging into bodies of relatively quiet water, where they drop their load of sediment as they lose their velocity. The coarser part of the rock material in transit is dropped as the current meets its first check, and the succeeding load of similar material is dumped basinward over the edge of that already deposited. This produces the sloping or cross-bedded structure constituting the foreset beds and a major portion of the delta. The finer sediment is carried farther on by the feeble current to settle in deeper water as layers more or less parallel to the bottom of the basin, where they form the bottomset beds. As the delta builds outward, gradually filling the basin of the lake, the shore line advances and the stream flows over its own deposits but drops part of its load over the fill as topset beds, which thus complete the delta structure.

The very fine rock materials, with grains or flakes of dustlike size, carried by streams entering the lake, are held in suspension as cloudlike masses which produce *turbidity currents* (Fig. 234). Such currents still carry part of the original load of sediment acquired by the stream. They may flow on the surface (overflow) if the lake water is heavier than that of the incoming current; but if the surface water of the lake is of less density, the heavy turbidity current sinks and flows downslope on any submerged surface composed of material of greater density, whether it be a lower mass of water (inflow) or the lake bottom itself (underflow), and so the extremely fine sediment may be transported to distant parts of the lake or reservoir. Eventually this fine, dustlike sediment settles out in quiet water, and the outflowing stream from the lake may be quite free from mechanical sediment of any kind. In Lake Mead, the artificial lake behind Hoover Dam, turbidity currents travel the full length (120 miles) of the reservoir and cease only at the dam itself.

Deltas are very common in the lakes of many regions the world over. The St. Clair River has built a delta filling a large area at the upper end of Lake St. Clair northeast of Detroit. The flat area, on which much of the town of Watkins, New York, is built at the head of Seneca Lake, is a delta nearly 3 miles long and more than 1 mile wide; the thickness of the fill is 500 or 600 feet and possibly more. Deltas are especially common

FIG. 234. Colorado River discharging into the upper end of Lake Mead, showing its turbid water plunging downward in gullylike courses to the lake bottom. This is the beginning of the turbidity current that may be traced along the bottom all the way to Hoover Dam. (*Photograph by Howard Gould.*)

in the lakes of Switzerland, where these bodies of water are the settling basins for streams carrying great quantities of sediment brought down from the high mountain areas. The town of Interlaken is located on the double delta built by streams entering from opposite sides and cutting the basin into two parts, thus forming the Lake of Thun and Lake Brienz. The turbid Rhone River is building an extensive delta, now 20 miles long and 1,000 feet thick, at the upper end of Lake Geneva and, if it continues, will eventually fill the basin. As the river leaves the lake at the city of Geneva, it is relatively clear and, having lost its load of sediment, has become an eroding stream.

Filling of Glacial Lakes. A special type of basin filling is found in the quiet marginal lakes of glaciated regions, where the finest sediment, or rock flour, from the glacial grinding process settled out beyond the turbulence of currents to form well-stratified silt and clay beds. Since the conditions under which these were formed appear to have been uniformly periodic, the thicknesses of successive layers are similar. But they are also seasonal, that is, summer and winter layers. The layers laid down during the summer are thicker, lighter-colored, and somewhat coarser or more silty than the thinner, darker, more organic layers deposited during the winter, when the supply was less and agitation of water was reduced by a frozen surface. These are the *varved clays* (Fig. 217). Each summer and winter pair constitute a year's sedimentation, or *varve*. The transition from summer to winter layer is gradual, but that from winter to summer is abrupt, probably due to sudden breakup of the ice cover at the end of the winter season. The varves are thus easily separated and, by counting the number of pairs of layers or varves in a deposit, the time required for their accumulation or for the filling of the basin may be determined.

Organic Filling. The remains of animals and plants accumulate on the bottoms and along the margins of lakes. This is especially well-shown around the edges of small, shallow lakes where aquatic vegetation is invading the basins. Here sediment lodges among the plants, covers up the relics of former living things, and helps to extend the shore line farther into the lake. Many animals and some plants living in lakes secrete calcium carbonate, others silica, to form their shells or skeletal parts. When such animals or plants die, their hard parts settle and accumulate as a portion of the bottom sediment of the basin. These hard parts often form a large part of the lake deposit, and in some places such remains are so abundant that they constitute the main basin-filling material, even becoming beds of economic importance.

Other Methods of Filling. Various other agents contribute to the filling of lake basins and hence to the extinction of lakes which they contain. Among these are wind-blown sand and migrating dunes. These latter may not only be responsible for the formation of basins that fill with water, but drifting into lakes they add to the filling of such basins. Dust, whether of volcanic or arid origin, contributes to the same end. During the blanketing of an area with volcanic dust, that which falls directly on the lake, together with the great quantity that is washed in immediately by the torrents of rain, may be sufficient to obliterate the lake entirely.

SWAMPS, OR MARSHES

Swamps are a widespread and important surface condition. Between 40,000 and 50,000 square miles of the United States, exclusive of Alaska, are rated as swamp or peat land. Minnesota alone has between 5 million and 6 million acres of such land, and Florida has a similar amount. Swamps, or marshes, are also referred to as peat bogs or merely as bogs, and in some regions the humus soil formed in them is loosely called muck.

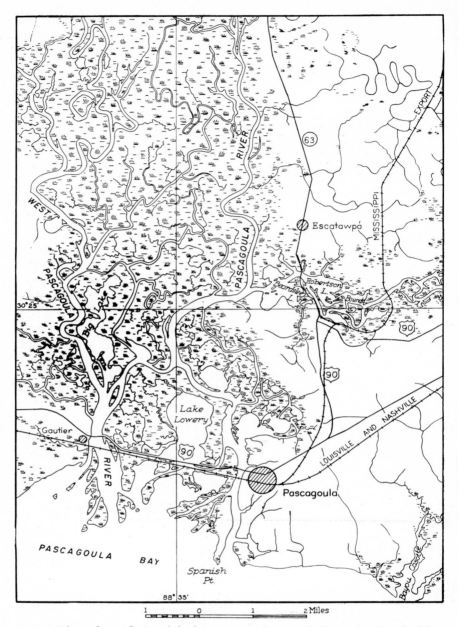

FIG. 235. Channel complexity of the lower part of Pascagoula River, showing the lakes and swampy area along the Gulf of Mexico at the southeast corner of Mississippi. (*U.S. Geological Survey Topographic Branch.*)

Swamps are areas of wet, soggy ground usually filled with spongy, decaying vegetable matter and more or less overgrown by water-loving plants. Such areas may be of large or small size and, as is the case with lakes, are closely related in development to the level of ground water. A few relatively small swamps occur on high ground or hillsides quite detached from the general water table of the region but usually found to be associated with an impervious subsoil and a perched water table or seepage from still higher ground. Hillside marshes of this sort may become the point of origin of a landslide by which most of the bog is transferred to lower ground. Some of the swamps lying high on the continents may be of very large size. Thus the marshes at the Bolivia-Brazil boundary cover thousands of square miles and contribute to the sources of important tributaries of both the Amazon and the Paraná Rivers.

Swamps are often the successors to lakes and sluggish streams, but this is not necessarily the case. Some are found on areas that never were lakes (Fig. 235), and coastal swamps may be the salt marshes of former tidal flats. Wherever there is a wide stretch of relatively flat-lying, poorly drained land and an abundant supply of water, a swamp is very likely to occur. Such conditions are more likely to be found on the poorly drained till plains of recent glaciation, along the flood plains and deltas of major streams, and along the coastal region adjacent to a broad, shallow Continental Shelf.

Muskeg Swamps. The ground moraine over large areas of north central United States and over still larger areas in adjacent parts of Canada is so nearly flat that water drains from it very slowly. The spongy black soil is made up largely of roots and root fragments, leaves, partly decayed vegetable matter, and fine rock waste. When this is saturated with water, it becomes a very favorable medium for the growth of plants desiring an abundance of water and so many such areas are overgrown by sphagnum moss, low shrubs and bushes, or other water plants, often so thickly set and tangled that it is difficult to penetrate and so wet that the region is almost impossible to traverse. The black larch, or tamarack, is a common tree growing in these swamps. Pools of open water are abundant. These are the muskeg swamps of the north central area of America, and patches of muskeg may be found at least as far north as Hudson Bay. In some parts of Canada the muskeg is developed directly over smooth, flat glaciated surfaces of the bedrock. Except where shattered by jointing, the rock is so impervious to water that little underdrainage is possible and the swamp lingers on indefinitely; others partially drain as the outlet is lowered.

Great areas of muskeg were encountered in western Russia during the building of the Moscow-Leningrad railway. They presented the same construction difficulties, such as the mushy material oozing out from

FIG. 236. Bedrock, lakes, and irregular patches of soggy swampland in the tundras, or barren lands, north of Great Slave Lake, Mackenzie District, Canada. (*Royal Canadian Air Force.*)

under the grade and the track settling, that were met earlier by the railway builders over Canadian muskeg. An even greater swamp of this type lies east of the Urals, in western Siberia, where the drainage basin of the Ob River is largely occupied by the Vasyugane Swamp—a typical muskeg. Under much of the European and Asiatic muskeg the bedrock is only a few feet below the surface, and in some of the swampy regions of Siberia there is developed an iron hardpan that likewise interferes with underdrainage and so produces conditions favorable to muskeg development.

Tundra. The Russian muskeg swamps are gradually succeeded northward, as on the American continent, by the lake and swamp areas within the subarctic and arctic wastelands. In Canada this transition begins near the southern limit of Hudson Bay, where the irregular timber line infringes here and there upon areas of the permanently frozen subsoil, over a large portion of which are developed a topsoil and vegetation characteristic of the tundras. These continue northward to the Arctic Ocean. In Europe, Asia, and North America much of this arctic area was covered by the recent continental glaciation. Now ground moraine, with all the topographic features common to that type of drift deposit, covers the surface. In northwestern Canada the drift is locally thin, and some large areas are bare rock (Fig. 236), with numerous intervening rockbound lakes and small patches of moss and lichen. "Barrens" and "barren lands" are terms applied to these Canadian regions more frequently than "tundra," of which they are a definite part.

For the most part the tundras are characterized by a black soil mingled with partly decayed roots and stems of mosses, lichens, sedges, and small hardy shrubs that grade upward into a mat of dead and living plants, the whole constituting the spongy, waterlogged surface. The sub-soil over much of the area is little known, except that it is frozen and remains in that condition most of the year. Only the top portion beneath the mat loses part of its frost in summer months. The depth of this surface melting, if any, varies with the length of the summer season and the distance from the outer margin of permafrost. Several feet or only a few inches may be affected by this melting, depending largely on the thickness of the surface mat and the efficiency of its blanketing effect.

This soggy soil condition, and its characteristic tundra vegetation, may extend even to higher ground where the subsoil is frozen and downward escape of moisture is prevented. In fact it may be found above the timber line in high mountains outside the Arctic Zone where permafrost occurs and where a *perched tundra* area is developed, like a swamp or lake on a perched water table. Boggy masses from such areas may be found traveling down slope under mass movement on a frozen subsoil wherever suitable conditions occur, leaving rounded and subdued slopes over areas from which permafrost has receded. Since the resulting steppes, or prairies, inherit a surface mat of vegetation or sod, this gentle topography may be expected to endure beyond the time when frost disappears as a permanent part of the subsoil.

The tundra soils inch out over the bare rock of the Canadian "barrens" from their tiny hold to cover greater surfaces and in time may spread over the whole bare-rock area. In northern Europe and in Siberia the timbered areas straggle northward along the streams, then feather out, and prairies, or steppelike areas, are included within the borders of the tundra, though most of the low, flat portion is best classified as swamp-land. In fact during the summer season this, and even some of the adjacent higher slopes, may have the appearance of a vast and continuous swamp through which man and beast plod in ankle-deep slush or mushy soil. In winter the whole region becomes a rolling or featureless snowy waste.

River-valley Swamps. The overflow from a river, carrying large quantities of fine sediment, may build the region adjacent into a flood plain of such low relief that the sluggish stream changes its course frequently and thus abandons parts of its channel. These flat areas are covered by sloughs, oxbow lakes, and secondary channels wandering through a maze of swampland. From Fort Snelling southward the Mississippi River, since glacial time, has built up its flood plain 90 to 100 feet or more and now flows on top of the fill. Its worked-over area exhibits many excellent examples of these adjacent swampy, water-soaked lands, such as those to be seen from the highway over the flats at La Crosse, Wisconsin, and at many other places.

The building of natural levees raises that portion of the flood plain situated along either side of the channel and leaves the more distant flat as swampland. Much of the farm land along the lower Mississippi lies on the levees near the river and slopes toward the sides of the valley, where the swampy areas are located. The drainage of this agricultural land is thus actually away from the main stream. The growth of the delta is extending these conditions, and especially the swamp areas, into the Gulf of Mexico.

Coastal Marshes. Gradational processes, with or without diastrophism, may convert large areas along the seacoast into marshes. These may be partly invaded by the tides or flooded by fresh water from the land, causing their waters to be brackish. There is thus among them every gradation from the salty tidal flat to a fresh-water swamp, and even shallow lakes in the early stage of marsh or swamp development. Notable examples are the Dismal Swamp with its Drummond Lake in southern Virginia, much of the Atlantic coastal area of North Carolina lying adjacent to Pamlico Sound, Okefinokee Swamp in southern Georgia, the southern tip of Florida, and essentially the whole Gulf coast of Louisiana, where shallow lakes and low, soggy lands are prevalent.

The swampland of southern Florida covers about 6,000 square miles, of which five-sixths is the typical saw grass- or sedge-covered Everglades, with its slight elevations, or "hammocks," bearing hardwood trees. The balance of the swamp area, being more tolerant of vegetable variation, is covered by cypress swamps, with here and there sandy areas covered by pine, and by wet prairies and mangrove swamps along the southern and southwestern coastal borders. All of these types more or less grade into the saw grass swamps of the true Everglades and thence into the sandy, pine-covered uplands of the north, east, and west. Lake Okeechobee occupies a shallow basin at the northern edge of the Everglades and spills over its excess water into the water-soaked regions to the south. The main water supply for the Everglades is the excessive rainfall (about 60 inches annually) and seepage or springs draining the ground water that falls as rain farther north. The muck or impure, peatlike soil and areas of sand overlie, by only a few feet, a limestone and marl surface that was sea bottom in geologically recent time. The Everglades are thus but a special phase of the whole southeastern coastal swampland of North America.

In many places along a sandy coast, sand dunes are prevalent with swampy land between dunes and mainland. These pass through the same history as other marshy lands and usually add grassy flats to the adjacent territory.

Fate of Swamps. Ponds, lakes, and shallow embayments are being gradually filled and converted into swamps or marshes by the methods that have been outlined or by others that are closely related. With more complete drainage development swamps of whatever origin may pass into woodlands, meadows, prairies, or dry-land flats as erosion proceeds. Others, depressed below drainage level, may be covered by later sedimentation, thus preserving the accumulations of vegetable matter, or peat, the shells and shell marl, the diatomaceous earth, the stratified sands and clays, along with all the other evidence of swamplike character, for a very long time. Eventually the peat may be changed to lignite, or even to coal, and the marl into limestone.

ECONOMIC ASPECTS OF LAKES AND SWAMPS

Natural products that are beneficial to mankind are constantly being taken from the lake waters or from the sediments that accumulate under the water. Saline lakes furnish salts, and many shallow lakes have extensive deposits of calcium carbonate in the form of a white, chalky marl. This calcium carbonate is used for agricultural purposes and also in the manufacture of cement. In some localities the remains of microscopic plants called diatoms, which secrete tiny shells of silica, accumulate to form beds of diatomaceous earth in lake basins. This material is excavated and used in the manufacture of abrasives, refractories, and other products. Extensive deposits of peat have been built up along the shores of lakes and bogs. In many localities in Europe peat cut from the bogs is dried and used as a fuel. Where lake basins have been filled or drained, either by natural or by artificial means, the exposed sediments become fertile soils. Large areas of lake soils are being cultivated in the "wheat belt" of North Dakota and western Minnesota, where many thousand square miles of fertile plains represent the drained basin of the extinct Lake Agassiz. Numerous coastal-plain swamps also have been drained or filled with sediments, leaving fertile soils high in humus. This is especially true along the southeastern coast of the United States, in Holland, and in Flanders. Drainage ditches in the Florida Everglades, south of Lake Okeechobee, have lowered the level of ground water about 4 feet and have converted a very large area of swampland into suitable agricultural land. Over that territory sugar cane plantations and winter truck gardens of great importance have since been developed.

The muskeg and low, soggy tundras of the Far North are suited to

Some Noted Lakes of the World [1]

Name	Location	Area, square miles	Max. depth, feet	Elevation above sea, feet
Caspian	Russia	170,000	3,200	−85
Chad	Sudan	10,000 to 50,000	8 to 20	840
Superior	United States–Canada	31,820	1,290	602
Aral	Russia	26,233	222	157
Victoria	Uganda-Tanganyika	26,200	270	3,720
Huron	United States–Canada	23,010	750	580
Michigan	United States	22,400	923	580
Baikal	Siberia	12,740	5,712	1,516
Tanganyika	Congo-Tanganyika	12,700	4,700	2,536
Great Bear	Northwest Canada	11,490	270	391
Great Slave	Northwest Canada	11,170	.....	495
Nyasa	Nyasa-Mozambique	11,000	2,580	1,650
Erie	United States–Canada	9,940	210	572
Winnipeg	Manitoba	9,398	70	712
Ontario	United States–Canada	7,540	778	245
Balkash	Russia	7,200	36	900
Ladoga	Russia	7,000	730	55
Onega	Russia	3,764	408	125
Rudolf	Kenya	3,475	.....	1,250
Titicaca	Bolivia-Peru	3,200	1,000	12,507
Nicaragua	Nicaragua	3,089	200	135
Athabaska	Alberta-Saskatchewan	3,058	.....	699
Reindeer	Saskatchewan	2,444	.....	1,150
Issyk-Kul	Russia	2,230	2,300	5,400
Koko Nor	Tibet	2,200	.....	10,000
Vanern	Sweden	2,149	292	144
Winnepegosis	Manitoba	2,086	38	831
Bangweulu	Northern Rhodesia	1,900	15	3,700
Nipigon	Ontario	1,870	.....	852
Manitoba	Manitoba	1,817	12	813
Urmia	Iran	1,750	50	810
Albert	Uganda	1,640	55	2,037
Dubawnt	Keewatin	1,600	.....	500
Great Salt	Utah	1,500	25	4,200
Van	Turkey	1,453	.....	5,643
Tana	Ethiopia	1,100	.....	5,690
Pyramid	Nevada	828	350	3,783
Okeechobee	Florida	725	16	15
Dead Sea	Palestine	360	1,300	−1,268
Salton Sea [2]	California	300	29	−244
Tahoe	California-Nevada	195	1,645	6,225
Chelan	Washington	85	1,500	1,079
Como	Italy	60	1,340	650
Crater	Oregon	25	2,000	6,239

[1] Data in this table are taken from various sources which do not agree in all details. However, the differences are seldom as great as 1 per cent. The area of Lake Chad varies with the season.
[2] This lake dates from 1904. Prior to that the area was a dry playa. Its depth and area are both variable.

reindeer and caribou ranching, and experiments for their utilization as such are under way. Certain types of vegetable are also produced, even over areas of permafrost and its boggy soil.

SUGGESTIONS FOR FURTHER READING

Diller, J. D.: Crater Lake, *U.S. Geol. Survey Prof. Paper* 3, 1902.

Gilbert, G. K.: Lake Bonneville, *U.S. Geol. Survey Mon.* I, 1890.

Gray, G. B. D.: Soviet Land, A. & C. Black, Ltd., London, 1947.

Lane, F. C.: The World's Great Lakes, Doubleday & Company, Inc., 1948.

Russell, I. C.: Lakes of North America, Ginn & Company, 1895.

Sellards, E. H.: The Florida Lakes and Lake Basins, *Florida Geol. Survey 3d Ann. Rept.*, pp. 47–76, 1910.

Shaler, N. D.: Sea-coast Swamps of the Eastern United States, *U.S. Geol. Survey 6th Ann. Rept.*, pp. 353–398, 1885.

Veatch, A. C.: Formation and Destruction of Lakes of Red River Valley, La., *U.S. Geol. Survey Prof. Paper* 46, pp. 60–62, 1906.

CHAPTER 13

The Ocean: A. General Features

Functions of the Ocean. The ocean supplies moisture to the atmos-phere, from which it falls as rain on all parts of the earth's surface. It is the ultimate source of the land waters which are so effective in carving the continents and which give life to plants and animals. Its basin is the place toward which land detritus is being carried and is the final resting place of all sediments. The ocean absorbs heat slowly and gives it up slowly. It is therefore a great regulator of climate. Extending from con-tinent to continent, it is the route over which marine life migrates and is the great highway of commerce, while its waters supply food for millions of people. From the geologic, the climatic, and the economic standpoint, therefore, the ocean is of vital, often dominating, importance, and its influence reaches every part of the earth's surface (Fig. 237).

Distribution. The ocean is that great body of water which occupies the depressed, basinlike portions of the earth's surface. It lies between and surrounds the elevated, or continental, portions of the earth. The partially separated water areas have different names. Thus there are the Atlantic Ocean, the Pacific Ocean, etc., somewhat independent but nevertheless connected at the surface and forming a common ocean.

The outlying divisions of the ocean are commonly called seas, as the Red, the Mediterranean, and the Caribbean Seas; but a nearly similar body of salt water may be called a gulf, as the Gulf of Mexico, or a bay, as Hudson Bay. The whole ocean, moreover, may be called the sea, and it is the usual practice to refer to its surface as sea level. Some of these divisions, or seas, are almost completely surrounded by land, whereas others are partly enclosed by island chains. They may be entirely within the shallow water or may lie in isolated portions of the great ocean basins themselves.

RELIEF FEATURES OF THE OCEAN BASIN

Sea Level. The surface of the ocean is the datum, or reference plane, for all topographic and geologic work. All level surfaces are theoretically parallel to mean sea level, and that surface is assumed to be constant. It is, of course, not level but is merely the surface of an oblate spheroid. It is not exactly the surface of an oblate spheroid, because the mobile waters are attracted by, and drawn up against, the sides of the basin nearest the greatest land masses, such as the huge mountain masses of the southwestern United States, the Andes of South America, or those of India. Differences in salinity (and therefore of weight) probably also affect sea level slightly.

Temporary changes in level, such as those produced by the tides, winds, and excessive rainfall, leave no permanent effect on the sea level but may cause marked effects on the coast lines, where the waves temporarily reach above their ordinary height.

FIG. 237. The Golden Gate, entrance to San Francisco Bay. This drowned water gap, giving ready access to the sea from sheltered harbors on the bay, is one of the most important arteries of commerce in the world. (*Spence Air Photos.*)

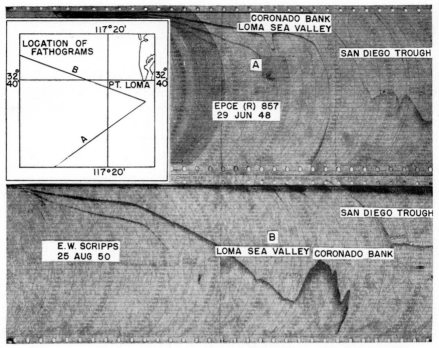

FIG. 238. A typical fathogram off San Diego, California. (*Allan Hancock Foundation.*)

Surveying the Ocean Floor. Mapping the depths of the sea involves two problems, (1) the determination of the exact geographic position at which the observation is made, and (2) the measurement of the depth itself. Each of these has its difficulties. Within sight of landmarks on shore the position of a ship at sea may be found by ordinary trigonometric methods by taking bearings with a sextant. Beyond sight of land the methods used include dead reckoning, astronomical fixes, great lengths of taut wire, radio compass, radio acoustic ranging, radar, Shoran, Loran, and SOFAR. Shoran and Loran utilize radio waves and special electronic equipment at shore stations and on board ship. SOFAR uses the transmission of sound waves from a bomb exploded at a depth in the sea where sound waves travel horizontally at a uniform rate (about 4,800 feet per second) to geophones placed at the same depth near shore.

The depth of the sea is determined by sounding. In shallow-water areas it is readily measured by a taut-wire sounding device, but in deep water the task is not so simple on account of the length of time required, the difficulty of maintaining a vertical cast, the bulk of great lengths of wire, the heavier equipment needed to handle it, the possible error in measuring it on a wheel, its stretch, and other difficulties. Hence echo sounding has largely replaced wire sounding except in certain areas or for special purposes.

An echo-sounding instrument measures the time required for a sound to travel to the bottom and the echo to return to the ship. High frequency or audio frequency may be used. Based on the velocity of sound in sea water, the instrument automatically registers the depth as the ship continues along on its course. A recording device may be used to make a continuous record which is convenient for later study of the depths traversed (Fig. 238). The speed of echo sounding contrasts sharply with the old, laborious method with a weight and line dropped to the bottom. By the latter method the "Challenger" expedition made only 505 deep-sea soundings during its cruise from 1873 to 1876, and the locations of many of these old soundings have been found to be in error by as much as 5 miles.

Sonic sounding, however, does not work well near underwater cliffs, and in very deep water the velocity of sound (and hence the computed depth) is affected by differences in temperature and salinity. Notwithstanding these limitations, sonic sounding coupled with good position fixes promises to make possible ultimately a fairly accurate survey of the topography of the ocean bottom. Charts based on sonic and other soundings already have been prepared for much of the shallow sea around the continental margins, for the Gulf of Alaska, and for certain other areas,

FIG. 239. Glauconitic shelly foraminiferal sand on shelf at 192 fathoms off northwest end of Santa Catalina Island. Note abundant sea urchins (*Allocentrotus fragilis* Jackson) and their trails. Bottom edge is about 3 feet wide. (*Allan Hancock Foundation.*)

but much of the sea is still to be surveyed in detail, although the records of numerous traverses now are available.

Further study of the ocean bottom has been carried out with the aid of seismic refraction surveys, gravity meters, current meters, undersea photography (Fig. 239), and sediment-sampling devices, including coring instruments capable of obtaining cores of bottom sediment as much as 70 feet long.

The Ocean Basin as a Whole. Although the depressed oceanic area within which the ocean lies is called a basin, it is noteworthy that, like the surface of the sea itself, the bottom also is the surface of an oblate spheroid and is convex outward. Water lies within it because the points on the bottom are nearer the center of the earth than are the adjacent points on the land.

The ocean basin proper occupies about two-thirds of the earth's surface, but there is an excess of water, and so the basin is somewhat more than full. Its waters, therefore, spread out over the low borders of the continental masses, covering them to depths which vary from near zero to hundreds of feet but which average about 70 fathoms at the outer edge. At places this inundated continental fringe, or border, is more than 100 miles wide, and the total shallow-water portion amounts to about 10 million square miles. The whole ocean, including the deep basins and the shallow areas, covers 72 per cent of the earth's surface.

Distribution of Depths. The ocean has an average depth of about 12,450 feet (2.36 miles), but half of it has a depth of 3 miles or more, and about 4 per cent of the sea bottom descends to the great depths, which range from nearly 4 to more than 6 miles. The greatest depths lie in the western part of the Pacific Ocean, where several soundings have exceeded 30,000 feet (Figs. 20, 440). The greatest known depth was found in the Marianas Trench, where sounding showed more than 6 miles (35,640 feet) of water. The relative percentages of the different depth zones is shown graphically in the upper part of Fig. 262.

Continental Shelves. The shallow portion of the ocean adjacent to the land is known as the Continental Shelf. It slopes seaward about 12 feet per mile from the shore to about the 70-fathom line, where the bottom begins to descend more abruptly into the abysmal depths. The Continental Shelf varies in depth at its outer edge and even more greatly in width along different parts of its extent. Its surface also is varied; in places it is fairly smooth, whereas elsewhere it is broken by channels, ridges, enclosed depressions, submarine benches, and other features. In places the bottom material is solid rock, and in others sand, mud, or even gravel. Along the coast of New England and adjacent parts of Canada the bottom in shallow water still retains many glacial features, among which are drumlins, some projecting above water as islands (Fig. 208).

Although the continental shelves are part of the continental masses and not merely an embankment of sediments, they are continually being built up and out by land-derived sediments discharged by streams or by the wind or by those worn from the coast line by the sea itself. Sinking of the coast line may cause the sea to spread farther over the low coastal areas of the continents, and conversely a rise of the coast line may convert a part of the Continental Shelf into a coastal plain on land. So the Continental Shelf is especially sensitive to changes brought about by gradation or by earth movements.

Continental Slopes. At about the 70-fathom line the slope of the sea bottom, as stated, generally becomes more abrupt. Even so its average slope is only about 320 feet per mile off mountainous coasts and about 185 feet per mile off wide coastal plains. Its lower edge grades imperceptibly into the main floor of the deep sea. The Continental Slope thus defined varies in width upward from a few tens of miles, but it is nearly everywhere a feature of the border of the ocean basin and is one of the most marked changes of level on the sea bottom. Its area is a little more than twice that of the continental shelves.

The continental slopes are thought to be the margins of masses of relatively light continental-type rocks which give way seaward to heavier rocks underlying the ocean basin proper.

Submarine Canyons. At many places the continental slopes and the outer parts of the continental shelves are characterized not by a smooth, even descent from shallow water to abysmal depths but instead by deep, V-shaped, steep-walled, valleylike depressions called *submarine canyons* (Fig. 240). Some of these canyons have tributaries with a dendritic pattern like that made by stream erosion on land. Some lie off the mouths of rivers, such as the Congo, Indus, Hudson, Delaware, or Columbia, whereas others have little or no counterpart on land nearby. Their lower reaches extend to depths of as much as 6,000 to 9,000 feet below sea level. Their walls in many places are rocky.

The origin of these submarine canyons is uncertain. They have been ascribed variously to erosion by turbidity currents of suspended mud, to mudflows and submarine slumping of recently deposited, highly water-soaked sediments on a steep outer depositional front, to erosion by rivers on land and subsequent submergence by downwarping and by eustatic change of sea level, to erosion by tidal currents or by currents formed by giant sea waves, to faulting, to sapping by submarine artesian springs, and to other causes.

Turbidity currents are known to occur in Swiss lakes and in Lake Mead and are thought to have broken telegraph cables at sea, but their adequacy to cut deeply into solid rock is questioned by many geologists. Certain of these gorges which have been under close observation, such

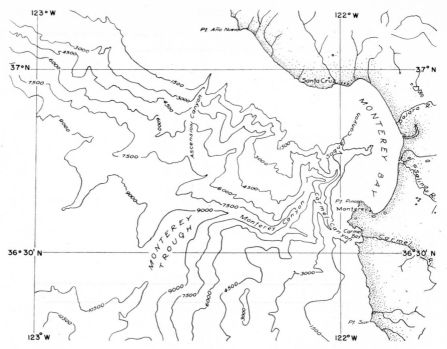

FIG. 240. Monterey submarine canyon off California coast. (*After Shepard and Emery.*)

as the Scripps Canyon off the southern California coast, occasionally show sudden deepening that seems to indicate submarine slumping, but perhaps only in canyons already formed otherwise. On the other hand the close resemblance of submarine canyons to valleys on land tends to favor subaerial erosion as part of their explanation. Erosion by streams during the Pleistocene lowering of sea level may have extended to present depths of a few hundred feet, but hardly thousands of feet. The opinions of geologists are divided over these causes or combinations of them.

Relief of the Deep-ocean Floor. The floor of the deep ocean is not a featureless plain; instead, it has a great variety of irregularities—ridges, both broad and narrow, submerged plateaus, oval basins, elliptical and elongate depressions, submerged mountains, flat-topped peaks, and the like (Fig. 19). The Mid-Atlantic Ridge, extending from Iceland nearly to Antarctica, culminates in the Azores and other small islands, but most of it lies under about 9,000 feet of water and about 6,000 feet above the deeper areas on either side. The Hawaiian Islands, of volcanic origin, stand on another great ridge more than 2,000 miles long in the mid-Pacific. The Gulf of Mexico (Fig. 241), Caribbean Basin, Mediterranean

Sea, Black Sea, Red Sea, and North Polar Sea, on the other hand, are examples of deep, almost landlocked basins on the sea floor.

Seamounts and Guyots. A notable feature of the ocean bottom is a series of submarine mountains, aptly named *seamounts*. Some of those in the Gulf of Alaska are shown in Fig. 242. A large number of flat-topped seamounts termed *guyots* (named for a geographer, A. H. Guyot, pronounced gē-yō) have been charted in the central and western Pacific between the Hawaiian Islands and the Marianas. Their summits, now submerged to a depth of about 4,000 to 6,000 feet, may represent volcanic peaks which were truncated by wave erosion in the geologic past or capped with broad coral reefs and subsequently were drowned by subsidence of the ocean bottom or by rise of sea level (Fig. 243).

Trenches and Deeps. Several deep elongate trenches occur on the floor of the Pacific (Fig. 440), especially at the foot of the continental

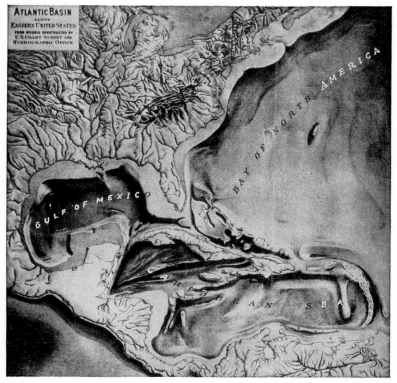

FIG. 241. Relief map of the Atlantic Basin, showing the Continental Shelf and depths of the Gulf of Mexico and the Caribbean Sea. (*From models of the U.S. Coast and Geodetic Survey and United States Navy Hydrographic Office.*)

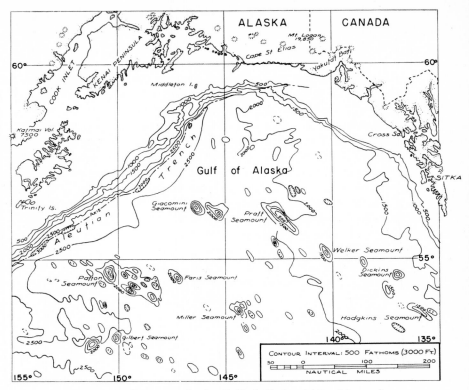

FIG. 242. Seamounts in the Gulf of Alaska. (*After Murray.*)

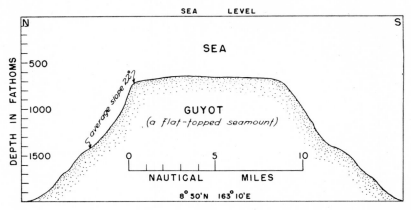

FIG. 243. North-south profile cross section of a guyot south of Eniwetok Atoll, at a depth of 620 fathoms (vertical scale greatly exaggerated). The flat top and beveled edges sloping 2 to 3 degrees are characteristic. (*After Hess.*)

slopes, as off the west coast of South America, or along the front of island arcs, as illustrated by the Aleutian Trench (Fig. 242). Other Pacific troughs are the Kurile Trench, Japan Trench, Mindanao, or Philippine, Trough, Marianas Trough, and Kermadec-Tonga Trough (northeast of New Zealand). The Java Trough in the Indian Ocean and the Puerto Rico Trough in the Atlantic Ocean are other examples.

The deepest-known soundings in the ocean have been found in these trenches—5,740 fathoms (34,440 feet) in the Philippine Deep by U.S.S. "Cape Johnson," 5,905 fathoms (35,430 feet) in the same trench by the German ship "Emden" in 1923, and 5,940 fathoms (35,640 feet) in the Marianas Trench by H.M.S. "Challenger" in 1951. In oceanographic usage a *deep* is any depression in the oceanic abyss that exceeds 6,000 meters (19,685 feet) in depth.

The origin of these deep-sea trenches is not known. While a few straight ones resemble fault troughs on land, most of them are thought to be formed by downwarping or infolding. That they lie along active and mobile belts of the earth's crust is indicated by the fact that numerous earthquakes originate beneath these troughs.

GENERAL FEATURES OF THE OCEAN

Temperature. The temperature of the ocean is dependent almost entirely on solar radiation. The slight heat received from the earth's interior and from the radioactivity of the sea bottom is negligible in comparison. The temperature varies greatly from equator to poles and from surface to the abysmal depths. At the equator the surface temperature averages about 80°F., whereas in the polar regions it is about 28°F., or near the freezing point of sea water. The water at the bottom of the deep sea varies from the 28°F. of the polar regions to about 35°F. in the lower latitudes. The temperature of sea water in general changes rapidly from the surface to the 600-fathom line, where it is about 39°F., then less

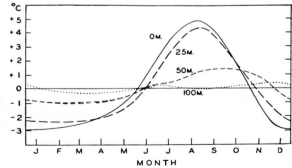

FIG. 244. Graphs showing the annual variation of temperature of different depths off the Bay of Biscay. (*m* = meters.) (*After Sverdrup.*)

rapidly to the 1,000-fathom line, and below that it is relatively constant at or slightly below 35°F. (Figs. 244, 245, 262). The great body of the ocean is therefore cold; and the heavy, cold waters that originate in polar and subpolar regions, creeping equatorward, dominate the circulation of the modern sea and the general climate of the bordering lands.

Salinity of Ocean Water. Sea water carries in solution great quantities of mineral matter, and thus it differs greatly from ordinary land waters. One thousand parts of sea water contains 34.4 parts by weight of mineral matter, or 3.44 per cent (Figs. 245, 246, 262). For 1 cubic mile of sea water this amounts to 151,025,000 tons. Murray estimates the total amount of sea water to be 323,722,150 cubic miles; and since each of these cubic miles contains 3.44 per cent of salts, the total in the sea is over 4,500,000 cubic miles of mineral matter with a specific gravity of 2.2. This is equivalent to about 20 per cent of the volume of all rock masses above sea level and if precipitated on the sea bottom would make a layer about 175 feet thick over the entire ocean floor.

Salts Present in the Ocean (After Dittmar)

	Per cent
Sodium chloride, NaCl	77.758
Magnesium chloride, MgCl$_2$	10.878
Magnesium sulfate, MgSO$_4$	4.737
Calcium sulfate, CaSO$_4$	3.600
Potassium sulfate, K$_2$SO$_4$	2.465
Calcium carbonate, CaCO$_3$	0.345
Magnesium bromide, MgBr$_2$	0.217
Total	100.000

About 32 elements have been found in sea water. In the order of amounts present in the sea some of these are chlorine, sodium, magnesium, oxygen, sulfur, calcium, and potassium. When the sea was originally formed, its waters may have contained some mineral matter in solution, and some may have been dissolved from the rocks of the area over which it spread, but probably the greater part of the solid matter has been contributed by streams, which obtained it by solution from the rocks of the land.

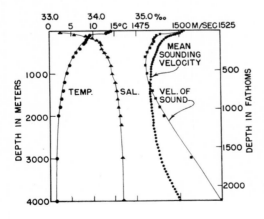

FIG. 245. Changes in temperature, salinity, and computed velocity of sound with increasing depth off southern California. The mean sounding velocity is the mean velocity from the surface to any specified depth. (*After Sverdrup, Johnson, and Fleming.*)

Approximate Composition of Sea Water [1]

Constituent	Concentration, milligram-atoms per kilogram of sea water	Constituent	Concentration, milligram-atoms per kilogram of sea water
Chlorine	535.0	Iron	0.0036
Sodium	454.0	Manganese	0.003
Sulfate	82.88	Phosphorus	0.002
Magnesium	52.29	Copper	0.002
Calcium	10.19	Barium	0.0015
Potassium	9.6	Iodine	0.00035
Carbon dioxide	2.25	Silver	0.0002
Bromine	0.81	Nitrite	0.0001
Strontium	0.15	Arsenic	0.00004
Aluminum	0.07	Zinc	0.00003
Fluorine	0.043	Hydrogen ion	0.00001
Silicon	0.04	Gold	0.00000025
Boron	0.037		
Lithium	0.015		
Nitrate	0.014		

[1] Compiled by T. G. Thompson and R. J. Robinson of the Oceanographic Laboratories, University of Washington. Taken from *Nat. Research Council Bull.* 85, p. 114, 1932.

The mineral content of river water, however, differs considerably from that of sea water, as shown by the accompanying table. River waters

Average Composition of Mineral Matter in River and Sea Waters (*After Clarke, U.S. Geol. Survey Bull. 770*)

Constituent	Percentage	
	River water	Sea water
Calcium	20.39	1.19
Silica, SiO_2	11.67	Tr.
Sodium	5.79	30.59
Magnesium	3.41	3.72
Ferric and aluminum oxides	2.75	0.00
Potassium	2.12	1.11
CO_3 radical	35.15	0.21
SO_4 radical	12.14	7.70
Cl radical	5.69	55.48
NO_3 radical	0.90	0.00
Total	100.01	100.00

contain relatively large quantities of calcium and of bicarbonate but only moderate quantities of sodium, magnesium, and chloride. The relative percentages of these substances are changed drastically and almost completely reversed in the sea.

Mineral matter is constantly being removed from the sea water by marine animals that use it in forming their shells, which are chiefly composed of calcium compounds. Still other parts of it have been removed by precipitation, either where the temperature has been rising and the carbon dioxide has been escaping or where excessive evaporation has been taking place. Evaporation also causes the formation of salt and gypsum deposits but probably is confined to shallow bays, coastal lagoons, and closed basins. Notwithstanding these removals, probably the mineral content of the sea is increasing. Common salt, NaCl, is accumulating in the ocean more rapidly than the calcium salts, because it is rejected by organisms in the making of their skeletons or shells and is removed by evaporation only where unusual conditions prevail.

Dissolved Gases. In addition to the solids, gases also are held in solution by sea water. Among the more abundant ones are nitrogen, oxygen, and carbon dioxide. As an evidence of the amounts of these gases, one may consider carbon dioxide. According to T. Schloesing, the sea contains 18 to 27 times as much as is contained in the atmosphere. Assuming that air contains 3 parts of CO_2 per 10,000, it is estimated that the atmos-

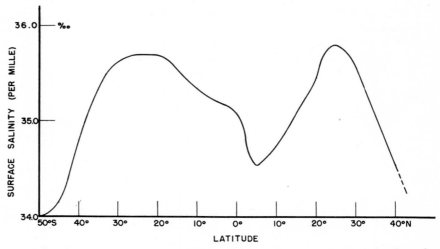

FIG. 246. Graph showing average surface salinity of sea water in relation to latitude. Salinity is highest near Lat. 25°N. and 20°S., because of high evaporation and low precipitation there. It decreases toward the equator and toward high latitudes. (*Data from Sverdrup, after Wüst.*)

phere contains 2,200,000,000,000 tons of carbon dioxide. The carbon in the carbon dioxide in the air is equivalent to about 1½ times that contained in the estimated coal reserves of the world. The sea contains 18 times as much as the atmosphere. The gases in sea water are chiefly gases that have been absorbed from the atmosphere, although some probably have been derived from submarine volcanoes or from the disintegration of organic matter or have been liberated from compounds through life processes. Oxygen is essential to nearly all life of the sea and to the process of oxidation in putrefaction, while carbon dioxide is the chief food material of the green and brown algae in the sea. Cold water is capable of holding a greater quantity of gas than warm water. The gases absorbed from the atmosphere in the cold regions are diffused through the deep waters of the ocean and released in the warm regions of the earth or wherever these cold waters come to the surface and are warmed.

Density and Pressure. The normal specific gravity of sea water is about 1.025, owing to its salinity. In cold polar seas it increases to about 1.028, whereas in warm tropical seas it decreases to about 1.022. Changes in the density with changes in temperature, pressure, dilution, and concentration are responsible for certain currents in the ocean (Fig. 262).

The pressure at any particular depth in the sea is equal to the weight of the water above it. One cubic foot of sea water from the surface weighs about 64 pounds. Accordingly at a depth of 1,000 feet the pressure is about 64,000 pounds per square foot; at a depth of 35,000 feet, it is more than 1,100 tons per square foot. Although water is nearly incompressible, the pressure at great depths is enough to cause a slight increase in its density. Otherwise sea level would be raised nearly 90 feet.

Life of the Sea. The marine environment has been divided into several life zones (Fig. 247), each with a certain type of fauna and flora.

1. *Littoral, or Tidal, Zone.* The littoral, or tidal, zone includes the area exposed between high and low tides. In this zone the ebbing tide lays bare the sea bottom, and the high tide covers it with water. It is always within the influence of strong wave action. For these reasons

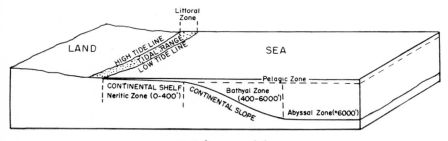

FIG. 247. Life zones of the sea.

living conditions are unusually difficult, and organisms must either be firmly attached to the bottom or burrow into the mud. Some find refuge in tidal pools, and others develop anatomical structures that enable them to survive periods of exposure to the air. Certain varieties of sea urchins occupy holes that they dig in solid rocks.

2. *Neritic Zone.* The neritic zone extends from the lowest tide line to the outer edge of the Continental Shelf. It is probable that a greater abundance of life per unit area flourishes in this environment than in any other place on earth. Since the water is less than about 400 feet deep, the area is lighted by the sun, food is abundant, and vast numbers of different species of organisms thrive on each other and on the materials in solution in the sea water. Conditions in the shallow inland seas of the geologic past were similar in many respects to those on the continental shelves of today.

3. *Bathyal Zone.* The bathyal zone is that part of the sea bottom between the depths of 70 to 1,000 fathoms. The higher parts of the area receive a little light, but even there plant life is rare. The floor of the sea in the bathyal zone has a prolific animal population despite the fact that plant life is limited. Since the rate of deposition of sediments is slow, bottom-living scavengers destroy much of the organic matter. The calcareous sediments consist largely of planktonic shells, and the siliceous deposits are mainly diatoms and spicules of sponges.

4. *Pelagic Zone.* The pelagic zone includes the waters of the great, expansive sea that lies beyond the littoral zone. The life of this zone includes the floating planktonic forms as well as the free-swimming forms in the open ocean. Algae and diatoms are the most common plants, and many varieties of animals inhabit this realm. Their resistant, inorganic hard parts contribute abundantly to the formation of sedimentary rocks.

5. *Abyssal Zone.* The abyssal zone includes that portion of the sea below a depth of 1,000 fathoms. This zone receives no sunlight, its temperature is near freezing at all times, and the pressure is greater than 1 ton per square inch. Since plants that require sunlight cannot live in this environment, the animals that depend on plant food must live on that which settles from the sunlit waters near the surface. The shells and bones of animals that live on abyssal bottoms indicate that only highly specialized creatures are able to live in these depths.

It is usually supposed that the first life on the earth appeared in the sea or in the brackish waters of the coastal swamp. With its introduction came biochemical activity. Many of the organisms which live in the sea have hard parts made up of calcium carbonate or of silica, and these are the materials which form the limestones and siliceous deposits. It is largely through living organisms and their ability to precipitate calcium carbonate and amorphous silica that the cementing materials for other sediments are obtained. The rock-building life of the sea therefore is a geologic factor of great importance.

The common lime- and silica-secreting forms of life belong chiefly to the lower plants, such as the bacteria, the diatoms, and the algae, and to the invertebrates among the animals (Fig. 248). It seldom happens that bacterial remains are long preserved in recognizable condition in the deposits which they are forming. Ancient limestones now wholly devoid of fossils may owe their origin to these organisms. Few of the marine plants, even of the algae, can be identified among the fossils so commonly occurring, and yet in the modern seas the calcareous algae can be found in the active process of rock building, often even exceeding the animal life of the region in the rapidity of their work. Thus on the typical coral island of Funafuti in the South Pacific two kinds of algae were found to have formed more of the rock than all the corals combined.

The diatoms have siliceous tests, or capsulelike shells. These accumulate in abundance under favorable conditions and give rise to thick deposits of "diatomaceous earth," or their siliceous material may be carried off in solution and contribute to the formation of flint or chert beds in adjacent limestones. The Radiolaria and certain of the sponges have siliceous skeletons which contribute to the formation of the same flints and cherts.

The lime-secreting animal life of the sea includes almost every group from the Foraminifera to the highest division of the invertebrates. Their remains are found in abundance in the deposits they form. The most prolific limestone builders occur among the Foraminifera, the Hydrozoa, the Anthozoa, the Crinoidea, the Echinoidea, the Bryozoa, the Brachiopoda, and the Mollusca in general. Other animal groups also make contributions but are seldom of such importance as those just mentioned. Certain areas of the shallow sea bottom, especially those comparatively free from land detritus, are crowded with these groups, and their remains accumulate in abundance to form limestone (Fig. 249).

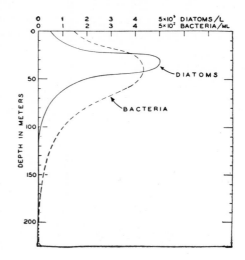

FIG. 248. Graphs showing the vertical distribution of bacteria and diatoms in the open sea. (*After Sverdrup.*)

FIG. 249. Foraminifera in Cretaceous marl from New Jersey. (Greatly magnified.)

CORAL REEFS

Certain calcareous marine algae and many of the calcareous or lime-secreting marine animals, including the corals, live in colonies and are reef builders. Since the coral is a conspicuous form in the reef and is readily recognized, these structures are commonly called *coral reefs*, even though their major portions may be built by algae, Hydrozoa, Bryozoa, or other forms of marine life. A coral reef is a belt along which the algae, corals, and associated marine animals live, their skeletons building up a platform on which these forms continue to grow.

Reefs of this sort have been an important factor in the formation of limestone since very ancient (Ordovician) time, and they still are of common occurrence in the warm, shallow waters of the tropical and subtropical oceans. The total area covered by growing coral reefs is estimated to be 500,000 square miles, and the detritus derived from them by wave action may cover more than twice that area.

Modern reef-building corals are confined to clear sea water with a temperature that does not fall below 68°F. and a depth that varies from a little below mean sea level to about 150 feet. They are thus a shore phase of islands or of low shelving coasts of continents. The most vigorous growth of the reef is toward the open sea, where the waves bring food, oxygen, and the necessary calcium for their skeletons. Opposite the mouths of rivers, where quantities of fresh water and land detritus are discharged, there is a break in the coral growth; tidal movements may

FIG. 250. Aerial photograph of a small atoll in the South Pacific. The coral rim encloses the lagoon that is connected with the sea through a narrow passage seen at the left. There is a heavy growth of trees above the level of high tide. (*Photograph by United States Navy Hydrographic Office.*)

preserve openings through the reef so that they form a disconnected belt along the coast.

Massive reefs built along the shore are termed *fringing reefs*. Those which are separated from the shore by a channel or a lagoon are called *barrier reefs*. Those which surround lagoons and are more or less circular in shape are called *atolls* (Fig. 250).

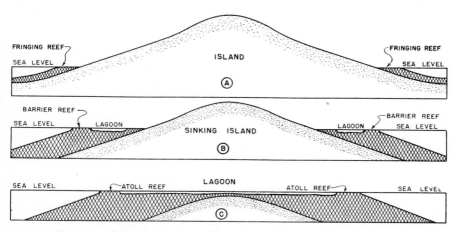

FIG. 251. Diagrams showing how an atoll may be developed. A, island with a fringing coral reef. B, same after subsidence; the fringing reef has grown upward and become a barrier reef. C, same after further submergence of the original island; the barrier reef has become an atoll.

Darwin suggested that an atoll is formed at a certain stage in the history of a fringing reef surrounding an island on a sinking sea bottom (Fig. 251). The fringing reef, which grows chiefly to seaward, is changed to a barrier reef separated from land by a lagoon as the island sinks; and then as the island sinks farther and disappears below sea level, the corals continue to build up the reef and it becomes an atoll. The waves break off fragments of the reef and pile them up above sea level on the lagoonward side. In time, land is thus formed, vegetation gets started, and a ringlike coral island results.

The most extensive coral reef of the present time is the Great Barrier Reef along the northeast coast of Australia. It is more than 1,000 miles long and varies from 10 to 90 miles in width. Behind this barrier is a channel 20 to 50 miles wide and 60 to 240 feet deep, which is thus protected and is used for coastwise shipping, while the adjacent coast also is freed from the violence of the waves.

SUGGESTIONS FOR FURTHER READING

Daly, R. A.: The Floor of the Ocean, The University of North Carolina Press, 1942.

Gardiner, J. S.: Coral Reefs and Atolls, The Macmillan Company, 1931.

Kuenen, Ph. H.: Marine Geology, John Wiley & Sons, Inc., 1950.

Ommanney, F. D.: The Ocean, Oxford University Press, 1949.

Shepard, F. P.: Submarine Geology, Harper & Brothers, 1948.

Sverdrup, H. U., M. W. Johnson, and R. H. Fleming: The Oceans, Their Physics, Chemistry, and General Biology, Prentice-Hall, Inc., 1942.

CHAPTER 14

The Ocean: B. Sea Movements and Their Effects

Types of Movement. Water is constantly in motion in the "restless" sea. Disturbances in any part of the ocean are transmitted to distances of thousands of miles, and hence the ceaseless motion.

These movements include waves, undertow, rip currents, long-shore currents, tides, surface ocean currents, subsurface oceanic creep and other density movements, piling up by storms, the spreading of river waters and heavy rains, and giant sea waves (tsunamis) caused by earthquakes.

One of the common causes of movement is the drag or friction of the wind as it passes over the surface. Such movements are subject to marked changes with the weather, and they vary according to the strength and direction of the wind. During heavy storms these movements are awe-inspiring, and their destructive power is very great. The pressure exerted by such waves may exceed 1 ton per square foot, and the height to which they may cause damage is illustrated by the lighthouse at Dunnet Head on the north coast of Scotland, where windows 300 feet above sea level have been broken by stones hurled up by the waves.

Very severe storms may cause the sea to rise and to move forward. Thus on Oct. 5, 1864, a violent storm changed the level of the sea at Calcutta about 24 feet and inundated a large area. On Sept. 8, 1900, a similar rise of the sea occurred during the Galveston storm; another hit Puerto Rico on Sept. 13, 1928. Such storms are of the typhoon or hurricane type and may cause marked destruction along coasts. In 1935 a hurricane struck the Keys off the south coast of Florida. The ocean swept through between islands where railroad embankments had been built, and the twisted rails with their ties attached were left 100 yards from their former locations. Much of the archway of the interisland viaduct was ruined, and both railroad and highway were washed out for miles. Waves rolled over part of the land and added to the destruction. Buildings and steel towers fell before their attack, and in a well-populated section, where the storm was most severe, a lone house remained after it had subsided.

Evaporation removes great quantities of water, increasing the salinity of the surface waters and therefore the density of the sea. This effect is most pronounced at the equator. Along the coast of India it has been found that evaporation from the free surface of the sea amounts to about 23 feet per year. The cold, dense waters from the polar regions, which creep equatorward and now fill the deep sea, rise in the warm latitudes and take the place of the vast quantities removed by evaporation or by surface currents. Changes in density of sea water, whether produced by evaporation, by the removal of calcium carbonate from sea water by lime-secreting life, or by other causes, will produce motion, and all such changes contribute to the circulation of sea water.

Rivers entering the ocean discharge great quantities of water at the coast line, where it tends to pile up. This comparatively warm, fresh water is lighter than the salt water of the sea, and so it floats for a time as it spreads out and mingles with the salt water of the sea. The Mississippi and other rivers entering the Gulf of Mexico contribute largely to the Gulf Stream as it passes out into the Atlantic Ocean. Excessive rainfall on any part of the sea also causes the water temporarily to pile up, and during its distribution motion is inevitable.

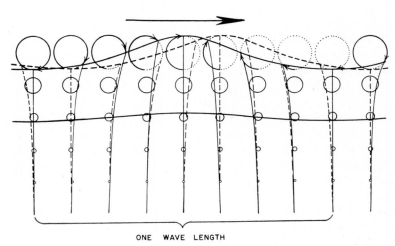

ONE   WAVE   LENGTH

FIG. 252. Sketch of a wave to show the relative movements of the water particles at different parts of the wave form and at different depths. The orbits are drawn to scale. The dotted lines show the progression of the wave a short time later. (*After Kuenen.*)

Earthquakes may cause waves of destructive violence. Such waves have been known to sweep inland 7 or 8 miles. Waves of this sort are *tsunamis*, but they frequently are called tidal waves, although they have no connection with true tides. Tides, of course, are caused by the attraction of the sun and moon.

Waves in Deep Water. The winds and other agents produce water waves. Wave motion is oscillatory, that is, each particle of water describes a nearly circular orbit, returning approximately to the point of origin of the motion (Fig. 252). Actually a small amount of water is driven forward or blown over the crest of the wave. The diameter of the orbit at the surface of the water is equal to the height of the wave, or the vertical distance between crest and trough.

The form of the wave approximates a trochoid, the line described by a dot on the spoke of a wheel rolled along on the undersurface of a table. The shape of a trochoid can vary from nearly a straight line (corresponding to a dot on the axis of the wheel) to nearly a cycloid (as by a dot on the rim), but most water waves are many times longer than high and have troughs wider and flatter than the crests. The length of the wave is the distance from crest to crest.

Most waves are $\frac{1}{20}$ to $\frac{1}{30}$ times as high as they are long, and exceptional ones $\frac{1}{12}$ to $\frac{1}{15}$ times. The ratio of the length to the height determines the amount of motion that is transmitted downward. For example, in a wave 100 feet long and 5 feet high, with a period of 4.4 seconds, the orbital diameter at the surface is 60 inches, whereas at a depth of 50 feet it is only about 2.5 inches, and at a depth of 100 feet it is scarcely $\frac{1}{8}$ inch. In a storm wave 500 feet long and 20 feet high, with a period of 10 seconds, the amplitude of the movement at a depth of 500 feet (equal to the wave length) is still about $\frac{1}{2}$ inch. It has been found that the motion decreases rapidly with depth, about $\frac{1}{2}$ for each $\frac{1}{9}$ wave length beneath the surface. Hence very little movement (only $\frac{1}{23}$ that at the surface) takes place at a depth of $\frac{1}{2}$ wave length. Under ordinary seas it is scarcely perceptible below 20 to 30 feet, although long, high storm waves reach to depths of 300 to 500 feet or more with sufficient vigor to move fine sand. Thus most waves are relatively superficial. The level at which wave motion becomes negligible changes from day to day and from season to season in keeping with the state of the sea.

The period of the waves usually is several seconds and only rarely longer than 10 or 12 seconds, although periods of 20 seconds or more have been observed.[1]

---

[1] In deep water the relations between velocity and wave length are expressed by the formula V = length/time (in seconds) = $\sqrt{gL/2\pi}$ = $gT/2\pi$. In the metric system, V = 1.56 (meters) $\times T$ (in seconds), L = 1.56 (meters) $\times T^2$; and V^2 = $1.56L$. The ratio of length to height is not fixed but varies.

FIG. 253. The upper margin of a wave leaving its mark on the sand beach and the water returning as backwash at Balboa, California.

A train of waves is not perfectly rhythmic but instead is somewhat irregular. Great storms at sea, especially, produce irregular or choppy patterns of simultaneous waves of different dimensions and orientations; so the surface of the sea is more like crumpled crepe paper than corrugated iron. As storm waves travel out from under the region of disturbed conditions into an area of relative calm, they preserve or increase their lengths and velocities but diminish in height as they pass into the common "ground swells" of the sea.

Wave heights and the velocities of the swell have been found to be governed by the velocity of the wind, the duration of the wind, the available fetch, and the time and distance of travel of both during growth in the generating area and during their decline in the area of calm. With the aid of weather maps of oceanic areas and with knowledge of the laws of waves and of swell it is possible to predict the arrival time and the height of the swell, as was demonstrated during World War II.

Breakers. As waves approach a shelving coast line, they begin to drag bottom when the depth of the water is about half the wave length. Hence the lower part of the wave is retarded by interference from the sea bottom,[1] while the surface portion because of its inertia tends to maintain the wave motion. The wave length and velocity are reduced, and so, to compensate, the crest of the wave rapidly becomes higher and the trough deeper, until finally the crest moves ahead of its supporting column of water, curls over, and "breaks" or "plunges" down over the side of the wave into the trough in a turbulent, foaming mass called "surf." The forward motion of the water then carries it bodily onshore as "swash" until its energy [2] is released in turbulence, friction, and work. The excess

---

[1] In shallow water the velocity is a function of depth, as $V = \sqrt{gd}$, where g is the acceleration of gravity and d is depth.

[2] The quantity of energy available is directly proportional to the square of the wave height times the wave length, or $E \propto H^2L$.

of water sloshed forward runs down the face of the beach as "backwash," only to be caught in the next wave and hurled toward shore again (Fig. 253).

As waves of the same height break at about the same distance from shore, a *line of breakers,* or *plunge line,* is formed but the position of the line of breakers shifts back and forth with changes in the height and wave length of the waves. As an approximation, the plunge line appears where the depth of the water is about equal to the height of the wave in deep water offshore. This depth usually is less than 10 feet and rarely exceeds 50 or 60 feet.

The terminology of the environs of the shore is shown in Fig. 254.

Interference of Waves. Automatically recording wave gauges, as at La Jolla, California, show that many waves are compound, that is, several waves of different lengths and heights are superimposed upon one another. When their crests coincide, they reinforce each other and rise to exceptional height. When the crest of one meets the trough of another, the waves are out of phase and nullify each other. Interference generally is readily visible to the eye when two sets of waves of comparable size approach the shore from somewhat different directions. Such interference is the basis no doubt for the popular notion that every seventh wave (or some other number) is unusually large.

Refraction of Waves. When a wave approaches a uniformly shelving shore obliquely, one end of the wave begins to drag bottom in shallow water while the remainder of it goes forward unhindered. The wave, therefore, tends to become bent, or refracted, in such a way as to strike the shore nearly head on, regardless of the original direction of approach.

A similar refraction of a series of waves, setting up crossing wave-train patterns, takes place over any shoal, against a rocky island or an artificial obstruction, from submarine canyons, or against a peninsula or headland protruding seaward. This refraction tends to concentrate the

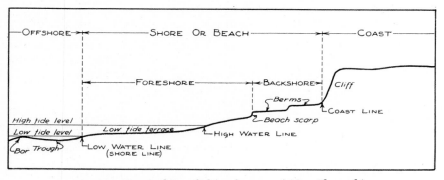

FIG. 254. Terminology of shore features. (*After Shepard.*)

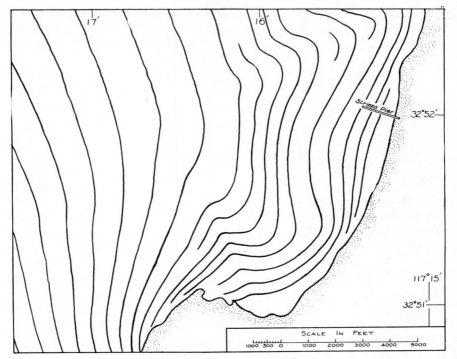

FIG. 255. Wave refraction near La Jolla, California. (*After Munk and Traylor.*) A southwest swell in the open sea at the upper left with a period of 16 seconds is turned, locally more than 90 degrees, to strike the shore nearly head on. The two bulges are less refracted, as they forge ahead over deeper water in the branching head of a submarine canyon.

energy of wave attack by convergence against the three sides of the headland and to disperse the wave energy in a bay (Fig. 255). On the other hand deep water near shore may transmit the waves with undiminished energy against the adjacent shore.

Refraction patterns appear on many photographs of irregular, rocky shore lines (Fig. 256).

Undertow. The water from the backwash of waves on the beach commonly has been thought to return to sea beneath the breakers as a sheetlike current along the bottom. This "undertow" has even been considered a hazard to swimming in the surf. Measurements with a current meter, however, though difficult at best, fail to prove the existence of any undertow. Inside the line of breakers turbulent mixing is the rule. As the only water that needs to be returned beyond the breakers is that blown along by the wind on the surface of the waves, the quantity of water involved ordinarily is small and its speed very low. Nevertheless, if there is any

322

FIG. 256. Curved wave fronts resulting from refraction, Curry County, Oregon. A small bay at the left is cut off by a bay bar (behind tree), and sand has accumulated in the lee of the small stacks. (*Oregon State Highway Commission.*)

undertow, its pulsating movements may help to shift mud and fine sand down slope seaward. The matter is a moot question.

Rip Currents. Rip currents [1] are strong currents of surface waters that flow seaward through the breakers wherever large breakers are found.

[1] F. P. Shepard, K. O. Emery, and E. C. LaFond, Rip Currents; a Process of Geological Importance, *Jour. Geology*, vol. 49, pp. 337–369, 1941.

"Feeder currents" come together in the surf, turn seaward as a rip in a narrow "neck" through the breakers, and then spread out in a "head" with swirling eddies (Fig. 257). These currents attain speeds of as much as 2 miles an hour; it is likely that they have been mistaken for undertow by swimmers. They make channels in sandy bottoms and should be important factors in moving large quantities of sediment away from the beach.

Longshore Currents. When waves strike the shore line obliquely, a longshore current is generated parallel to the coast line. This current is capable of transporting sediment along the foreshore as *shore drift*. The movement in shallow water probably is complex dynamically. Tests with floats indicate velocities inside the breaker zone as high as 3 knots. Deep water at the mouth of a bay may tend to interrupt the transport until a bar has been built across it, and a point of land may divert the current seaward so as to shift the deposit of sediment out to sea, although in places sand is carried round rocky headlands. Various modifications result from other local conditions.

Oblique waves, somewhat refracted, also shift gravel and sand along the beach. The combined effect of the oblique swash of the waves and of the gravity return of the water almost directly down slope causes particles

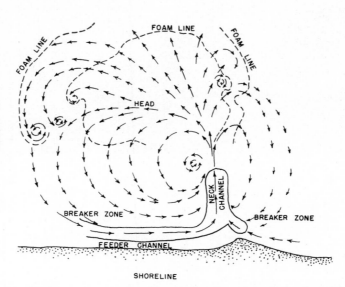

FIG. 257. Sketch of a rip current, showing a feeder channel, neck, head, and foam lines in relation to the breaker zone and shore line. The lengths of the arrows indicate relative velocities. (*After Shepard.*)

of rock to oscillate up and down the beach in saw-tooth paths (Fig. 258). Naturally the trajectories, modified in form by gravity, are more pronounced for sand than for pebbles. These alternations shift the materials along the beach; hence the term *beach drift*. This movement may carry pebbles many miles from their sources, sometimes at very rapid rates as shown by tests with marked stones or bricks, and may carry sand tens of miles or more. The quartz sand of the beaches of the east coast of Florida has been shifted southward from Georgia and the Carolinas.

Tides. The periodic rise and fall of the sea, rising twice in 24 hours and 52 minutes, is the *tide* (Fig. 259). It is produced by the differential attraction of the sun and moon on the earth. This attraction is effective on both land and sea, but the sea is more mobile and therefore yields more readily to the pull thus set up.

The sun, moon, and earth lie in nearly the same plane, but they continually shift their positions with reference to each other. The total gravitative effect of the sun and moon on the earth is constantly acting, but the pull is in different directions as their positions change; hence the effect on the earth varies from time to time.

Because of its nearness the moon produces the most marked results. The sun's tide acts more as a modifier of the moon's tide, and when these two bodies are in the same straight line, the effects are added and the result is an unusually high tide. Considering only the more effective force, the surface of the sea is pulled out, or caused to bulge, on the side nearest

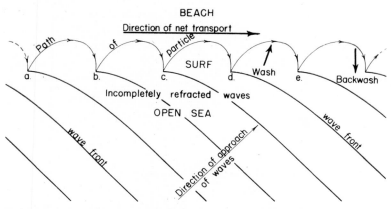

FIG. 258. Beach drift caused by oblique approach of waves. The inclined uprush of each wave carries particles of sediment diagonally up the beach, and the backwash returns them nearly directly downslope. In the meantime the next succeeding wave will have moved forward. So the particles are caught by the next swash and hurled up beach again. The net movement is from *a* to *b*, *b* to *c*, and so on, but many trips from many waves are required to move more than a wave length, instead of the single trips shown.

the moon, while on the opposite side of the earth a similar, but slightly smaller, bulge is produced.

Figure 259 illustrates the generation of tides. The distance from the earth to the moon is approximately fifty-nine times the radius of the earth ($AM = 59r$); the distance from the center of the earth to the moon is 60 earth radii ($EM = 60r$); and the distance from the moon to the far side of the earth is 61 radii ($BM = 61r$). Since the attraction of mass for mass varies inversely as the square of the distance, it follows that the attraction at A, E, and B may be represented as $(\frac{1}{59})^2$, $(\frac{1}{60})^2$, and $(\frac{1}{61})^2$, respectively. Thus the water at A is attracted toward the moon with a greater force than that of the earth, which is centered at E. However, the earth is attracted toward the moon more than the water at B. Because of these differences in attraction the water at A, being nearest the attracting mass of the moon, is pulled farther than E, and thus A tends to be pulled away from E. At B, which is at the greatest distance from the moon, the attraction is less than at either A or E. Therefore, the water at the far side of the earth is left behind to almost the same extent as that on the near side is pulled forward. In the area between C and D the water is drawn away, and low tide results. Since the earth rotates once in 24 hours, the region along any meridian will experience a high tide every 12 hours and 26 minutes.

In the open ocean the tidal variation of sea level probably does not exceed 2½ or 3 feet, but along the continental borders the differences between high and low tide are much greater, whereas in narrow bays with broad seaward openings, partly as a result of resonance, as in the Bay of Fundy, it may exceed 20 or even 50 feet. The tide usually comes in as a series of waves, each reaching higher and higher until the crest of the rise is attained, after which recession sets in, and this continues until low tide. At certain places, however, the rise of the tide is sudden, coming in

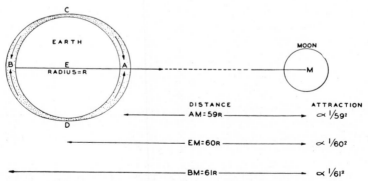

FIG. 259. Diagram illustrating the origin of tides. (*After Holmes.*)

as a wall-like wave of water, known as a *bore,* which may be 25 feet high. The bore is especially well-developed on the coasts of China and India. Wherever the tide runs through restricted passages, such as narrow straits or bays or between islands, currents are developed which scour the bottom and shift about the loose materials. The tide is not a very important agent of erosion. There are broad belts of the surface, adjacent to the

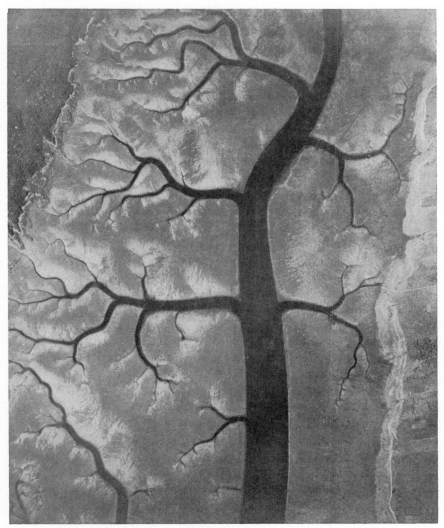

FIG. 260. Drainage pattern in the tidal mud flats at low tide, near Yarmouth, Nova Scotia. Scale about 1,200 feet to 1 inch. (*Vertical photograph by Royal Canadian Air Force.*)

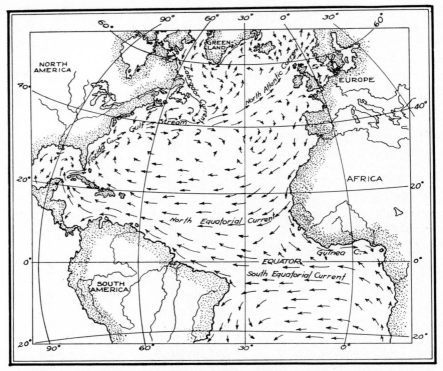

FIG. 261. Surface ocean currents in the Atlantic. The westward equatorial currents, the Gulf Stream, and the large gyral in the North Atlantic are outstanding features. (*After Schott.*)

sea, however, that are usually referred to as tidal flats. These are covered by water part of the time and during the remainder of the day or night are exposed to the ordinary weathering processes (Fig. 260).

Ocean Currents. In regions where the winds have more or less constant direction, such as in the trade-wind belts, the surface waters are dragged along in the same direction with a velocity less than that of the wind itself (Fig. 261). Since these winds blow from the northeast north of the equator and from the southeast south of the equator, the water is being urged toward the equator from both sides and there drifts westward as one current which would encircle the earth if the ocean covered the entire earth. This *equatorial drift,* contributed to and modified by numerous other factors, is the origin of the currents in equatorial oceans. Thus in the North Atlantic the westward-drifting equatorial waters strike the eastward-projecting portion of Brazil, and part is deflected up along the north coast of South America, striking the eastern terminus of the Greater and Lesser Antilles, where it is again divided, part of it crossing the Caribbean

Sea and entering the Gulf of Mexico. Augmented by the great quantity of water being poured into the Gulf by rain and rivers, it emerges through the Straits of Florida as the Gulf Stream. Similar currents are formed in the South Atlantic; and in the Pacific Ocean, where the equatorial drift is more pronounced.

These ocean currents are not due to wind alone. The surface heating of the equatorial waters and their consequent expansion, together with their cooling in the polar regions, are in themselves sufficient to produce circulation. Far out at sea the Gulf Stream can be recognized by its color, due in part to the excess of fresh water which has poured into it. The shape of the Continental Shelf, the configuration of the coast line, and the rotation of the earth modify these currents and control their movements to some extent; but as long as the generating forces act, they keep moving. The chief effects of such currents are climatic, as they carry little sediment.

Subsurface Ocean Currents. Cold polar surface water sinks in the North Atlantic off the coast of Greenland and creeps southward as a "depth current" as far as Lat. 60°S. (Fig. 262). Beyond that position cold antarctic winter water dives below it as a "bottom current." Another current, the "intermediate current," flows northward from Lat. 50 to 60°S.

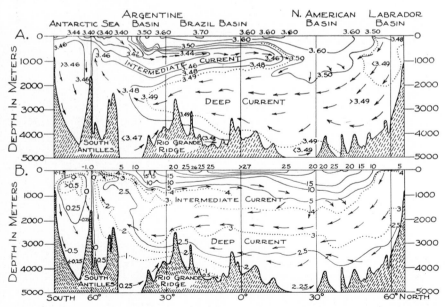

FIG. 262. North-south profile of subsurface density currents in the Atlantic Ocean, based on differences in salinity (A) and differences in temperature (B). (*After Wüst via Schott.*)

to about Lat. 30°N. at a depth of about 1,000 meters. Other near-surface currents sink at about Lat. 30°N. and 30°S. and flow at a depth of about 600 meters toward the equator, where they well up and begin to return along the surface. Thus a complicated circulatory system prevails in the Atlantic, delicately balanced in dynamic equilibrium between heating, cooling, dilution by fresh water, and concentration by evaporation, and modified by the shape of the basin, configuration of the bottom, the earth's rotation, and perhaps other factors.

Cold antarctic water also flows northward into the Indian and Pacific Oceans, which likewise have complicated circulatory currents below the surface.

Radiocarbon measurements by J. L. Kulp indicate that this deep oceanic circulation requires thousands of years to complete the cycle.

In partially enclosed basins special considerations apply. In the Mediterranean Sea, for example, evaporation greatly exceeds the precipitation and runoff. Hence a strong current of 4 kilometers per hour flows from the Atlantic Ocean through the Strait of Gibraltar to make up the difference. By long-continued evaporation all the water in the Mediterranean has become extra saline (3.8 per cent), so that its increased density causes a current to flow out into the Atlantic over a "sill" or submerged ridge separating two basins in the Strait of Gibraltar beneath the inflowing current. There it flows along the bottom until its density from its high salinity (offset somewhat by its high temperature) is balanced by that of the deep Atlantic water. Then it fans out as a great subsurface tongue of warm extrasaline water that spreads as far west as the Azores and from the equator to Ireland before it loses its identity by mixing.

If the sill in such a basin were very shallow, so that only an incoming current could flow, the continued concentration of salts within the basin in a dry climate ultimately would produce such a high salinity that deposition of some of the salts would result. Some of the deposits of gypsum and rock salt of the geologic past may have been formed under these conditions.

In a partially enclosed basin under a humid climate, on the other hand, the excess of water, being lighter, flows out to sea along the surface. If the sill is shallow, as in many Norwegian fiords, the subsurface water in the basin becomes stagnant, its oxygen is used up, most organisms die, and hydrogen sulfide forms. The lack of ventilation by subsurface currents affects the life and sediments in such a basin.

WORK OF WAVES AND SHORE CURRENTS

Methods of Wave Erosion. Movements in sea water produce mechanical effects of vast importance owing to the mass of the moving water and its velocity. Thus the waves beating upon a coast gradually wear it away. In loose materials the *impact* of the waves alone is sufficient. In solid rocks the water takes advantage of joints, pries blocks loose by hydraulic pressure, and eventually *quarries* away block by block great masses of rock. Erosion by impact and by quarrying is covered by the term *hydraulicking.*

Waves also erode by *abrasion,* as the rock fragments quarried out by the waves or rolled down into the water are hurled back by the waves against the shore. Rock fragments are thus effective tools in cutting the shore line or undercutting promontories. The overhanging rock then topples into the sea, and more tools are supplied to continue the attack. The tools themselves, of course, are worn by *corrasion* and undergo reduction in size, or *attrition,* as they are carried back and forth as on a washboard. Shells and rocky materials are reduced by grinding between coarser pieces. They are worn finer and finer as they are dragged or rolled to and fro on the beach by the moving water.

The compression and decompression of air, despite the cushioning effect, enable the waves to reach and to quarry beyond the water itself. Currents *scour* the bottom in shallow water and thereby assist in shore erosion. Sea water also *dissolves* mineral matter from the rocks, especially from coral or other limestones.

Results of Wave Erosion. The cliff developed by undercutting of waves is known as a *sea cliff* (Fig. 263). Such cliffs, on the south shore

FIG. 263. Sea cliff and caves at La Jolla, California. (*Photograph by Arnold, U.S. Geological Survey.*)

FIG. 264. The wave-notched base of a sea cliff near Nanaimo, British Columbia. (*Courtesy of Canada Department of Interior.*)

FIG. 265. (Below) Elevated sea terrace, sea cliff, and wave-cut terrace exposed at low tide, near Devils Punch Bowl State Park, Oregon. Both terraces bevel the tilted layers of sandstone and mudstone. (*Oregon State Highway Commission.*)

of Nantucket Island, have been cut back by the waves as much as 6 feet per year. Many cliffs show a horizontal *notch,* or *nip,* at the base, as a result of the chopping or sawing action of the waves (Fig. 264).

On rocky coasts the continued advance of the sea by erosion and retreat of the sea cliff produces a beveled rock bench, the *wave-cut terrace, strand flat,* or *wave-cut platform,* which is partly exposed at low tide (Fig. 265). A multitude of *flutings, grooves, furrows,* and *scour pits* and other small-scale features on its surface testify to abrasion of its surface in the turbulent surf. Unusually resistant materials may be left standing as *rock reefs.* In places the returning water from the spray and splash of storm waves rotates the water and sediments caught in small rock basins, grinding the holes deeper and producing the familiar *tidal pools* ("crabholes"). Jug-shaped holes of this origin are known on the north shore of Lake Superior, but they are more common on seacoasts.

In rocks which are highly jointed or broken by faults wave erosion may quarry out *sea caves.* If erosion breaks through the roof or top of the cave, it forms a *spouting horn,* or *blowhole* (called *gloup* in England). Because most rocks are close-jointed, at least locally, caves may be expected along any rocky shore line subjected to vigorous attack by waves,

FIG. 266. A wave-eroded natural bridge, Otter Crest, Oregon. A former arch (Elephant Rock) at upper left has lost its "head" and "trunk."

FIG. 267. Group of sea stacks, Bandon, Oregon. (*Oregon State Highway Commission.*)

FIG. 268. Joint chasm being eroded along a fracture in basaltic lava. Note the "tools" in the lower right.

as along the New England and Pacific coasts. Occasionally caves formed on opposite sides of a narrow promontory may break through to form a pierced rock, or natural bridge (Fig. 266). When the bridge, or arch, falls, the seaward mass becomes an island, or *sea stack* (also called *chimney rock,* or *skerry*). Most stacks, however, develop by the isolation of resistant masses of rock by the removal of the less resistant rocks surrounding them (Fig. 267) without any intermediate natural bridges. Indentations without roofs quarried out by the waves are *joint chasms* (Fig. 268).

Waves easily discover differences in the resistance of rocks on shore, and so they erode differentially. Rocks which are weak because of joints or because of a lack of induration are eroded back to form *coves,* while more resistant rocks stand out to form *headlands.* In detail a shore line of coves and headlands becomes minutely irregular, or *crenulate.* In unconsolidated rocks, however, such as gravel, sand, clay, or glacial till, a cliffed shore line may remain straight.

When the maximum irregularity has been developed and erosion is balanced on coves and headlands alike by differences in exposure, the shore line is said to be *mature.* Thereafter the shore line advances upon the land without significant change in form.

Shore Transportation. It is also the job of waves and longshore currents to remove the products of erosion. During this removal the materials are subjected (1) to further wear in transit (with resulting *attrition* and *rounding*) (Fig. 269) and (2) to *sorting* as to size, shape, and specific gravity in the perpetual milling action of the sea. The fine particles stay in suspension and eventually settle offshore.

Shore Deposition. Storm waves commonly toss coarse materials far up on shore out of reach of the ordinary waves, and of course the slackening of any of the waves or longshore currents also leads to deposition.

FIG. 269. Three building bricks in successive stages of rounding by wave erosion. (*From F. H. Lahee, Field Geology, 5th ed., p. 44, Fig. 19, 1952.*)

FIG. 270. Bayhead beach, Emerald Bay, Laguna Beach, California. The highway is on a sea terrace. (*Spence Air Photos.*)

Materials carried by traction on the bottom are deposited as a result of a reduction in velocity of a current across deep water where a part of its energy is used to move a thicker, slower-flowing sheet of water.

Beach Deposits. The oversize, the overload, or the rejects from the surf "mill" accumulate along the shore as a beach embankment, or beach ridge. The term beach is used broadly for the entire area along the sea extending from the line reached by high tide and the highest storm waves to the low tidemark, but along a rocky cliffed coast much of the beach as thus defined may be nearly barren of deposits, whereas along a sandy coast a sandy beach may be nearly continuous. Local accumulations of gravel or sand in bays are *bayhead beaches* (Fig. 270), and those at the heads of smaller indentations are *pocket beaches.*

The materials of beach deposits vary greatly in grain size, from sands through pebbles and cobbles to boulders. In the sequence of seasonal changes a beach characterized by gravel in winter may be converted to a wide belt of sand in summer. Where most of the beach pebbles are flattened, disk-shaped ones produced by a gliding wave motion, they may overlap so as to form a *shingle beach* (Fig. 271).

Certain beaches are composed of shell fragments or of coral sand, for example the "pink beach" of Bermuda, or of olivine sand, as in the

FIG. 271. Shingle beach of Lake Ontario near Olcott, New York. (*Photograph by Gilbert, U.S. Geological Survey.*)

Bay of Naples, but by far the greater number are mainly quartz sand. Local concentrations of native gold, magnetite ("black sand"), zircon, rutile, cassiterite (tin ore), and other useful minerals in some deposits form the basis of certain beach placer mines.

Where an excess of sand is present, as at the mouth of a river, a wide series of beach ridges may be added to the shore so as to extend the land seaward as a *prograded shore*. A good example is Clatsop Plains just south of the mouth of the Columbia River.

Wind-blown sands derived from beaches commonly pile up on shore as coastal dunes.

Barrier Beaches. On a number of gently sloping sandy shores the waves and currents have built up ridges of sand to form strips of land some distance offshore (Fig. 272). Such ridges are known as *barrier beaches* (*offshore islands,* or *island bars*). The area behind the barrier beach is more or less shut off from the open ocean as a lagoon.

The origin of these barrier beaches is not well-understood. Johnson [1] thought that they were formed just landward of the line of breakers, mainly by the throwing of sand thereto from the seaward side until a chain of islands and finally a ridge were built near sea level. The sand could be thrown somewhat above sea level by storm waves and then whipped up still higher into dunes by the wind. Recent observations show, however, that the line of breakers is a place of maximum turbulence

[1] D. W. Johnson, Shore Processes and Shoreline Development, pp. 365–367, 1919.

337

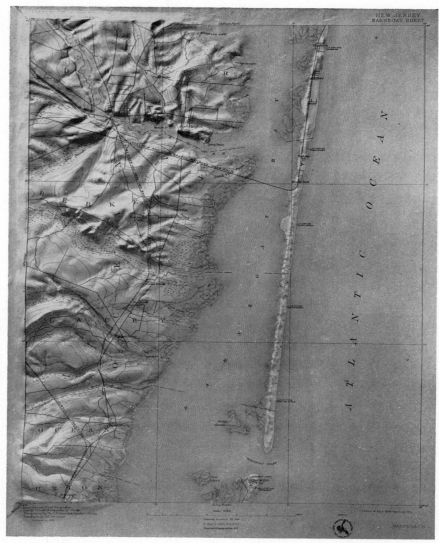

FIG. 272. Model of part of New Jersey coast, showing long barrier beach and environs. (*Aero Service Corporation.*)

instead of sedimentation and that it is characterized by a furrow, or trough, instead of a ridge, although a low sandbank (or a series of bars and intervening troughs, sometimes called balls-and-lows) may lie beside the trough. The trough and bar change with the state of the sea, but none ever has been seen to form a barrier beach.

Another possible explanation is that the barrier beaches were begun as relatively simple beaches on a nearly flat sea bottom during the ice age when sea level was lower than it is now. As sea level slowly was restored, the waves gradually may have driven the beach ridges landward and upward to their present positions. It is noteworthy that the valleys behind the lagoons are drowned by the postglacial rise of sea level.

Barrier beaches in apparently different stages of development and modification by longshore drift are common along the Atlantic Coast from New Jersey southward and along the Gulf coast of Texas. Some of them are single ridges, and some are multiple; some are islands, and some are connected to the mainland at one or both ends; and many of them have subsidiary deposits along their edges and in the vicinity of tidal inlets. A modified lagoon with associated deposits is shown in Fig. 273.

Bars and Spits. A longshore current shifts sediments parallel to the coast line, but owing to the tendency of a current to continue in a straight line it fails to follow an indentation that may be produced by a drowned

FIG. 273. Aerial photograph of coastal zone of northeastern Australia. Former tidal flats channeled by streams. (*Photograph by United States Air Force.*)

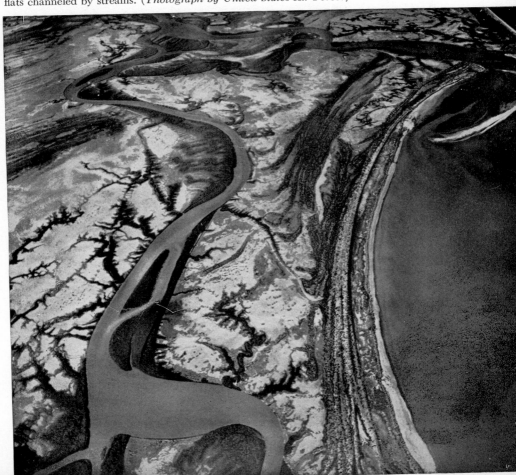

FIG. 274. Bay-mouth bars and coastal lagoons near Eureka, California. The lagoon in the center is cut off from the Pacific Ocean by a sand bar. A similar lagoon occurs below (south). (*Fairchild Aerial Surveys, Inc.*)

river valley or by a bay of any origin. Where the longshore current passes from shallow to deeper water at the entrance of such indentations, or bays, deposition is almost certain to take place. A ridge which becomes a land projection, or *spit,* is thus built up. When a spit is built almost or entirely across the entrance to the bay, it becomes a *bay-mouth bar* (Fig. 274). Bars cut off the indentations and tend to simplify the form of the coast line. Islands become connected with the mainland or with each other in a similar manner. Such islands are said to be *tied,* and the bars acting as the lines of connection are called *tombolos* (Fig. 275). They are numerous along the New England coast, where several islands in succession may be tied together, and the string thus formed may be connected with the mainland. Nahant, Massachusetts, is a land-tied island. The Rock of Gibraltar is similarly united to the coast of Spain.

If the free end of a spit is beaten by violent storm waves or by those of seasonal storms, it may be deflected or cut back and the terminal materials thus turned back may be deposited as a *recurved spit,* or *hook* (Figs. 277, 278). By prolonged deposition the curved end of the hook may be extended until it reaches the mainland and forms a *loop.*

Cuspate Forms. Where sediment-laden longshore currents are deflected seaward on both sides of a point of land, a projecting spit with cusped or curved sides is built out as a *cuspate spit* (Fig. 276), or, on a larger scale, a *cuspate foreland.* Cape Fear, North Carolina, and Cape Canaveral, Florida, are outstanding examples of cuspate forelands.

FIG. 275. Land-tied islands, Spruce Head Islands, Maine. (*Photograph by Bastin, U.S. Geological Survey.*)

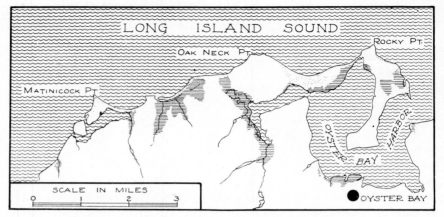

FIG. 276. A youthful shore line of submergence undergoing simplification, near Oyster Bay, Long Island, New York. Matinicock Point has the form of a cuspate spit. Oak Neck Point is a cliffed headland flanked by bay-mouth bars. (*After Oyster Bay Topographic Map, U.S. Geological Survey.*)

Submerged Bars. Besides the shore deposits that are obvious because they stand above sea level, waves and longshore currents also make bars beneath the water surface (Fig. 274). These, according to local conditions, take the shape of variously oriented ridges, sandy shoals, and anomalous forms that are not readily classified.

In addition, a mantle of sediments is distributed over the sea bottom below the level of wave and current activity. This has been called a *wave-*

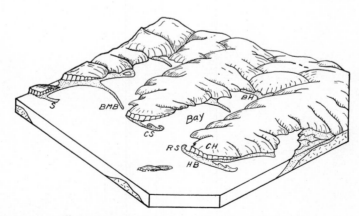

FIG. 277. Diagram illustrating the land forms developed along a coast line of submergence. *S*, spit; *CS*, complex spit; *RS*, recurved spit; *HB*, headland beach; *BH*, bayhead beach; *CH*, cliffed headland; *BMB*, bay-mouth bar. (*After D. W. Johnson.*)

built terrace or *shore-face terrace* by some authors, and thought to be continuous with the surface of the wave-cut terrace, but such a constructional terracelike embankment is said not to be found in the present sea. Instead, the sediments seem to be spread unevenly. The Pleistocene changes of sea level may be partly responsible for this irregularity.

All the various constructional features formed by waves and currents are subject to change from season to season and from year to year; and so a beach, spit, barrier beach, bay-mouth bar, or submarine bar may show very different outlines within a decade.

Problems of Control of Shores. To protect harbor works and other water-front property, man builds sea walls, bulkheads, revetments, breakwaters, and the like, but these prove difficult to maintain against the fury of the sea unleashed in storms. Jetties commonly are used to protect navigation inlets, where they also interrupt the longshore transport of sand. Accretion of sand then normally occurs on the upcurrent side, as at Lake Worth Inlet, Florida, where jetties interfered with the southward sand drift. In certain situations artificial changes may result in starvation of the beaches farther down the coast on the lee side, as at Palm Beach, where erosion of the beach followed the construction of the Lake Worth Inlet jetties. Construction of a breakwater in 1929 to protect the harbor at Santa Barbara, California, caused about 300,000 cubic yards of sand per year to collect in front of the breakwater. By 1934 the capacity was reached and sand began to go round the end of the breakwater and to fill in the harbor; by 1952 more than 5 million cubic yards of sand had accumulated in the harbor behind the breakwater. Part of the fill has been used to stock-pile the beach down drift, where beach erosion had become serious.

To stabilize beaches or to induce prograding, a series of groins

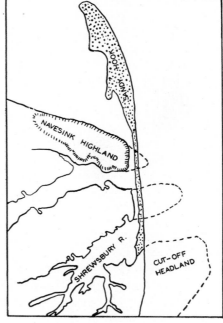

FIG. 278. Diagram showing the erosion of headlands and the deposition of the eroded material as a bar and hook at Sandy Hook, New Jersey, at the entrance to New York Harbor. (*After Loomis.*)

may be built perpendicular to the shore athwart the shore drift. The interference with the natural balance by such forced deposition may lead, however, to erosion elsewhere. Considerable success has been had at moderate cost on the coasts of New Jersey, Florida, California, and Lake Michigan with artificial nourishment of beaches by sand dredged or pumped from nearby sources, as at Atlantic City, Palm Beach, Santa Monica, and Chicago.

Long breakwaters placed offshore parallel to the coast line provide shelter for small ships, but they also create a wave shadow, where the effects of wave refraction, wave diffraction, and modification of the shore currents cause deposition on the beach front. Thus a 2,000-foot breakwater built about 2,000 feet offshore at Santa Monica, California, led to a somewhat cuspate accumulation of sand onshore, which in 30 years has grown to be several hundred feet wide. Sea stacks and islands offshore have a similar effect in their lee.

By anticipating the effects of various engineering structures on the work of waves and longshore currents, it is possible to select a design appropriate to a particular setting with reasonable success and to take steps to counteract undesirable changes resulting therefrom.

CLASSIFICATION AND DEVELOPMENT OF SHORE LINES

Johnson's Classification. A widely accepted classification of shore lines proposed by Johnson groups shore lines in four main categories:

1. *Shore lines of emergence,* characterized by a nearly flat coastal plain covered with unconsolidated marine sediments. Terraces onshore and barrier beaches offshore also are typical.

2. *Shore lines of submergence,* characterized by drowned valleys, deep bays, bold headlands, and islands.

3. *Neutral shore lines,* which do not show the effects of either emergence of a former sea floor or submergence of former land. These include (a) delta shore lines, (b) alluvial-plain shore lines, (c) outwash-plain shore lines, (d) volcanic shore lines, (e) coral-reef shore lines, and (f) fault shore lines.

4. *Compound shore lines,* which show features that are a combination of at least two of the preceding classes.

This classification has met with some objections. Because of sea-level changes during the ice age the supposedly stable "neutral" shore lines actually have undergone both emergence and submergence. Moreover, for the same reason nearly all shore lines are compound. Thus shore terraces and drowned valleys, of opposite significance, occur together in many places.

Shepard's Classification. To avoid these difficulties, Shepard has proposed another classification, which may be summarized as follows:

I. Primary, or youthful, coasts and shore lines, configuration due primarily to nonmarine agencies
   A. Shaped by terrestrial erosion and drowned by deglaciation or downwarping
      1. Drowned river-valley coasts (ria coasts)
      2. Drowned glacial-erosion coasts (with deep estuaries, fiords, or glacial troughs and basin depressions)
   B. Shaped by terrestrial depositional agencies
      1. River-deposition coasts (deltaic coasts, drowned alluvial plains)
      2. Glacial-deposition coasts (partially submerged moraines, partially submerged drumlins)
      3. Wind-deposition coasts (prograding sand dunes)
      4. Vegetation-extended coasts (mangrove coasts)
   C. Shaped by volcanic activity
      1. Coasts with recent lava flows
      2. Shore lines due to volcanic collapse or explosion (breached calderas)
   D. Shaped by diastrophism
      1. Fault-scarp coasts
      2. Coasts due to folding
II. Secondary, or mature, coasts and shore lines, configuration primarily the result of marine agencies
   A. Shore lines shaped by marine erosion
      1. Sea cliffs straightened by wave erosion
      2. Sea cliffs made irregular (crenulate) by wave erosion
   B. Coasts and shore lines shaped by marine deposition
      1. Shore lines straightened by building of bars across estuaries
      2. Coasts prograded by wave and current deposits
      3. Shore lines with offshore bars and longshore spits
      4. Coral-reef coasts

His subdivisions of coastal regions are (1) coasts with young mountains, (2) coasts with old mountains, (3) coasts with broad coastal plains, and (4) glaciated coasts.

Development of Shore Lines. To illustrate the progressive development of shore lines, let us consider the changes wrought with time on two different types of coasts, one a ria coast (a shore line of submergence of Johnson), and the other a coast with a wide coastal plain (a shore line of emergence of Johnson).

The first of these may be thought to begin with long estuaries, bold headlands, and islands. During the youthful stage sea cliffs are cut on the exposed headlands and on the seaward shores of the islands. The resulting sediments are deposited as spits to make "winged headlands," and bay-mouth bars are extended across the deeper waters of the bays (Fig. 277). The dismembered tributaries of the drowned valleys build deltas in the sheltered portions of the bays. As these processes continue, the islands are cut away and the headlands recede (Fig. 278). Spits and bay-mouth bars simplify the outline of the shore line, and it approaches maturity. The mature stage is characterized by high sea cliffs (crenulate or straight, according to the resistance of the material) and by wide, wave-cut terraces. The terraces extend seaward as far as the original headlands that were removed by wave erosion. The shortened bays are filled with delta sediments, and the shore line is shortened and simplified to the greatest extent. It is then mature. After this stage is reached, the shore line retreats slowly, and the wave-cut terraces are widened until the force of the wave action is lost as the waves have to cross the wide, rocky platforms.

The second type of coast may be considered to begin with a nearly flat coastal plain underlain by newly exposed, unconsolidated marine sediments (Fig. 279). Most of the irregularities of the sea bottom have been obliterated by the deposition of sediments. Erosion, however, begins immediately, and the stage of early youth is characterized by the development of barrier beaches or offshore bars. Shallow-water lagoons lie between the offshore bars and the shore line (Fig. 272). The lagoons are gradually filled by sediments from the land, by the growth of vegetation, and by other less evident agencies. During the stage of late youth the waves continue to beat on the barrier beaches and to drive them landward. The lagoons are changed into tidal marshes (Fig. 279), and the marshes may be completely filled. As wave action continues, the barrier beaches are forced back onshore and eliminated and the shore line is made straight and simple. It is then similar to the mature stage of a

FIG. 279. Diagram illustrating a coast line of emergence. (*After D. W. Johnson.*)

shore line of submergence. During the succeeding stage a wide, wave-cut terrace is developed as the shore moves landward.

SUGGESTIONS FOR FURTHER READING

Johnson, D. W.: Shore Processes and Shoreline Development, John Wiley & Sons, Inc., 1919.

Kuenen, Ph. H.: Marine Geology, John Wiley & Sons, Inc., 1950.

Shepard, F. P.: Submarine Geology, Harper & Brothers, 1948.

———: Submarine Topography of the Gulf of California, memoir 43, part III, Geological Society of America, 1950.

CHAPTER 15

Sedimentation and Sedimentary Rocks

Origin of Sediments. On the basis of origin, sediments may be classified as (1) land-derived, or terrigenous, (2) organic, (3) volcanic, (4) magmatic, and (5) extraterrestrial, or meteoritic. Of these the land-derived gravels, sands, silts, and clays are by far the most abundant. Land-derived solutions yield various chemical precipitates, including sodium chloride, calcium and magnesium carbonates, and iron, manganese, and phosphatic and barite concretions and nodules. Some of these inorganic precipitates may be separated with difficulty from those of biochemical origin. These terrigenous materials, both solids and solutions, are formed by the disintegration and decomposition of rocks of all kinds and represent the end products of erosion.

Organic sediments are those formed from constituents that were once dissolved in water and later extracted through the activity of plants and animals. Many organisms use inorganic substances in the development of their protective and supporting structures, such as bones, shells, and tests. These structures contain phosphates, sulfides, iron oxides, calcium and magnesium carbonates, silica, and other constituents in varying amounts that accumulate as sediments when the organisms perish. Other organisms bring about chemical reactions that lead to the precipitation of sediments. Peat and coal are composed of the altered remains of plants.

Sediments of volcanic origin include all fragmental materials ejected from volcanoes. They consist of fine volcanic dust, ash, cinders, bombs, and submarine lava flows.

Sediments of magmatic origin are not extensive. They represent dissolved substances that were transported from within the earth by the heated waters associated with magmas. Much of the material reaches the surface in hot springs, where it may be deposited on land, as it has been in Yellowstone Park, or the springs may discharge on the floor of the sea and add their dissolved load to the sea water.

The extraterrestrial materials come from outer space and result largely from the oxidation or burning up of meteorites in passing through the earth's atmosphere. The material from the meteorites then falls as the finest dust on land and sea alike.

The main route of derivation of sediments is shown diagrammatically in Fig. 280. The great bulk of the sedimentary material is derived by the weathering and erosion of earlier rocks and the transportation and redeposition of the products so formed. Locally the volcanic contributions may be large. The principal agents of transportation are gravity, streams, glaciers, waves and shore currents, wind, ground water, and organisms. In transit the fragmental materials are subject to attrition, rounding, and sorting as to size and specific gravity.

Sedimentary rocks resulting from the breaking up of other rocks are *clastic* rocks. These include loose gravels, sands, and muds, as well as the consolidated conglomerates, sandstones, and shales. Rocks derived only indirectly from other rocks through their decomposition, solution, and redeposition are *nonclastic*. In general they are formed through the agency of some form of life or by chemical precipitation.

Classification of Sedimentary Rocks. The different physical states of the sedimentary materials, whether solids or solutions, require different modes of transportation, which therefore tend to segregate the two principal groups of sediments, namely, (1) clastic, or mechanical, sediments on the one hand, and (2) chemical and organic precipitates, or nonclastics, on the other. Mixtures, however, are very common, such as sandy

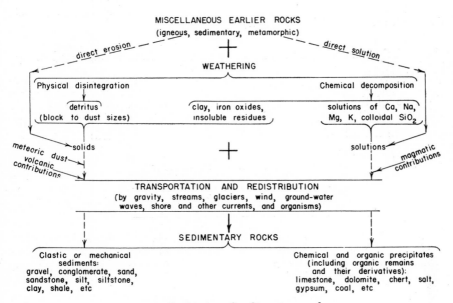

FIG. 280. Derivation of sedimentary rocks.

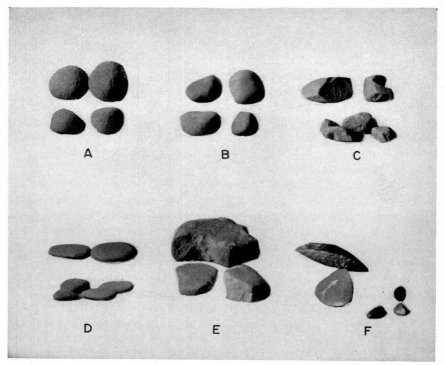

FIG. 281. The shapes of pebbles. *A*, rounded; *B*, subrounded; *C*, angular; *D*, disklike; *E*, faceted and striated glacial; *F*, dreikanter, faceted by wind-blown sand. (About one-fourth natural size.) (*After Grout.*)

shale, shaly limestone, carbonaceous shale, gypsiferous shale, and many others.

The clastic sediments are classified further mainly on the basis of the size of the constituent fragments, as boulders, cobbles, pebbles, granules, sands, silts, and clays. Several size classifications have been proposed; the following classification is commonly accepted:

Classification of Fragments

Name of fragment	Diameter, millimeters
Boulder	256 or more
Cobble	64 to 256
Pebble	4 to 64
Granule	2 to 4
Sand	$\frac{1}{16}$ to 2
Silt	$\frac{1}{256}$ to $\frac{1}{16}$
Clay	Smaller than $\frac{1}{256}$

Clastic sediments also may be classified according to the agent of deposition, such as gravity deposits (residual accumulations, talus piles, landslides, mudflows), aeolian, or wind-blown, deposits (dune sands, loess), fluviatile deposits (channel gravel, sand bars, flood-plain silt), marine deposits, etc., but this procedure requires interpretation that may be difficult or uncertain. In some instances the shapes and surface markings of the pebbles and even of the sand grains may serve as clues to their history (Figs. 281, 282).

Sediments of chemical and organic origin are even more difficult to classify, as they are widely different in texture, composition, and conditions of deposition. The simplest scheme is to classify them on the basis of their chemical or mineralogical composition. Some are calcareous (limestone of many varieties); others are ferruginous (bog iron ore, hema-

FIG. 282. Photomicrograph of quartz sand grains somewhat battered and worn during their transportation.

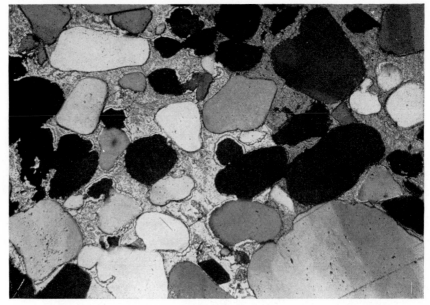

FIG. 283. A quartz sandstone cemented with calcite, as seen in thin section.

tite rock), phosphatic (phosphorite), or siliceous (chert, flint, diatomite, geyserite), etc. Many of them are marine; others are products of fresh-water lakes, of salt lakes, of springs, or of other geologic settings.

Relative Proportions of Sediments. The crust, or outer 10 miles of the earth is estimated to have the following composition: 95 per cent igneous rocks and 5 per cent sedimentary rocks. Of the sedimentary rocks on the continents about 58 per cent are shales, about 22 per cent sandstones (and conglomerates), and 20 per cent limestones (Pettijohn), whereas calculations of their chemical composition, in relation to that of the average igneous rock (the ultimate source), show that of all sediments 70 per cent should be shales, 16 per cent sandstones, and 14 per cent lime-stones (Holmes). Notwithstanding the abundance of shales on land, it is clear that part of the shaly material must have been lost to the deep sea. In any event the preponderance of shale, about two-thirds or more, is very striking. The minor types of sediment such as coal, gypsum, phosphate rock, and chert make up less than 1 per cent of the total volume.

Consolidation of Sediments. As sediments increase in thickness, the lower beds are pressed together by the weight of the overlying beds and are rendered more compact. Lateral pressure or any other movement may bring the rock particles closer together, driving out water, decreasing the pore space, and consolidating the rock, especially a shale. Nevin [1] estimates that compaction reduces pore space in mud from 50 per cent at

[1] Charles M. Nevin, Structural Geology, 4th ed., p. 210, 1949.

a depth of 100 feet to 33 per cent at a depth of 500 feet, to 18 per cent at 4,000 feet, and to 10 per cent at 6,000 feet.

Nonclastic sediments are consolidated in part by compaction, also, and in part by recrystallization into strongly coherent masses.

In medium- and coarse-grained clastic sediments the most important consolidating process, however, is cementation. The ground waters percolating through the sediments carry calcium carbonate, silica, iron oxides, or other cementing materials into the pore spaces between the fragments and there deposit them, thus cementing the grains or larger fragments into a solid mass. The common solid clastic sedimentary rocks are the results of this process (Fig. 283).

In general, the older sediments are more highly consolidated than the younger ones, but there are exceptions in which either they never were consolidated or the cementing material has been dissolved and removed so as to restore them to a loose condition.

Textures of Sediments. The textures of most sediments may be described by the terms fragmental, crystalline, oölitic, pisolitic, spherulitic, and colloform (Fig. 284).

Fragmental textures range from very fine-grained clays to coarse boulders or blocks. They occur in clastic or mechanical sediments.

Crystalline textures occur in evaporites and other rocks precipitated from aqueous solutions. The crystals may be microscopic as in chert,

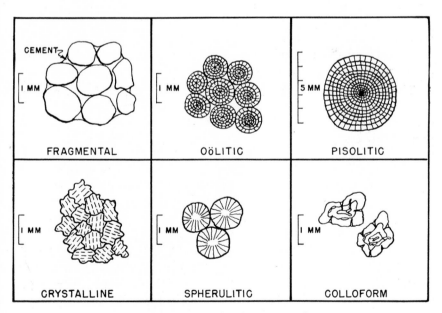

FIG. 284. Textures of sedimentary rocks.

FIG. 285. Rhombic dolomite crystals in the Oneota formation, as seen in thin section.

fine-grained as in common limestone, or coarse-grained as in some rock
salt or certain limestones. The grains in crystalline rocks commonly have
no definite crystal outlines but instead are so crowded together as to interlock irregularly in a sort of mosaic. In some sedimentary rocks well-
formed crystals have developed later by recrystallization or by replacement (Fig. 285).

The term *oölitic* means egglike (Greek *oion,* egg; cf. Latin, *ovum*).
An oölitic limestone is made up almost entirely of small shotlike bodies
crowded together into a solid mass. The individual spherules are composed of concentric shells of calcite deposited about some minute grain,
such as a grain of sand or a fragment of a shell (Fig. 289). When the
spherules are about the size of peas, the rock is said to be *pisolitic* (Greek
pison, pea). Particles showing a radial internal structure but lacking the
concentric laminations of oölites and pisolites are *spherulitic.*

Oölites are found among the rocks of all geologic ages, and in many
instances the evidence suggests that the small spherules were formed by
accretionary growth during the deposition of the material that later was
consolidated. Oölitic sands are now forming on the shores of Great Salt
Lake, Utah, and off some of the coral islands of the Pacific. These modern
oölites are calcareous, but in some older rocks the oölites are composed
of chert, hematite, or other substances, apparently as a result of replace-

ment of the original calcite. Other oölites and pisolites, less regular in structure, occurring in bauxite, phosphorite, and some iron ores, also have been formed by replacement of earlier substances.

As oölites are about the size of sand grains, they are readily subject to transportation and redeposition, and so some oölitic rocks are cross-bedded.

Particles with *colloform* (Greek *kolla*, glue) texture result from the coagulation of bits of colloid, or gel, which subsequently loses water, shrinks, and hardens. Their roundish forms, amorphous internal structure, and shrinkage cracks help to identify them. Crystallization later may obscure their colloidal origin.

Organic forms resulting directly from the activities of organisms, such as shells, bones, teeth, fragments of coral, siliceous skeletons of diatoms and Radiolaria, calcareous tests of Foraminifera, and amorphous or replaced pellets of excrement, usually are classified as organic structures instead of textures. The particles range in size texturally from microscopic grains through silt and sand grades upward to very coarse pieces.

Color. Sedimentary rocks may be white, neutral, or highly colored. The color generally is caused by the presence of carbonaceous matter or of various iron compounds, chiefly the oxides. The carbonaceous matter usually occurs as finely divided organic material mingled with the sediment, but the iron compounds may occur as finely divided sediment, as cementing material, or as coating for the individual grains of the sediment, or they may be within the mineral grains of the sediment.

The color of a sedimentary bed is characteristic only over limited areas and may differ with the degree of weathering to which it has been subjected. Thus many limestones having a wide range of original colors may weather to buff, and the residual clays resulting from their solution may be red. Gray or black shales may weather to a red clay. The red iron oxide which colors the clay may be the oxidation product of pyrite, disseminated through limestone or shale so finely that its presence is scarcely detected in the fresh rock.

CHARACTERISTICS OF COMMON SEDIMENTARY ROCKS

Arkose. Arkose is a rock composed of the residue of disaggregated, granular, acid igneous rocks. Its constituents are mainly unaltered feldspar and quartz. It is a sandstone in which fragments of orthoclase feldspar are abundant. If the original rock was basic and the feldspar plagioclase, the derivative is called *graywacke*. Arkose deposits are common among the land-laid formations and especially among those accumulating in arid or semiarid mountainous regions, where the chemical processes of decomposition are slow and where other processes of weathering are more effective.

Breccia. A rock composed of the cemented angular fragments of other rocks is a *breccia*. It is evident that the angular constituents of breccia have not been transported by water far from the source of the material. Breccias are common along fault zones or in ancient talus accumulations. They grade into conglomerates as the fragments show signs of rounding as a result of transportation by water.

FIG. 286. Ancient conglomerate exposed on the Laurentian peneplane.

Conglomerate. Conglomerates are gravels that are held together by some kind of cement (Fig. 286). Many conglomerates are made up chiefly of quartz pebbles, because quartz is the most common mineral that possesses great resistance to disintegration and wear. Flint, chert, and jasper also are common, although the pebbles of a conglomerate may be made up of any kind of rock fragments. Thus there are limestone conglomerates and also shale conglomerates. Unassorted pebbles, such as those found in an ordinary gravel bed of the glacial drift, especially where there is a high percentage of calcium carbonate in the associated drift, may be cemented into great masses of rough conglomerate which look like weathered concrete.

Sandstone. A sandstone is a bed of sand cemented to form a coherent mass. The cement may be the light-colored calcium carbonate or the red, yellow, or brown iron oxide. If quartz sand is thoroughly cemented by silica, the rock is quartzite. Sand is made of grains smaller than pebbles. The grains may be subangular or well-rounded. Their surfaces may be pitted owing perhaps to impact in transit, or they may be frosted like the surface of ground glass. Thus they tell something of the history through which they have passed as fragments. Most sands are made up chiefly of quartz fragments, but sands made of fine grains of olivine are found along the Bay of Naples, sands of calcium carbonate are found at Bermuda, and sands composed of gypsum are found in New Mexico. Certain sands are composed of magnetite, and others partly of tin oxide or of gold, but all such sands are unusual. Sandstones grade through coarse-grained sands into conglomerates and through fine-grained sands into shales. Sandstones that contain an appreciable amount of calcium carbonate are calcareous sandstones (Fig. 283); if they contain clay, they are argillaceous sandstones. Occasional pebbles may occur in sandstones; these are strung along a bedding plane or occur here and there in the sand. Such a rock is not a conglomerate but a pebbly sandstone. A coarse sandstone, especially if the grains are sharp, is a *grit*.

Greensand. Grains of glauconite may be common to abundant in a sandstone. In some sandstones they are more abundant than quartz grains. Such rock is called greensand, or a glauconitic sandstone. It is common among some of the older sediments and is now forming in the ocean.

Shale. Shale is composed of compacted or cemented beds of mud or clay. It includes the finest products of rock decay that are swept farther out to sea than any other clastic sediment. Shales usually are thin-bedded, showing frequent changes in the fineness of materials composing them. Such changes in grain may be due to seasonal changes, or they may represent differences in rainfall or some other change that affected the amount or character of sediment brought down by streams. Shales that contain sand are arenaceous; those that contain calcium carbonate are calcareous; and those containing iron are ferruginous. Those containing large amounts of organic matter are carbonaceous shales. The latter usually are black, and some grade into beds of coal. Some of the ancient shales remain as beds of clay and differ from the deposits originally formed only in that they have been pressed together slightly.

Thin-bedded limestones or sandstones often are referred to as shaly, and many of them grade into shale.

The weathering of limestones may give rise to beds of clay which represent the insoluble residue of the limestone. Red clay beds may be so formed. When covered by later sediments, these residual clays mark ancient erosion surfaces.

Limestone. Limestone, the most abundant nonclastic sediment, consists of a solid rock made up mainly of the shells and the skeletal materials of lime-secreting plants and animals. Such organisms extract this material from sea water to form their hard parts. The spaces between the shells are filled by fine calcareous materials resulting from the grinding action of waves. Limestones are formed in relatively clear, shallow water where life is abundant and where the neighboring land areas are too low to contribute large quantities of clastic sediments. Living bacteria may cause the precipitation of calcium carbonate in sea water, and under exceptional conditions limestone may be deposited by chemical precipitation, but the greater number of limestones, whether fossiliferous or not, probably are composed of material that once formed organic remains (Fig. 287).

Limestones may grade into shales by the addition of clay to the cal-

FIG. 287. A slab of fossiliferous Devonian limestone from western New York. (*Photograph by Hardin, U.S. Geological Survey.*)

careous sediments. They may grade into calcareous sandstones in like manner by the addition of sand and through them into ordinary sandstones.

Dolomite. If a large part of the calcium in a limestone is replaced by magnesium, the rock is dolomite (Fig. 288). Dolomitization is a common

FIG. 288. Massive bedded dolomite along Stockton Hill in the Gilmore Valley at Winona, Minnesota.

process in limestones of all ages and often is accomplished during the process of sedimentation or by substitution of magnesium for calcium before the limestone is covered by later beds.

A limestone in which no such change has taken place is rare. If there has been only a small amount of replacement (10 to 20 per cent), the rock usually is referred to as a dolomitic limestone. Dolomites and dolomitic limestones are less soluble than ordinary limestones, hence endure longer on exposure. On weathering of limestone, calcium carbonate is dissolved and removed more rapidly than magnesium carbonate, and the proportion of magnesium carbonate is increased.

Chalk. Chalk is a special type of limestone usually composed of small shells, or of their fragments, cemented together. Foraminifera shells, or tests, constitute a large part of the material, but shells of other organisms also are commonly present.

Chalk usually is soft, porous, and white or gray, and some of it is massive in appearance. The chalk cliffs of Dover, England, are an example. Some of the chalks of the Southwest, particularly of Texas, grade into resistant beds that are as well-indurated as ordinary limestones, and such beds are found capping buttes and mesas of the region.

Marl. The porous masses of shells and shell fragments that accumulate on the bottoms of many fresh-water lakes are shell marls. Large amounts of marls are formed by the lime-secreting alga, *Chara*. The best-known example of Chara marl occurs at Pyramid Lake, Nevada. The term marl is used also to designate certain marine sediments presumably formed at the outer margin of the shale mud, in which clay and finely divided shell fragments are mixed. The term is applied also to soil in which clay and calcium carbonate are present in about equal amounts. Marine muds that are composed chiefly of calcium carbonate are called marls by some, but this practice is not general. The greensands of New Jersey usually are called greensand marls.

Coquina. Coquina is a limestone composed of loosely aggregated shells and shell fragments. This term usually is applied to the more recent deposits of cemented shell heaps, such as those forming off the coast of parts of Florida, but it is applied also to similar shell masses belonging to much older formations in which the mass is well-consolidated.

Oölite. An oölite is a rock in which the particles consist of small, concentrically built-up particles resembling fish roe (Fig. 289). The term oölitic generally is applied to the texture of the rock only, for in composition oölites may be siliceous, calcareous, phosphatic, or ferruginous. Commonly a sand grain or a shell fragment forms the center of the accretionary growth.

Tufa and Travertine. Calcareous deposits made about the mouths of springs, generally earthy, porous, or spongy, are *tufa*. Deposits of calcite

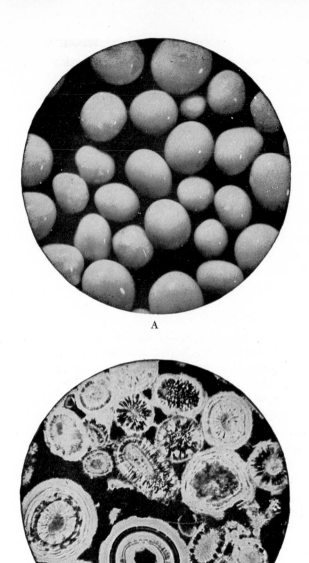

A

B

FIG. 289. A, photomicrograph of oölites from the southeast shore of Great Salt Lake. (Enlarged 15 diameters.) (*Photograph by A. J. Eardley.*) B, photomicrograph of thin section of cemented oölites from Great Salt Lake. The more or less complete radial and concentric structures are shown. (Enlarged about 35 diameters.) (*Photograph by A. J. Eardley. Reprinted by permission from Twenhofel, Principles of Sedimentation, 1st ed., copyright 1939, McGraw-Hill Book Company, Inc.*)

in limestone caves, commonly banded (as in Mexican onyx), laminated, or stalactitic, are *travertine.*

Chert and Flint. Chert is a compact, dense, siliceous material that occurs both as separate distinct layers and as roundish nodules distributed through beds of other rocks, chiefly limestones. Either the silica was deposited in colloidal form as a primary precipitate, or silica-bearing waters have partially replaced the associated sediments. The preservation of earlier textures and structures, including organic forms, in some instances indicates replacement. The secondary silica for such replacement may have come from re-solution of primary silica of colloids or of hard parts of sponges or other siliceous organisms or from water squeezed out of other sediments during their consolidation. Both primary and secondary methods of deposition of chert are probable in nature.

Flint, a dark gray to black variety of chert, is essentially silica with some water, although the names chert and flint are used interchangeably. In the Stone Age, man used flint (or chert) to fashion arrow points, and later he used it with steel to kindle fire. *Agate* is usually a banded, ornamental variety of chert. Granular ferruginous chert containing 15 to 35 per cent iron in the Lake Superior region is called *taconite.*

Diatomaceous Earth. Diatoms are minute plants that have siliceous skeletons. They live in great numbers in the sea and in fresh-water lakes. When they die, their siliceous capsules, or skeletons, accumulate to form diatomaceous earth. At many places their accumulations form papery gray to white layers interbedded with shales. Such beds have high porosity, and they may contain much water, but when dried they will float on water. At Lompoc, California, and at other places, thousands of feet of diatomaceous shales are found.

Coal. Coal is formed by the compacting and partial decomposition of vegetation accumulated in ancient peat bogs. It is preserved through submergence and by a covering of later beds (Fig. 290). The coal bed usually

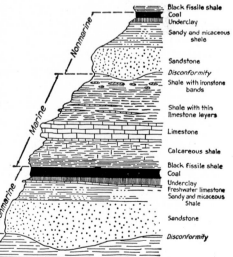

FIG. 290. Section showing typical relations of coal beds to associated strata in the eastern interior coal basin.

is found in the same location in which the plants, now coal, grew. This is indicated by the flat or unrolled condition of the leaves, the old stumps with roots still penetrating the soil below, and the lack of other sediments mixed with the plant remains. A few coals, however, have been formed from vegetation drifted into bays or estuaries. The alteration of vegetation into peat, lignite, and various other grades of coal is a process usually requiring a long time. The grade of coal produced is dependent upon the kind of material and the amount of alteration, through pressure and heat, that has taken place since the bog deposit accumulated. Coal is included among the sedimentary rocks, but it is merely an accumulation of fossil plants.

Phosphate Rock. Most igneous rocks contain small amounts of the mineral apatite, a calcium phosphate. Ground water dissolves the phosphate, and plants and animals utilize it in their life processes. Small amounts of phosphate are carried to the sea and are deposited there in beds. Such beds, raised above the sea, have become available to man, and the phosphate rock is used in large amounts for fertilizer. The largest deposits of rock phosphate in the United States are found in Montana, Idaho, and Wyoming, where they are associated with limestone and cover extensive areas. Valuable deposits are found also in Florida, South Carolina, Tennessee, and Kentucky.

Some phosphate deposits have formed by replacement of coral or other limestone, particularly where ground water has leached the phosphate and carried it downward until it was precipitated by limestone.

Salt and Gypsum. The composition of sea water is stated on page 308. When sea water is evaporated to dryness, the salts fall out of solution and are deposited. The least soluble salts are deposited first. Calcium carbonate and iron oxide, if present in the water, are the first to be precipitated. Gypsum [1] follows, and often with it some anhydrite is formed. After gypsum, sodium chloride, or common salt, is deposited. The bitter salts consisting of sulfates and chlorides of potassium and magnesium are precipitated last. They are so soluble that they are not always deposited where salt and gypsum form, and if they are deposited, commonly they are dissolved again. Great beds of salt and gypsum are interbedded with sedimentary rocks in Texas, Kansas, Michigan, Ontario, Ohio, New York, and many other places. Wherever soluble salts are formed, they are likely to be dissolved again unless they are protected to some extent against solution by water. In general, where they are found preserved, muds and clays have been deposited above them and keep out water.

Red beds, mainly red sandstones and shales, at many places are associated with salt and gypsum. These are red because they contain small amounts of disseminated hematite, and it is believed that they have

---

[1] Common salt, NaCl; gypsum, $CaSO_4 \cdot 2H_2O$; anhydrite, $CaSO_4$.

formed in part under arid conditions. Salt and gypsum are precipitated under arid conditions in bodies of water that have been cut off from the sea or in embayments that extend landward from the sea where the water flows into the embayment and is evaporated. This process is illustrated in the Gulf of Karabugaz on the east side of the Caspian Sea.

Karabugaz Gulf is only about 50 feet deep, and it covers about 7,500 square miles. It lies in a semidesert region and is partly separated from the Caspian Sea by sandspits, which form a barrier that prevents free circulation between the sea and the gulf. The waters of the Caspian Sea contain about 1.3 per cent mineral matter. Evaporation removes the water from the surface as fast as it is being brought in through the restricted connection with the sea. The water of the gulf becomes more highly concentrated than that of the Caspian Sea, and the less soluble salts are precipitated. Such marginal lagoons, or gulfs, are not uncommon, and in areas of great evaporation salt deposits may form in them.

Salt water and brine often are encountered in deep drilling, and crystals of salts may occur in shales or in other sediments below the surface. The brines of eastern Ohio and adjacent regions contain bromides in addition to common salt. These brines may be sea water trapped in the sediments at the time of their formation, but some of them are more concentrated than sea water and probably have been changed greatly since they formed a part of the sea.

Bedded Iron Ore. Iron in various forms is an abundant substance, and on weathering under reducing conditions it may be dissolved and carried in solution to fresh-water bogs or to the sea, where it is precipitated by chemical or biochemical reactions. In certain beds it has formed in large amounts. These by surface enrichment under oxidizing conditions may become iron ore.

Sedimentary Rocks of Lesser Importance

Adobe	Argillaceous soil used for making sun-dried bricks.
Bone bed	A rock, commonly limestone, containing numerous bones, usually fishbones.
Buhrstone	Porous cherty or siliceous rock formerly used for millstones.
Caliche	Soil cemented by calcareous, nitrogenous, or other salts that rose and were deposited by evaporation at the surface.
Chalcedony	Cryptocrystalline silica, probably a precipitate from a colloidal state.
Catlinite	A red clay "slate" containing abundant diaspore; carves easily and was used by Indians for making pipes. Pipestone.
Fire clay	A tough clay usually found underlying a coal seam. Makes refractory bricks.
Fuller's earth	Fine earthy clay with low plasticity.
Guano	Phosphatic and nitrogenous materials formed from the excrement of animals.
Gumbo	Clayey soils which become sticky mud when wet.
Ironstone	A rock containing iron, commonly with clay or sand.
Jasper	A siliceous red or variously colored rock resembling chalcedony.

FIG. 291. Sample cores of laminated (varved) clay, showing seasonal layers. From deposits at Haverstraw, New York, and New Haven, Connecticut. (*Courtesy of American Museum of Natural History.*)

PRIMARY STRUCTURAL FEATURES OF SEDIMENTS

Stratification. The arrangement of sediments in layers, or strata, is their most distinctive structural feature (Fig. 288). The stratification may be marked by a change in color, although this condition is more likely to be referred to as banding. Stratification usually means layers of sediments that readily separate along bedding planes owing to different sizes and kinds of material or to some interruption in deposition, permitting changes to take place before more material was deposited. The difference in character of sediments may result from (1) variations in currents, (2) seasonal changes (Fig. 291), (3) climatic changes, (4) fluctuations of sea level, or (5) marked changes in the types or number of organisms. The individual layers range in thickness from a fraction of an inch in some clayey muds to many feet in coarser sediments. If the bedding planes are near together, the sediment is "thin-bedded"; and if they are far apart, it is "massive," or "heavy-bedded." When the beds are laid down, they are generally nearly parallel to the surface over which they are deposited. As a rule they are approximately horizontal. At many places, however, the surfaces of deposition are undulating, and inclined stratification results. Sediments may be deposited in orderly sequence upon surfaces inclined as much as 30 degrees. The steepest slopes formed by deposition are found in small bodies of water or protected bays where there is slight agitation and very limited spreading of sediments.

Cross-bedding. Sediments that show parallel bedding at an angle to the planes of general stratification are *cross-bedded* (Fig. 292). Coarse sediments, such as pebbles and sand, are more likely to show cross-bedding, although some sandy shales and limestones are cross-bedded. Wherever steep slopes are produced by the rapid deposition of sediments, whether in rivers, lakes, or the sea, as at the front of a delta or on offshore bars, barriers, etc., inclined stratification occurs. Succeeding beds again may assume a horizontal position, and the cross-bedded layers thus may be interstratified with horizontal ones. Wind-laid deposits, such as sand dunes, characteristically are cross-bedded, and in them also cross-bedding is produced by rapid deposition at the front of steep slopes of the growing deposit (Fig. 89).

Graded Bedding. When a turbulent mixture of particles of different sizes, shapes, and densities is brought to the site of sedimentation, the coarser, heavier, and more nearly spherical grains tend to settle more rapidly than the others. As the smaller, lighter, and more angular ones follow in a more or less progressive series, the bed of sediment finally accumulated tends to show a segregation of the particles determined by their relative rates of settling. Thus the bottom portion of a bed may

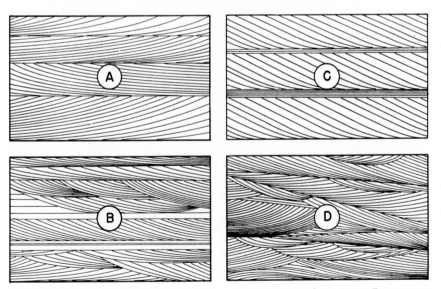

FIG. 292. Types of cross-bedding. *A*, ordinary marine near-shore type; *B*, common fluvial-current type; *C*, torrential-stream type; *D*, aeolian type, or dune structure.

consist of coarse or heavy particles, whereas the upper portion is made up of relatively fine or light particles. Such an arrangement is called *graded bedding* (Fig. 293). Repetition of the process may develop graded bedding within each of the succeeding layers.

Where sedimentary rocks have been upended or possibly overturned by earth movements, graded bedding is useful to a geologist as a means of distinguishing the original tops and bottoms of the beds.

Lenticular Beds. Massive beds, such as sandstones or limestones, at many places decrease rapidly in thickness and may be seen even to "pinch out" when traced along the face of a cliff. Lenticular bedding is common especially in the deposits made at the outlets of rivers or in stream deposits generally, but it is not limited to such localities. At the margin of one kind of sediment, where it grades into another kind, the change often takes place through an interbedded area in which the ends of the beds are lenticular, or pinched out. Thus the bedding evidently is not parallel, although it is not to be classed as cross-bedding. Irregularities in bedding are to be expected and may be brought out by comparing outcrops that are separated by several miles, although such features may be found in adjacent outcrops.

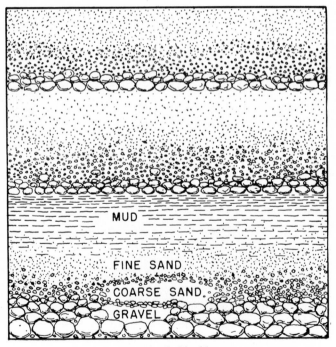

FIG. 293. Graded bedding.

Mud Cracks. Mud cracks are due to the shrinkage of the mud on drying (Fig. 294). This results in the removal of some of the water in which the mud accumulated as a sediment. Where formed in marine beds, mud cracks are a marked characteristic of sediments accumulating at or near the shore line or where the muds are exposed to the drying effects of the sun part of the time. Some mud cracks are several inches wide and ten times as deep. Such cracks, when the mud is thoroughly dried out, may remain open for several years even in regions of moderate rainfall. Where water again accumulates over them and sedimentation is renewed, the cracks are filled by this later and perhaps different kind of sediment. Such sediments, when thoroughly indurated, preserve the mud cracks as a feature of the solid rock. Where a mud-cracked area is drying rapidly, under certain conditions the patches thus blocked out on the upper surface may peel and roll up into cylinders. These, if preserved in the oncoming sediment, may resemble pebbles and produce a desiccation conglomerate.

Ripple Marks. Ripple marks usually are formed by the drag of the waves as they strike and travel over the bottom in relatively shallow water (Figs. 295, 296). They consist of a series of small, almost equally spaced ridges of sand or other fine sediment with rather sharp crests. The slopes of the sides show the type of motion which formed them (Figs. 297, 298). Oscillatory or undulatory movements give rise to ripples

FIG. 294. Mud cracks in sediments on floor of dry stream bed. (*Courtesy of U.S. Geological Survey.*)

FIG. 295. Ripple marks left by receding tide at Windsor, Nova Scotia. (*Courtesy of E. M. Kindle, Canada Geological Survey.*)

FIG. 296. Ripple marks preserved in the consolidated transitional beds at the base of the Beekmantown dolomite, Perth, Ontario. (*Courtesy of M. E. Wilson, Canada Geological Survey.*)

with symmetrical sides, whereas currents give rise to ripples with asymmetrical sides, the long slope being in the direction from which the current came. Under similar conditions, as the undulation dies out in deeper water, the crests of the ripple marks are more closely spaced, although the coarseness or fineness of the sediment composing them also may be a factor in the spacing. Waves in shallow water may be too violent at the contact of water and sediment to produce ripples. Their action is destructive, and any ripple marks that may have been formed during a more quiet sea are obliterated. Sand waves, or giant ripple marks, have been observed. These usually are formed in narrow bays by tidal currents. The wind forms ripple marks in land deposits such as sand dunes, and these resemble some of those formed in the water.

Rill Marks. As the tide retreats or the storm waves die down, the water left in the sand of a beach finds its way back to the sea and produces little rivulets which branch again and again like the distributaries on a delta plain. These are known as rill marks. Commonly they are observed on beach sands and frequently are found in consolidated sediments, where at places they have been mistaken for plant impressions.

Wavemarks. Wavemarks are formed on the sloping sands of a beach by the outer margin of the spent wave. They may be indicated by smooth-lying fine sand grains at places partly covered by fragments of shells and bits of mica. These wavemarks may be festooned with loops landward and the angles marked by heaps of shells or other light sediments. Sea-

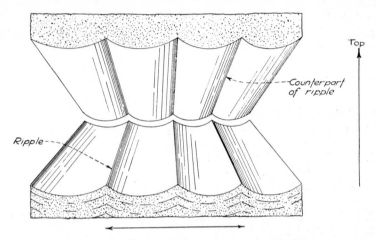

FIG. 297. Oscillation ripple marks. (*After Shrock.*)

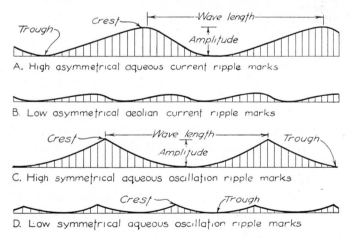

A. High asymmetrical aqueous current ripple marks

B. Low asymmetrical aeolian current ripple marks

C. High symmetrical aqueous oscillation ripple marks

D. Low symmetrical aqueous oscillation ripple marks

FIG. 298. Profiles of current and oscillation ripple marks. (*After Shrock.*)

ward from the marginal mark often may be found various patterns produced by the returning water. Of these some have an imbricated design like overlapping scales.

Raindrop Impressions. Raindrop impressions are produced by rain or by the splash of wave action or by water dripping from vegetation, and they may be preserved in the mud along the shore or on other mud flats. For their preservation probably it is necessary for partial drying or hardening of the mud to take place before the mud is covered and then that it be covered quickly by another layer. Such marks are not commonly found, but at places excellent examples are preserved.

Raindrop impressions, wavemarks, rill marks, ripple marks, mud cracks, and the like, give lasting evidence of the conditions under which the original sediments were laid down.

Fossils and Their Significance. Many sedimentary rocks contain remains of ancient life known as fossils. The word fossil is derived from the Latin word *fossilis,* meaning dug up. As originally used, it referred to any curious object dug out of the earth. Today the term fossil is applied to any organic remains or direct evidence of organisms preserved in the rocks of the earth's crust.

Fossils may be classified as follows:

1. Actual remains of organisms:
    a. Soft parts only.
    b. Hard and soft parts.
    c. Hard parts only.
2. Impressions or replacements of original substances, molds, casts, etc.
3. Tracks, trails, burrows, etc.

Since plants as a whole have fewer hard parts suitable for preservation than animals, plants are not so well-represented by fossils as are animals. However, some very fine plant fossils do occur as carbonized remains or as impressions of leaves or stems in mud or sand deposits that later become shales or sandstones. Others have had their woody fibers gradually infiltrated with and filled in by silica, producing such fine specimens of silicified wood as may be found in the petrified forests of Arizona. Still other plants are preserved as coal, which is fossil vegetable matter. Cell structure may still be seen in thin sections of coal.

The bones, teeth, shells, and general skeletal matter of animals are more likely to be preserved (Fig. 299); but the tracks, trails, burrows, or impressions of animals also may form fossils. In some cases the entire animals have been preserved, constituting unique fossils of great value. The best-known of these are the fossil insects in the Baltic ambers and the woolly elephants frozen in the gravels of Siberia.

Such remnants of ancient life show its development through the long

FIG. 299. Thickly crowded fossil shells embedded in a silty sandstone. (*Photograph by W. T. Lee, U.S. Geological Survey. Reprinted by permission from Moore, Historical Geology, copyright 1933, McGraw-Hill Book Company, Inc.*)

ages of earth history. Not only are the more primitive forms of life found to characterize the earlier periods in earth history, but the developmental changes of modern forms are recorded in the fossils that may be found in succeeding time intervals of that history. Thus the modern single-toed horse preserving the splint bones of two additional toes on each foot may be traced back to an earlier horse which had three functional toes, and that horse back to a still earlier one which had five toes.

Since fossils show the development from the more primitive to the more complex forms of life, it follows that a fossil-bearing rock is dated by the character of the life existing during the deposition of the rock that contains it. Thus geologists have come to recognize certain fossil forms as indices, or guides, to certain geologic units. Some of these are called horizon markers because they are found only within certain horizons, or groups of beds. If, then, the fossils occurring in the sedimentary rocks of two widely separated areas are alike, it follows that these sediments were accumulating during approximately the same period of geologic history.

SECONDARY STRUCTURAL PECULIARITIES

Certain minor structural peculiarities may develop after sediments have been consolidated.

Concretions. Concretions (Fig. 300) (Latin, *concretus*, grown together) are variously shaped masses, or nodules, of seemingly foreign

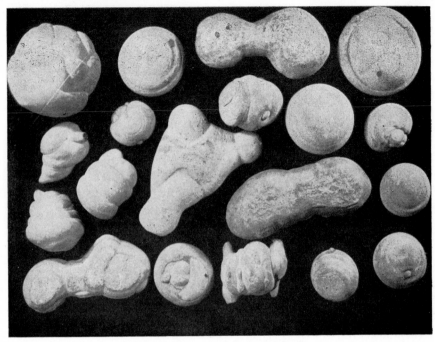

FIG. 300. Concretions from clay beds.

material that often occur in sedimentary rocks. They range in size from less than 1 inch to several feet in diameter, and certain loglike cylindrical ones have lengths of 10 feet or more. Concretions usually differ in composition from the rocks in which they occur. Generally they are formed from one of the minor constituents of that rock. In limestone and chalk, concretions generally are of flint, chert, or pyrite; in shales, they are generally of calcite, chert, pyrite, or siderite, but barite and gypsum occur abundantly in certain localities. Concretions in sandstone generally are impure oxides of iron, pyrite, or calcite.

Concretions usually are spherical, lenticular, or discoidal, more rarely cylindrical or irregular in shape. At many places the stratification of the beds in which they occur may be seen to thicken on entering the concretion, and those above are arched up, whereas those below are pressed down. Even cross-bedding may be found in concretions. At places fossils occur partly within the concretion and partly in the surrounding rock, or the center of the concretion may be one of the characteristic fossils of the formation in which it occurs. At some places concretions are abundantly fossiliferous, although the surrounding rock may be nearly destitute of fossils.

Concretions commonly show a concentric structure as if made up of a series of concentric spheres each fitting within the next larger. Those common in the black shales of Ohio are relatively smooth on the outside and separate easily from the enclosing shale. Many of them, in certain regions, are coated with a layer of pyrite, and rusty ones look like old cannon balls. At Kettle Point, Ontario, the large spherical concretions occurring in the Huron shale are composed of long, slender crystals of brown carbonate which radiate from the center. The concentric shells of some concretions differ in composition so much that weathering affects them differently. It thus happens that a shell inside the surface layer may disintegrate and leave the center loose. Such partly weathered concretions have been mistaken for fossil peaches or walnuts and are often referred to as rattle stones. It is evident that concretions were formed in place and since the deposition of the beds enclosing them, that they have grown up gradually from the center, and that they have partly displaced and partly incorporated the rock which originally occupied the places where they are found.

The material of which the concretion is formed was probably once disseminated in the host or enclosing rock, from which it was dissolved by ground water and carried to the place where the concretion is now found, often to be precipitated around some nucleus such as a fossil. Once started around the nucleus, precipitation continued, and the concretion increased in size.

Some concretions have been cracked or broken by jointing, and the cracks have been filled, veinlike, by material differing slightly in composition from that of the concretion. Such concretions are *septaria* (Fig. 301).

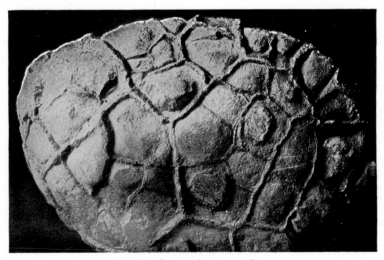

FIG. 301. A septarian concretion.

Since usually they are disklike in shape and show an irregular pattern resembling slightly the pattern on the back of a turtle, they have sometimes been mistaken for fossil turtles. Concretions are so abundant in certain limestones and in other sedimentary rocks that the whole rock is referred to as a concretionary mass.

Geodes. Geodes (Greek *ge* + *eidos*, earthlike) are cavities partially filled with crystals (Fig. 302). The filling grows inward from the surface of the cavity, and the crystals in the hollow space commonly point toward the center. Most of them are composed of quartz or calcite, but some are composed of other material that was deposited from solution by ground water. They are common in all kinds of rock.

Cone-in-cone Structure. This structure consists of a series of nesting concentric cones a fraction of an inch to 4 or 5 inches high with bases somewhat smaller (Fig. 303). These cones usually have wrinkled, fluted, or striated surfaces, but some may be relatively smooth, and in certain ones the conical surfaces are polished. The apices may be unusually sharp and the bases flaring. The cones may occur singly or in various combinations with adjacent individuals. They frequently form a double series with the bases of the two sets in opposite directions. This structure is common in lenticular calcareous beds, often in association with concretions in shales. Cone-in-cone structure is regarded as a secondary feature of layers containing fibrous calcite and is probably the result of fracture aided by the chemical action of ground water, although compacting or pressure also may be a factor.

Stylolites. Stylolites (Greek *stylos*, column) are striated, or slickensided, columnar and variously shaped projections of rock that form an interlocking and interpenetrating series along partings in carbonaceous rocks such as limestones (Fig. 304). The projections vary in

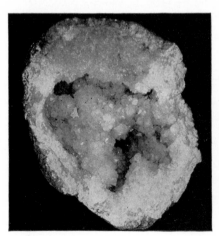

FIG. 302. A geode lined with quartz crystals.

FIG. 303. Cone-in-cone structure.

length from a fraction of an inch to 1 foot or more and are equally variable in width. Such sutured contacts may bind the two parts together so firmly that the rock will break as readily elsewhere as along the original parting plane. Stylolites result from different amounts of solution along a bedding plane or crevice, and their formation

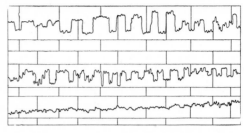

FIG. 304. Stylolites (columns and corroded surfaces) developed by solution along bedding planes of limestone under vertical pressure.

is promoted by the increased effectiveness of solution under different pressures at the points of contact on the two rock surfaces.

ENVIRONMENTS OF DEPOSITION

Places of Deposition. Eventually the products of weathering find their way to the sea, although some are temporarily lodged in various continental environments such as flood plains of rivers or in lakes. Most realms of accumulation pass laterally into each other, either as the gradual transition between the waters of the deep and shallow sea or as the flood-plain environment which passes into that of the delta and the latter in turn into the shallow-water marine realm. Likewise, both flood plains and deltas have shallow lake basins in which sediments accumulate.

The basins and other places where sediments are deposited are continental and marine. Since these two realms come into contact along the seacoast, it follows that an area adjacent to the shore line has some of the characteristics of both. Thus a third division of mixed continental and marine conditions may be included. The various places where sediments accumulate may be tabulated as follows:

Continental	Mixed continental and marine	Marine
Terrestrial:	Littoral	Shallow sea
Desert	Lagoon	Intermediate sea
Glacial	Estuary	Deep sea
Fluvial:	Delta	
Piedmont		
Valley flat		
Lake		
Swamp (paludal)		
Cave (speleal)		

CONTINENTAL SEDIMENTS

Desert Deposits. At the present time approximately 11 million square miles of arid desert regions exist on the surface of the earth. The sediments of these regions accumulate by wash from upland slopes, by intermittently torrential streams, by deposition from waters of playa and saline lakes, and by the deposition of wind-blown sediments. Most desert sediments are more or less etched, frosted, and polished. This is true especially of the coarser lag materials over the rocky desert platforms. The valley and gully deposits are composed of coarser detritus that extends up the valleys into the highlands and down the valleys to alluvial cones and fans. These coalesce laterally to form piedmont slopes so that many desert mountains appear to rise out of gravel deposits. The fine sands and silts of the playa and salt lakes dovetail with the dune and piedmont deposits. Stratification is conspicuous in the laminated clays of the lakes and playas, whereas most of the gravels on the piedmont slopes are unstratified. The aeolian sediments are characterized by wedge-shaped, cross-bedded units.

Glacial Deposits. Glacial sediments, or those deposited by ice, are unstratified, unsorted mixtures of coarse and fine sediments (Fig. 201) that are bordered laterally by and are interbedded with stratified sediments of eskers, outwash plains, and glacial lakes. The fine-grained sediments of the glacial lakes may be varved (Fig. 291). An individual varve may consist of clay and silt in various proportions, or it may be all silt or nearly all clay. The coarser the material, the thicker will be the summer as compared with the winter layer. Glacial sediments commonly rest with a sharp contact on striated and grooved rock surfaces, but they may be carried far beyond the outer ice margin or the terminal-moraine belt and may be mingled with the sediments originating by the common rock-weathering processes in distant regions. Such mixed sediments gradually lose their glacial peculiarities and take on the characteristics of ordinary river sediments except that they may retain fragments of rocks belonging to drainage basins other than that in which they find lodgment. Thus the upper Mississippi River has received glacially derived materials from Hudson Bay and the St. Lawrence drainage basins, transported them to the Gulf of Mexico, and built them into its own delta.

Fluvial Sediments. Fluvial sediments are those deposited by the flowing water of streams. They represent the products of aggradation on piedmonts, valley flats, and the upper surfaces of deltas. Piedmont sediments accumulate about the bases of mountains as a result of soil creep, rainwash, rock streams, mudflows, and intermittent streams. The present extent of piedmont deposits in western United States has been estimated as being equal in area to that of the mountains above them. In the Cucamonga district of California the deposits are more than 1,000 feet thick. They are composed of boulders, cobbles, gravel, sand, and silts. The sediments are poorly sorted and are indistinctly bedded, with the coarser fragments nearer the base of the mountains.

The sediments of the valley flats differ from those of the piedmonts in that they show better sorting and stratification, fewer large fragments, and more organic matter. Since most streams alternately aggrade and degrade, the sediments have but temporary lodgment. Many flood plains contain lakes and swamps, both of which shift their positions as the streams change the location of their channels over the valley flats. There thus results a dovetailing of lake clays and silts with swamp mucks and peats, and these in turn alternate with sand and gravel transported by the streams. Many of the sedimentary rocks of the Great Plains region were originally deposited as fluvial sediments.

Lake Sediments. The processes operating in the filling of lake basins have already been discussed (page 287). The type of sediment being formed in a lake may be greatly influenced by the origin and location of the lake basin. Thus lakes in mountain valleys may be expected to receive more coarse material than those in the broad alluvial flats and delta regions of old-age streams; among the sediments of glacial lakes much of the fine material may be still in the form of "rock flour" rather than clay resulting from mature weathering; the sediments of saline and alkaline lakes may be expected to include appreciable amounts of chemical precipitates, etc. In general lake sediments consist of gravels, sands, clays, marl, tufa, peat, iron and manganese oxides, iron carbonates, salt, gypsum, and other saline products of evaporation.

MIXED CONTINENTAL AND MARINE SEDIMENTS

Littoral Deposits. The sediments that accumulate where the oceans and the continents meet are a mixture of material derived from the land and from the sea. They accumulate along the shore zone and in the lagoons and estuaries. Conditions of deposition in the littoral zone are not everywhere the same. Some shore zones consist of bare, rocky platforms; others are nearly vertical sea cliffs; and still others are composed of gravels, sands, muds, shells, and shell fragments. These sediments grade into each other alongshore and grade seaward by imperceptible stages into the offshore marine deposits. The sediments of the shore zone are derived mainly from the shore by wave action. The waves are aided by frost, by undercutting, and by the wind. The work of the wind is more important, however, in generating waves and currents that carry sediments to the beaches. The materials of the beach vary with the source of supply and the vigor of the wave action. Upon a boisterous or surf-beaten coast the materials may be boulders or large cobblestones. Where the supply of finer materials is extensive, even on exposed coasts, the material may be pebbles or it may be sand. On rocky coasts beaches of boulders and cobblestones commonly form at the heads of indentations, although at places sand may occupy such positions. These *pocket beaches* are found along the coast of California at Carmel, at La Jolla, and at many other places. They are merely lodgment places in which the rock fragments are ground to fine particles and from which they are finally swept to sea by the returning water. The grinding process is caused by surf rolling up and down the beach dragging the boulders, cobblestones, and pebbles back and forth over each other and over the rock-shod bottom. As agitation ceases and the sediments finally are deposited, they are graded in the order of size from the shore outward.

Lagoon and Estuary Deposits. In the marginal lagoons the waters range from fresh water to waters with a salinity greater than that of the adjacent sea. The sediments that accumulate there likewise exhibit a considerable range. Land-derived sediments are brought by streams and wind; marine sediments are brought by currents from the sea; and organic and chemical precipitates are produced from the salts in solution. Calcareous marls are precipitated by plants and invertebrate animals and to some extent by direct chemical precipitation. In stagnant lagoons the activity of bacteria leads to the formation of hydrogen sulfide, which causes the precipitation of black iron sulfide in the accumulating sediments. In such black muds carbonate shells dissolve and are replaced by iron sulfide. At places where there is extensive evaporation the salinity may become so great that beds of salt and gypsum are deposited.

Delta sediments also accumulate in the mixed continental and marine realm (page 203).

Cave Deposits. Cave deposits are, for the most part, the products of precipitation from underground water. However, much fine clastic sediment may descend through cracks and crevices in the rocks of the bottoms of sinks, and, together with the insoluble residue of the beds undergoing solution, it may be distributed throughout the ramifying caverns beneath. In the loess-covered region of the Mississippi Basin, water dripping from the roofs of caves leaves much loess in the calcite that forms stalactites and stalagmites. During the active cave-forming stage the walls of cracks and caverns may be coated with such material. As a result many of these caves lack the beauty of those in other regions where such conditions are absent.

Other clastic materials may fall from the ceiling or walls of the cave or may be brought in by wind or by rodents or other animals to make so-called "cave earth." Artifacts, hearthstones, charcoal, bones, and other materials resulting from the occupation of caves by prehistoric man may be included; hence cave deposits are important in archaeology. Excrement of bats, rats, ground sloths, and other animals has accumulated in some caves to form *guano*, in places in sufficient volume to be used as sources of nitrate and phosphate fertilizers.

MARINE SEDIMENTS

The realms of marine sedimentation include the shallow epicontinental seas, the continental, or intermediate, slopes, and the deep sea (Figs. 247, 305). Sediments of this character cover a large portion of the land surface of the earth, and of course they are being laid down on the bottom of the present ocean.

Shallow-sea, or Neritic, Deposits. The shallow sea is that portion of the ocean basin extending from the low-tide level to an average depth of about 70 fathoms (Shepard). It includes the major portion of the Continental Shelf, together with such epicontinental seas as the Baltic Sea and Hudson Bay. It covers about 11 million square miles in tracts varying in width from a few miles to several hundred miles. The shelf is especially wide in the North Polar Sea along the coast of Siberia. Its average slope is only about 2 fathoms per mile; so the sediments deposited on it are practically flat-lying.

The distribution, extent, and depths of the shallow sea vary in geologic time with the nature and extent of diastrophic movements. Where the sea level rises, the deeper portions of the shallow sea are added to the intermediate slopes and the lowlands along the coast are flooded so that the former littoral zone is added to the area of the shallow sea. During the geologic past when large areas were reduced to low peneplanes, a rise of sea level extended the shallow sea far into the interior of the continents and added many thousands of square miles to the realms in

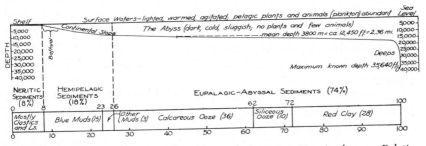

FIG. 305. Distribution of marine sediments in relation to position in the sea. Relative areas of depth zones in per cent are shown above and of bottom sediments below. (*Data from Kuenen.*)

which shallow-water deposits accumulated. Most of the marine sedimentary rocks of the continents of today accumulated in such basins.

The shoreward portion of the shallow sea bottom lies within the range of wave and current action. Where such currents are generated, the sediments are sorted so that the coarser materials are deposited near shore and grade into finer deposits seaward. There are many exceptions, however, to this generalization, for, along low shores with few streams, fine muds and calcareous sediments may accumulate far up toward the beach. A study of the sediments from the Continental Shelf along the eastern coast of the United States shows that the distribution of sediments is extremely irregular.

In general, rock bottom and coarse sediments occur off rocky points or rocky sea cliffs onshore, or wherever strong currents affect the bottom, as between islands, in narrow straits, or on shoals (Shepard). Sand prevails on the Continental Shelf off sandy coasts or in areas of moderate currents. Mud is deposited off large river mouths, in sheltered areas near shore, and in depressions on the Continental Shelf.

The great bulk of shallow-sea sediments is made up of detritus derived from land by way of streams, glaciers, dust- and sandstorms, shore erosion, and explosive volcanoes. Part is contributed by corals, calcareous algae, shellfish, and chemical precipitation.

Where the supply of land detritus is small, the sediments on the sea bottom may consist chiefly of the remains of organisms and of chemical precipitates. Some precipitates may be formed in the sea by reactions between constituents of different origin which produce insoluble compounds. It is not known to what extent calcium carbonate is precipitated by a purely inorganic process. It is doubtful whether simple precipitation takes place to any appreciable extent in the ocean under usual conditions, and probably most marine calcareous sediments are of organic origin. Such sediments form in comparatively shallow water, where lime-secreting organisms live in abundance but where there is relatively little sediment being carried in from the adjacent land. Partial disintegration of the shells, due to the grinding by waves or to solution, may destroy their original structure before they have been transformed into solid rock, or recrystallization may destroy remnants of forms that are left. The resulting unfossiliferous rock might be mistaken for a direct chemical precipitate.

The calcium carbonate content of the offshore sediments is influenced by temperature, depth, salinity, degree of saturation of the water with calcium carbonate, and the activity of living organisms. It increases as the surface salinity rises. The rate of rise in carbonate is greatest between salinities of 34 and 36 parts per thousand.

The structural features of offshore marine sediments are variable.

Deposits near shore are usually lenticular beds, with much cross-bedding and a great range in size of particles. Ripple and current marks have equally great variation in trend and in extent of development. Where the sea floor has steep slopes, the sediments may slump and develop crumpled and irregular bedding planes. In deeper waters the strata are more nearly uniform, and the stratification is distinct. Some chemical sediments show well-defined seasonal laminations.

The rate at which sediments accumulate cannot be determined with a high degree of accuracy. Attempts have been made to arrive at average rates of deposition, but the most that can be expected is a mean for each basin of accumulation. The rate of erosion of a given region has been compared with the area of the basin receiving sediments, but figures obtained in this way are, at best, quite inaccurate. Attempts have been made also to divide the total thickness of the column of sediments by the length of geologic time arrived at by the study of radioactive disintegration. This method may also have an extremely wide margin of error, as it does not take into account long periods when there was no deposition. The relative rates indicated in the accompanying table are reasonably accurate, but the total number of years listed for 1 foot of each type of sedimentary rock should be considered as nothing more than a rough estimate.

Estimated Rate of Sedimentation in the Epicontinental Seas of the Geologic Past (From Schuchert)

Type of rock	Time required to deposit a thickness of 1 foot, years
Sandstone	450
Shale	900
Limestone	2,250

Umbgrove, in 1945, computed that 9,000 meters of sediments accumulated in four geosynclines in Indonesia over a period of 60 million years at an average rate of 15 centimeters per 1,000 years, or 1 foot in about 1,800 years. Other areas yielded computed rates of as little as 1 foot in 9,000 to 20,000 years or more.

Intermediate and Deep-sea Deposits. Beyond the Continental Shelf the ocean bottom descends rather abruptly to the sea floor with an average depth of 2½ miles below the surface. This descent is the Continental Slope, or outer margin of the true continental mass. It begins at an average distance of about 40 miles from the coast; hence, in general, it is covered by those fine sediments of land origin which remain in suspension for a long period. These collectively are called the blue muds and owe their color to the presence of organic matter and to the deoxidized condition of the iron. Landward they grade into the shallower water deposits, and seaward they pass into the oozes and red clay of the abysmal depths. The blue muds probably cover 15 million square miles of the ocean basin. They have been encountered at distances from land as great as 200 miles, and out from the mouths of great rivers, such as the Amazon, they extend a distance of 1,000 miles. Volcanic mud, pieces of pumice, and scoria have been picked up by dredges more than 200 miles distant from the volcanic islands of Hawaii. Land-derived vegetation is strewn over the sea bottom at places even at a distance of several hundred miles from the land and in 200 fathoms of water. Such vegetation was found off the coast of Central America on both the Atlantic and the Pacific sides, where nearly every haul of the "Challenger" dredge brought up fruits, seeds, leaves, twigs, branches, and parts of the trunks of trees. This organic matter contributes to the deoxidizing agents of the blue-mud zone, but probably little is preserved in fossil form.

Areas and Depths below Sea Level of the Various Sediments on the Marginal Slopes of the Marine Environment (*From the Report of the "Challenger"*)

Sediment	Area, square miles	Mean depth, fathoms	Depth limits, fathoms
Coral (and algal) muds	2,236,800	740	1,820
Coral (and algal) sands		176	
Volcanic muds	600,000	1,033	260 to 2,800
Volcanic sands		243	100 to 420
Green muds	850,000	513	100 to 1,270
Green sands		449	900
Red muds	400,000	623	120 to 1,200
Blue muds	14,500,000	1,421	125 to 2,800

With increasing distance from shore the land-derived materials assume less and less importance. In the deep abyss many sediments are of volcanic, pelagic, glacial, and meteoric origin. At great depths the pressure is tremendous. It rises at the rate of more than 1 ton per square inch per mile of depth, so that at a depth of 4 to 6 miles the weight on each square inch is 5 to 7 tons. The temperature is approximately 35°F. at all times; and since currents and waves of the near-shore type do not exist, there is no appreciable motion of the water. There is no light other than that emitted by the phosphorescence of deep-sea organisms. Fewer organisms exist than in shallower waters. The chief organic sediments consist of the hard parts of organisms which lived in the upper, lighted waters. These surface-dwelling forms are chiefly simple types of plants and animals collectively called the *plankton*. They consist of small Mollusca, Foraminifera, and Algae, which secrete calcium carbonate, together with diatoms and radiolarians, which secrete siliceous skeletons. When these organisms die, their remains sink to the bottom, where the undissolved residue, together with volcanic, meteoric, and other dusts form oozes, or slimy deposits, that accumulate very slowly. These oozes are named according to the most abundant remains composing them. Thus there are the globigerina oozes, the pteropod oozes, the diatom oozes, the radiolarian oozes, etc., but they all grade into each other.

Globigerina ooze is by far the most extensive, and it is now forming over an area of 50 million square miles (Fig. 305). Diatom ooze is formed mainly in the cool waters of the North Pacific and of a belt surrounding Antarctica. The radiolarian ooze is found in some of the deepest parts of the sea.

Owing in part to the increase, with depth, of the carbon dioxide in sea water, the percentage of calcium carbonate in the bottom deposits decreases in general with depth. This is because the carbon dioxide and water form a weak acid which dissolves the calcium carbonate. Considering the oozes and muds of various origin together, the calcium carbonate content of the deposits on the sea bottom is as follows:

Variations with Depth in Calcium Carbonate of Bottom Deposits (After F. W. Clarke)

Fathoms	Per cent	Fathoms	Per cent
Under 500	86.04	2,000 to 2,500	46.73
500 to 1,000	66.86	2,500 to 3,000	17.36
1,000 to 1,500	70.87	3,000 to 3,500	0.88
1,500 to 2,000	69.55	3,500 to 4,000	None

In the greater depths of the ocean the bottom is covered by a very fine red clay (most of it really chocolate-brown), which is composed of terrigenous clay, insoluble portions of the plankton shells and other organic matter, volcanic ash, and meteoric dust from the heavens. Moulton [1] states that more than 20 million visible meteors enter our atmosphere daily; those of telescopic magnitude may number 100 billion per day. Most of them disintegrate in their passage through the air and settle as fine dust over land and sea. From the amount of kinetic energy of their high velocities transformed into light it is estimated that even the bright ones weigh only a very small fraction of an ounce. If most of them are no bigger than a grain of sand, the total weight of such material reaching the earth yearly would be only 50 to 200 tons according to their size and density. A very liberal estimate of their size and weight would

[1] Forest Ray Moulton, Astronomy, p. 305, 1931.

increase the total increment to about 50,000 tons a year. Although three-fourths of this is scattered over the ocean basin, the amount is trivial. It is evident, therefore, that sedimentation on the deep-sea floor from this source is exceedingly slow.

The rate at which sedimentation is taking place may be appreciated from the fact that dredging on the sea floor often brings up the inner ear bones of the whale; these are the most resistant parts of the whole skeleton and have thus accumulated on the sea bottom through many generations of whales, and yet they are so thinly covered by the red clay that frequently the dredge will bring them up, sometimes as many as 90 in a single haul. At Station 285, in the South Pacific, a single haul of the "Challenger" dredge brought to the surface 1,500 sharks' teeth, many of them representing extinct species, in addition to immense numbers of very small teeth and fragments. Evidently they had been accumulating for a very long time, and although manganese-coated they were practically without sedimentary covering. The red clay occupies about 40 million square miles of the sea bottom, and most of the known area is in the Pacific Ocean.

Schott has estimated the rate of red-clay deposition in the Atlantic Ocean to be 1 centimeter in 1,200 years and of globigerina ooze 1 centimeter in 265 to 1,700 years.

Thickness and Rate of Sedimentation of Recent Marine Sediments in the Deep Sea in Equatorial Atlantic Ocean since End of Glacial Epoch (From W. Schott)

	Blue mud	Glo-bigerina ooze	Red clay
Average thickness, centimeters	35.50	24.06	17.14
Greatest observed thickness, centimeters	66.00	42.50	26.50
Smallest observed thickness, centimeters	18.00	10.50	10.00
Average rate of sedimentation, centimeters per 1,000 years	1.78	1.20	0.86
Greatest observed rate of sedimentation, centimeters per 1,000 years	3.30	2.13	1.33
Smallest observed rate of sedimentation, centimeters per 1,000 years	0.90	0.53	0.50

A core sample, 194 centimeters long, composed of alternating layers of red clay and globigerina ooze, obtained in the southeastern Pacific Ocean, was computed from radioactive materials to be at least 800,000 and possibly 990,000 years old at its bottom end. The bottom end of another core, 138 centimeters long, obtained farther south and hence composed entirely of red clay, was found to be possibly 1,231,000 years old or more. The indicated rates of sedimentation in the two cores, therefore, are 1 centimeter in about 4,100 (or possibly 5,100) years and 1 centimeter in about 8,900 years, respectively. Comparable results have been obtained from similar cores obtained from the bottom of the Atlantic Ocean. The alternations in such cores of globigerina ooze (attributed to warm water conditions) and of red clay (corresponding to cold water conditions) are thought to record a series of interglacial and glacial climates during a large part of the Pleistocene ice age. When one can capture a million years of accumulation of sediments in the deep sea in a core only a few feet long, the rate of deposition must be slow indeed. The continued study of deep-sea core samples is a very promising line of research.

Although the chalk beds of England and France are chiefly the remains of Foraminifera and a large part of the Monterey series at Lompoc, California, consists of the remains of diatoms, it is doubtful whether these or any beds found on the present continents correspond to the deep-sea oozes or the red clays. Steinmann reports them in the Alps and the Apennines, and others consider some of the radiolarian cherts of the northern Appalachian region to be deep-sea deposits; but even if these should prove to be true abysmal deposits, the total known land area would be small.

STRATIGRAPHIC RELATIONS OF SEDIMENTS

Conformity and Unconformity. As a result of the deposition of a continuous series of beds, one kind of rock is said to lie on the other with *conformity*. If, however, there is an erosion surface between any two beds, there is evidently a discontinuity in deposition. A region of deposition may be elevated, or uplifted, and thus converted into one of nondeposition or of erosion, and after an interval the same region may be depressed so that sediments again are deposited on the old surface. If the beds below the erosion surface are tilted so that they form an angle with the beds lying on top of it, the contact is called an angular *unconformity* (Fig. 306); but if the beds above and below the erosion surface are parallel, the contact is called a *disconformity*. The actual erosion surface in either case may be even or uneven depending on whether or not it had been base-leveled.

Overlap and Offlap. In the normal course of events the sea may gradually encroach upon the land as the process of base-leveling advances. The deposition of the coarser sediments follows the retreating coast line, and therefore it takes place progressively farther to landward. This causes the newly deposited sediments to cover up the margin of the lately formed sediments and the basal beds to rest in turn on an erosion surface of continually changing age. The result is an unconformable contact known as an *overlap* (Fig. 307).

A

B

FIG. 306. A, photograph of an unconformity between the Laramie sandstone and the Wasatch conglomerate. (*Photograph by Fisher, U.S. Geological Survey.*) B, sketch of the unconformity shown in A.

The reverse, however, takes place when the coast is rising and coarse sediments are laid down farther and farther seaward on top of the finer sediments. The sea is retreating, and each succeeding, or younger, division leaves a portion of the older one exposed to landward. This type of contact between differing sediments has been called *offlap* (Fig. 308). The conditions which form offlap may be followed by those of *onlap*, and the top sandstone of emergence in the offlap may be followed directly by the bottom sandstone of submergence in an onlap, thus producing a compound, or double, series with the contact lying within the sandstone that represents both the emergence and the submergence.

Lateral and Vertical Variations. Sediments may grade laterally or vertically into other kinds of sediments, forming intermediate or mixed types. On the usually gently sloping coastal portion of the Continental Shelf the coarser gravels are deposited near shore and are succeeded gradually by

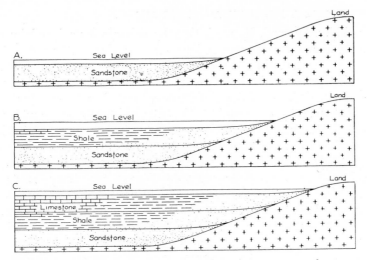

FIG. 307. Diagram showing an overlap, resulting from progressive submergence of a land area or a progressive transgression of the sea. *A*, beach sands are deposited on an old land surface; *B*, muds that later form shale cover much of the sand as the shore line moves inland; *C*, calcareous oozes that form limestone are deposited over the previous muds, as the sites of deposition of sands and muds shift landward.

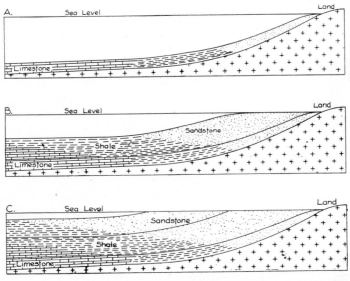

FIG. 308. Diagram showing an offlap, resulting from progressive emergence of a land area or a progressive recession of the sea. *A*, near-shore sands give way laterally to muds and calcareous sediments; *B* and *C*, as the sea recedes toward the left because of filling or of slow uplift of the land, sands are deposited over the offshore muds and muds are deposited over calcareous oozes that later form limestone.

finer pebbles, by sand, by mud, then by calcareous mud and by ooze. Wave action and shore currents, however, may disturb the regularity of this gradation seaward and hence interfere with the regular order of sediments that produce the sedimentary rocks. But the calcareous muds formed from shell deposits and their fragments do not form limestones unless the quantity of land-derived sediment accumulating with them is small. Limestones usually are formed in shallow water where lime-secreting life is abundant and off coasts that are near enough to base level so that the streams are carrying very little clastic sediment to the sea. A vertical section of the sediments forming off a coast thus may show gradations from conglomerate to sandstone to shale and finally to limestone as the adjacent land is reduced and clastic land-derived sediments fail.

The lateral variations of a sedimentary unit give rise to *facies*, that is, different rocks in different geographic areas. Where these unlike subdivisions shift positions in the course of time, because of changes of location of shore lines or of supply of sediment or other factors, the resulting stratigraphic column becomes complex vertically as well as horizontally. Repeated lateral shifting of the sites of deposition of sands, muds, and calcareous matter causes the edges of these deposits to dovetail, or interfinger, with one another. Detailed studies of such lateral changes of facies are especially important in the search for petroleum.

Tectonic Control of Sedimentation. As shown by cross-bedding, ripple marks, fossils, and other features, a large part of the sedimentary rocks on the continents are shallow-water marine sediments. In several mountain ranges these sediments are tens of thousands of feet thick. The inference is then that the accumulation of such great volumes of sediments in shallow water was made possible or was induced by progressive subsidence of the sites of deposition. The character of the sediments depended in part upon the degree of balance between the rate of subsidence and the rate of filling and in part upon contemporaneous changes in the source areas. Notable uplift adjacent to the basin would supply a great bulk of coarse arkosic sediment, whereas long-continued erosion of a stable land would change the sedimentary substances reaching the sea largely to fine muds and solutions. Hence sedimentary rocks, by their composition, texture, thickness, areal distribution, and other characteristics, reflect the complex interplay of a number of factors, of which tectonic movements are perhaps the most influential.

Interpretation of Sedimentary Rocks. Because of the dependence of many characteristics of sedimentary rocks upon the environments of their origin all sedimentary rocks tend to record the conditions of sedimentation existing at the time they were deposited. *Every rock tells a story.* Sandstones, for example, show ripple marks, wavemarks, cross-bedding, tracks, burrows, etc., just as do sands of the seashore today. Other kinds of sedimentary rocks, by their composition, structure, texture, fossils, and other features, also carry telltale signs of conditions of the past, and so an interpretation of ancient sediments is made possible by a knowledge of what is taking place under similar conditions today. Thus the present is the key to the past.

Ancient epicontinental shallow seas, former ice sheets, extinct lakes, and other features of the past are recorded by their sediments. Such sediments tell not only the environments of deposition but also something about their derivation, the relief of the land from which they came, the climate under which they were weathered, and other geographic conditions of the past.

As sediments have been accumulating in an orderly succession throughout the past ages as veritable tablets of stone, they constitute the main documents of geologic history.

SUGGESTIONS FOR FURTHER READING

Kemp, James F.: Handbook of Rocks, 6th ed., D. Van Nostrand Company, Inc., 1940.

Krumbein, W. C., and L. L. Sloss: Stratigraphy and Sedimentation, W. H. Freeman & Co., 1951.

Pettijohn, F. J.: Sedimentary Rocks, Harper & Brothers, 1949.

Shrock, R. R.: Sequence in Layered Rocks, McGraw-Hill Book Company, Inc., 1948.

Spock, L. E.: Guide to the Study of Rocks, pp. 144–190, Harper & Brothers, 1953.

Trask, Parker D.: Recent Sediments; A Symposium, American Association of Petroleum Geologists, 1939.

CHAPTER 16

Volcanic Phenomena

The term *vulcanism* is used to embrace all aspects of volcanic activity. This includes the generation and movement of magmas within the earth's crust as well as the forceful ejection of lavas and fragmental volcanic debris at the surface of the earth (Fig. 309).

Heat within the Earth. Many observations may be made which furnish direct evidence that the interior of the earth is hot. At points about 50 feet below the surface, in the intermediate latitudes, the ground temperature is constant at about 50°F. Nearer the surface the changes are caused by daily and seasonal temperature changes in the atmosphere, but at depths greater than 50 feet the temperature increases gradually with depth. Observations in deep wells and in mines show an average increase of 1°F. for every 60 feet downward into the rocks of the crust. Boreholes have been drilled to depths of more than 20,000 feet, and the rise of temperature has been found to continue to their bottom limits. At greater depths the rate of increase may not be so high as it is nearer the surface, but extruded lavas and boiling hot springs indicate that the whole interior of the earth is very hot. An indication of the intensity of the heat is the fact that lavas issue from the earth at temperatures which range from 600 to 1200°C.

The origin of the heat within the earth is not yet fully understood. According to a view long held by many geologists this heat is simply a residue from the heat of an originally molten condition of the whole earth, which in spite of its great age is still intensely hot a few miles beneath the surface. If one ignores the heat supplied by the sun, the heat loss from the earth is very small. The actual rate of loss is controlled by the heat conductivity of the rocks and by the temperature change with depth. It has been estimated that if the internal heat were cut off entirely, the surface temperature of the earth eventually would fall only about 0.01°C. because rocks are poor conductors of heat. It is apparent, therefore, that even if there were no other source of heat within the earth, it would be losing its original heat at a very slow rate.

It is quite possible, however, that the earth is becoming hotter day by day. Beginning in 1895 it was discovered that certain atoms disintegrate spontaneously to yield other atoms of less complex structure and that this change is accompanied by the liberation of large amounts of energy in

FIG. 309. The volcano Ngauruhoe, New Zealand. (*Copyright, National Geographic Society. Reproduced with permission.*)

the form of heat. The most radioactive, naturally occurring elements are uranium and thorium, which are universally present in all rocks in extremely small quantities. It has been demonstrated that they are more concentrated in granites than in the dark-colored, basic igneous rocks and that the amount of radioactive matter diminishes in depth. Computations based on the known content of radioactive matter and the thickness and area of the granitic foundations of the continents indicate that this granite alone would seem to be able to supply more heat due to radioactivity than is escaping at the surface of the earth. If there are areas near the surface where the rocks are relatively enriched in radioactive substances, the heat generated by radioactivity in those places will accumulate slowly and, because rocks are poor conductors of heat, will remain localized and eventually, after several long units of geologic time, may become so great as to liquefy the rocks and produce bodies of magma.

Much more extensive sampling and measurement of radioactivity are needed before positive conclusions can be reached regarding the importance of radioactivity in the formation of magmas. The concept is significant, however, for it indicates a newer trend in geologic thought from that of a century ago, when students of earth history concluded that the earth was cooling off because it is giving off heat.

FIG. 310. Lava stream from vent on southwest rift of Mauna Loa, Hawaii, June, 1950. (*Photograph by Macdonald.*)

Magma. Magma is the parent material of igneous rocks. It is a natural, very hot fluid, formed beneath the surface and made up largely of mutual solutions of silicates with some oxides and sulfides and usually some steam and other gases which are held in solution by pressure. Magma has been defined as molten rock material, but this definition is not entirely satisfactory because it fails to point out that magma contains volatile constituents which are driven off as it solidifies but which nevertheless are important prior to and during crystallization. In reality, magma as such has never been sampled, for it exists only beneath the surface. That which reaches the surface is called *lava,* and it differs from magma in that most of the volatile materials and gases escape as the magma reaches the surface.

Magma is characterized by a composition that is predominantly silicate, by temperatures ranging from 500 to 1200°C., and by mobility that allows it to flow, even though only a part of it is a liquid. It has been maintained that magmas are essentially dry, but this opinion has been largely discarded, for water has been found to be universally present in volcanic fumes and also in gases evolved from crystalline igneous rocks when heated in the laboratory. It has been suggested that magma formed deep within the earth may contain an appreciable amount of hydrogen which becomes oxidized nearer the surface to produce water. Such formation of water within the earth is still conjectural, but current estimates suggest the presence of 1 to 8 per cent of water in magmas.

The formation of magma may take place in any portion of the earth where the temperature becomes sufficiently high to melt or dissolve the rocks. Not all rocks melt at the same temperature, and furthermore many factors other than temperature influence the melting point. Where magma forms, the liquid rock is lighter in weight than the adjoining solid rock and the dissolved gases make it still lighter. Hence the magma is forced upward as it is subjected to the tremendous pressures of the surrounding heavier rock. At a depth of slightly more than 100 miles the pressure is roughly 1 million pounds per square inch. The upward movement of the magma is aided by its mobility and by the expansive force and fluxing ability of dissolved gases it contains. Some of it may eventually reach the outer part of the earth's crust, where the rocks are cracked and fissured, and thus make its way through such openings to the surface. There the molten materials may be poured out as lava flows (Fig. 310), or great quantities may be broken and pulverized by explosive forces which eject it in solid form. These lava flows and fragments, ranging in size from great blocks weighing many tons down to particles as fine as dust, accumulate to form volcanoes.

Volcanoes. A volcano is a conical hill or mountain formed around an opening in the earth's surface through which hot rock fragments, gases, and lavas are ejected. As the solid materials accumulate around the conduit, they build up a cone which increases in size until a huge volcanic mountain is formed. A cone so constructed is called a volcano. However, the term includes both the vent in the earth and the mountain built around it [1] (Fig. 311).

FIG. 311. Mayon, a stratovolcano in Philippine Islands, 7,616 feet high. (*After Chester H. Reeds, American Museum of Natural History.*)

Volcanoes vary in size from small conical hills to some of the loftiest mountains on the earth's surface. The Hawaiian Islands are volcanoes that reach a height of nearly 14,000 feet above sea level, and they are built on the floor of the Pacific Ocean where the sea is 14,000 to 18,000 feet deep. Some of the highest peaks in the Andes are volcanoes, and, in the Cascade Range of western United States, Mount Baker, Mount Rainier, Mount Adams, Mount Hood, and Mount Shasta are volcanoes which recently have become extinct (Fig. 312).

Volcanic Eruptions. The eruption of a volcano is often preceded by earthquakes and by loud rumblings like thunder, which may continue on a gigantic scale during the eruption. The land rumblings of Tambora on Sumbawa Island, Dutch East Indies, in 1815, were heard over an area with a radius of about 1,000 miles. During this eruption, which is the greatest one recorded by man, about 38 cubic miles of material was thrown out. The loud rumblings are probably due to the movement of gases and molten rock that are held in under great pressure. Preceding the eruptions fissures often are opened, lakes are drained, and hot springs appear at many places.

[1] The name volcano was first applied to Mount Etna in Sicily and to some of the Lipari Islands north of Sicily. It is derived from the name of Vulcan, the Roman god of fire, who was supposed to dwell in the volcano.

The nature of a volcanic eruption is determined largely by the type of materials ejected from the volcanic vent. These products are gases, molten rock, or solid fragments. A given volcano may emit all three

FIG. 312. Map showing distribution of volcanic mountains in Washington, Oregon, and California. (*After H. Williams.*)

types of product, but in many regions a certain product predominates. Thus the Hawaiian volcanoes generally discharge very hot and highly fluid lava from which the enclosed gases escape readily. Such eruptions are nonexplosive. On the other hand, some volcanoes erupt with great explosive violence. Mount Pelée on the island of Martinique in the West Indies is a typical example. In May, 1902, it began to erupt in a series of violent explosions, but no lava was discharged during the eruption. A type of eruption intermediate in character between those on the island of Hawaii and Mount Pelée is that of the volcano Stromboli located in the Mediterranean Sea north of Sicily. Stromboli erupts every 10 or 15 minutes with mild explosions that hurl small masses of partially solidified lava into the air. Most of the fragments, both large and small, fall back into the crater. Since the interval of time between eruptions is short, the magma in the crater does not have time to cool and solidify. Furthermore, heat is continuously being brought to the surface by gases streaming up from greater depths. Steam also issues from openings and forms a cloud which reflects the light from incandescent lava. This light, often visible at night, served the navigators of ancient times, and Stromboli came to be known as the "lighthouse of the Mediterranean."

Materials Ejected by Volcanoes. The solid fragmental material hurled from volcanic vents is called *pyroclastic debris*. Large solid pieces are referred to as blocks, and the more or less elliptical pieces with spirally twisted ends are known as *volcanic bombs* (Fig. 313). The smaller intermediate sizes are called *lapilli*, or cinders, and the finer material is *ash* and dust. Some volcanic blocks are exceedingly large. In 1930 the volcano

FIG. 313. Volcanic bombs. (*Photograph by Grout.*)

Stromboli hurled blocks weighing 2 tons for a distance of more than 2 miles from its crater, and some of the solid fragments were only partially solidified when they were thrown. During their flight through the air the gases they contained escaped and gave the fragments a vesicular, cellular, or spongy character.

The liquid rock that issues from a volcano is lava. In many instances the lava does not flow over the rim of the crater but issues through secondary vents, or fissures, in the sides of the cone. The character and appearance of lava vary with its chemical composition and temperature. When it issues from the earth it may be red- or white-hot but it soon cools on the surface and becomes darker in color. In general, the more siliceous lavas are quite viscous. The degree of viscosity determines the rate at which the lava flows and the angle of slope at which it may come to rest before it solidifies. Thus the nature of the lava determines the steepness of the slope of many volcanic mountains.

Large amounts of gas issue from the vents of most volcanoes, and, of the many gases that escape, steam is by far the most abundant. Some of it is formed by heating ground water and surface water that have come in contact with the hot products of the volcanoes. Much of it, however, is believed to be steam that was dissolved in the magmas. Chlorine and sulfur gases issue with steam from certain volcanoes, and these may be in part the products of heated sea water but probably in a large measure are of magmatic origin.

The gases arising from the Valley of Ten Thousand Smokes a few miles northwest of Katmai, Alaska (Fig. 314), have been closely studied. An eruption in 1912 scattered ashes 6 inches deep as far as 150 miles away. In this valley steam issues from hundreds of vents in large amounts, and it is probable that a buried intrusive lies below the valley. Hydrochloric and hydrofluoric acids, sulfur, and boron compounds rise with the steam. Zies estimated that 1,250,000 tons of hydrochloric acid and 200,000 tons of hydrofluoric acid issue annually. The steam and chlorine compounds might be derived in part from sea water, but this is improbable, since they are associated with large amounts of hydrofluoric acid, and fluorine is very sparingly present in sea water. The steam which constitutes 99 per cent of the gas issuing from the vents is very hot, about 97 to 650°C. The steam and vapors carry with them many metals in appreciable amounts, among them iron, lead, zinc, molybdenum, copper, arsenic, antimony, tin, and silver, which were identified in the incrustations along fissures through which the gases rise. The gases issuing from a vent of Mount Pelée in 1902 were examined by Lacroix and were found to consist of water vapor, with hydrogen chloride, carbon dioxide, carbon monoxide, sulfur, methane, hydrogen, nitrogen, oxygen, and argon. These gases issued at a temperature of 400°C.

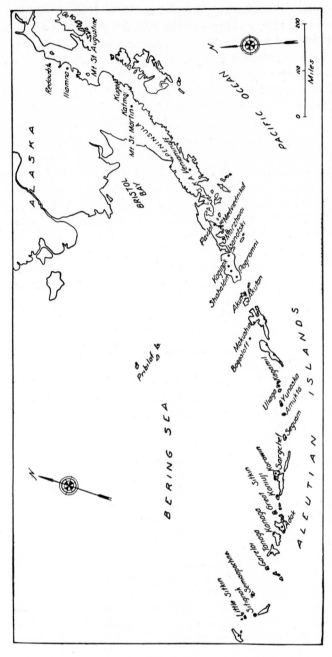

FIG. 314. Map showing locations of volcanoes of Alaskan peninsula and Aleutian Islands.

The volume of output of volcanic material from volcanoes varies greatly. Iceland leads all other districts in the output of lava, and the Dutch East Indies lead the world in volume of fragmental deposits for the period of human history. In general, the oceans and subarctic regions are at present the great lava producers; the continental borders and the equatorial belt produce most products of explosions. The output series in the following tables are taken from Sapper.

	Cubic kilometers fragmental
1. Java belt	185.0
2. Central America	58.0
3. Alaska-Aleutian	30.0
4. Iceland	10.0
5. South America	9.5
6. Japan	8.2
7. Philippines-Molucca	6.5
8. Kamchatka-Kurile	6.0
9. New Zealand–Tonga	4.1
10. North America–Antilles	3.5
11. Mediterranean	3.5
12. Melanesia	3.1
13. Atlantic Ocean	2.2
14. Indian Ocean–Africa	2.0
15. Central Pacific	1.5

In order of lava output the series is as follows:

	Cubic kilometers lava
1. Iceland	15.5
2. Central Pacific	11.0
3. Indian Ocean–Africa	8.0
4. Atlantic Ocean	5.5
5. Mediterranean	5.1
6. Kamchatka-Kurile	5.0
7. Japan	3.5
8. Alaska-Aleutian	2.0
9. New Zealand–Tonga	2.0
10. North America–Antilles	1.5
11. South America	1.2
12. Philippines-Molucca	1.2
13. Central America	0.6
14. Java Belt	0.5
15. Melanesia	0.1

Kinds and Shapes of Volcanic Cones. There are three main types of volcanic cone, namely, cinder cones, lava cones, and composite cones. The *cinder cones* are steep-sided, symmetrical, cone-shaped volcanoes built up of angular fragments erupted from the earth in violent explosions. If the material thrown out consists of large, solid fragments, the cone will have steep walls with slopes of 30 or 40 degrees. If the material consists chiefly of finely broken rocks or dust, water and wind will carry it farther away from the vent, so that the volcano will have gentler slopes. Volcanoes that throw out both large fragments and dust are of the explosive type and generally eject gases in considerable amounts. Volcanoes of this type include Vesuvius, Krakatao, Mount Pelée, and many others.

Lava cones are more nearly flat and are composed of many superposed layers of lava which issued at a high temperature and therefore in a highly fluid state. Since basic lavas are more fluid (less viscous) than

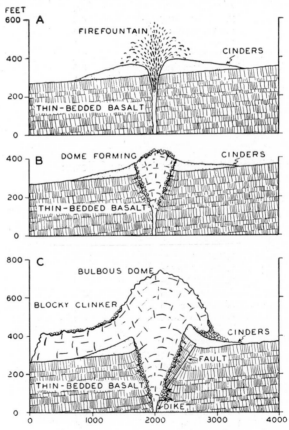

FIG. 315. Stages in the formation of bulbous volcanic domes. (*After Stearns.*)

acidic lavas, they form volcanoes with gentler slopes. Such nearly flat cones, similar to those in Hawaii, are called *shield volcanoes* (Fig. 325). Mauna Loa on the island of Hawaii is a shield-shaped dome about 60 miles long and 30 miles wide. It is one of the most prolific lava producers on earth. Its slope near its base is only 2 degrees, but it increases summitward to 10 degrees and flattens out again above an altitude of 10,000 feet. Its total elevation is 13,675 feet above sea level, but its base rests on the floor of the sea where the ocean is approximately 15,000 feet deep. Thus the mountain is in reality more than 28,000 feet high.

Vents are opened on the flanks of volcanoes, and material is ejected from them. From these vents are built up subordinate cones with characteristic slopes and craters. These volcanoes which are developed on the sides of older volcanoes are *parasitic cones*. It is believed that the central vent had become choked with the solidification of lava and that molten matter rose in fissures radiating from the central vent. Since the openings developed on the flanks are lower than the central vents, lavas more readily may rise from them. Parasitic cones are developed on the flanks of Etna, Vesuvius, and other volcanoes.

Composite cones consist of layers of lava and cinders. Such cones are generally intermediate in steepness between cinder cones and lava cones. The presence of both lava and cinders indicates that a volcano of this type at times ejected fragmental materials and at other times discharged fluid lavas. The fragmental materials of successive explosions form layers of different textures and colors and thus produce a stratification that records the angle of rest of the material ejected. This stratification is made more conspicuous by the sheets of lava interbedded with the layers of pyroclastic fragments. Volcanoes which possess such well-marked stratification are called *stratovolcanoes* (Fig. 311), and those which are mainly viscous magma form bulbous volcanic domes (Fig. 315).

Craters, Calderas, and Other Features of Volcanoes. The top of a volcano generally is marked by a pit, or crater (Figs. 316, 317). This pit is usually funnel-shaped and represents the vent through which material is ejected, widened near the top by explosions and by the sliding back of the volcanic matter of the rim or by the lava in the crater melting and dissolving the rock of the funnel. The crater may be widened to great size, and subsequently upon its floor another cone is built up of material ejected from the vent.

The explosion at Mount Katmai produced a crater more than 2 miles in diameter and 2,000 to 3,500 feet in depth. In a valley a distance northwest of the volcano, numerous fissures were opened, and rock debris was strewn over the valley floor. Gases still issue from these vents, and the area is now called the Valley of Ten Thousand Smokes.

A caldera is a huge circular pit resulting from an explosion or collapse

FIG. 316. Amboy Crater, San Bernardino County, California. (*Spence Air Photos.*)

FIG. 317. Small, circular lava lake at foot of wall of Halemaumau Crater, September, 1920. (*Photograph by J. A. Jaggar.*)

of a former volcanic cone. Most calderas are of great size, and many of them are very wide as compared with their depth. However, there is no distinct line of demarcation in size between a crater and a caldera. The term caldera is taken from the huge pit in the Canary Islands, called La Caldera, which is more than 3 miles in diameter and is surrounded by cliffs nearly 3,000 feet high. Two splendid examples of depressions of this type are the calderas at the summits of Kilauea and Mauna Loa in Hawaii. The caldera of Kilauea is 2½ miles long and 1¾ miles wide, and that of Mauna Loa is 3½ miles in length and 1¾ miles in width. Both these calderas were formed by the collapse of the summits of shield volcanoes. Such collapse results from the withdrawal of the lava column from below the shield-shaped cone, either by eruptions onto the surface or by movement of magma within the earth's crust. The presence of concentric fault escarpments bounding the pits is evidence of the downward movement of the summit of the cones. Furthermore, the steep inner walls of many calderas are marked by concentric or interweaving fissures, marking the slips and faults caused by the down-dragging core. Where magma is injected into the concentric fissures, ring dikes (page 422) are formed.

Many great calderas are known, and some are very large. Possibly the largest in the world occurs in the ancient volcanic field of northern New Mexico where the Valle Grande is 18 miles long and 15 miles wide. Smaller pits, as much as 3 miles in diameter, were formed by gigantic explosions that blew away the summits of former cones. Subsidences on a much larger scale have occurred where eruptions of lava took place along fissures rather than from central vents. Some of such *volcano-tectonic* depressions are enormous, like those of Lakes Tabo and Ranan along the rift zone of Sumatra, one of which is approximately 60 miles long and 20 miles wide.

At certain places which may be distant from volcanic areas, low ridges occur around craterlike pits. The material in a given ridge consists largely of fragments of the country rock, but minor amounts of volcanic debris may be present. These structures are interpreted as embryonic volcanoes in which the volcanic activity has been limited to the opening of a vent through the country rock. Such *explosion pits* are common in east central Europe west of the Rhine River in the region known as the volcanic Eifel. Since many of these pits, which range from ¼ to ½ mile in diameter, are filled with water, they are called moors, or maars.

Nonvolcanic Craters. Meteor Crater near Winslow, Arizona, is a pit almost 1 mile in diameter and 500 feet deep in a region of recent volcanic activity (Fig. 318). The presence of abundant fragments of meteoritic iron found in and around the crater was interpreted as evidence that the crater was formed by the explosive impact of a large meteorite or a swarm

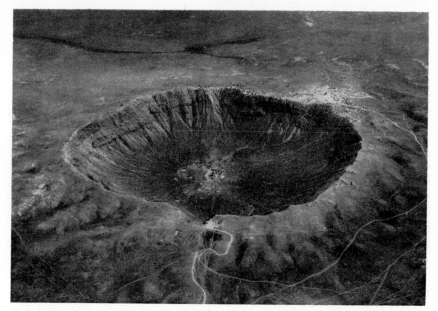

FIG. 318. Meteor Crater near Winslow, Arizona. (*Spence Air Photos.*)

of meteorites. On the other hand the presence of numerous thick strata of soluble rocks such as salt, gypsum, and limestone, together with numerous fractures along which there has been slumping, has led a few geologists to conclude that the crater was formed by the collapse of a low structural mound as a result of subterranean solution. A shower of meteorites undoubtedly fell in the vicinity, but the relationship between the shower of meteoritic fragments and the origin of the crater is still uncertain.

Dimensions of Other Craters of Known Meteoritic Origin

Crater	Width, feet	Depth, feet	Ratio of width to depth
Meteor Crater, United States	3,900	570	6.8
Wolf Creek Crater, Australia	2,800	170	16.5
Boxhole Crater, Australia	575	52	11.1
Texas Crater, United States	530	18	29.4
Henbury Crater, Australia	360	60	6.0
Henbury Crater, Australia	240	25	9.6
Henbury Crater, Australia	30	3	10.0
Wabar Craters, Arabia	328	40	8.0
Campo del Cielo Crater, Argentina	183	16	11.4
Siberian Crater, U.S.S.R.	164	13	12.5

Chubb Crater on the subarctic tip of Quebec Province, Canada (Fig. 12) is thought to have been formed by the impact of a huge meteorite. This crater is much larger than Meteor Crater in Arizona. A recent survey indicates that Chubb Crater is 11,500 feet in diameter from rim to rim; the lake in the bowl of the crater is more than 2 miles across and as much as 1,300 feet deep. The rim of the crater stands 500 feet above the level of the lake and is composed of angular blocks of granite. It is estimated that 5 billion tons of granite were shattered by the impact. Other huge meteorites are known to have struck the earth, making craterlike depressions. One weighing more than 50 tons lies where it fell in southwest Africa, and one weighing nearly 37 tons was found by Peary near Cape York. It is now on display in the Hayden Planetarium in the American Museum of Natural History in New York City. Three meteorites ranging in weight from 11 to 27 tons have been found in Mexico.

Mud Volcanoes. Gas issuing at the surface of the earth may carry with it particles of sand and clay which are deposited at the vent, and as the process continues, a cone is built up. If water is present, the sand and clay form mud, which dries and hardens at the surface of the mound, and gas accumulates below the hardened surface until the pressure is sufficient to blow off the top of the cone, imitating on a small scale the eruption of a true volcano. Some of these mounds, or "volcanoes," are built to considerable heights. The famous Bog-Boga mud volcano in the Baku region near the Caspian Sea is more than 100 feet high. Many mud volcanoes are found in oil and gas fields, and some of these are far removed from true volcanic areas. They are formed by the gas that escapes from gas-bearing strata. Other mud volcanoes are found in areas where steam, probably volcanic, escapes through mud. Those at the southeast end of the Salton Sea, near the mouth of the Alamo River to the west of Niland, California, emit steam and gases that have a slight odor of sulfur (Fig. 319).

Distribution of Volcanoes. Volcanoes may form on mountains or plateaus, on low plains, and on the bottom of the sea. They are widely distributed both chronologically and geographically (Fig. 320). They were active at many periods in the geologic past, for their products are found in all the great rock systems. In many series their products are very sparingly present, however, and in others they are concentrated. Evidences of them are widespread in both the earliest-known rocks and in very late geologic time. In comparatively recent geologic time volcanoes existed at most places where they are active today, but in the intervening epochs there were periods of great igneous activity and other periods of relative quiescence over most of the earth's surface.

Locally volcanoes are grouped in belts, and it is believed that such

FIG. 319. Mud volcanoes 50 to 75 feet high near mouth of Alamo River west of Niland, California. (*Photo by Frashers.*)

belts are located along fractures or along fractured zones. On the other hand, certain volcanoes seem to be independent of other volcanoes.

The Pacific Ocean is essentially bordered by a volcanic belt which has been called the "circle of fire." Another belt extends westward from Baluchistan, through Persia, through Asia Minor, the Mediterranean, the Canary and Azores Islands, trending toward the West Indies. In two other areas volcanic activity is notably concentrated. One of these includes the West Indies, northern South America, Central America, and southern Mexico. The other is on the opposite side of the Pacific Ocean and nearly west of the East Indies group. It includes Sumatra, Java, New Guinea, and the Philippine Islands. In addition to these volcanic areas around the Pacific Ocean, volcanoes are found at many places in the Pacific, where they are arranged in northwest-trending zones. Next to the "circle of fire" surrounding the Pacific Ocean and the belt extending eastward through the Mediterranean Sea to Baluchistan is the great belt of the Atlantic Ocean, which includes West Spitsbergen, Jan Mayen Island, Iceland, the Azores, Madeira, and the Canary and Cape Verde Islands. A third belt extends from Palestine southward through Arabia,

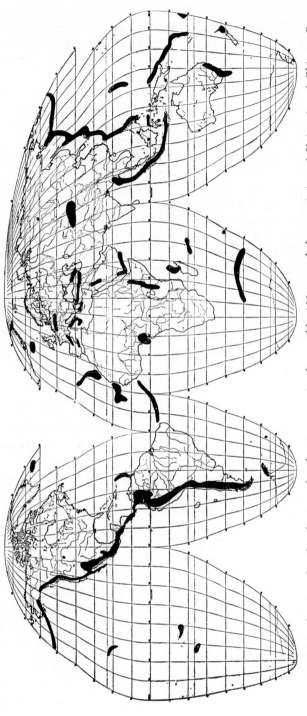

FIG. 320. Map showing the distribution of volcanic areas in the world. (*Map used by permission of University of Chicago Press.*)

407

the Red Sea, Abyssinia, and East Africa to Madagascar. These belts include nearly all the active and recently active volcanoes of the world.

Volcanic Eruptions in Historic Time. About 450 volcanoes have been observed in activity. There are also hundreds of others that have been affected very little by erosion and that must have been active in very recent times. A volcano in eruption is "active." One that has ceased to erupt is "dormant." If it is believed that the volcanic processes have subsided and that the volcano will not erupt again, it is said to be "extinct." It is difficult to distinguish between an extinct volcano and a dormant one, and many volcanoes supposed to be extinct have erupted with great violence. Mount Vesuvius was regarded as extinct in A.D. 79, when its first eruption in historic time occurred.

In the Phlegraean Fields, a densely populated area west of Naples, in 1538 the eruption of Monte Nuovo took place. A new opening was formed, and in 3 days a cone was built up to a height of 500 feet. The eruption lasted a week, died down, and the volcano has not been active since.

Vesuvius. Vesuvius, the best-known volcano, is situated 7 miles southeast of Naples in a densely populated region. The height of the mountain varies but it is about 4,000 feet above sea level. Before 1906 it was 4,275 feet high, but that year it was reduced several hundred feet by explosions. A great ridge known as Mount Somma half encircles the present active cone. This outer ridge partially encloses a huge crater formed in prehistoric time in which the present active cone is situated. In A.D. 79 the ancient crater had been quiet so long that trees were growing in it, but that year an explosion blew off a large part of the cone of Vesuvius, burying the cities Pompeii, Herculaneum, and Stabiae. Little or no lava was ejected, but much dust, ash, and steam issued, forming a pasty mud that flowed down the slopes and overwhelmed dwellings. Pompeii and Herculaneum were covered to depths of 25 to 50 feet. Gases were exhaled, and these either poisoned or suffocated the citizens. Since A.D. 79 Vesuvius has erupted often. In 1631 a violent eruption attended by the ejection of lava, dust, and steam killed many people. Lava streams flowed to the sea and dust was carried as far as Constantinople, about 800 miles away.

Etna. Mount Etna on the east shore of Sicily rises to an elevation of about 10,758 feet and covers 460 square miles. The crater of the volcano is about 1,500 feet deep. Eruptions as early as the eighth century B.C. are recorded. A violent one in 1169 overwhelmed Catania, and many eruptions have occurred since. The temperature of a lava stream in 1892 was 1060°C. at the depth of 1 foot.

Krakatao. One of the greatest eruptions recorded is that of Krakatao, a small island between Java and Sumatra. A great volcano existed in this area, and in prehistoric times its top was blown off, leaving a circular chain of islands around the crater. Subsequent eruptions built up small islands within the ring, one of which was Krakatao, with its summit 2,623 feet above sea. In 1877, earthquakes were noted in this region, and in 1883 an eruption began throwing out pumice and dust. This increased in violence, and on Aug. 26 gigantic explosions began which lasted 3 days. Nearly all the island was blown away, and a hole 1,000 feet below sea level was blasted out. Fragments were hurled 17 miles high, and in 15 days the dust from the volcano borne by air currents had encircled the earth. Dust darkened the air so that lamps were used in daytime at Batavia 100 miles away. The sounds of explosions were heard hundreds of miles away. Sea waves 100 feet high were generated, and these upon reaching the shores of neighboring islands destroyed many towns.

Mount Pelée. Mount Pelée is situated at the north end of Martinique, an island of the West Indies (Fig. 321). On May 1, 1902, its crater blew out, belching dust and cinders. Telegraph cables to the island were broken. On May 8 great explosions occurred, and a great black cloud of hot gas and dust rolled from the mountainside like a hurricane and overwhelmed and destroyed the city of St.-Pierre, killing nearly 30,000 people. The cloud was so dense with dust that it seemed to act like a liquid. The destruction of life appeared to result from the action of particles of hot dust on the membranes of the respiratory organs. During the course of the eruption a "spine" rose from the crater, its top reaching an elevation of 5,276 feet above sea level and 1,000 feet or more

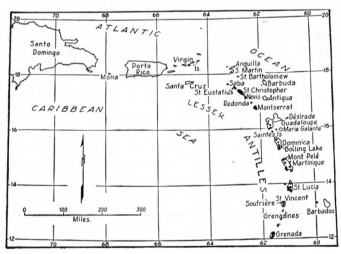

FIG. 321. Map of volcanic area in Caribbean Sea. (*Volcanoes located chiefly from Sapper.*)

above the level of the crater. The huge, needlelike shaft of rock rose gradually almost vertically above the crater, pushed up by pressure from below. Its sides were scratched and slickensided, and it was evidently made of solid or nearly solid material that had formed in the vent. The spine soon disintegrated, and in 1907 a mere stump remained, surrounded by broken fragments of the spine.

Hawaii. Hawaii, the largest island of the Hawaiian chain, is built up of volcanic matter, which rises high above the level of the sea (Fig. 322). Mauna Loa in the southern part of the island has an elevation of 13,675 feet. It has a crater 2 miles wide and 1,000 feet deep. Kilauea, 4,050 feet high, is 20 miles away but is part of the great mountain mass. The great difference in elevation of these two vents is assumed to indicate that they derive their lavas from independent sources and probably very deep ones. Mauna Loa, the "summit" crater, is not drained by the lower one. It has been the more active volcano in recent time and is often violent at periods when the lower crater is only mildly active. Numerous flows have been expelled from fissures or from the summit crater, some of them reaching the sea (Fig. 322). The crater of Kilauea

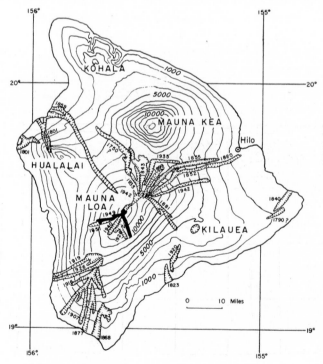

FIG. 322. Map of Hawaii, showing five coalescent cones and several recent lava flows. Contour interval 1,000 feet. (*After Stearns and Macdonald.*)

is about 1½ miles in diameter. It is crusted over in the main, but in part of the crater the vent, Halemaumau, is active.

A new eruptive phase of Mauna Loa began in January, 1949. Lava broke out along a series of fissures extending part way across the summit caldera and a short distance down the southwest rift. Along the southwest wall of the caldera lava fountains as much as 800 feet high built a large cone of pumice and fine cinder and spatter in its crater. Lava flooded more than half the floor of the caldera and filled to overflowing a small pit crater adjoining the caldera on the south. A flow spilled out of the pit crater and moved 4 miles southward. The total volume of extruded lava was approximately 77 million cubic yards (Figs. 324, 325).

Mount Lassen. In the western part of the United States there are many volcanoes that have been in eruption in late geologic times. Their cones and craters are still intact and are little affected by erosion. Several of these volcanoes are reported to have erupted in historic time, but these reports have been questioned. Mount Lassen in northern California is the only volcano in the United States proper that has had eruptions in the present century (Fig. 312). These eruptions began in May, 1914, and there have been several eruptions since then, during which a small crater

FIG. 323. Ropy pahoehoe lava, Kilauea, Hawaii. (*Photograph by Mendenhall, U.S. Geological Survey.*)

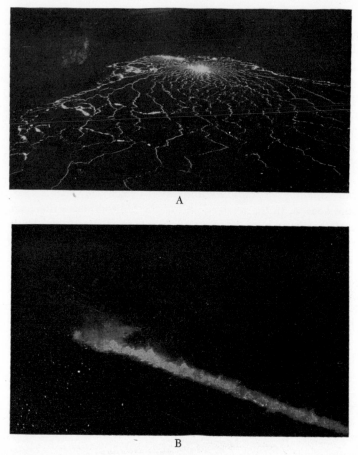

A

B

FIG. 324. Photographs taken at night at Halemaumau Crater, Hawaii. (*Courtesy of G. A. Macdonald.*) A, bright crack pattern in solidified crust on lava lake; B, large, glowing fracture at southwest edge of lava lake.

formed at the top of the mountain, and from it issued gases, ashes, and volcanic cinders. Explosions took place in 1915.

Katmai. Mount Katmai is situated where the Alaskan peninsula joins the mainland. It erupted violently on June 6, 1912; very few people lived anywhere near the volcano, but the explosion was heard 750 miles away at Juneau and even far north at Dawson and Fairbanks across the Alaska Range. During the explosion 3 to 5 cubic miles of dust and ash were thrown into the air. The dust continued to fall for 3 days, and when all had settled, it made a deposit 10 inches deep at Kodiak, 100 miles away, whereas at Katmai, about 12 miles from the volcano, the deposit of dust and ash was 3 feet thick.

Ngauruhoe. The volcano Ngauruhoe is one of a group of three major volcanic mountains on North Island, New Zealand (Fig. 309). It is located about 80 miles southwest of the celebrated hot-spring district of Rotorua. Its cone rises 7,500 feet above sea level and nearly 4,000 feet above the surrounding hills. In 1949 it suddenly became violently active for a short period of time. The activity began with the blasting out of a plug of debris from one of the crater's two intermittently active vents, followed by the issue of avalanches of lava. At intervals during the eruption, huge red-hot blocks were hurled as much as 2,000 feet above the summit of the cone, and a plume of ash and vapor rose nearly 1 mile above it.

Submarine Volcanoes. Violent submarine eruptions repeatedly have been observed in the volcanic belt of the Aleutian Islands (Fig. 314) and in the south central Pacific Ocean area (Figs. 326, 327). Cones may be built several hundred feet above sea level, but when volcanic activity declines, the small volcanic islands are soon destroyed by waves.

Pantelleria, a small island which lies between Sicily and Cape Bon, Africa, is wholly volcanic. A submarine eruption took place on Oct. 17, 1891, about 3 miles northwest of the island. Red-hot bombs were hurled high into the air, and an island 1,500 feet long and 9 feet high formed, which was soon washed away by waves.

FIG. 325. Lava fountain at the vents at an altitude of 8,500 feet on southwest rift of Mauna Loa, June 7, 1950. (*Photograph by G. A. Macdonald.*)

In 1831 Graham Island rose from the sea between Pantelleria and Sicily where the water had been 500 to 600 feet deep. The water boiled, black clouds rose, and within 2 months a cone 200 feet high and about ½ mile in diameter was built above sea level. It has since been destroyed by wave action.

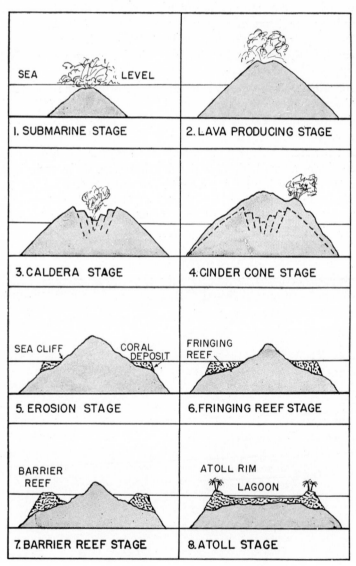

FIG. 326. Stages in the geologic history of a volcanic island in the central Pacific. (*After Stearns.*)

FIG. 327. Birth of a volcanic island off the coast of Japan. (*Photograph by United States Navy.*)

Fumaroles. The term fumarole is from the Latin *fumariolum*, which means smoke hole. Fumaroles are vents in the earth's crust from which steam and other gases issue. They are common in regions of active volcanoes and also in areas of decadent volcanism. Many intrusives do not reach the surface but probably supply heat and gases to the regional ground water. The steam of fumaroles is in part from heated ground

Gases Issuing from Volcanoes and Fumaroles

Steam, H_2O	Sulfur dioxide, SO_2
Oxygen, O_2	Hydrogen sulfide, H_2S
Nitrogen, N_2	Hydrochloric acid, HCl
Argon, A	Hydrofluoric acid, HF
Carbon dioxide, CO_2	Ammonia, NH_3
Carbon monoxide, CO	Sulfuric acid, H_2SO_4

waters, but some of the water may be derived from the intrusive magma which supplied most of the other gases. The temperature of the steam that issues from certain fumaroles is well above the boiling point of water, and temperatures as high as 650°C. have been measured.

Hydrogen sulfide and carbon monoxide are poisonous gases. Sulfur dioxide and carbon dioxide are suffocating gases, the latter collecting at low places in the topography. Thus where these gases issue from vents, animals may be killed, as in Poison Valley, Java, where it is said that many bones of men and animals killed by gases have been found.

Solfataras. Solfataras (Italian *solfo,* sulfur) are fumaroles which give off sulfur gases. At places the hydrogen sulfide gases oxidize on exposure to the air and form sulfur which accumulates in considerable amounts, so that the rocks near the solfataras may contain commercial quantities of sulfur. One of the best-known vents yielding sulfur compounds is La Solfatara, west of Naples. The last eruption of this volcano occurred in A.D. 1198. Since then steam and sulfur compounds have issued. At places in Mexico, Japan, and elsewhere deposits formed by volcanic emanations are worked commercially for sulfur. This is formed by the action of the air on hydrogen sulfide vapors, as follows:

$$H_2S \quad + \quad O \quad = \quad H_2O \quad + \quad S$$

hydrogen   oxygen   water   sulfur
sulfide

Utilization of Volcanic Gases. In the volcanic area of Tuscany, Italy, there are steam jets and pools of hot water boiling by natural heat. Notwithstanding the corrosive character of the hot gases, plants for generating electric power and for producing boric acid have been erected there, and boreholes cased with iron tubing allow steam to issue at an average pressure of 2 atmospheres and at 100 to 190°C. At Larderello 150 metric tons of steam per hour is available from 135 boreholes, and it is used in turbine engines to generate electric power. Ammonium carbonate, sodium carbonate, and boric acid are recovered from the steam and hot water. Likewise in the Coast Ranges of California, about 40 miles north of San Francisco, in an area of hot springs, wells have been drilled to obtain steam for generating power.

Postvolcanic History of Volcanoes. After a volcano becomes extinct, destructive erosional forces dominate and sooner or later the mountain disappears. On the land, streams and glaciers are the most effective agents, while, on the volcanic islands, streams and wave action are most destructive (Fig. 326). Sea cliffs and wave-cut terraces are developed around extinct volcanoes in the open sea, and all stages, from cones only slightly eroded to those almost completely obliterated, may be observed. The erosion of composite cones on land may leave the lava column of the throat of the volcano standing as an isolated rock shaft called a *volcanic plug*. Dikes of igneous rocks may radiate from the plug, and remnants of the volcanic material ejected from the volcano may occur in concentric zones around the former volcanic vent. Eventually these are all removed, and the intrusive masses such as laccoliths, sills, and stocks (Fig. 39) are exposed at the surface.

Fissure Eruptions. A form of extrusive igneous activity that does not produce volcanic cones is that of fissure eruptions. Lavas commonly rise along fissures, and at many places volcanoes also are arranged in lines which suggest a connection with fissures. Great floods of very liquid lava have been discharged from such fissures far removed from volcanoes. Some of the flooded areas are covered by flows of basalt and other lavas which, taken together, amount to hundreds or thousands of feet in thickness. Because of the absence of volcanic cones it is commonly assumed that lavas issued from fissures. H. S. Washington, who studied many of these flows, suggests that they be called *plateau* flows, not because the lavas are all found high above sea level but because the word implies flatness.

Some of these basaltic flows are of very great extent. The Deccan flows of India cover an area of 200,000 square miles and probably average 2,000 feet in thickness. In the northwestern part of the United States, in Washington, Oregon, and Idaho, the Columbia River basalts cover about 225,000 square miles and have an average thickness of about 500 feet (Figs. 328, 329). Large areas of similar rocks are found also in northern Michigan and Wisconsin and along the north shore of Lake Superior. Washington studied the rocks from all these regions and has shown that they are characterized by high iron content, particularly by high ferrous iron, and for that reason were highly fluid lavas. On account of their

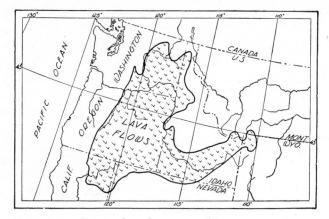

FIG. 328. Map showing lava flows in northwestern United States.

FIG. 329. Lava flows and piles of talus exposed in wall of valley tributary to the Columbia River. (*Photograph by Washington Department of Conservation and Development.*)

lower viscosity, basic lavas move faster and farther than acidic ones. Some of them are known to have moved as fast as 10 or 12 miles an hour. In Hawaii a basic lava has flowed more than 40 miles, and one in Iceland flowed nearly 60 miles.

As the top of a lava flow is more exposed, it cools more rapidly than the lower part; consequently the top often forms a crust which rests on the lower part. Because of movement the crust breaks into numerous blocks, and these blocks are largely light vesicular material. The masses of fragments floating on the lavas form great islandlike bodies, large parts of which project above the liquid. At places essentially all the surface of the flow is covered with the loose blocks. After cooling, the voids between the blocks form great systems of openings which extend for miles without interruption. Such openings later may serve as important channels for moving waters. The brecciated vesicular tops of lavas are well-developed in basic flows. They are common features of the lava fields but are best known in the ancient basic lavas of Keweenaw Point, Michigan. Light fragments of rock floating on the lavas are so numerous in certain lava streams that they hide from view completely the liquid flow; and when the stream advances on land, it moves forward like a stone wall, only the solid matter being visible (Fig. 330).

Lavas that contain numerous fragments of their broken crusts are called *flow breccias*. In the western United States there are series of lava flows extending over thousands of square miles which are made up of flow breccias in which the total mass of the fragments of the breccia is not much less than the lava matrix which cements them.

In Hawaii the relatively smooth lava surfaces are called *pahoehoe*, and the rough ones are called *aa*. These names have come into general use. Lava also assumes a pillowy surface, and in certain flows the pillows are outlined by irregular curving joints that are believed to have formed where the lava was poured out under water.

Caves in Lava Flows. Some lava flows show great caves that probably were formed by the flow of lava from below the solidified crust. Government Cave, 23 miles west of Flagstaff, Arizona, is a cavern in lava which flowed from the west side of San Francisco Mountain. The cave is about ¾ mile long and 20 to nearly 50 feet high. A thick flow of lava was poured out from a volcanic opening, and the upper part, being exposed to the air, cooled first. Later a low opening was provided, and the liquid lava flowed out from below the solid roof, leaving the cavity as it now is. Small stalactitelike pendants of lava hang from the roof.

Spatter Cones. As a lava cools, a crust forms on its surface. The moving of the lava causes the crust to fracture. If gases have accumulated below the solid crust, the portion still liquid may be under pressure due to impounded gas. The lava and gas are expelled through the fissures, and the molten lava builds up a small chimneylike "spatter" cone, or "driblet"

FIG. 330. The advancing front of Zapicho lava flow at Parícutin Volcano, Mexico. (*Photograph by W. F. Foshag.*)

cone. Such cones commonly are 15 or 20 feet high or less. They are not connected with the main volcanic vents but are merely features of the solidifying lava mass.

INTRUSIVE VULCANISM

The underground movement of magma cannot be observed while it is in progress, but the rock masses resulting from the solidification of such magmatic intrusion become accessible to view after they have been uncovered by erosion.

The term *pluton* is given to any body of intrusive igneous rock of any shape or size. Such masses differ greatly in composition and texture and in their relation to the enclosing rock. Furthermore, magmas are very different in their degree of fluidity or viscosity, and consequently a given intrusive mass represents the line of least resistance for that particular magma. On the basis of their shape or form and their structural relation to the enclosing rock they are classified as *dikes, sills, laccoliths, volcanic necks, stocks,* and *batholiths* (Fig. 39).

Dikes. Dikes are rudely tabular bodies of igneous rocks that fill former fractures in the earth's crust (Fig. 331). They may cut across the structure of the intruded formations, or they may cut massive, structureless igneous rocks of older age. They vary in width from less than 1 inch to many feet and in length from a few yards to many miles. Dikes 10 miles

FIG. 331. Dike with offshoots, Cornwall, England. (*Courtesy of Geological Survey and Museum, London.*)

long are common in Iceland, and the Cleveland Dike in England is more than 100 miles long. The Great Dike in Rhodesia is 300 miles long and, in places, more than 5 miles wide.

Most dikes are formed by the injection of magma in preformed fractures, but some may be in fractures formed by the tensional forces produced by the intruding mass of magma; still others are dikelike replacements along fractures and are produced by solutions moving through a fracture and altering the rock walls of the fracture. In the first case the pressure exerted by the magma may push apart the walls of the fracture, and the wedging action of the magma may play an important part in extending the fracture farther.

In certain areas dikes radiate from volcanic centers, and these may be accompanied by concentric or arcuate dike patterns. In other localities they are parallel, or they may form intersecting systems. In the Sunlight area of Wyoming (Fig. 332) there are thousands of radiating dikes, averaging about 4 feet in width, and extending 5 to 7 miles from the central area. Concentric systems are termed *ring dikes*. In the Belknap Mountains of New Hampshire two distinct rings occur around a central core of older schists. The outer ring dike has a diameter of about 7 miles and a width of nearly 1 mile. An inner ring is smaller but nearly as wide.

Ring dikes that dip inward steeply toward the central core are called

FIG. 332. Radiating dikes of the Sunlight area, Wyoming. (*After Parsons.*)

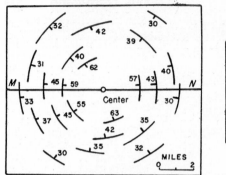
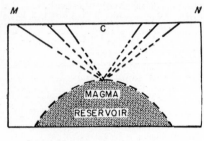

FIG. 333. Concentric dikes, or cone sheets. Left, map view; right, cross section along line M-N. (*After Billings.*)

cone sheets (Fig. 333). If the dips of the cone sheets in Scotland are projected downward, they meet at a focus approximately 3 miles beneath the present surface. Such a focal point is believed to lie near the top of the magma reservoir from which the molten rock materials were injected upward into the fractures.

The original fractures into which the dikes are injected are caused both by tension and by compression. Some are produced by the pressure of magma as it moves upward toward the surface, and others result from compressive forces exerted by the magma in the conduit within the cone of the volcano. In either case, systems of fractures result.

The Spanish Peaks district of Colorado is noted for its system of dikes, which have been sculptured in relief by erosion. The dikes are 2 to 100 feet or more in thickness and dip at high angles. Some stand as wall-like masses as much as 100 feet above the surface and extend a few hundred yards to 10 or 15 miles beyond the plutonic center.

Sills, or Intrusive Sheets. Sills, like dikes, are tabular intrusive masses. They differ from dikes in that they lie parallel, or nearly parallel, to the bedding planes of the enclosing rocks. Most sills are connected with dikes which are the feeding channels along which the magma reaches the bedding planes it invades. Some sills are small, covering areas of only a few acres, but others are very extensive. They range in thickness from a few inches to a few thousand feet; most are less than 100 feet thick. Sills usually lie in an approximately horizontal position, like the sill of a door, except where they were intruded into tilted or folded strata or where the strata have been folded after the sill was intruded.

One of the best-known sills in the United States is the one that crops out along the west side of the Hudson Valley from Jersey City to Haverstraw. This thick sill with conspicuous columnar jointing forms the Palisades of the Hudson. The columns, similar to palisade structure, are the result of shrinkage cracking during cooling. Similar jointing occurs in sills at Mount Tom and Mount Holyoke, Massachusetts, at East and West Rocks at New Haven, Connecticut, and in the Trap Mountains near Orange, New Jersey. The great Whin Sill of northern England has an average thickness of about 160 feet and extends over an area of several thousand square miles. This sill intrudes nearly flat-lying limestone and in general is almost parallel to the beds it intrudes.

In some areas sills appear in great *swarms*. A typical example is the enormous sill swarm injected into the Karroo series of relatively flat-lying sedimentary rocks in South Africa. This swarm consists of many hundreds of sills ranging from a few feet to more than 1,000 feet in thickness. The total volume of magma that solidified to form these sills and related dikes approaches that poured out to form the Columbia River lava plateau.

Laccoliths. A laccolith is a large lenticular mass of igneous rock similar in origin to a sill. If a sill lifts up the overlying beds or raises its cover into a domelike structure, the solidified mass of igneous rock is a *laccolith* (Fig. 334). The magma is supplied from below through a small pipe, or fissure, and the intrusive mass is inferred to have a flat base resting on sedimentary strata.

Laccoliths occur in a great variety of shapes and sizes. Many are oval, and some are quite irregular. The Henry Mountains in southern Utah have long been considered laccolithic domes. They range from ½ to 4 miles in diameter and from 2 to 10 cubic miles in volume. This group of domes shows all stages of progressive erosion, with most of them sufficiently eroded to disclose their igneous cores, or centers. Recent studies have shown that the igneous bodies forming domes of the Henry Mountains may be *stocks* rather than laccoliths. A stock is a larger, floorless, domelike intrusive rudely circular in horizontal cross section.

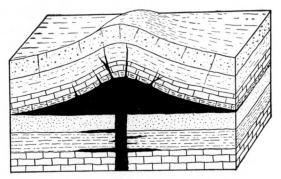

FIG. 334. Ideal cross section of a laccolith. The igneous rock (black) intrudes the beds and arches them up.

FIG. 335. Columnar jointing. Devils Tower National Monument, northern Wyoming. (*Courtesy of National Park Service.*)

A group of domes less deeply eroded rises from the plain northwest of the Black Hills. Little Sundance Mountain, which is one of this group, is a dome 3 miles in circumference at its base. This supposed laccolith has had only a part of the sedimentary strata of its roof removed by erosion, and the core is not yet exposed.

Volcanic Necks, or Plugs. The filled vents through which the magma moved that fed volcanoes are termed necks, or plugs. They are cylindrical masses, subcircular in ground plan and as much as several thousand feet in diameter. In volcanic areas where erosion has reached the late topographic stages, volcanic necks may rise 2,000 feet or more above the surrounding country. Such features develop where the rocks in the vents are more resistant to erosion than the pyroclastic materials of the cinder cones. In the plateaus of northwestern New Mexico and adjoining areas in Arizona more than 150 plugs mark the sites of former volcanoes. The various volcanic buttes rise to different heights, and furthermore their bases stand at various altitudes, so as to indicate that each is a separate intrusive mass and not part of a single extensive lava flow.

The vents may be filled with heterogeneous brecciated material, or the magma in a vent may solidify to form felsitic intrusive rock. Where such fine-grained rocks are formed, vertical columnar jointing (Fig. 335) may develop in the upper part of the vent and curve outward toward the enclosing walls near the base of the volcano. The columns are the result of cooling, with the joints forming approximately at right angles to the cooling surface. At the top of the neck the cooling surface is the upper surface of the magma in the crater, and therefore the joints are vertical, but toward the base of the neck the cooling plane is the wall of the vent, and consequently a radial pattern of joints is developed in that portion of the intrusive mass.

Batholiths. Batholiths are the largest and originally the deepest intrusive bodies of igneous rock known. They are believed to have been the feeding masses of laccoliths, dikes, sills, and volcanoes formed at higher levels. They are so large that they are never sufficiently exposed to permit measurement of all three dimensions. Some are 50 to 100 miles wide and more than 1,000 miles long. Most of them are aligned parallel to mountain ranges, except in very deeply eroded areas, where such alignment is not evident. Batholiths differ from laccoliths in that none is known to have a floor. They extend downward to great but unknown depths, and nearly all of them, where their contacts are exposed, are found to broaden downward. It appears improbable that they broaden downward indefinitely, and some indirect evidence would seem to indicate that they taper downward at depths of several miles.

Most batholiths occur as the cores of folded mountain systems. They were emplaced either at times of crustal deformation or shortly thereafter. The Coast Ranges batholith of British Columbia, the Idaho batholith, and the Sierra Nevada batholith (Fig. 336) is each along a zone where mountain-building diastrophism took place. Of these, the largest is the Coast Ranges batholith, which is 1,250 miles long and 80 to 120 miles wide. Its surface area is about 100,000 square miles. The largest one wholly within the United States is the Idaho batholith, which is exposed over an area of 16,000 square miles. Similar great intrusive masses are exposed in the Patagonian Andes (Fig. 336) and along the cores of other great mountain chains. Most batholiths are composed essentially of granite or closely related granitoid rocks.

Structurally, batholiths are of two types, *concordant* and *discordant*.

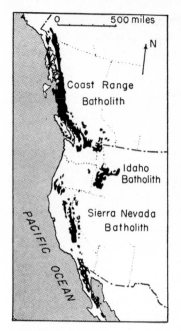

FIG. 336. Batholithic intrusives of western North America and southern South America. (*After maps by Geological Society of America.*)

An intrusive body, or pluton, is said to be concordant if the contacts are parallel to the bedding or schistosity of the older rocks, and it is discordant if the contacts cut across the structure of the country rock. Batholiths intruded during crustal deformation tend to have concordant contacts, and so the roof rocks arch over the top somewhat as the dome-like beds arch over a laccolith. The discordant, or transgressive, types, which cut across trends of folds and other structures of their surrounding walls, were emplaced at the end of a period of intensive diastrophism.

The roofs, or upper surfaces, of batholiths are irregular and undulating (Fig. 39). The small, domelike parts of their roofs that extend upward into the invaded rocks are *cupolas*, and the low sags of the invaded rocks that project or hang downward from the roof are *roof pendants* (Fig. 39). The walls slope steeply outward, but in many batholiths the contact that separates the granite of the intrusive mass from the wall rock is not sharp. Instead a zone, or aureole, of recrystallized rocks surrounds the granite and consists of intimately penetrating masses of granite and small layers, or bands, of foliated metamorphic rocks known as *injection gneiss*. Beyond the margins of some batholiths the invaded rocks show a gradation from typical sedimentary and metamorphic characters to various mixed types and finally to granite. Such field evidence indicates that shales, sandstones, slates, and even basalts can be transformed into granite by partial replacement and the addition of materials from the invading magma. Still other batholiths have swarms of *inclusions* of wall rock near the margins. Some inclusions are sharply angular and fresh, whereas others appear partly assimilated and deformed, indicating that they were softened by heat and stretched out in the direction of movement of the magma. Dark-colored, wavy streaks of half-assimilated hornblende and mica schist inclusions are called *schlieren.*

The manner in which such gigantic masses of magma make room for themselves is not yet fully understood. Some geologists believe that the very hot magma moves upward by engulfing and subsequently dissolving large quantities of the rock in its path. By such a process, called "magmatic stoping," large blocks are loosened from the roof, spalled off by heating, and fall into the liquid magma, where they are dissolved in part or sink to great depths. In this way the magmatic chamber conceivably becomes enlarged, and the magma works its way upward into the earth's crust. The presence of large blocks of partly assimilated invaded rock in granite areas far from the margin of the batholith indicates that stoping actually takes place, but its quantitative importance is not known. Mechanical shattering may be as important as shattering due to heating, because the roof rocks are undoubtedly subjected to enormous tensional, compressional, and torsional forces.

Other geologists think that batholiths are emplaced by forceful injection. This may be the process by which concordant batholiths are emplaced. The great mass of magma simply pushes its way into the older rocks, driving them aside or ahead as it moves upward. Where a lighter granitic magma rises through older, heavier rocks, the intrusive force may be entirely due to gravity, and since most large batholiths are related to zones of crustal deformation, the magma may also have been pushed around by diastrophic forces. Still other geologists hold that granites are made *in situ* by "granitization." This aspect of batholithic injection is discussed further in connection with the origin of folded mountains (Chapter 20).

Stocks. A stock is an igneous intrusion having the essential features of a batholith, but it differs in being smaller. If its areal extent is less than 40 square miles, the mass is called a stock. Some seemingly small intrusives which are called stocks may be cupolas of batholiths.

Age Relations of Intrusives. Except in rare instances, igneous rocks do not contain relics that may be used to determine the age of the rocks as fossils are used to determine the age of a sedimentary bed. The relative age of an igneous rock frequently may be determined, however, by observing its relations to associated rocks. If a rock intrudes another rock, it is younger than the rock invaded (Figs. 337, 338), and if it is covered by another flow or sedimentary bed that was laid down above it, it is

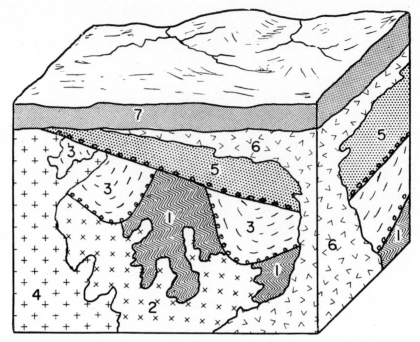

FIG. 337. Diagram showing age relations of igneous rocks. Numbers 3 and 5 represent folded and tilted sediments. All others are igneous rocks with their numbers listed in chronological order.

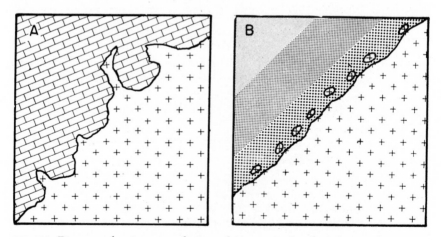

FIG. 338. Diagrams showing age relations of igneous and sedimentary rocks. *A*, the intrusive igneous rock (plus signs) is younger than the rock it intrudes. This relationship is an intrusive contact. *B*, the igneous rock (plus signs) was exposed by erosion, and sediments containing pebbles derived from the igneous rock were deposited on it. This is an erosional contact, and the igneous rock is older than the overlying sediments.

older than the flow or bed. The determination of age relations of intrusives is an essential part of the systematic study of an area, and particularly is it important in areas containing mineral deposits, which commonly are related to the same magmatic reservoir that supplied the material of the intrusive. An intrusive that contains fragments of another rock is younger than the rock that supplied the fragments. When an intrusive alters another rock near its contact, it is younger than that rock. Certain intrusives are fine-grained or glassy near their contacts with other rocks, whereas a few feet away from the contact they are more coarsely crystalline. The chilled margin is evidence that the intrusive rock is later than the cooling surface that chilled it. If one igneous rock is regionally metamorphosed and another one nearby is not, the metamorphosed rock is the older; or if any regional change has taken place in one rock and the other rock is not affected, the altered rock is the older, for obviously both rocks would have been altered if both had been present when regional alteration took place.

SUGGESTIONS FOR FURTHER READING

Coleman, S. N.: Volcanoes New and Old, The John Day Company, Inc., 1946.
Foshag, W. F.: The Birth of Paricutin. *Smithsonian Inst. Ann. Rept.*, pp. 223–234, 1946.
Jaggar, T. A.: Volcanoes Declare War, Paradise of the Pacific, Ltd., 1945.
Russell, I. C.: Volcanoes of North America, The Macmillan Company, 1924.
Stearns, H. T.: Geology of the Hawaiian Islands, *U.S. Geol. Survey, Div. Hydrography, Bull.* 8, 1946.

CHAPTER 17

Igneous Rocks

Igneous rocks, as their name implies, are the products formed by the cooling or solidification of magma that formed deep within the earth. A distinction is commonly made between those which have crystallized far below the surface and those which solidified from lavas that were poured out on the surface. Deep-seated masses such as batholiths, laccoliths, stocks, sills, and dikes are *intrusive* bodies of igneous rock, whereas the term *extrusive* is applied to the magma that reached the surface and was discharged or extruded as hot lava or as fragments of volcanic debris (Fig. 39).

Structures and Textures. The structure of most igneous rocks, as distinct from sedimentary strata, is massive; but some show flow structures, and others have distinct joint systems. Lava rocks commonly show banding. Furthermore their materials are rarely uniform but include colored spots and gas cavities, for as they flow, they drag out the different kinds of material and these form bands. Columnar joints are present in many tabular igneous masses such as sills and dikes. In these the joints are developed normal to the cooling surface. In flat sills the columns are upright (Palisades-like) (Fig. 339), and in vertical dikes they are horizontal. Much of the jointing is caused by the contraction resulting from the cooling of magma during solidification.

The *texture* of igneous rocks refers to the size and shape of the mineral grains or crystals of which they are composed and to the pattern of their arrangement. Most rocks contain mineral grains, but some are predominantly volcanic glass or mixtures of glass and mineral grains. On the basis of texture they are classified as (1) glassy rocks, (2) fragmental rocks, (3) aphanitic or felsitic rocks, (4) porphyritic rocks, and (5) granitoid rocks.

A *glassy texture*, as the name implies, is that of glass or slag which has no definite minerals. It results when a magma is chilled so quickly that the minerals have no opportunity to form. Massive glass is called *obsidian* (Fig. 340), and porous or vesicular glass with fine, closely spaced pores,

430

FIG. 340. Obsidian. (*Courtesy of Ward's Natural Science Establishment.*)

431

FIG. 341. Photograph of a fragment of a rhyolite flow. The gray areas represent reddish-brown rhyolite. The black bands are obsidian, or black glass. The dark gray areas of the upper part of the figure show cavities formed by expanding gases.

is pumice, whereas that with fewer and larger voids is called *scoria*. The pores in *pumice* and scoria are the result of expanding gases, which tend to make a frothlike surface on the lava. On solidification the frothy texture is retained (Fig. 42).

A fragmental igneous rock is made up of fragments of volcanic material. They are *pyroclastic* (fire-broken) rocks, containing fragments of different sizes and compositions. The loose pieces range from fine dust or ash through volcanic sand, lapilli, cinders, and bombs to huge blocks. Rocks composed of consolidated volcanic dust and ash are called *tuffs*, whereas the term *breccia* is used if most of the fragments are more than 1 centimeter in diameter. Tuffs and breccia that have been partially remelted and fused by the collapse of pumiceous particles are known as *welded tuffs*. The extremely coarse explosive breccias are also commonly called *agglomerates*.

A *felsitic* rock is one in which the mineral constituents are so small that they cannot be distinguished by the naked eye. They are commonly mere specks less than 0.5 millimeter in diameter. The rock is crystalline but so very fine-grained that it appears homogeneous. Such a texture results from rapid cooling during which crystallization proceeds from many centers and small crystals form (Fig. 341). Felsitic rocks also may be scoriaceous or vesicular.

A *porphyritic* rock is composed of relatively large, isolated crystals enclosed in a groundmass, or matrix, of smaller crystals or of glass (Fig. 342). In some porphyritic rocks the matrix is a mixture of fine mineral grains and noncrystalline glass. The larger crystals, because of their prominence in the rock, are called *phenocrysts* (apparent crystals). Phenocrysts may have sharp edges and well-formed crystal faces, or they may be corroded and somewhat irregular. They also range greatly in size. In some rocks they are several inches in diameter, and in others the crystals may appear no larger than pinheads.

A porphyritic texture indicates two phases of crystallization: (1) the formation of the phenocrysts, which form early and remain suspended in the magma; (2) the formation of the groundmass, which may be finely crystalline or glassy or both because of a change of circumstances during solidification.

When vesicular lava has been filled with such secondary minerals as quartz, zeolites, epidote, or calcite, the fillings are called amygdules and the rock is *amygdaloidal*. Amygdules differ from phenocrysts in that the vesicles they occupy are almond-shaped or tubelike in form (Fig. 343) with irregular or oval cross sections, whereas phenocrysts have angular crystal outlines.

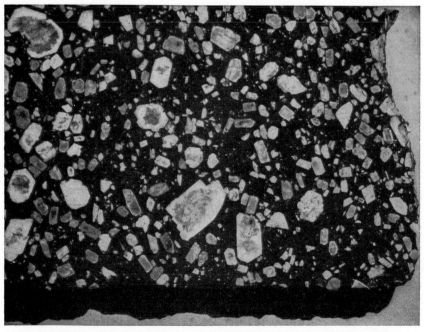

FIG. 342. Trachite porphyry, Bannockburn Township, Ontario. (*Courtesy of Ward's Natural Science Establishment.*)

A *granitoid*, or coarse-grained, rock is one in which all the leading mineral constituents may be seen with the naked eye (Fig. 344). The grains are generally of nearly uniform size and may be quite fine or very coarse. The average granite has grains 3 to 5 millimeters in diameter. Exceptionally coarse crystalline aggregates of the same minerals as a granite are called pegmatites, and the texture is *pegmatitic*. The coarser the grain size, the more slowly the magma cooled.

Factors Causing Textural Variations. The texture of an igneous rock reveals the manner of its formation. If cooling is slow, crystallization proceeds from few centers and large crystals will form. If cooling is rapid, it proceeds from many centers and small crystals form. If fluids are present, they tend to lower the temperature of crystallization, because they promote diffusion, or movement, of material through the magma, so as to permit the growth of larger crystals. A magma may be fluid at a temperature so low that it would solidify readily if the gases were not present. If such a magma flows out upon the surface, the gases escape and the molten matter solidifies quickly to form an aphanitic rock or a

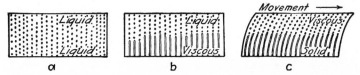

FIG. 343. Drawings illustrating the development of bent-pipe vesicles. *a*, gas bubbles rising through a liquid lava; *b*, pipelike vesicles forming in partly viscous lava; *c*, owing to movement of the viscous lava, the pipelike vesicles are bent in the direction of movement which is indicated by the arrow. Pipe-shaped amygdules are formed by subsequent filling of the vesicles.

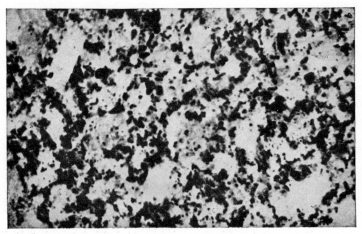

FIG. 344. Granite. (*Courtesy of Cold Spring Granite Co.*)

glass. If some crystals had formed at depth before eruption, phenocrysts would be present and the rock would be porphyritic. In general the basic magmas, which are low in silica and high in iron and magnesia, are much more liquid than the silicic magmas, and consequently the crystals or grains of minerals tend to grow to larger size in basic lavas than in the more viscous siliceous magmas. This is not true in many deep-seated rocks, however, for pegmatites, which have the largest crystals, are of siliceous composition, but they formed in residual magmas high in fluids and gases.

Textural variations are influenced also by the mode of occurrence of igneous rock masses. Since the texture of an igneous rock depends mainly on the rate at which a magma or lava solidifies, it follows that large intrusive masses will form coarser-textured rocks than thin lava sheets or thin dikes and sills. In general the rocks that occur as great batholiths are of granitoid texture, whereas dikes and sills are composed of fine-grained, or felsitic, rocks. Thin lava flows generally are glassy. Not all small bodies of rock, however, are fine-grained. The volume of rock in a volcanic neck is not great, but notwithstanding its small volume the rock commonly is coarse-grained. The coarse texture is due to slow cooling because the constant upward passage of molten material heats the rocks surrounding the conduit of the volcano and when the magma in the conduit finally solidifies, it cools slowly inasmuch as the surrounding rocks are also hot.

COMPOSITION OF IGNEOUS ROCKS

The chemical composition of the magma from which an igneous rock is formed determines the mineral composition of the solidified product. Inasmuch as magmas vary in composition, the igneous rocks crystallized from them may grade into one another by imperceptible gradations. Some rock types are so closely related that any rigid classification is impossible. Mineralogically most igneous rocks are composed of the feldspars and one or more of the micas, pyroxenes, or amphiboles. Quartz and olivine may or may not be present.

Rocks of high silica content are called *acidic* or *silicic* because of their high proportion of the acid-forming radical, silica (SiO_2) (Fig. 345). They are, as a rule, light in color and of relatively low specific gravity. *Basic* rock, on the other hand, contains a predominance of bases such as lime, magnesia, and iron. They are dark-colored or green and heavy because of their content of iron-bearing minerals. Since rocks are found that form an unbroken series with a silica content ranging from 80 per cent down to 40 per cent, it follows that some are neither acidic nor basic. Rocks transitional between the two groups are called *intermediate*.

Igneous Rocks

Mode of occurrence	Texture	Acidic rocks — Light-colored minerals predominate — Orthoclase and ferro-magnesian minerals		Basic rocks — Dark-colored minerals predominate — Plagioclase and ferro-magnesian minerals	
		With quartz	Without quartz	With hornblende	With pyroxene
Batholiths, stocks, and laccoliths	Granitoid	Granite	Syenite	Diorite [1]	Gabbro [2]
Intrusive sheets, dikes, laccoliths	Porphyritic with many phenocrysts	Granite porphyry	Syenite porphyry	Diorite porphyry	Gabbro porphyry
	Porphyritic with few phenocrysts	Rhyolite porphyry	Trachyte porphyry	Andesite porphyry	Basalt porphyry
Surface flows	Felsitic, some partly glassy	Rhyolite	Trachyte	Andesite	Basalt
		Felsite group		Basalt group	
Volcanic cones, flow surfaces	Glassy	Dense: obsidian Finely vesicular: pumice Coarse pores: scoria		Basalt obsidian	
Beds, crudely stratified	Fragmental	Fine fragments: ash and tuff Coarse fragments: cinders and breccia			

[1] With quartz the rock is quartz diorite, and its felsitic equivalent is dacite.
[2] With olivine the rock is olivine gabbro.

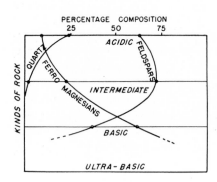

FIG. 345. Diagram showing relative percentages of quartz, feldspar, and ferromagnesian minerals in acidic and basic igneous rocks.

Granites and Related Rocks. Granites are granitoid rocks consisting of orthoclase, quartz, and a small amount of mica or of some ferro-magnesian mineral. Since the proportions of minerals and rates of crystallization vary, many kinds and colors of granite have been formed. In some granites the mica is white (muscovite); in others it is black (biotite). In certain granites hornblende is present, and it may be more abundant than the micas. In a few granites the micas are absent altogether. The average granite contains 60 per cent feldspar, 30 per cent quartz, and 10 per cent dark minerals. Most granites contain pink or reddish orthoclase, and since it is the most abundant mineral, it gives the rock a pinkish color. In gray granites the feldspar is white or gray, and thus the dark biotite and hornblende show more plainly. This color combination gives a salt-and-pepper effect like a white area sprinkled with black.

Very coarse crystalline aggregates of the same minerals as granite occur in fractures near the borders of granite intrusions. Such rocks are called *pegmatites*, or giant granite. Many of the crystals in them are perfectly formed and very large. The feldspars commonly are 1 foot or more in length; some of those in Maine are as much as 20 feet across. The mica plates are 12 to 15 inches wide; some have been found that weigh many tons. In the pegmatite mines in the Black Hills, the mineral spodumene (a lithium-bearing silicate) occurs as crystals 40 feet in length and 4 feet in thickness. Pegmatites are said to have been deposited by magmas unusually high in fluids.

In some pegmatites the feldspar and quartz have a curious intergrowth such that the quartz makes patterns on some of the cleavage faces of the feldspar that resemble certain ancient characters used in writing. Such rocks, composed mainly of quartz and orthoclase, are called graphic granites (Fig. 346).

If a magma like that which at depth solidified to form granite had flowed out upon the surface, the molten matter would have chilled before there was time for the molecules to organize themselves to form crystals. The resulting rock would be partly or entirely glassy; or if crystals were formed, generally they would be small. Such a rock is rhyolite; if it were essentially all glass, it would be called obsidian.

Syenites and Related Rocks. Syenites are formed from magmas that contain less silica than those which crystallize to form granite. In syenites the silica is almost or entirely taken up in the formation of silicate minerals, and little or none remains to form quartz. The average syenite is composed of orthoclase and hornblende with plagioclase, apatite, and magnetite as accessory minerals. When plagioclase is present in larger amounts, the rocks are called monzonites, which represent a transition to the diorites.

FIG. 346. Graphic granite, Hyble, Ontario. (*Courtesy of Ward's Natural Science Establishment.*)

The felsitic equivalent of a syenite is trachyte, which may be more or less porphyritic. Most trachyte porphyries have a groundmass, or matrix, of minute feldspar crystals and little or no glass.

The syenites are not very common rocks. They formed most commonly toward the edges of great bodies of granite where silica was scarce, or they were formed as small, independent intrusives near the margins of granite batholiths.

Diorites and Related Rocks. A diorite is a coarse-grained rock composed of plagioclase feldspar and one or more of the common ferromagnesian minerals. The dark mineral is usually green hornblende, but augite and other pyroxenes and biotite occur in some varieties. The feldspar is more abundant than the dark minerals. Most diorites contain little or no quartz, but if quartz is present, the rock is *quartz diorite.*

The fine-grained, or felsitic, equivalent of diorite is andesite. The andesites are generally dark gray in color and are transitional between the light-colored rhyolites on the one hand and the dark green to black basalts on the other. An andesite with prominent phenocrysts of striated feldspar is an andesite porphyry. The rock may be glassy in part, but andesite obsidian is rare and can be distinguished from rhyolite obsidian only by chemical analysis. A quartz-bearing andesite is called dacite.

Gabbros and Related Rocks. A gabbro is coarse-grained and contains essentially the same minerals as diorite, but the dark minerals predominate, and the plagioclase is subordinate. Because the ferromagnesian minerals are most abundant, the rock is dark gray to black and of high specific gravity. Gabbros containing olivine are called olivine gabbros.

Basalt is the fine-grained equivalent of gabbro. The basalts are closely related to the andesites and connected with them by transitional forms. They are very common volcanic rocks formed by the rapid crystallization of basic-lava flows. Many are scoriaceous or amygdaloidal. Basalt porphyries have conspicuous phenocrysts of plagioclase or pyroxene or both in a dark basaltic matrix.

A diabase is similar in composition to a gabbro or a basalt. It is the name used for a texture in which the feldspar crystals are long, narrow, and lath-shaped with the ferromagnesian minerals in the interstices. The term dolerite is used for a basic rock of intermediate grain size that does not have a diabasic texture.

The term traprock is a common field name for various kinds of dark, heavy, basic rocks which cannot readily be identified without a microscope. The term was first used in Europe on account of the stairlike appearance of the eroded edges of a series of flows (*treppe*, stairs).

Massive basalt glass, or obsidian, is relatively rare. However, vesicular basic glass called scoria is abundantly present at the surfaces of lava flows and in cinders. It differs from pumice in that the composition is more basic, the vesicles are larger and more irregular, and the color is reddish brown to black.

MAGMATIC DIFFERENTIATION IN SILLS AND OTHER PLUTONS

Many thick basic sills and laccoliths have a higher percentage of heavy ferromagnesian minerals at or near their bases than throughout the bulk of their mass. The diabase sill, more than 900 feet thick, that forms the bluffs across the Hudson River from New York has a zone near its base containing nearly 65 per cent of ferromagnesian minerals and 35 per cent plagioclase, whereas the bulk of the sill is composed of approximately 60 per cent plagioclase. Apparently the heavy iron-bearing minerals crystallized early and sank to the bottom during the course of crystallization. Narrow, chilled zones at the top and at the bottom of the sill have identical composition, and so it is inferred that they represent the composition of the injected magma before it had time to separate into gravitative differentiates.

Similar observations of differentiated zones have been made in certain laccoliths where the rock of the lower part of the intrusive mass is different from that in the middle and upper parts. Heavy minerals such as magnetite and pyroxene generally are more abundant in the lower rocks, whereas quartz and feldspar predominate in the upper positions so as to suggest differential crystal settling. Furthermore, at many places, deep-seated igneous rocks are found to grade one into the other. Thus a light-colored granite may grade into a darker diorite or even into a gabbro. Neither rock intrudes the other, and therefore they are believed to be of the same age. Hence, if once homogeneous, some sort of separation must have occurred.

In the great batholiths, magmatic differentiation probably is carried out on a vastly larger scale than in sills and laccoliths with magmatic chambers of restricted size. The batholiths, however, are so large that the operation of the processes is more difficult to interpret, and moreover the floors of batholiths do not come under observation. Nonetheless the predominance of granite in batholiths tends to support the theory of wholesale differentiation.

Doubtless, differentiation due to gravity also occurs in a volcanic conduit and in a volcano's reservoir of magma at greater depth. During a dormant period, the magma in the feeder, or neck, of a volcano may solidify, and, below this plug, the heavier minerals that slowly crystallize out first may sink and leave a lighter and more silicic magma near the top of the reservoir. When the volcano erupts again, the first flows, or pyroclastics, will be highly silicic and the later ones more basic. As many as five different kinds of lava, presumably the products of such a separation, were erupted from San Francisco Mountain in northern Arizona. This extinct volcano, rising 5,000 feet above the plateau on which it was built, has been dissected by erosion sufficiently to expose to view the five kinds of eruptive rocks in its make-up.

SUGGESTIONS FOR FURTHER READING

Daly, R. A.: Igneous Rocks and Their Origin, McGraw-Hill Book Company, Inc., 1914.

——: Igneous Rocks and the Depths of the Earth, 2d ed., McGraw-Hill Book Company, Inc., 1933.

Grout, F. F.: Petrography and Petrology, McGraw-Hill Book Company, Inc., 1932.

Harker, A.: The Natural History of Igneous Rocks, Methuen & Co., Ltd., London, 1909.

Pirsson, L. V.: Rocks and Rock Minerals, 3d ed. by Adolph Knopf, John Wiley & Sons, Inc., 1947.

Shand, S. J.: Eruptive Rocks, 3d ed., John Wiley & Sons, Inc., 1947.

Diastrophism and Its Resulting Structures

There is abundant evidence that, during the earth's geologic past and even during historic times, the earth's crust has been warped, tilted, and uplifted or depressed so as to result in relative changes of position of the rock formations. Such changes are grouped together under the term *diastrophism*, which includes all movements of parts of the solid earth with reference to each other. The movements may be in any direction, upward, downward, inclined, or horizontal, and they may be either extremely slow and gradual or sudden and violent (Fig. 347).

Diastrophic movements take place for two different reasons: because of the earth's elasticity and also because of its plasticity. The earth's elasticity may be crudely illustrated by pressing a finger on a toy balloon. When the finger is removed, the depressed surface at once assumes its original form. In like manner a steel ball responds to temporary localized pressure on its surface, for even though such a ball has great rigidity, it yields a little without breaking and without internal flow of the steel. When the pressure is removed, the ball instantly resumes its original shape. Thus a steel ball will bounce. If the pressure is great and prolonged, however, the bonds among the atoms of steel are broken, the atoms slip past one another, and the steel actually flows, though the rate of movement is very slow. Such internal displacements are permanent, and the ball will not return to its original spherical form. This latter type of deformation is nonelastic, but plastic, and requires a long period of time. Since the earth possesses both elasticity and plasticity, both types of deformation are possible.

Vertical Movements. Direct evidence of the change of level may be seen in the fossiliferous marine sedimentary rocks that compose the high plateaus bordering the Grand Canyon of the Colorado, which are now at an altitude of 7,000 feet, or in the folded beds of similar origin in the

441

FIG. 347. Elevated and eroded sea terrace near Brookings, Curry County, Oregon. (*Photograph by Oregon State Highway Commission.*)

Appalachian and Rocky Mountains. In The Himalaya sediments that were deposited below sea level have been elevated nearly 30,000 feet. The uplift of the land in relation to the sea may be observed along many coast lines (Fig. 347). Sea cliffs with their associated terraces, sea caves, and chimney rocks may be seen inland a number of miles from the present coasts, and the coastal plains such as the flat Atlantic and Gulf Coastal Plains from central New Jersey southward indicate that the land has been elevated or that the ocean has withdrawn. If the ocean had withdrawn, the abandoned shore lines would be found at many places behind the present shores; but since the abandoned shores are found only in restricted areas, the conclusion is warranted that the land has been raised and that only these restricted areas have been affected. Some of the ancient shore lines, moreover, are higher above the sea at some places than at others. The sea is essentially level. It is a little higher on shores near great mountain ranges, where high rock masses attract the water by gravitative pull, but the differences in the level of the sea's surface are relatively small. The mean sea level is the most nearly constant level available, and it is taken as a datum for measuring the elevation of the land surface.

A classic record of movement in historic time is provided by the ancient Roman public market now known as the temple of Jupiter Serapis on the coast near Naples, Italy. The columns have been bored by *Lithophagus* 18 feet above the floor of the temple, and their shells are found in the holes. The temple was built by the early Romans; subsequently the land was submerged, and later it was raised above the sea.

Evidence of land emergence also is to be found far within the continents, where rocks containing the remains of marine shells are exposed far above the present level of the sea. Such rocks were deposited in the seas as essentially level beds. At places now they are warped and tilted, and the inference is warranted that they have been elevated and also deformed.

Off the coast of Italy, on the island of Capri, a famous sea cave known as the Blue Grotto was used as a shelter by the Romans (Fig. 348). They cut an opening in the roof of the cave to admit more light into the underground retreat. Today the cave is flooded, and the opening in the roof is partly submerged.

Evidence of subsidence is furnished by various observations on different parts of the continents. These include such things as the presence of tree stumps with their roots spreading out in the position in which they grew, but now 1,000 feet underground and 600 feet below sea level in a coal mine in Illinois. One must conclude that this tree once grew on land at the surface of the earth above sea level. Evidence is furnished also by irregular shores such as the rugged coast of New England with its numerous islands, shoals, and drowned valleys. Soundings have shown that there are submarine canyons extending more than 100 miles into the sea. Probably these were formed in part by rivers and thus would indicate that the land once may have stood at a higher level than it does today (Fig. 349). However, a careful examination of the coastal region of Maine reveals the presence of isolated areas of marine sediments which contain shells of various species of marine life that still thrive in the sea. These sediments are more than 100 feet above present sea level. Thus one must conclude that the latest crustal movement in that region was one of uplift. However, the amount of uplift was much less than the subsidence that preceded it and is part of the general upwarp of the northeastern part of the continent that began when the weight of the great continental glacier was removed from that portion of North America.

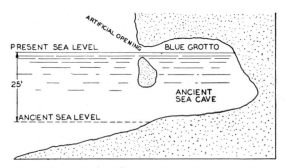

FIG. 348. Generalized section of the Blue Grotto on the coast of the island of Capri, showing evidence of subsidence. (*After Von Kuebel.*)

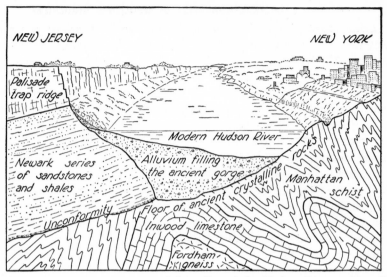

FIG. 349. Generalized cross section of the valley of the Hudson River at New York City, showing subsidence and filling of a valley. (*Redrawn after Scott. Courtesy of C. P. Berkey.*)

A large number of observations assure us that the earth is virtually everywhere sensitive to heavy loads of wide span. Extensive loads of prolonged application, such as widespread, thick ice sheets, cause the earth's crust to be depressed by plastic flow under the load. When, after thousands of years, the ice melts away, the unloaded region rises by a plastic response. The rise is greatest where the ice was thickest, and this may ultimately result in an updoming of the surface. Such actual updoming is recorded by elevated beaches, not only along the northeastern coast of North America and the coasts of Fennoscandia, but also in many other regions that have or had separate icecaps. These include Great Britain, Iceland, Spitsbergen, Patagonia, and New Zealand.

Rate of Movement. The movements of the land are generally slow. Direct measurements have been made in countries bordering the Baltic Sea by placing markers on its shores. It is found that the rate of elevation at places is 2 feet in 100 years. The northern coast of Norway and Sweden has been raised more than 400 feet.

Not all movements, however, are slow. Displacements of the earth's surface during the San Francisco earthquake amounted to 21 feet, and during the earthquake in Japan in 1923 the bottom of Sagami Bay moved more than 1,000 feet, but probably in part at least by submarine slumping. After a great earthquake in Alaska in 1899, it was found that part of the shore of Yakutat Bay had been lifted up as much as 47 feet. The earlier beach with its pebbles and marine shells is now high and dry above the reach of the highest waves.

Kinds of Movement. The movements of the earth are of two types, *orogenic* and *epeirogenic*. By orogenic (mountain-making) movements the mountain masses are raised up. Nearly all great mountain ranges are anticlinoria, that is, the dominant folding is upward at the central parts of the folds. The formation of mountain folds generally is attended by strong horizontal movements along the circumference of the earth, which result in folding and in crumpling of the strata.

By epeirogenic movements land masses of continental magnitude are raised and lowered with little folding. These movements raise segments of the earth's surface above the sea, where degradation prevails, and depress other segments below sea level, where aggradation is dominant. Thus the whole trend of geologic events is changed by such warpings. Most epeirogenic movements are radial, since they take place along the radii of the earth.

The causes of diastrophic movements will be discussed in a subsequent chapter on mountains.

STRUCTURES RESULTING FROM DEFORMATION

It may be observed at many places that the strata forming the earth's crust have been tilted and warped out of their original horizontal position. The structures resulting from diastrophic forces may be classed as (1) gentle tilts or warps, (2) folds, (3) joints or fractures without appreciable displacements, and (4) fractures with displacements called faults.

Attitude of Strata. The attitude of a rock formation is its position with respect to a horizontal surface and to compass directions. In order to show the position of an inclined surface such as a bedding plane in sedimentary rock, two observations are necessary: (1) the angle of slope of the strata; (2) the direction of the intersection of the strata with a horizontal plane. The surface of the earth may be considered to be a horizontal plane.

The term *dip* is used to designate the angle of inclination or the amount a bed is tilted from the horizontal position. The direction of dip is in the direction of steepest inclination of the dipping bed and is expressed in terms of the four cardinal points as determined by a compass. For example, a bed may have a dip of 30 degrees toward the northwest. The dip is an angle in a vertical plane and is measured downward from the horizontal plane. The angle is measured by an instrument called a clinometer.

The term *strike* designates the direction of the intersection of a stratum with a horizontal plane. The direction of strike is measured by means of a compass, the dial of which is graduated to degrees. Thus, if the line of intersection of the bed and a horizontal plane (*BD*, Fig.

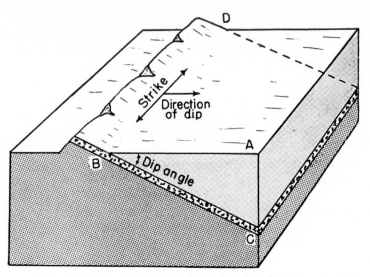

FIG. 350. Diagram illustrating the dip and the strike of a tilted stratum. *ABC* is the angle of dip. *BD*, a horizontal line, is the direction of strike. The direction of dip is toward the right at right angles to the direction of strike.

FIG. 351. Aerial view of eroded inclined strata in northern Appalachians. (*Photograph by John Rich.*)

350) extends in a direction 40 degrees east of north, the strike is recorded at N.40°E. The direction of dip is always measured at right angles to the strike (Fig. 351).

The compass (Fig. 352) used for geological mapping usually contains a clinometer also, which is either a pendulum or a mounted level. Thus the same instrument may be used for determining the direction of strike and the amount of the inclination, or angle of dip. Dip and strike together define the position, or *attitude*, of a stratum with respect to a horizontal surface and to compass directions. Horizontal strata have no dip and therefore can have no strike; both terms apply only to tilted or folded beds.

Warping. Most large areas of sedimentary strata were originally deposited as horizontal beds. If the sea floor on which they were deposited was not lifted up uniformly, the rocks are bent into gently sloping structures such as irregular basins or domes that may be many miles in diameter. Furthermore, the margins of areas of intensive orogenetic diastrophism are rarely sharp and distinct. Marginal zones are commonly warped by uplift or depression, and gently inclined or tilted strata are the results of such movements. Uniformly tilted beds are *homoclines.*

Folds. Where rock strata have been subjected to pressures beyond the elastic limit of the rocks, they may yield slowly by bending or folding into more or less symmetrical series of folds with alternating crests and troughs. The principal types of folded structure are monoclines, anticlines, synclines, and domes and basins (Figs. 353, 354).

A *monocline* is the flexure connecting horizontal or gently inclined strata on either side of the flexure. Where strata are arched up as in the crest of an upfold, they form an *anticline;* downfolds, or troughs, are *synclines.* Each of these may have various modifications. In mountainous or formerly mountainous regions where folds are very numerous, nearly parallel anticlines and synclines are common.

FIG. 352. Brunton compass.

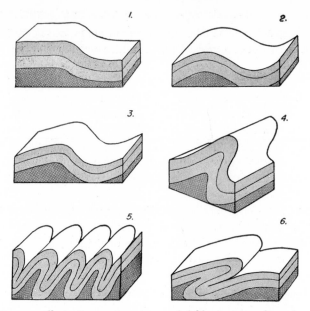

FIG. 353. Diagrams illustrating various types of folds. 1, monocline; 2, symmetrical anticline and syncline; 3, asymmetrical anticline and syncline; 4, inclined or overturned anticline; 5, isoclinal folds; 6, recumbent fold.

FIG. 354. Aerial view of eroded anticlinal fold. (*Photograph by John Rich.*)

The axial plane of a fold is the plane that may be considered to pass through the center of the fold (Fig. 355). The axis is the line which the intersection of the axial plane makes with each of the bedding planes of the folded series. If the axis is inclined, the fold is a plunging fold (Fig. 356). The two sides of a fold are called limbs. If the limbs dip at about the same angle, the fold is said to be symmetrical; if one dips at a higher angle than the other, the fold is asymmetrical. An overturned fold is one in which one limb is at places doubled under, so that it lies below the other (Fig. 353).

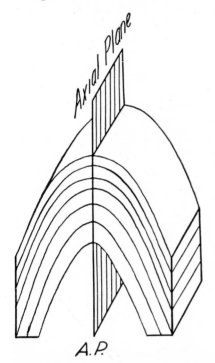

FIG. 355. Sketch showing the axial plane of an anticlinal fold.

In mapping it is common practice to map the intersection of the axial plane and the surface of the earth as the axis of the fold, that is, to map the line from which the rocks dip in opposite directions. Such a line is really the surface trace of the axis.

A recumbent fold is an overturned fold in which the limbs are essentially horizontal, and an isoclinal fold is one in which the two limbs dip equally in the same direction (Fig. 353).

An anticline may coincide with a hill and a syncline with a valley, but after erosion the anticlines commonly lie in the valleys and the synclines form the hills.

Many structural features are so small that the structure is seen at a glance; and in arid mountain regions where vegetation is scarce, large structural features may be seen with little difficulty, especially from the air (Fig. 358). In general, however, the larger structural features are discovered only by mapping the area (Fig. 359).

Folds Due to Settling. The folds of the earth's surface, in general, are due to compressive stresses acting along the earth's circumference. Certain minor folds, however, are believed to have been formed by the settling of rocks above an ancient irregular surface. Figure 360 shows a series of shales and sandstones deposited above a rigid hill. If, as a result of pressure, water is squeezed out of the shales and the shale shrinks 20 per cent, the overlying rocks will be let down above the ancient hill and the rocks away from the summit of the hill will be let down more because the shales are thicker than at the summit. The sandstone (Fig. 360) will dip away from the center of the hill, forming an anticline. According to certain investigators, some of the minor structural features in the oil fields of Kansas and Oklahoma have been formed by this process, which is commonly referred to as *differential compaction*.

Systems of Folds. A large system of folds, including both anticlines and synclines, in which the dominant folding is upward is an *anticlinorium* (Fig. 361). A *synclinorium* is a system in which the dominant folding is downward.

The areas of the great mountain folds are characterized by uplifts that extend for hundreds and even thousands of miles. The axes of the major anticlines of a mountain region overlap each other, and small anticlines are developed on the flanks of larger ones.

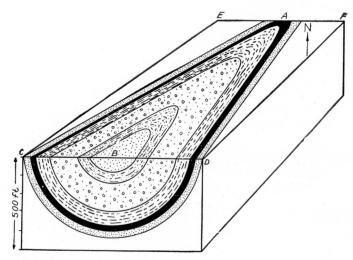

FIG. 356. Block diagram of a syncline plunging toward the southwest. *ECDF* represents the plane of the earth's surface. At *A* the formation shown in black is at the surface, but at *B*, owing to the plunging of the fold, the same formation is more than 300 feet below the surface.

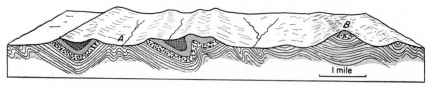

FIG. 357. Cross section of the Appalachian Mountains near Rogersville, Tennessee, showing deeply eroded folds and the relation between ridges and folds. *A*, anticlinal valley; *B*, synclinal ridge. (*After Keith.*)

FIG. 358. Aerial photograph of eroded plunging fold in North Africa. The anticline in central foreground plunges toward the upper left. (*Photograph by United States Air Force.*)

During the formation of great mountain ranges by folding the areas between the mountains also are affected. In the great downfolds, or structural basins, between the mountain ranges the rocks have a general dip away from one mountain range, and they rise toward another. Between the areas of great mountain folds are smaller folds, and since many of these have axes that are parallel to the greater folds of the neighboring mountains, it is believed that they were formed at about the same time and that they are the results of the same forces. The arrangement of the minor folds in Wyoming is illustrated by Fig. 362, which

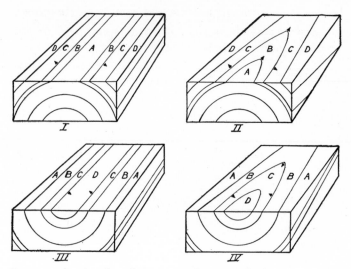

FIG. 359. Diagrams showing the relative age and structural relations of strata included in simple folds. *A* is the oldest stratum that crops out at the surface; *D* is the youngest. I, symmetrical anticline; II, plunging anticline; III, symmetrical syncline; IV, plunging syncline.

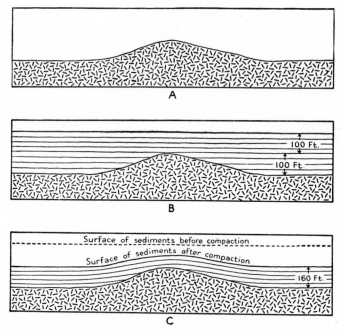

FIG. 360. Diagrams showing a fold resulting from the settling of sediments. *A,* erosional ridge; *B,* same ridge covered by unconsolidated sediment; *C,* same but after compaction of sediment. (*After Billings.*)

shows the positions of the major mountain uplifts and of the smaller anticlinal folds around them. Essentially the area of the entire state has been involved in the uplifts that formed the Black Hills, Bighorn Mountains, Shoshone Mountains, the Laramie, and other mountain ranges of Wyoming.

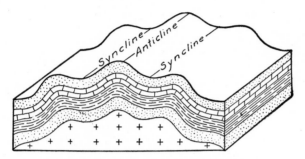

FIG. 361. Sketch showing an anticlinorium.

Subsurface Relations of Folds. Folded beds commonly lie one above the other like cards in a flexed pack. If an upper one which may be seen at the surface is folded, lower ones also will be folded. The subsurface relations of strata in folds may be depicted by *structure contours* which, like a topographic map, show the configuration of a surface by lines of equal elevation, generally referred to mean sea level as the datum plane. For a discussion of the methods used in the construction of structural contour maps, see Appendix B.

Crustal Compression. The processes of folding involve compression of the earth's crust, as is illustrated by Figs. 363, 364. In Fig. 363 the bed represented by *AB* is 6 miles long, and the distance after folding is 4 miles. The length of the area formerly covered by the bed *AB* has decreased one-third by folding. The compression shown by Fig. 364 is 10 per cent. It is estimated that the shortening produced by the crustal folding attending the formation of the Appalachian Mountains near Harrisburg, Pennsylvania, including the crystalline belt, has amounted to 100 miles; and the compression due to the folding of the Alps has resulted in shortening the earth's visible crust about 125 miles.

Domes and Basins. A dome is a roughly symmetrical upfold in which the beds dip in all directions from a point (Fig. 365). Circular, symmetrical domes are rare, but elongated, oval-shaped domes are very common and occur as parts of many large anticlines. Every gradation may be found between circular domes, elongated domes, and anticlines. In some regions domes are isolated structures in areas of horizontal strata;

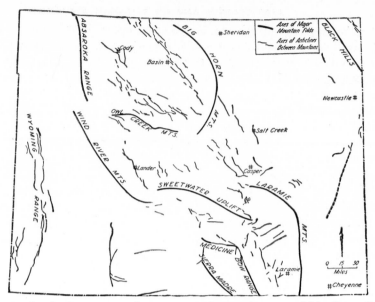

FIG. 362. Sketch of Wyoming, showing axes of major mountain folds (heavy black lines) and intermontane minor folds (light black lines). (*After Hares, Heald, Richardson, Woodruff, Collier, and others, U.S. Geological Survey, Wyoming Geological Survey.*)

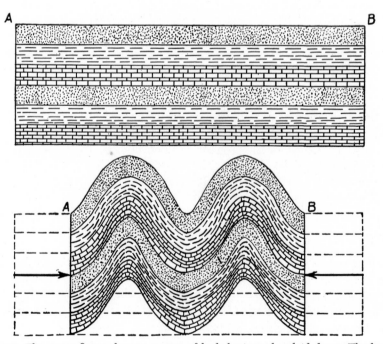

FIG. 363. The upper figure shows a system of beds horizontal as laid down. The lower figure shows same after folding. *AB* in lower figure is two-thirds as long as *AB* in upper figure. The shortening is one-third.

more commonly, however, they occur associated with other folds. The Black Hills of South Dakota are a single oval dome which rises above the Great Plains and is not connected with other folds. This dome has been deeply dissected by erosion, so that its structure may be readily observed.

A basin is the opposite of a dome. It is a concave structural depression in which the strata dip toward the center from all sides rather than away from it in all directions. In a basin the strata resemble a stack of saucers, each one smaller in surface area than the one next below. The term basin is used also with reference to erosion, and it is necessary, therefore, to distinguish between the basins formed by folding and those produced by agents of erosion. The topographic expression may be common to both, but the structure may be entirely different.

Joints. When subjected to a sufficiently great stress, rocks are strained and eventually yield, by deformation, by flowage, or by rupture. If the

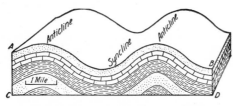

FIG. 364. Diagram showing anticlines and synclines of folded beds. The curved line *AB* represents a line 7 miles long. The distance *CD* is 6.3 miles long. By folding the distance *AB* is shortened about 10 per cent.

FIG. 365. Aerial photograph of eroded dome in North Africa. Rocks dip outward in all directions from crest of dome at *C*. (*Photograph by United States Air Force.*)

yield is by rupture, fractures result and those along which there has been no appreciable displacement parallel to the plane of the fracture are referred to as joints. The joints are responses to the application of forces of tension, compression, shear, or torsion (Figs. 366, 367).

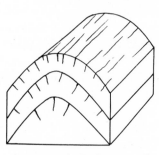

FIG. 366. Block diagram of a simple anticline, showing tension joints along the crest.

All rocks are much weaker under tensional stress than under compression, and therefore it is reasonable to find tension joints very widely distributed throughout the earth's crust. Undoubtedly many of the irregular fractures are due to the warping and twisting to which the rocks were subjected during gradual crustal movements. This is true especially in marine sedimentary rocks that were originally deposited below sea level and later elevated by regional uplifts. Such vertical movements would rarely be perfectly uniform over a wide area, and consequently the beds would be subjected to torsional or shearing stresses of such magnitude that they yielded by fracturing. Tensional joints also are formed along the crests of anticlines, where they are produced as a result of the stretching of the rock strata.

Field observations indicate that joints are much more numerous in some places than in others. Where they are abundant in sedimentary rocks, they commonly are arranged in intersecting sets at fairly large angles to each other and, in each set, the joints are nearly parallel (Figs. 368, 369). Such associated sets constitute

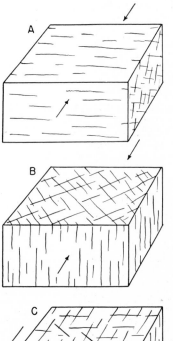

FIG. 367. Shear fractures produced by stresses in directions indicated by long arrows. *A*, with easy relief upward; *B*, with easy relief laterally; *C*, horizontal shearing stress. Four tension fractures (*T*) are shown. (*After Nevin.*)

a *joint system.* In such systems one set of the system is commonly more strongly developed than the other and extends for long distances across a thick series of beds. Such sets are known as *master joints* as contrasted with minor fractures, which may be limited to a single stratum.

Joints likewise are formed by tensional stresses caused by the contraction resulting from the cooling of magmas in necks, dikes, sills, and lava flows. Columns ranging in diameter from a few inches to several feet form at right angles to the cooling surface, especially in the tabular masses (Fig. 339). The Devil Postpile in California, the Devils Tower in Wyoming (Fig. 335), and the Giant's Causeway in northern Ireland are perhaps the best-known and most spectacular examples of such columnar jointing.

In addition to the joints caused by shrinkage due to cooling, igneous

FIG. 368. Vertical jointing in Portage beds, Cayuga Lake, New York. (*Photograph by Kindle, U.S. Geological Survey.*)

FIG. 369. Intersecting joint systems in northern Australia as seen from the air. Joints have been enlarged by weathering and erosion to form gullies. (*Courtesy of United States Air Force.*)

rocks may have many joints and systems of joints that are the result of crustal movements long after the rock was solidified. Many such joints are the results of compressive stresses. A block of granite under compression develops a system of joints nearly at right angles to each other. Many granites and other coarse-grained igneous rocks are regularly jointed into rectangular, more or less cubical blocks or long prisms. The presence or absence of such joints determines not only the method of quarrying but also the size of the blocks that may be quarried. At only a few places are joints spaced sufficiently widely to permit the quarrying of blocks from which to make perfect monoliths as much as 50 to 100 feet in length.

Faults. Fractures in the earth's crust along which slipping has occurred are called faults. The essential feature is differential movement parallel to the surface of the fracture. Faults occur in all types of rock, but they are most easily detected in sedimentary rocks, where the offsetting of definite strata is readily recognized. The amount of displacement may be only a fraction of an inch, or it may be tens of thousands of feet. In either case it is not possible to determine whether one side of the fracture stood still while the other side moved or whether both sides took part in the movement. All that can be observed is that, of two points

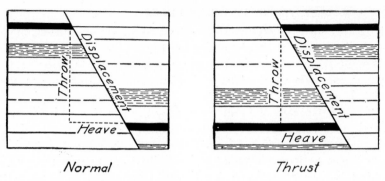

Normal   Thrust

FIG. 370. Diagrams showing cross sections of a normal fault and of a thrust fault. The figures illustrate displacement, throw, and heave.

that once were opposite each other in the walls of the fracture before the faulting took place, one has moved in relation to the other (Fig. 370).

The plane of the fracture along which displacement took place is the *fault plane*. This plane is rarely flat for any considerable distance, and consequently the term *fault surface* would be more appropriate. If a fault could be traced its entire length, it would be found to die out to zero displacement at its two ends (Fig. 371). In other words, the amount of displacement is commonly at a maximum near the middle of its length and diminishes toward its extremities. In some regions there is a tendency for faults to occur in groups, or zones, in which movement takes place along a number of closely spaced fractures instead of on a single fault surface, and in other districts there are fault zones in which the separate faults are arranged in an overlapping order. Where such overlapping relationships exist, the faults are said to be *en échelon*.

Where the masses of rock involved in faulting are of great size and

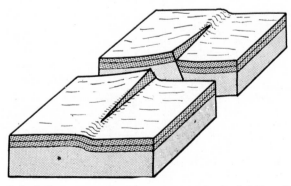

FIG. 371. A fault dying out and passing into a monoclinal fold at both ends.

weight, the enormous pressures keep the faces of the fault blocks in close compressional contact and, as a result of the friction between blocks, the fault plane is smoothed and in many places polished to a slick surface to which the term *slickensides* is applied. Such surfaces may resemble glaciated surfaces, but they are usually more glazed. Fault *striae* are scratches on the walls of faults formed by the abrasion of hard rock or mineral particles against them. On some fault surfaces two sets of striae cross each other, showing different movements at different times. When the fault surface is not clean-cut and definite, there may be more or less crushing of the wall rocks during the act of slipping. If the fragments that result are coarse, the material is called a *fault breccia*, and if reduced to a fine powder, it is termed *gouge*. The fragments at a fault surface are made up of the rocks that the fault crosses, and often the fragmental material is a mixture of many kinds of rocks.

Fault surfaces are generally inclined, but a few are vertical. Since most faults are inclined, one wall will overhang the other and conse-

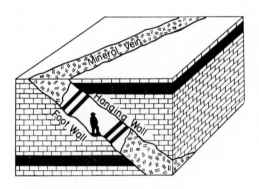

FIG. 372. Diagram showing the relation of the hanging wall to the footwall of a fault. The man stands on the footwall, and the hanging wall, which in this case has moved up, "hangs" above his head. A mineral vein has been deposited along the fault surface.

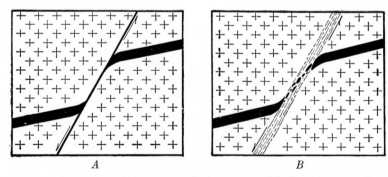

FIG. 373. A, cross section of a vein curved near a normal fault; B, cross section of a vein curved near a normal fault with broken fragments of the vein in the fault gouge between segments of the vein. The sections show drag.

quently it is customary to speak of the rock above the fault plane as the *hanging wall* and that below the fault as the *footwall*. These are mining terms and are applied to both faults and veins. The footwall is the rock on which the miner stands as he works a vein, and the hanging wall is the rock above his head (Fig. 372).

In faults of considerable displacement the ends of the adjacent strata or of veins are bent upward or downward according to the direction of movement on the fault plane. The dislocated ends of the beds are bent back from the direction of movement of the wall in which they form (Fig. 373). Such bending adjacent to the fault is called *drag*.

The block that appears to have moved up is the *upthrow side* of the fault, and that which appears to have moved down is the *downthrow side*. The striae and grooves on the fault walls do not record the direction of movements, as they show only that the movement has taken place in one of two directions, and they do not show which block has moved. On some fault planes there are raised places which are due to hard spots in the rocks. They are worn deeper in the direction from which the movement came. When the hand is passed over it, the fault surface will feel smoother where the movement of the hand coincides with the direction of movement of the abrading material than when the hand is moved in the opposite direction. Although it is often impossible to determine the extent of movement along a fault, the lost segment of a faulted bed or vein often may be discovered by mapping the area.

Fault Scarps. Many faults break the surface as well as the rocks beneath. Where one side of a fault moves up with relation to the other, it may give rise to a cliff, or *fault scarp*, the height or prominence of which will de-

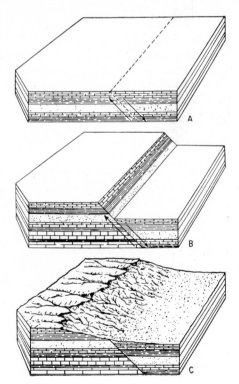

FIG. 374. Diagrams of a fault cutting horizontal strata. *A*, the fracture before displacement; *B*, after displacement but before erosion; *C*, after erosion of the fault scarp.

FIG. 375. Fault scarp forming shore of MacDonald Lake, near Great Slave Lake, Mackenzie District, Canada. (*Royal Canadian Air Force.*)

pend upon the amount of displacement and its recency in geologic time (Figs. 374 to 376). At many places erosion has reduced the upthrow block to the same level as that of the downthrow block.

The east side of the Sierra Nevada is a series of fault scarps several thousand feet high that serves as the west boundary of the Great Basin of Nevada and Utah. This basin is bounded on the east by the somewhat lower fault scarp of the Wasatch Mountains. Both the mountainous escarpments have been made so irregular by erosion as to obscure their faulted character. In the Appalachian Mountains there are many faults but rarely any fault scarps. There the faulting occurred so long ago that erosion has reduced the upthrow side of the faults to the same level as the downthrow blocks.

Rate of Faulting. Displacements of a fraction of an inch to 20 feet or more have taken place in a few minutes along fault planes. In Owens Valley, California, in 1872, a slipping occurred along a line 40 miles long which resulted in a displacement of 5 to 20 feet. Such sudden movements nearly always produce earthquakes. At places in some mines faulting is observed to be taking place continually, but at a very slow rate. If long-continued, the total displacement resulting from such movements may be great, but no surface changes may be detected, since erosion cuts away the upthrow side as fast as it is elevated. If most faulting is assumed to be slow, it follows that a fault with a displacement of several thousand feet was active for a very long period of time and that the total displacement was accomplished by hundreds of small, sudden slips.

Kinds of Faults. If the hanging-wall block of a fault appears to have moved down, the fault is called a *normal fault;* if it appears to have

FIG. 376. Vertical air view along the San Andreas fault zone in San Luis Obispo County, California. The position of the fault is indicated by the straight, dark furrow between the hills to the right of center. The streams from the mountains at left follow along the fault for several thousand feet before breaking through the fault scarp. (*Photograph by Fairchild Aerial Surveys, Los Angeles.*)

FIG. 377. Chief Mountain in northwestern Montana, an erosional remnant of the Lewiston overthrust fault. Ancient metamorphic rocks resting on Cretaceous sediments.

risen, the fault is a *thrust,* or *reverse, fault* (Figs. 377 to 379). Faults that cut across the dip of the beds and lie at right angles to the strike are *dip faults* (Figs. 380, 381); those which lie parallel to the strike of the beds but cross the dip are *strike faults* (Figs. 382, 383); and those which cross both dip and strike are *oblique faults* (Fig. 384). Dip, strike, and oblique faults may be either normal or reverse. By normal faulting certain beds may be cut out of the series where it crops out at the surface, as is shown by Fig. 383A, where bed 7 lies against bed 9 and beds below 7 are concealed. Beds may be cut out also by reverse faulting, as is shown by Fig. 383B, where beds 4 and 7 are adjacent and beds 5 and 6 are cut out by erosion. In folded areas an anticline may pass into a normal fault, and a recumbent fold may pass into a thrust fault.

In the main, reverse faults dip at low angles, and in general such "low-angle faults" dip 0 to 45 degrees, although some are steeper. Many low-angle faults are ruptured folds broken along an axis of folding (Fig. 378).

Great thrust faults are found at many places. Some are traced scores

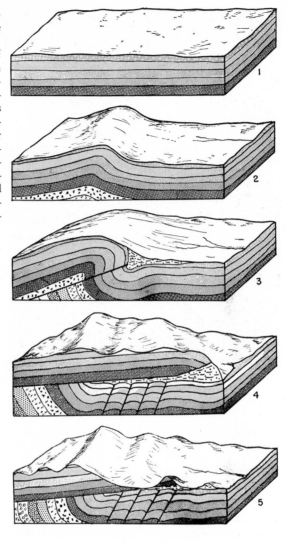

FIG. 378. A series of diagrams showing the probable sequence of events (1 to 5) in the formation of Chief Mountain in northwestern Montana. Old geologic formations were thrust eastward more than 10 miles along a low-angle fault surface overriding younger strata (3 to 5). Chief Mountain (5) is an erosional remnant of ancient pre-Cambrian rocks resting on and surrounded by younger Cretaceous strata. (*After Hussey.*)

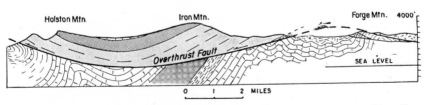

FIG. 379. Generalized cross section from Bristol, Virginia, to Mountain City, Tennessee, showing extensive overthrusting. (*After Butts.*)

465

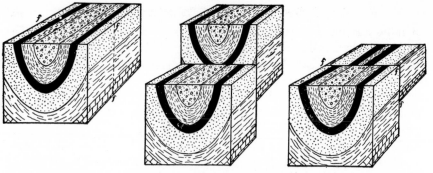

FIG. 380. Diagrams illustrating a dip fault cutting a syncline. Faulting was followed by peneplanation.

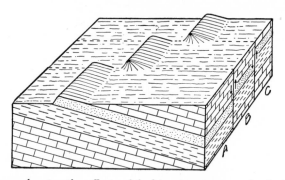

FIG. 381. Diagram showing the effects of faulting in an area with tilted beds of unequal hardness. The faults are vertical dip faults. Block *B* moved upward with relation to *A*. Block *C* moved upward with relation to block *B*. There was no horizontal displacement. The faulting was followed by erosion, and hogback ridges remain. The apparent displacement of the ridge is not due to horizontal movement, but it is the result of monoclinal shifting of the outcrop during the erosion of the vertically elevated blocks.

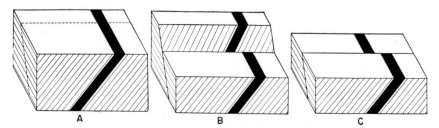

FIG. 382. Diagrams showing structural relations of a dip fault cutting a homocline. *A*, dotted line at right angles to strike shows position of fracture before displacement. *B*, after displacement but before erosion of fault scarp; hanging wall in foreground. *C*, both hanging wall and footwall eroded to a common level with apparent horizontal displacement along fault.

of miles and have horizontal displacements of more than 20 miles. The Lewiston overthrust (Chief Mountain) fault of Montana (Fig. 377), one of the best-known overthrust faults in the United States, has a displacement of 10 miles or more.

Some faults are neither normal nor reverse but in movement and position are merely vertical or horizontal instead. Still others involve longitudinal movement parallel to a nearly vertical plane, as on the San Andreas fault of California (Fig. 376). Such a fault is a *rift* or *tear fault*.

Horsts and Graben. A block depressed between two faults is a *graben* (Fig. 385), and a block raised between two faults is a *horst* (Fig. 386). Faulting and tilting of faulted blocks may go on together, and thus parallel ridges, or "saw-tooth" mountains, may form. Such block faulting has taken place on a large scale in the Great Basin area of Arizona, Nevada, and Utah and also in the San Francisco Bay region of California (Fig. 387).

Horsts and graben occur in almost every complexly faulted area. The Death Valley region has many examples. The Vosges Mountains in France and the Black Forest in Germany are two horsts which face each other across the broad and deep trough or graben of the Rhine Valley. An outstanding example of graben structures in the present topography of the continents is the Great Rift Valley of eastern Africa, which consists

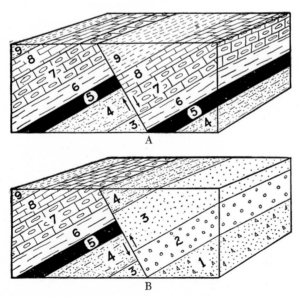

FIG. 383. Diagrams of strike faults. A, showing how certain beds may be repeated by normal faulting followed by erosion; B, showing how beds (5 and 6) may be cut out from their usual outcrop positions by reverse faulting followed by erosion.

of a series of down-faulted blocks which are now partially covered by lakes, Lake Tanganyika, Lake Albert, Lake Nyasa, and others occupy basins produced by the faulting. Lake Tanganyika is more than 4,000 feet deep with the floor of its basin lying 1,600 feet below sea level. Another large graben forms the valley of the Jordan River and that of the Dead Sea. For much of its length this valley is also below the level of the

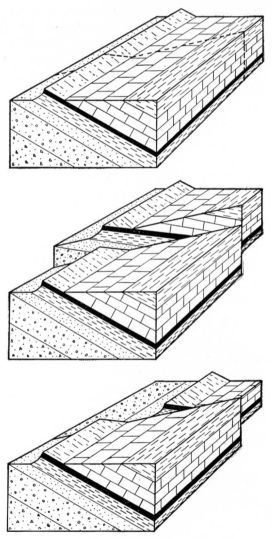

FIG. 384. Diagrams showing an oblique fault cutting inclined strata. Faulting was followed by erosion.

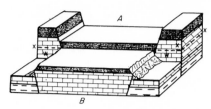

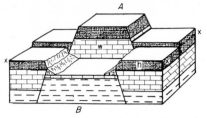

FIG. 385. Diagram of a graben at *A*. After extensive erosion, block *A* is reduced to the level of a peneplane at *xxx*, and the more resistant rock (*stippled*) is removed from the highlands. If the peneplane is rejuvenated, the less resistant rock (*w*) may erode more rapidly than the more resistant rock (*stippled*) so that the lowland of block *A* in the background may become the upland of block *B*. (*Redrawn after Lahee.*)

FIG. 386. Diagram of a horst at *A*. After extensive erosion, block *A* is reduced to the level of a peneplane at *xxx* after the more resistant rock *h* is removed from the high block. If the peneplane is rejuvenated, a valley may then develop as shown in block *B* in the foreground. Thus the lowlands of block *A* may become the highlands of block *B*. (*Redrawn from Lahee.*)

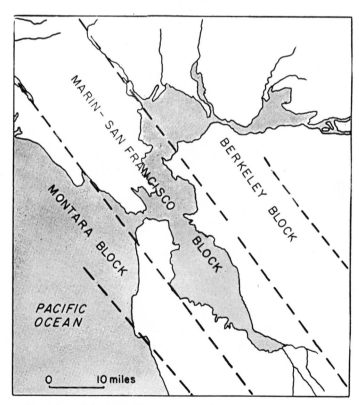

FIG. 387. The system of fault blocks in the San Francisco Bay region. (*After Lawson, U.S. Geological Survey.*)

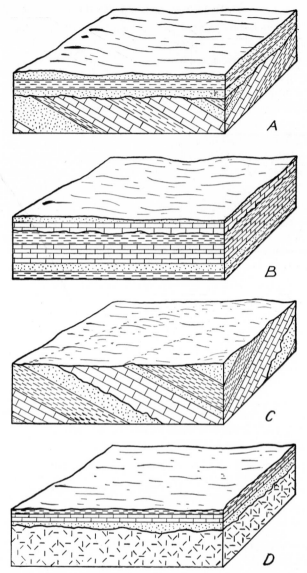

FIG. 388. Diagrams illustrating unconformable relations of sedimentary rocks. A, an angular unconformity with a discordance in bedding. B, an erosional unconformity or a disconformity; neither series of strata is tilted or folded. C, a disconformity with both series tilted. D, a nonconformity where sedimentary beds rest on the eroded surface of igneous rocks.

Mediterranean Sea. The surface of the Dead Sea is more than 1,300 feet below sea level.

Unconformities. An unconformity is a surface of erosion or non-deposition that separates younger strata from older rocks. Where rocks are laid down one above the other in uninterrupted succession, they are conformable. When they are eroded and submerged and later rocks are laid down upon them, the relationship is an unconformity (Fig. 388). The plane of contact between the two beds or series of beds is the plane of unconformity. Commonly this is not a geometrical plane but an undulating surface.

The relief on the unconformity may amount to hundreds or even thousands of feet. The early Paleozoic sedimentary rocks of the Grand Canyon were deposited on a surface with a relief of more than 800 feet, and the upper Paleozoic rocks around Boston, Massachusetts, rest upon an unconformity with a relief of at least 2,100 feet. If the beds below and above the plane of unconformity have the same dip, the relation is an erosional unconformity or a *disconformity*. If the beds of the lower series were folded or tilted before beds of the later series were laid down, the two series of beds are discordant. The beds dip at different angles, and this relationship is an *angular unconformity* (Fig. 389). Unconformities may be developed between eroded intrusive igneous rock and sedimentary strata. This relationship is referred to as a *nonconformity*. An unconformity indicates a long chain of geologic events, and the relation therefore is highly significant.

Recognition of Unconformities. To recognize an unconformity all evidences of erosion between the deposition of the older and younger series of rocks must be investigated. Thus, if the dividing surface between the older and the younger series is irregular (Fig. 389), this may suggest that it was once an erosion surface. An ancient soil or weathered zone between two series of rocks shows that there is a buried erosion surface. If the lower series of rocks is more highly folded than the later one, there is a discordance of bedding which indicates unconformity (Fig. 389). If the lower series of rocks contains many veins or dikes and these are absent from the upper series, one may infer that an erosion surface exists between the two series. If sedimentary rocks lie upon a surface of igneous rock and there are no evidences of intrusive relations, it is probable that the contact is an erosion surface.

An abrupt change in the character of the rocks suggests that a change of conditions occurred. Thus a conglomerate, which is a near-shore sedimentary rock, suggests an ancient shore line. If the conglomerate contains fragments of the underlying formation, it is evidence of an erosion interval. A basal conglomerate at the beginning of a new series, containing

FIG. 389. Angular unconformity near Socorro, New Mexico. (*Photograph by Chapman, U.S. Geological Survey.*)

fragments of different rocks from the older series, particularly is significant. Conglomerates are found within formations, and some of them seem to be made up of fragments of rocks broken by waves during heavy storms. These intraformational conglomerates do not denote unconformities and are to be distinguished from basal conglomerates.

SUMMARY OF EVIDENCES OF UNCONFORMITY

1. Discordance in bedding. The underlying series of beds is more highly folded than the overlying series.

2. Erosion surface. The beds of the upper series rest upon an erosion surface of the older series.

3. Basal conglomerate. The lowest beds of the upper series contain pebbles of rocks of the older series.

4. Differences in degree of deformation. The older rocks are faulted, folded, or metamorphosed more than the younger series.

5. Differences in veining and intrusion. The older rocks contain closely spaced dikes and veins not present in younger series.

6. Differences in character of rocks. An intrusive igneous rock is in contact with sedimentary beds but does not exhibit intrusive relations, showing that it was eroded before the upper beds were deposited.

7. Marked differences in fossils occurring in the beds in contact.

SUGGESTIONS FOR FURTHER READING

Billings, M. P.: Structural Geology, Prentice-Hall, Inc., 1942.

Blackwelder, E.: The Recognition of Fault Scarps, *Jour. Geology*, vol. 36, pp. 289–311, 1928.

Bucher, W. H.: The Deformation of the Earth's Crust, Princeton University Press, 1933.

Lahee, Frederick H.: Field Geology, 5th ed., McGraw-Hill Book Company, Inc., 1952.

Nevin, C. M.: Principles of Structural Geology, 3d ed., John Wiley & Sons, Inc., 1942.

CHAPTER 19

Differential Stream Erosion and Its Effects

The shapes into which the land is sculptured by stream erosion and mass wasting are determined to a great extent by the composition and sub-surface structures of the rocks of the region, that is to say, land forms commonly reflect the structure of their component rock. It follows, there-fore, that where the rocks are not homogeneous the cycle of stream erosion produces topographic features very different from those found where valley development takes place in uniform rocks.

Trend of the Stream's Course. There are various causes which lead to the selection of the course followed by a stream in its journey to the sea. A valley may owe its position and its trend to one or more of the follow-ing factors: (1) the original slope and natural irregularities of the sur-face; (2) differential erosion; (3) jointing; (4) faulting; (5) folding.

1. A river whose course has been determined by the original slope and the irregularities of that slope is a *consequent stream* (Fig. 390). Such streams are characteristic of coastal-plain areas where the surface is comparatively uniform and regular with a gentle slope to the sea. Many of the streams along the Atlantic and Gulf Coasts of the United States are of this type. Other consequent streams flow off volcanic cones, across lava fields, or over irregularly rolling plains of glacial deposits. The overflow of a lake also takes a consequent course.

2. As erosion proceeds, new channels develop, independent of the original topography. In the absence of any directional control, as in areas of flat-lying sediments or of massive crystalline rocks, the headward growth and multiplication of tributaries produce a *dendritic* drainage pattern (Figs. 391, 392). At many places, on the other hand, the stream courses are directed by differences in the structure and character of the bedrock formations. The streams tend to follow the softer, or weaker, beds. Such variations lead to differential erosion so that eventually a stream

474

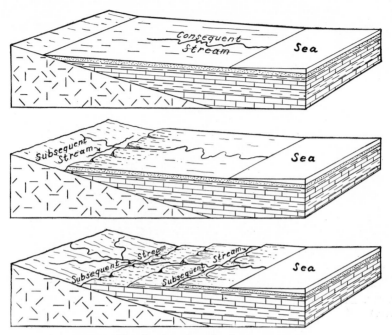

FIG. 390. The development of subsequent streams.

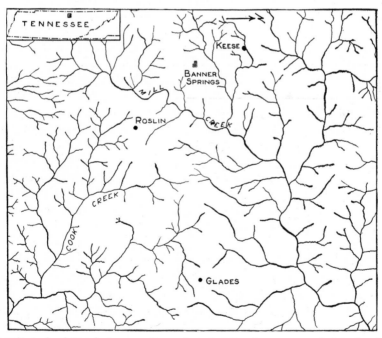

FIG. 391. A dendritic drainage pattern characteristic of an area underlain by horizontal strata or massive crystalline rock of uniform hardness.

FIG. 392. Dendritic drainage in central Africa. (*Photograph by United States Air Force.*)

may undergo marked changes in position and direction and alter its original consequent course. Rivers formed in this way are called *subsequent streams* (Fig. 390) because they have been developed by subsequent erosion determined by structure. Topographic features produced by differential erosion are described on pages 483–488.

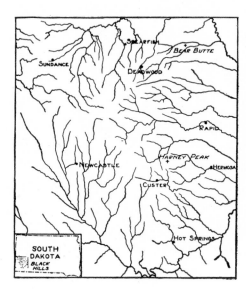

3. The position of a valley often is controlled by the direction of the joints or fissures in the bedrock of the area which it drains. Guided by such joints during headward erosion, the streams develop angular drainage patterns (Fig. 394). This is true especially of small tributary streams, as is characteristically shown in the Colorado Plateau, in Connecticut, and

FIG. 393. A radial stream pattern developed on the surface of the domelike uplift of the Black Hills in South Dakota.

also in Ontario, where large areas of strongly jointed rocks are exposed at the surface.

4. In regions where faulting has taken place on a large scale, many valleys follow the fault zones for great distances because the fractured rock there is relatively nonresistant to erosion. At some places long, narrow blocks of the earth's crust have been depressed to form valleylike basins, which later become stream channels. The Dead Sea Basin and the Jordan Valley are typical examples. In California Owens Valley has a similar history; and in Germany a large portion of the valley of the Rhine is a structural trough flanked by the Vosges and by the Black Forest mountains in which many of the steep slopes facing the valley are escarpments produced by the displacement of the rocks along fractures.

5. Long, parallel mountain folds influence the trends of valleys by governing the directions of the major consequent streams which follow the troughs of the folds. Small streams flow from the crests of the folds into the troughs, where they unite to form the larger ones. At such places the walls of the valley are the limbs of the folds; and since the courses and profiles of the valleys are determined by the structure of the rocks through which they pass, they are *structural valleys*. Certain tributaries of the Columbia River in central Washington follow such valleys. Subsequent valleys, carved from folded rocks, also are influenced by the trend of the folds (Fig. 395).

Stream Piracy. In the process of valley development each stream continues to extend or to modify its drainage basin until all its divides become stationary. During this process it frequently happens that one stream finds conditions for growth and extension more favorable than another, on the opposite side of the

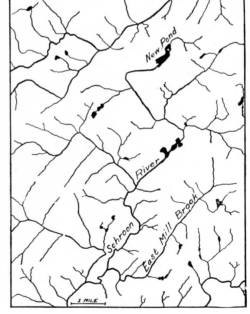

FIG. 394. A rectangular stream pattern near Elizabethtown, New York. The pattern is characterized by right-angled bends in both the main stream and its tributaries. It is controlled by right-angled jointing or faulting of the rocks.

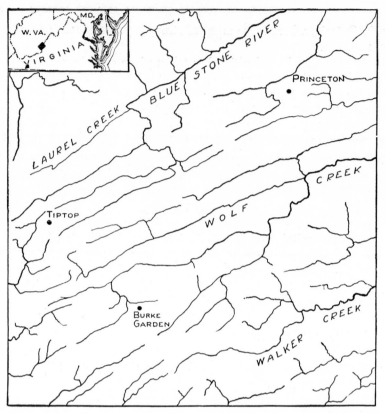

FIG. 395. An adjusted stream pattern characteristic of the mature stage of an erosion cycle in a region of folded or tilted strata of different degrees of resistance to erosion. The arrangement resembles a trellis.

divide, and, by the extension of tributaries, cuts back until it steals some of the headwaters of the less favorably situated stream and diverts them to its own channel. Such invasion is *stream piracy,* and the stream whose territory has been invaded is said to have been *beheaded* by the pirate stream (Fig. 396). The conditions which may give a stream an advantage over an adjoining one are (1) a greater volume of water, (2) softer rocks in which to excavate its channel, and (3) higher gradient due to a shorter course to the sea. If the amount of precipitation is greater on one side of a mountain range than on the opposite slope, the streams receiving the greater volume of rainfall will have a higher velocity and therefore will erode more rapidly and will be able to extend their headwater tributaries farther than streams on the opposite side of the divide.

If streams drain regions with tilted strata in which different types of sedimentary rock alternate as a result of tilting, the larger streams tend to follow the outcrops of the less resistant beds and their smaller tributaries join them nearly at right angles. Where such conditions prevail, the larger streams flowing in the softer rocks often behead the streams that cut across the hard strata. During high water the higher stream overflows into the valley of the deeper stream and establishes a channel which later becomes permanent.

Where a stream flows across tilted strata, a *narrows*, or a *water gap* (Fig. 397), is developed where the valley crosses the harder beds. If a stream is diverted from the water gap by piracy, the narrow portion of the beheaded valley is called a *wind gap*. Such gaps are common in the

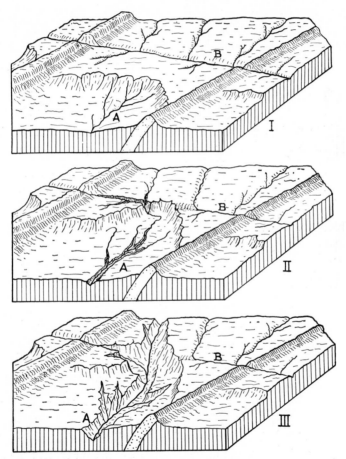

FIG. 396. Diagram illustrating stream piracy. I, the tributaries at *A* are advancing by headward erosion toward the valley of the stream *B*. II, the stream *B* has been beheaded or captured, and its headwaters are diverted to the pirate stream *A*. III, the valley of *A* is extended and deepened. (*Based on a drawing by Davis.*)

FIG. 397. The Delaware Water Gap where the river cuts across the level-topped ridge known as Kittatinny Mountain. (*Aero Service Corporation.*)

Appalachian region, and at many places they served as passes through the mountains for the early pioneers traveling by wagon to settle in Kentucky and Tennessee. It is estimated that 300,000 people passed through the Cumberland Gap in their migration westward during the last quarter of the eighteenth century. Some of the gaps of the Blue Ridge became strategic points during the campaigns of the Civil War.

Antecedent Streams. Some well-developed streams continue to follow their long-established courses regardless of later warping of the surface on which they formed. These streams antedate the local transverse uplift and have been able to deepen or adjust their channels as fast as the change in attitude has taken place. They are *antecedent streams,* and the Columbia River is regarded as a classic example.

Stream Erosion in Flat-lying Strata. Where the strata are horizontal or but slightly inclined, the valley form is determined by the nature of the rock formations. If excavated in strata of uniform resistance, the valley slopes show few irregularities, and the angle of the slope is determined by the ratio of lateral erosion to the deepening of the channel. As erosion continues, successive layers are exposed and in an area of maturely dissected topography the outcropping beds swing out around the spurs between tributaries and up into the tributary valleys. If followed upstream on one side, a given stratum at the level of the stream crosses the stream and turns back on the other side.

Rock Terraces. By differential weathering and erosion the resistant layers are etched into relief, and the slopes of the valley become terraced.

Such structures are *rock terraces* since they are cut in solid rocks rather than in alluvium.

The downward slope of a rock terrace is the exposed edge of a hard stratum and usually is steep and clifflike, whereas the slope rising above the terrace is formed by the eroded edge of the softer stratum above and normally is a gentle slope covered with weathered rock waste. If the resistant beds are thick, extensive escarpments may develop, as is shown on a magnificent scale in the Grand Canyon of the Colorado River (Fig. 127). As the topography becomes more mature, the terraces are cut back farther from the channel and broad, flat areas many miles in width and parallel to the stream may be developed on both sides of its valley.

Mesas and Buttes. In regions of horizontal sedimentary strata or where sheets of lava cover soft clays or partially indurated sediments, flat-topped areas are isolated by the headward cutting of tributary streams as the region passes from youthful to mature topography. Such plateaulike areas are *mesas,* from the Spanish word meaning table. The level top of a mesa consists of a resistant horizontal bed that tends to protect the less resistant strata below it. Where erosion reduces a mesa to a flat-topped hill, it becomes a *butte* (Figs. 398, 399). Many of the striking mesas and buttes in the semiarid plains of New Mexico and Arizona are remnants of former plateaus dissected by erosion (Fig. 400). Other buttes are erosional remnants of volcanic necks, dikes, or other steep-standing resistant rock structures.

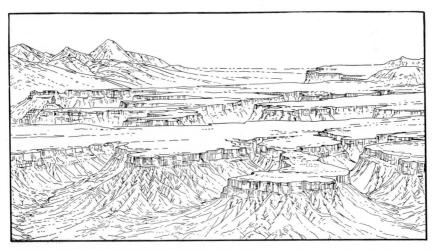

FIG. 398. A sketch showing the development of mesas and canyons by the erosional dissection of a high, semiarid plateau in the southwestern United States. Mesa Verde, Colorado. (*U.S. Geol. Survey Prof. Paper 60.*)

FIG. 399. Red Butte, Wyoming. (*Courtesy of U.S. Geological Survey.*)

Badlands. Under special conditions the differential erosion of flat-lying beds produces peculiar and striking types of topography (Figs. 400, 401). Among these are the *badlands,* which are well-developed in the northwestern Great Plains region of United States and Canada, especially in the Dakotas, Wyoming, and Montana. Badlands are flat-topped, or buttelike, hills with rugged, barren slopes. The ruggedness is due chiefly to numerous gullies cut in the slopes of slightly consolidated sediments, in which certain layers are sufficiently resistant to erosion temporarily to arrest denudation. A semiarid climate is favorable to the development of

FIG. 400. Erosional remnants, Monument Valley, Utah. The talus slopes indicate that wasting still continues. (*Spence Air Photos.*)

FIG. 401. Badlands carved by rainwash and gullying in the Painted Desert near Holbrook, Arizona. The varicolored, nearly flat-lying beds, though generally soft, offer differing resistance to erosion. (*Spence Air Photos.*)

such features, for under such conditions the rainfall is concentrated in a few heavy showers, and thus there is the maximum runoff and hence the maximum of erosion with the minimum rainfall. The semiarid climate is largely responsible for the lack of vegetation on the slopes, and this lack results in the exposure of the loosely consolidated material to the torrents of water.

Erosion of Tilted Strata. Where a region underlain by tilted strata (Fig. 402) is eroded toward maturity, the inclined beds are exposed and some of the alternating layers are more easily eroded by the streams than others, with the result that they tend to flow, as far as possible, on the less resistant beds and to cut across the resistant ones, thus flowing as short a distance as possible on resistant beds. The less resistant strata, therefore, become the sites of valleys, and the resistant strata stand up as ridges or mountains. Such changes in the course of a stream by means of which it develops a definite and stable relation to the subsurface rock structures are called "structural adjustment."

The Hoosic Valley of Massachusetts, the Shenandoah Valley of Virginia, and the Lehigh Valley of Pennsylvania are all examples of valleys that are eroded in relatively soft rocks.

The adjusted streams, flowing parallel to the strike, frequently cut vertically through the weaker strata until they encounter a hard or resistant bed and then shift down the dip, developing a valley with a dip slope on one side and a steep escarpment on the other (Fig. 403). Such lateral shifting down the dip is *monoclinal shifting,* and the valley is

483

FIG. 402. Erosion of inclined strata exposing dip slopes. Creation Rock, Red Rocks Park, near Denver, Colorado. (*Courtesy of Denver Tourist Bureau.*)

asymmetrical because of the difference in profile of the two slopes. When parallel streams flow at right angles to the strike of slightly inclined beds, the strata crop out in parallel belts with sharp bends.

Cuestas. Where warping has tilted the rock strata to low angles, as along the Atlantic Coastal Plain, where the beds dip seaward from 5 to 12 degrees, erosion develops ridges on the more resistant layers, and from the crest of such a ridge there is a steep slope facing landward and a gentle descent toward the coast. Such a ridge with steep erosional escarpments on one side and dip slopes on the other is a *cuesta* (Fig. 404). Where there are alternating beds of hard and soft formations, there will result alternating zones of lowlands and highlands in roughly parallel bands. An example is the Black Prairie of Alabama, bordering the Appalachian Mountains, consisting of a belt of lowlands formed over easily eroded sediments. At the margin of the prairie is a cuesta which faces the

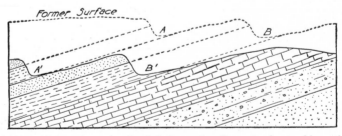

FIG. 403. Diagram showing monoclinal shifting of valleys. As the earth's surface was lowered from the upper profile shown by the dotted line to the profile shown by a continuous line, valleys A and B moved down the dip of the strata to A' and B'.

lowland and rises abruptly about 200 feet from the surface of the
lowland.

Hogbacks. Where strata are inclined at high angles (Fig. 405), the
ridges produced by differential erosion have slopes that are nearly equal.
The side corresponding to the cuesta escarpment develops a more gentle
slope, and the dip slope of the opposite side is steep. A ridge with such a
profile is a *hogback*. They are commonly developed on the flanks of folded
mountains such as those of the Rocky Mountain system, where they are
conspicuous especially along the east margin of the Front Range in
Colorado and Wyoming. Eastward toward the plains there are all grada-

FIG. 404. A deeply eroded fold in the sedimentary rocks of French West Africa. The
tilted beds on the left form a well-developed cuesta. (*United States Air Force.*)

FIG. 405. Hogback upheld by resistant sandstone, Comb Ridge, Utah. (*Spence Air Photos.*)

tions from hogbacks with steep slopes formed in highly tilted beds, through cuestas formed where the inclination is low, to mesas and buttes in the horizontal strata of the plains; and all are simply remnants of erosion that assume different profiles as a result of the different attitudes of the rock formations.

Erosion of Folds. On symmetrical folds, such as a series of parallel anticlines and synclines, the initial consequent streams flow in small gullies on either side of the crests of the anticlines and drain away from their axes. These small streams discharge into the synclines, where the major streams flow along the axes of the synclinal troughs. As tributaries cut back into the flanks of the anticlines, they develop gorges that soon become sufficiently deep to develop lateral gullies of their own, and working in rocks that were fractured during folding these tributary gullies rapidly cut deep into the axial portion of an anticline, where, in many of them, numerous fractures and joints hasten the process of denudation. In time, the divides between the tributaries that flow on the crests of the folds are narrowed and lowered, and lateral erosion widens their valleys until the valleys are pushed down the flanks of the anticlines. Stream conquest, or piracy, between adjoining folds follows, and eventually the streams along the crests of the anticlines become the master streams, and the major valleys become anticlinal valleys (Fig. 406). The synclinal divides stand high in relief and form broad ridges and, at places, mountains.

Lookout Mountain is an example of a synclinal divide which terminates at the north in a steep escarpment 1,500 feet high at Chattanooga, Tennessee, and extends southwest over 50 miles into Alabama. A deep anticlinal valley 4 to 5 miles wide flanks Lookout Mountain on the west, and still farther westward beyond this valley is another broad synclinal plateau.

Curved Valleys and Zigzag Ridges. Where symmetrical folds pass through a cycle of erosion, the resistant layers form parallel ridges that are paired on the two limbs of a fold. If, however, the axis of a fold is not horizontal but is tilted so that it plunges into the earth, the erosional ridges present a different topographic pattern. If the folds plunge steeply, some of the pairs of ridges end after the layers producing them plunge below the regional base level. When the plunge is less steep, they converge in the direction of plunge and eventually join to form a continuous ridge with a sharp, elbowlike flexure and with a valley shaped like one end of a canoe within the flexure. If several resistant layers are present, each will form an encircling ridge with curved valleys separating them. A series of alternating plunging anticlines and synclines, therefore, produces zigzag ridges (Fig. 407), such as characteristically are developed on the Appalachian peneplane in Pennsylvania and Virginia.

Erosion of Domes and Basins. On a newly uplifted domelike structure the initial streams form a series of radial valleys extending in all di-

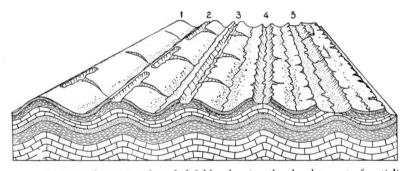

FIG. 406. Diagram of a series of eroded folds, showing the development of anticlinal valleys and synclinal divides. The maximum fracturing is along anticlines. Fold 1 shows three tributaries that flow into the synclinal valley between folds 1 and 2. In fold 2 the tributaries have developed valleys along the axis of the anticline. In fold 3 the tributary in the foreground has captured the headwaters of the second tributary, and in fold 4 all the tributaries have been captured by one downstream beyond the diagram. In fold 5 the stream has cut through the resistant sandstone on the crest of the anticline, and therefore it can erode downward more rapidly than the stream in the syncline between 4 and 5. Eventually it diverts the water of the stream in the syncline as shown by the tributaries to the right of 5. Thus the syncline becomes a divide. (*After Lobeck.*)

rections from the crest of the dome. These *consequent* streams may unite to form one or more trunk streams at the lower margin or base of the structure. As erosion cuts through the strata on the summit of the uplift, the formations begin to crop out in a series of narrow belts around the crest of the dome (Fig. 8). If beds of varying hardness are present in a series of sedimentary strata, the harder sandstones and limestones form ridges and streams adjust themselves to the softer, shaly layers. In this way the radial valleys are converted into concentric or *ring* valleys, and the ridges are transformed into hogbacks which stand concentrically around the center of the uplift. Because of the steep escarpments facing the valleys, some of the more conspicuous sandstone ridges rim the valleys. Examples are found in Montana and South Dakota.

As structural basins pass through a cycle of erosion, they tend to show similar concentric features, but with the escarpments facing outward. The structural relations are similar to those observed in a low nest of shallow plates, in which the largest is placed at the bottom and the smallest at the top. In such a nest the outer edges of the plates correspond to the encircling ridges of harder rock that rim the basin as the region is base-leveled. The lower peninsula of Michigan and the Paris Basin in France show such structural relations.

Superimposed Streams. Although streams tend to adjust their valleys to the structure of the rocks they encounter, the courses of certain streams do not conform to the structure. These obviously are out of adjustment and require explanation. Where tilted beds, for example, have been peneplaned and covered by later flat-lying beds, the new drainage system may be wholly independent of the hidden structure of the underlying tilted beds. As such a system, by continued erosion, is let down onto

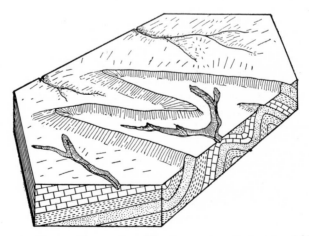

FIG. 407. Zigzag ridge produced by the erosion of plunging folds.

the surface of the tilted beds, the streams cutting downward in valleys begun in the horizontal beds may be compelled to cut across the tilted beds. Such streams are *superimposed* (Figs. 408 to 411).

In the Appalachian region the Hudson, Delaware, Susquehanna, and Potomac Rivers are considered to be superimposed from a former cover of sediments subsequently removed. In the Rocky Mountain region many rivers, including the Bighorn, Madison, Platte, Arkansas, Green, Snake, and others, are superimposed very impressively in spectacular canyons across mountain ranges. In the Grand Canyon the Colorado River is

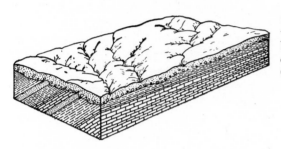

FIG. 408. Diagram showing valley development in a flat-lying stratum that rests on the eroded edges of folded strata Compare with Fig. 409.

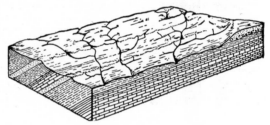

FIG. 409. Diagram of the region shown in Fig. 408 after erosion has removed the horizontal bed. The streams are not in structural adjustment because the old drainage is superimposed upon the tilted strata.

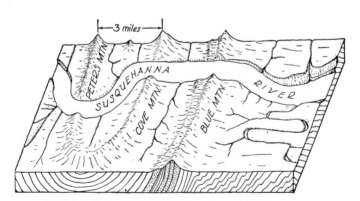

FIG. 410. A superimposed stream flowing over truncated folds. The Susquehanna River near Harrisburg, Pennsylvania. (*After D. W. Johnson.*)

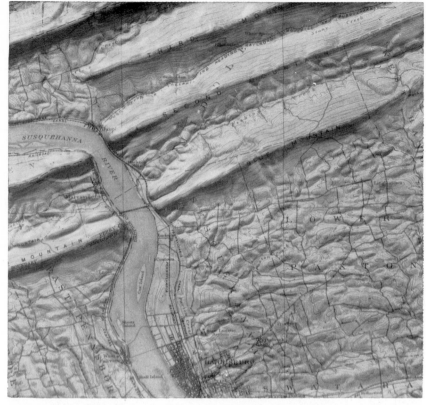

FIG. 411. Photograph of part of relief map showing the water gaps of the Susquehanna River crossing Second Mountain and Blue Mountain near Harrisburg, Pennsylvania. (*Aero Service Corporation.*)

superimposed on ancient crystalline rocks that underlie the nearly horizontal rocks of the Colorado Plateau.

FEATURES DEVELOPED UNDER SPECIAL CONDITIONS

Waterfalls and Rapids. The geologic significance of waterfalls may be slight, but from a scenic point of view they form a fascinating part of a river system. There is no sharp distinction between a rapid and a fall. Steep rapids are commonly called falls, and, when small, both are referred to as *cascades,* and where an enormous volume of water falls over a precipice, the term *cataract* is used.

Falls and rapids occur at many places and are formed under various conditions. Wherever the bedrock is made up of layers that have different degrees of resistance to erosion, the resistant layers hold back the streams in their trenching processes. Since the less resistant beds farther downstream are still being cut away at the old rate, there is a lack of adjustment between that part of the stream above and that which lies below the outcrop of the resistant layers. There are thus developed a series of rapids which get steeper and steeper with continued erosion and finally become a waterfall. Among the structural conditions favorable for the formation of falls are the following: (1) harder sedimentary rocks overlying softer ones in a nearly horizontal series; (2) igneous sills or flows interbedded with flat-lying sedimentary strata; (3) successive igneous flows of varying resistance; (4) dikes of igneous rock or any hard layer in other formations; (5) vertical joint planes in massive rocks. Falls may be developed in tributary streams as a result of a rapid deepening of the main valley. Thus as a waterfall recedes past the mouth of a tributary, the minor valley is left hanging or out of topographic adjustment and the smaller stream then falls into the gorge of the newly deepened main stream or valley. In this

FIG. 412. Niagara Falls from the air. The river begins to cascade near the upper end of Goat Island (*right center*), finally plunging over the limestone brink, most of the water going over the Canadian Falls (*lower right*). (Scale 1 inch = 1,000 feet.) (*Courtesy of Spartan Air Services Ltd., Ottawa.*)

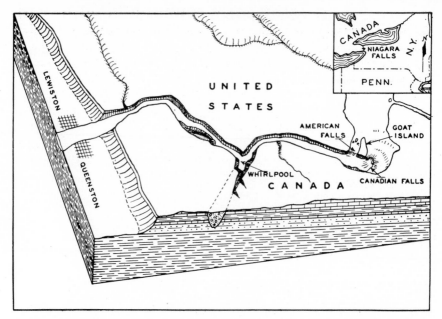

FIG. 413. General setting of Niagara Falls and Gorge. The falls began at the cuesta scarp at the left and have receded about 7 miles. An earlier gorge is buried near the Whirlpool. Goat Island separates the American from the Canadian Falls. (*After Gilbert.*)

way a series of waterfalls may have developed on the tributaries, each one downstream having receded a little farther from the gorge of the main stream. A similar condition may develop through glaciation during which the ice may have eroded the trunk valley below the bottom of the side valleys and, when the glacier recedes or disappears, these latter are left hanging with falls at their junction with the major stream, which has succeeded the glacier in the main valley.

Niagara Falls (Fig. 412) offers a magnificent example of an escarpment formed in nearly horizontal beds where a resistant rock caps notably weaker strata. This cataract plunges about 160 feet over a brink-making limestone about 80 feet thick, beneath which is a very soft shale formation. The falls are divided into two parts by an island in the stream channel. The American Falls has a frontage of about 1,060 feet, and the Horseshoe, or Canadian, Falls has a curved frontage of nearly 2,800 feet. Approximately 500,000 tons of water per minute, or nearly 94 per cent of the water of the river, passes over the Canadian Falls. This great body of water has carved out a gorge 200 feet deep beneath the level of the water below the falls, so that the total depth of the gorge from the rim to the bottom of the water is about 360 feet (Fig. 412). As the swirling water behind the falls loosens the soft, shaly formation, it removes it piecemeal and undermines the capping limestone, until finally the limestone cap remains as an inadequately supported overhanging ledge from which large masses of rock plunge into the pool at the bottom of the falls. This process of undercutting is termed *sapping*. Thus, foot by foot, the escarpment has receded up the river, leaving the deep gorge that marks its course from Lewiston at the edge of the cuesta forming the Niagara

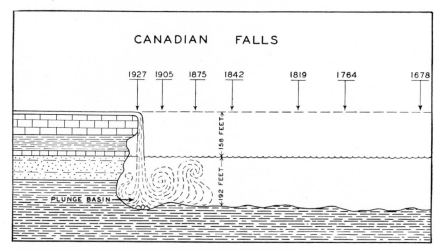

FIG. 414. Canadian Falls, showing its retreat by sapping of relatively weak rocks beneath a resistant cap rock of limestone. (*After Gilbert.*)

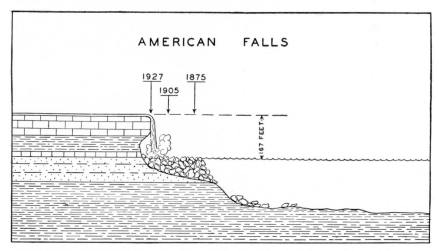

FIG. 415. American Falls, showing its smaller form and slower retreat. Compare with Fig. 414. (*After Gilbert.*)

escarpment, 8 miles south of Lake Ontario, to its present position about 7 miles farther south (Figs. 413 to 415).

The rate of recession of Niagara for an extended period is difficult to determine. A series of factors of unknown value enter into the problem, such as the variation of the river volume and the increase in thickness, toward the south, of the capping limestone rock. Measurements have been made from time to time, and by a comparison of records it has been ascertained that the average rate of recession for 42 years was approximately 3 feet a year (Fig. 414). The Canadian Falls is now receding much more rapidly than the American Falls, because of its greater volume of water. Since the American Falls receives scarcely 6 per cent of the stream's water, it is receding only a few inches per year. If the falls had receded 3 feet per year, 12,320 years would have been required for it to recede 7 miles.

Other Waterfalls. Along the north shore of Lake Superior many high-gradient streams have cut steep gorges into the Keweenawan lava flows and exposed conglomerate beds separating the successive layers of basaltic rock. At many places the conglomerates or softer amygdaloidal flows are more easily eroded than the overlying massive basalts, and numerous waterfalls result.

At Yellowstone Falls an irregular mass of more resistant igneous rock crosses weaker rocks in which the deep canyon of the Yellowstone River is excavated (Fig. 416). Such falls will not recede a very great distance, for gradually the resistant mass will be cut away, and as it is worn down, the softer formations upstream will be eroded to the gradient of the river, the crest of the falls will sink, and the falls eventually will disappear or become rapids.

In mountains that have been glaciated, the trunk-stream valley commonly is eroded deeper than tributary valleys because the glacier of the trunk stream is much thicker than the glaciers of the tributary streams. When the ice has melted, these glacial valleys again become watercourses and the water of a tributary stream falls into the main stream over a steep precipice. Many of the highest waterfalls of the world were formed this way. Yosemite Falls in California (Fig. 417) plunges over a granite cliff into the Merced River Valley with an initial drop of 1,430 feet. It then cascades for about 800 feet over a jagged surface with a steep slope and finally plunges 320 feet more over a vertical cliff to the flood plain of the river. Prior to glaciation, the Merced Valley possessed a typical V-shaped profile, but during the Great Ice Age a glacier slowly ground its way through the valley, deepened it greatly, and shaped its sides into vertical cliffs over which the tributaries now discharge as falls.

Vertical joints in massive rocks influence stream erosion much as bedding planes in inclined strata (Fig. 418). Such joint planes are widened by erosion, and large blocks of rock may be removed from the stream bed. As the blocks are removed, a vertical cliff may be developed over which a falls is initiated. In New York near Ithaca, and also at Trenton, falls are developed in jointed limestone.

In mountain ranges where zones of hard rocks cross stream beds such rocks are eroded more slowly than the softer rocks below them. Vertical escarpments may not be developed, and under such conditions the water leaps from ledge to ledge in a series of sparkling cascades, which may grade imperceptibly into rapids. Along the east margin of the Appalachian Mountains, roughly paralleling the Atlantic Coast, the Piedmont plateau

FIG. 416. Lower Falls and Grand Canyon of the Yellowstone River. Yellowstone National Park, Wyoming. (*Courtesy of Northern Pacific Railway.*)

FIG. 417. Yosemite Falls, in Yosemite National Park, California. A tributary falls discharging from a hanging valley. (*Courtesy of Southern Pacific Railroad.*)

area is bordered by a coastal plain composed of sands and clays not yet indurated into solid rock strata. Streams, flowing from the Appalachian highlands toward the Atlantic, pass from the hard crystalline rocks to the soft unconsolidated sediments nearer the coast, where they cut more rapidly and develop rapids and falls along the line of contact of the two different types of rocks. Because of the great number of cascades along a relatively narrow zone the region is referred to as the *fall zone.*

Under exceptional conditions, falls may originate by damming due to the deposition of material in the stream bed by processes other than stream erosion. Landslides, glacial deposits, or lava flows may form temporary rapids.

Plunge Pools. At the base of a waterfall the falling mass of water commonly excavates a basin called a *plunge pool.* Such a pool below the 400-foot abandoned waterfall at Dry Falls below Grand Coulee, Washington, forms the basin of Fall Lake, about 80 feet deep and half a mile wide. The progressive recession of a waterfall tends to lengthen a plunge pool headward and thus to form an elongate basin on the valley floor.

Potholes. Where rapidly flowing streams produce eddying currents, there is a tendency toward the concentration of the energy of the stream at certain places along the channel. If water that is carrying silt is given a rotary motion by the eddies at such points, it tends to grind out round or kettle-shaped excavations in the bedrock of the valley floor (Fig. 419). These are *potholes,* or *giant's cauldrons.* Once a rounded depression is started, the swirling currents in the excavation have their velocities increased during periods of high water and the rate of deepening is accelerated. Certain potholes are spiral-shaped and have a larger diameter near the bottom than at the top. They may be formed in massive igneous rocks such as basalt or in granite or in softer sedimentary strata such as limestone or shale. The currents below a waterfall or along walls of a high-gradient stream with rapids favor their development. They vary

FIG. 418. Giant Stairway Falls, Paradise Creek, Alberta. The fall escarpment consists of a series of low, steplike falls. The treads and risers of the steps are joints. (*Geological Survey of Canada.*)

FIG. 419. A pothole being scoured out by stream action. (*After R. S. Tarr.*)

in size from a few inches to 10 or 20 feet in diameter and are variable also in depth. Some of the larger potholes in Interstate Park at Taylor's Falls, Minnesota, are 20 feet in diameter and are sunk 50 feet or more in solid basalt. Pothole formation can assume a very important role in the development of steep, gorgelike valleys, such as that of the inner portion along the Colorado River above Hoover Dam or the canyon of the ancient outlet of Owens Valley, near Little Lake, California (Fig. 420).

Canyons and Gorges. Where extensive areas stand at high altitudes, swiftly flowing streams tend to develop deep valleys; and if the conditions promoting widening are wanting, precipitous-walled valleys—canyons or gorges—are developed (Fig. 421). Arid regions, traversed by streams that have their headwaters in snow-capped mountains or in regions of more abundant rainfall, are usually favorable to the development of canyons, especially if the valley is cut in firm rock capable of standing as steep cliffs. Lateral cutting, due to the eddies deflected toward the side of the stream, and weathering of the steep rock slopes exposed to the atmosphere broaden the canyon so that the lofty walls gradually are cut back and the distance from rim to rim becomes wider. The canyon walls in arid areas remain comparatively steep, however, because there is little side wash.

Grand Canyon of the Colorado. The great trenches which the Colorado River and its tributaries have cut into the plateaus of the southwestern part of the United States are the greatest canyons known. Their total length is over 500 miles, and their depths are measured in thousands of feet. Here the great size and extraordinary beauty of the canyons are the result of the following conditions: (1) a large volume of water; (2) high velocity; (3) an abundance of sediment with which to corrade; (4) great thickness of firm rocks to penetrate before reaching grade; (5) an arid climate with little weathering and side wash on the walls of the canyon.

The Colorado River has a total length of about 2,000 miles and drains an area of about 225,000 square miles, most of which is a high plateau 6,000 to 8,000 feet above sea level. It trenches the high plateau of northern Arizona with a colossal canyon 220 miles long and more than a mile deep. Where it reaches this great depth, the total width from rim to rim is 8

FIG. 420. Potholes northeast of Little Lake, California, where the former outlet of drainage from Owens Valley plunged over a lava cliff into the canyon below. (*Copyright 1952, Automobile Club of Southern California.*)

FIG. 421. Big Thompson Canyon, north of Denver, Colorado. A steep-walled canyon cut through steeply dipping sedimentary and metamorphic rocks. (*Courtesy of Denver Tourist Bureau.*)

to 12 miles but its width at the bottom is only slightly greater than that of the stream. If the slopes of the canyon were uniform, it would have an angle of less than 15 degrees, but the inequalities of hardness of the sedimentary strata have produced gigantic steplike slopes, or rock terraces, some of the steep faces of which drop vertically for more than 1,000 feet. The upper series of rocks in which the canyon is cut is composed of flat-lying beds of limestones, sandstones, and shales (Fig. 43). Beneath this the stream has disclosed ancient crystalline schists and massive igneous formations.

Natural Bridges. An arch of rock across a valley, an exceptional and striking feature of the topography, may be formed in numerous ways. (1) Where a surface stream disappears into the joints of the bedrock of a valley, it may flow underground for some distance and then reappear at the surface. As erosion continues, a "valley" is excavated beneath the surface and where that surface does not cave in, the rocks will span the valley as a bridge. (2) If the rock of a stream bed is jointed above a waterfall, some of the water may descend through a joint and then follow a bedding plane until it issues into the main channel below the falls or behind the curtain of water forming the falls (Figs. 422, 423). The joint is slowly enlarged until the channel becomes large enough to accommodate all the water, and the mass of rock from the escarpment that produced the waterfalls upstream to the position of the vertical joint remains as a natural bridge (Fig. 423). In Two Medicine River in Glacier National Park this process is now in progress, and a natural bridge is partially developed. (3) Where ancient peneplanes have been rejuvenated, many of the meandering streams become deeply entrenched and the lateral swinging of a stream against the clifflike walls undercuts the neck of a meander at the level of the water. This process continues from both sides until a hole is cut through and the stream flows through the perforation, leaving an arch of rock as a bridge over the stream. The famous Rainbow Natural Bridge in San Juan County, Utah, is an example of a bridge

FIG. 422. Trick Falls, Glacier National Park. A natural bridge in early stage of formation. Some of the water flows through a joint system not seen and reissues near the foot of the falls to rejoin the part of the stream that flows over the falls. (*Photograph by Ethel M. Rodgers.*)

FIG. 423. Natural Bridge, Virginia. Lace Falls, which probably formed the bridge during recession, cascades into the gorge several hundred yards farther upstream. (*Photograph by Charles D. Walcott.*)

so formed. (4) Where the tributary streams are extended into steeply sloping divides by headward erosion, the watershed may be reduced to a very narrow ridge. If the divide is capped by a resistant formation overlying soft sand or shale, the divide may be perforated under the more massive cap rock. (5) In the petrified forest of Adamana, Arizona, a silicified log has been undermined by stream erosion until a very unusual natural bridge spans the valley. The trunk of the petrified log, which is about 3 feet in diameter, lies diagonally across a canyon about 30 feet wide and 200 feet deep. The rock in which the log was embedded is poorly cemented and therefore easily eroded. (6) In the volcanic areas of the West many natural bridges have been formed by the incomplete collapse of the roofs of lava tunnels. (7) Other natural bridges are made by wave erosion, by sandblasting by the wind, and by differential weathering.

SUGGESTIONS FOR FURTHER READING

Atwood, Wallace W.: The Physiographic Provinces of North America, Ginn & Company, 1940.

Bryan, Kirk: The Retreat of Slopes, *Assoc. Am. Geographers Annals,* vol. 30, pp. 254–268, 1940.

Cotton, C. A.: Landscape as Developed by the Processes of Normal Erosion, 2d ed., John Wiley & Sons, Inc., 1948.

Johnson, Douglas: Stream Sculpture on the Atlantic Slope, Columbia University Press, 1931.

Kindle, E. M., and F. B. Taylor: Niagara Falls Folio, *U.S. Geol. Survey Folio* 190, 1913.

King, Lester C.: Canons of Landscape Evolution, *Geol. Soc. America Bull.,* vol. 64, pp. 721–751, 1953.

Leopold, Luna B., and Thomas Maddock: The Hydraulic Geometry of Stream Channels and Some Physiographic Implications, *U.S. Geol. Survey Prof. Paper* 252, 1953.

CHAPTER 20

Mountains

The word mountain is a term applied loosely to all eminences of small summit area that rise to considerable heights above their surroundings; there is no sharp distinction between hills and mountains (Fig. 424). An elevation that appears to be no more than a small hill in the rugged portions of the Rocky Mountains would seem to be a great mountain if transported to the plains of the interior of the continent. Many geologists would restrict the term to those eminences which display mountainous structures—folds, faults, and intrusions.

Mountains differ in their modes of origin and in their life histories. One may be eruptive, resulting from the extrusion of lavas. Another may be the result of the intrusion of an igneous body into other formations, the latter being eroded away from the igneous mass after it has cooled and hardened, leaving it standing out as a hill or mountain. Still another may be the result of direct uplift above the surrounding region.

Mountains are formed also as the result of simple folding or tilting of blocks produced by faults. Many mountains are formed by two or more of these processes working together. Adding to these the variation in the character of the rocks, the different positions to which strata are tilted or folded, and the effects of these differences upon erosion, it is readily understood why mountain structures are so varied in different localities.

Modes of Occurrence. Mountains occur as isolated peaks, irregular groups, parallel ridges or ranges, and complex systems. The broad, mountainous belt in western North America, from the eastern border of the Rocky Mountains to the Pacific Coast, is commonly referred to as the North American Cordillera (Fig. 425). A similar belt in southern Europe and Asia is designated as the Eurasiatic chain or mountain zone.

Mountain peaks are high masses, more or less conical in outline, that rise above their surroundings. They may be either mountains of accumulation, such as the volcanic cones on the islands in the Mediterranean, on the floor of the sea, or along certain coasts of the Pacific Ocean, or ero-

504

sional remnants, such as Mount Monadnock in New Hampshire or Stone Mountain in Georgia.

Irregular groups of mountains vary in size and arrangement from small mountainous areas like the Little Rocky Mountains of Montana or the La Sal Mountains of Utah to larger, irregular units such as the Front Range of Colorado and Bighorn Mountains of Wyoming.

Mountain ridges and ranges are long, narrow, mountain masses that may represent the arches of anticlinal folds or the outcropping ridges of resistant rocks, remaining after the folds have been deeply eroded. Such folds are seen in the Coast Ranges, the Wasatch Range, the Pyrenees, and other mountain ranges.

A mountain system consists of several more or less parallel ranges in the same region. Thus the term Laramide system often is used in referring to a series of the ranges of the Rocky Mountains.

Dissected Plateaus. Mountainlike topography may be carved from a featureless plateau. Where diastrophic movements raise broad plateaus above the surrounding region, the gradient of the streams is increased and the rate of stream erosion is accelerated. In time the plateau becomes extensively dissected by steep-walled canyons, and the ridges and pyramids representing the remnants of the plateau stand so high above the stream valleys that they are like mountains (Fig. 426), but they lack the

FIG. 424. Mountainous topography viewed from Dead Indian Hill, Wyoming. (*Photography by Northern Pacific Railroad Company.*)

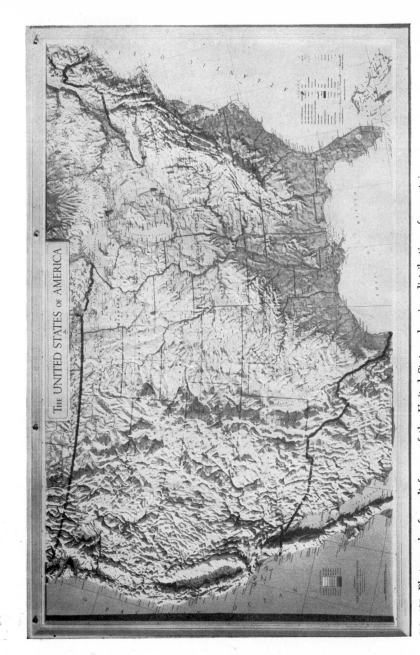

FIG. 425. Photograph of a relief map of the United States, showing distribution of mountains. (*Courtesy of Aero Service Corporation.*)

usual mountain structure. An early stage of such dissection is seen in the region of the Colorado Plateau in Arizona, where gorges more than a mile deep have been cut by the Colorado River and its tributaries. The divides between tributaries are irregular, flat-topped mesas and sharp ridges that are notched or broken into a series of isolated peaks and truncated pyramids that rise from the depths of the gorges. Their bases are far below the plateau, and they are dwarfed by the magnitude of the plateau from which they are carved. At Zion Canyon, Utah, horizontal strata lying 4,000 to 8,000 feet above sea level are cut by canyons several thousand feet deep (Fig. 427). In this region many of the pyramids that represent the divides between smaller tributaries exhibit well-developed rock terraces separated by precipices and long, vertical cliffs.

The so-called Catskill Mountains in New York were carved by erosion from a former extensive high plateau in which the strata are nearly horizontal. The sandstone and shale beds of which they are composed end abruptly in the steep cliffs of one of the ridges and reappear at approximately the same level in an adjoining ridge. The whole plateau is maturely dissected into mountainlike features of diverse height, with scores of summits between 3,000 and 4,000 feet above sea level. There is some evidence of glacial action in the present topography, but features due to ice erosion are not pronounced.

Residual forms of high relief may be formed also from plateaus of

FIG. 426. A mountainous area carved from elevated, gently tilted, and thrust-faulted beds. Valley and bordering mountains of Grinnell Glacier in northern Montana. (*Spence Air Photos.*)

FIG. 427. Mesas and pinnacles carved from the pyramids between tributary valleys. Zion National Park, Utah. (*Courtesy of Union Pacific Railroad.*)

homogeneous crystalline rocks, such as the Absaroka Plateau east of Yellowstone Park and the Columbia River Plateau of Washington and Oregon. Given sufficient time, stream and glacial erosion will carve such areas into peaks and ridges of mountainous proportions. The form of the topography carved from such plateaus depends upon the nature and arrangement of the rocks out of which they are sculptured.

Residual Mountains. A number of large monadnocks occur on various old, peneplaned areas, and some are of mountainous proportions. Such residual mountains are generally composed of rock that is exceptionally resistant to erosion. Mount Monadnock, for which such features are named, occurs in southwestern New Hampshire. It is more than 3,000 feet high on a peneplane that stands nearly 1,200 feet above sea level. Stone Mountain near Atlanta, Georgia, is another typical example. It is a dome-shaped residual mass of light gray granite with a remarkably steep slope, standing nearly 700 feet above the general level of the old peneplaned surface. Many residual peaks of similar origin occur also in the Rocky Mountains. Longs Peak, with an elevation of 14,255 feet, stands as a remnant on the South Park peneplane. Mount Evans, Pikes Peak, Bald Mountain, Arapahoe Peak, and many others have had a similar origin.

Volcanic Mountains. Volcanoes may occur singly or in irregular groups. They vary in size from low mounds to lofty peaks (Fig. 428). Some are built up in low-lying regions, but commonly they are superimposed on the crests of mountain ranges that owe their origin to other processes. The form of the cone depends very largely upon the nature of the materials of which it is composed. Most volcanic mountains consist of successive layers of ash, dust, and coarser pyroclastic fragments, interbedded with sheets of lava. Those which eject great quantities of solid rock fragments, as a rule, have higher and steeper peaks than volcanoes which emit highly fluid lavas.

Many of the highest peaks in the world, such as Aconcagua (23,080 feet), Chimborazo (20,498 feet), and Cotopaxi (19,613 feet) in the Andes and Kilimanjaro (19,710 feet) in Africa, have been built mainly by volcanic processes. In the United States typical examples are Mount Shasta (14,380 feet), Mount Rainier (14,408 feet), Mount Hood (11,225 feet), and Lassen Peak (10,577 feet).

Mount Shasta rises almost 2 miles above its base. It is a volcanic cone composed of alternating lavas and tuffs. The base of the cone at about 5,000 feet above sea level is 17 miles in diameter. It has an average slope of about 15 degrees. The slope of the upper third is about 35 degrees, but this flattens toward its base, where the slope is less than 5 degrees. The volume of the cone is estimated to be more than 80 cubic miles.

Volcanic action may become so general along definite lines or zones on the earth's surface that whole mountain ranges may result from the accumulation of volcanic debris. This is shown along the chain of the

FIG. 428. Mount Fuji, Japan. (*Courtesy of Katsuo Jamada.*)

FIG. 429. Rugged mountainous topography formed by the erosion of folded strata in northern Hunan Province, China. (*Photograph by United States Air Force.*)

Aleutian Islands of Alaska, where a mountain range over 1,000 miles long is now being built on the floor of the sea, mainly through volcanic activity. Vulcanism played a part also in the formation of the Cascade Range, extending from northern California northward into British Columbia. Along this zone Mounts Shasta, Lassen, Hood, Adams, St. Helens, Rainier, Baker, and other volcanoes contributed enormous quantities of volcanic materials during the formative stages of the mountain range.

Some high volcanic mountains occur in closely associated groups, such as the San Francisco Mountains on the plateau southeast of the Grand Canyon in Arizona. There an area of 2,000 to 3,000 square miles, centering near Flagstaff, is covered by lava flows and dotted by several hundred volcanic cones, the highest of which is 12,700 feet above sea level or about 5,000 feet above the level of the plateau.

In Hawaii it appears that activity has gradually shifted along a westnorthwest east-southeast line for 1,000 miles. Mauna Loa, at the eastern end of the island group and the highest present active crater of the chain, lies nearly 14,000 feet above sea level, rising from a base 16,000 feet below sea level.

Folded Mountains. The major mountain systems of the world are a series of strongly folded ranges which express themselves as single ridges or as a group of closely associated ridges (Fig. 429). They differ from other types of mountain in that they represent a sequence of geologic processes that are distinctive in many respects but comparable in others. A feature common to all is the great thickness of shallow-water clastic sediments such as conglomerates, sandstones, and shales, with subordinate limestone strata, that are included in the folds.

In eastern North America, to the west of the Appalachian Mountains, the sedimentary rocks are at most a few thousand feet thick, whereas, in the mountains, rocks of the same age attain many times this thickness. Furthermore, in the interior of the continent, the rocks are mainly limestones and dolomites, whereas clastic rocks or their metamorphic equivalents predominate in the mountains. This relationship in both thickness and types of rock has been observed in other mountain ranges such as the Alps, Urals, Andes, and the major ranges of western United States.

Further evidence of the shallow-water environment in which the clastic sediments accumulated that are now in the mountain folds is furnished by the presence of fossils of typical shallow-water forms of marine animals. Such associations occur in the rocks of many mountain ranges, through stratigraphic sections as much as 40,000 feet thick. One must conclude, therefore, that the surface on which the sediments and the remains of animals accumulated was never far below sea level during the long periods of time during which they were deposited. This would be possible if the crust in these areas was depressed at a rate approximately equal to that at which the sediments accumulated. Such downwarps of the solid crust that are filled with sediments have been called geosynclines (Figs. 430, 431).

Geosynclinal troughs tend to develop in linear mobile belts at or near the margins of relatively rigid or stable regions such as the pre-Cambrian shield of north central North America. Such belts consist of a depressed trough of deposition and an adjacent geanticlinal zone, or welt, which tends to rise as the geosyncline is depressed. In the Appalachian region

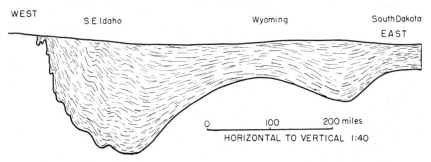

FIG. 430. Cordilleran geosyncline showing the downwarp in southeastern Idaho that filled with sediment prior to the folding of the Rocky Mountains. (*After Kay.*)

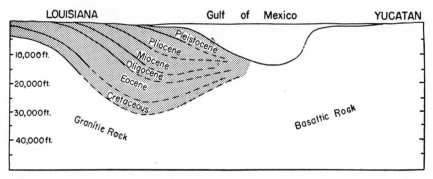

FIG. 431. Diagrammatic section of the geosyncline now in process of formation along the north coast of the Gulf of Mexico. (*After Barton et al.*)

the thickening and coarsening of the sediments toward the east suggest that most of them were derived from a rising land mass to the east of the present mountain folds. This would imply that the sediment came from the Piedmont region, the Coastal Plain that is now covered with younger rocks, or the Continental Shelf area that is now submerged by the epicontinental sea, and probably from all three.

The theory of isostasy (page 576) has been called upon to explain the continued sinking of geosynclinal troughs and the continued rising of the adjacent geanticlinal zones, or welts. The theory has two weaknesses, however, for it gives no adequate explanation of the compressive forces that later folded the outer crust, nor does it account for the great uplift that takes place after the trough has been filled. It is obvious that the corrugations which result from folding are partly responsible for the high altitudes of mountains, as may be seen in the Jura. But in the great mountain systems of the earth where folds are now deeply eroded, mountains of extraordinary height would result if the eroded folds were restored. In other words, there has been both uplift and folding. The uplift may have taken place during the closing stages of compressional folding or long thereafter, arching up the whole mountain system into an elongated bulge.

For many years it was generally accepted that both the folding and the uplift was caused by the shrinking of the earth because of cooling. It is evident that if the interior shrinks, the outer crust would be obliged to wrinkle to accommodate itself to the smaller internal volume. Undoubtedly the earth is slowly losing heat at the surface, as is indicated by the increase in temperature with depth as measured in mines and oil wells, but it is now generally thought that all the heat escaping at the surface is of radioactive origin. Furthermore, if cooling is causing the earth to shrink, that shrinking should shorten every great circle of the earth equally, but the distribution of folded mountains does not have such a systematic pattern. Shrinkage provides a convenient explanation for the great compressive forces that might have produced folds, but the amount of shrinkage that would have had to take place to explain all the folded mountain ranges, irrespective of their distribution, is far in excess of what could have been caused by the known rate of loss of heat.

Orogenic Cycles. It has been demonstrated that a surprisingly great deficiency in the force of gravity exists along the front of the arcuate island mountain chains in the East Indies, and similar conditions have been reported in the West Indies. This is interpreted to mean that these narrow zones are not in isostatic equilibrium (page 514) with adjoining areas because the mass is far less than it should be. These areas of low density are thought to be belts underlain by rocks whose density is less than is usual at equivalent depths elsewhere. The magnitude of the gravity deficiency indicates that the lightweight crustal rocks extend to depths of 30 to 40 miles. Such isostatically unbalanced conditions may be accounted for by postulating that these low-gravity areas are belts where the upper crust of low density (Fig. 22) has been forcibly bent or dragged down, somewhat similar to the downwarping of geosynclinal troughs. Most geosynclines, however, are much wider than these belts of negative-gravity anomalies.

Various theories have been advanced to explain the mechanics of an orogenic cycle, but none is entirely satisfactory. The diagrams in Figs. 432, 433 illustrate in a simplified and diagrammatic way four stages in such a cycle. The right half of each diagram represents a "mobile belt" consisting of a zone of deposition and a borderland, or geanticlinal, zone, or welt. The diagrams are represented as extending downward through the sial and sima of the rigid crust of the earth. Stage 1 is the initial stage of downward warping to below sea level, with sediments derived from the foreland. Processes of subsidence and fill continue, and at stage 2 a typical geosyncline has developed; the borderland is rising and thrusting toward the geosynclinal trough. It should be noted also that the low-density sial may be depressed into the denser and hotter sima. The subsiding trough becomes more mobile as it reaches greater depths, and in stage 3 thrust faulting and folding are pronounced, and the borderland is elevated to supply sediments to the bordering trough. Some of these sediments may be derived from older sediments that were deposited in the trough but later brought to the surface by thrust faulting. At this stage the depressed sial may reach a depth where the temperature is adequate to melt it and permit the formation of magma that makes its way upward into the zone of thrust faulting and folding along the margin of the geosyncline. Granitic batholiths are then intruded, and some magma may be poured out as lava flows or hurled out under explosive forces to form volcanic cones.

A probable cause of the fusion may have been the accumulation of heat from radioactive disintegration which is more pronounced in the outer granitic shell (sial) than in the deeper basaltic zone (sima). Starting at the base of the downwarped sial (stage 3), fusion would proceed upward, and, in some mountain systems, volcanic activity at the surface may have served to dissipate the heat and thus halt the upward progress of batholithic invasion. It is known that the granitic (sial) shell of the earth varies from one region to another, being thickest beneath most mountain chains, where deep "roots" undoubtedly project downward into the basaltic layer.

At a still later stage of an orogenic cycle there is vertical uplift of the entire series of local mountain ranges that were formed by the folding and faulting. This is accompanied by a withdrawal of marine waters as the area of deposition and former downwarping is elevated above sea level (stage 4). There is good evidence, however, that some uplift and con-

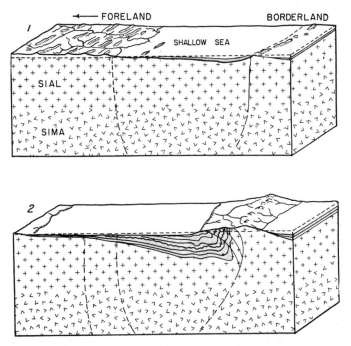

FIG. 432. Diagrams showing early possible stages in the history of a complex mountain system. 1, initial downwarping to below sea level; 2, geosynclinal trough developed and borderland rising and thrusting toward trough.

current erosion of mountain ranges take place during their folding. The presence of unconformities between sedimentary series that accumulated in the geosyncline and an abundance of coarse clastic sediments in some beds of the outer, gently folded parts of mountain chains testify to such uplifts. Furthermore, in many old mountain ranges the summit uplands have relatively low relief (Fig. 434), and the gently sloping surfaces of the upland cut across rocks that vary greatly in composition and structure indicate that the area must once have been eroded to a low plain.

The succession of events as outlined in Figs. 432, 433 is oversimplified, and much is speculative, but it is in accord with facts that are known from field observations and from experimental evidence. Mountain histories are undoubtedly varied and complex, and therefore a simple generalization cannot be made for all parts of any one system, much less for all great systems. The evidence now available, while abundant, is still not sufficient to permit accurate interpretation of the mechanism of mountain building, but even intelligent guesses may have real value, for they

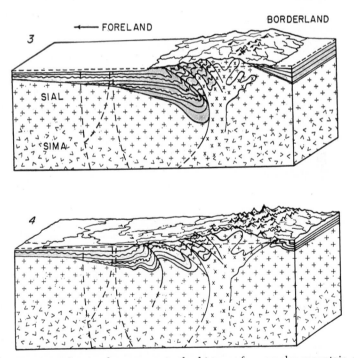

FIG. 433. Diagrams showing later stages in the history of a complex mountain system. 3, the sial is depressed into the hotter sima, and magma is formed and intruded into sediments of trough as faulting and folding continue; 4. vertical uplift and withdrawal of sea, followed by erosion. (*After Weeks.*)

FIG. 434. Beartooth Mountains north of Yellowstone Park, showing the low relief of their summits. They represent an uplifted peneplane, partly dissected by streams and former glaciers. (*Photograph by Northern Pacific Railroad Company.*)

suggest tests and the reexamination of evidence which may modify or validate earlier concepts.

Thrust-faulted Mountains. Complex folding usually is accompanied by fracturing, and where the rocks are broken by continuous fractures, displacement, or faulting, may take place as deformation continues. Most intensely folded mountain structures show that both folding and faulting were involved in their formation. Thrust faulting is a very common structural feature in mountains formed by compressional forces. The Highlands of Scotland are illustrations of mountains built by a shortening of the earth's crust through a series of distributive overthrust faults. In the United States both the southern Appalachians (Fig. 435) and the north-

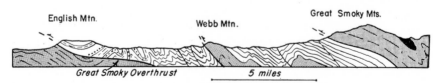

FIG. 435. Generalized section across the Great Smoky Mountains and adjacent foothills, showing overthrust faults in the southern Appalachians. (*After King.*)

ern Rockies show overthrust faulting on a large scale. In northern Montana the Front Range is represented by the Lewis and the Clark Ranges. Both ranges have high, craggy peaks reaching altitudes of 6,000 to 10,000 feet. The whole structure is a synclinal block, each limb cut off by a steep outer face. The two ranges are formed by the upturned edges of the strata, dipping 5 to 30 degrees toward the central trough. The entire block of the earth constituting the ranges has been thrust eastward by one of the greatest faults known. Ancient dolomites, quartzites, and argillites which make up the mountains have been pushed eastward over the younger Cretaceous shales of the plains. The thrust plane is nearly horizontal. It can be traced 7 miles in the direction of thrusting, but the extent of the thrust was greater, because the overthrust block has been reduced by erosion. Field evidence shows that the thrust was at least 10 miles horizontally, and it may have been much greater (Fig. 378). Chief Mountain, an erosion remnant in northern Montana, is a mass of pre-Cambrian rock standing on Cretaceous formations 8 miles east of its origin. Drilling on the plains of Alberta indicates that the eastward thrust may have been 25 miles in that area, where a similar contact is penetrated.

Block-faulted Mountains. Where faulting takes place on a large scale, mountains may be produced by differential movement of adjacent blocks along fractures in the earth's crust. This may be accomplished by elevation or by depression along one side of a fracture, leaving the other block, or segment, of the earth in its original position, or by a combination of the two types of movement. Where there are great systems of intersecting or parallel fractures along which there has been differential movement, mountains known as fault, or block, mountains are produced (Fig. 436). In most cases block mountains represent segments of the earth which probably have maintained their positions while the adjoining blocks have broken away and subsided. The most notable examples of this type of mountain structure are found in the Great Basin area in the southwestern part of the United States. This region is bordered on the east by the Wasatch Range and on the west by the lofty Sierra Nevada. It extends for nearly 800 miles north and south and for 500 miles east and west. The basin area is traversed by numerous, approximately parallel mountain ranges, with their axes somewhat irregular but generally extending north and south. Many of the ranges rise 3,000 to 5,000 feet above their bases and are outlined by normal downthrow faults the escarpments of which are but slightly altered by erosion. Such faults are a result of lateral tension rather than compression.

The abrupt change from valley floor to mountain slope, together with the uniform slopes of the mountain sides, is a striking characteristic of basin and range structure. In the more arid portions of the basin the slopes range from 20 to 90 degrees. In the southern part of the basin many of the fault blocks have been so deeply dissected by erosion that their original form has been almost completely destroyed. In this region many of the intermontane depressions are so filled with rock waste deposited by intermittent streams that some of the mountains are partly buried by alluvial cones and talus slopes of debris derived from the weathering of the fault escarpments.

Faulting and crustal warping of great magnitude resulted in the formation of the Sierra Nevada on the eastern border of California. These mountains form a continuous range about 75 miles wide and nearly 400 miles long. They represent a huge block of resistant rock uplifted by faulting and tilted toward the west. For this reason the crest of the range is near its eastern margin, and the eastern slope is steep and cliff-like. Where the crest line is highest, the average eastward slope from crest to foot is more than 1,000 feet per mile. In contrast to the steep eastern front is the gentle westward slope, which descends gradually from 9,000 feet on the east to 1,000 feet above sea level at the margin of the central valley of California. Along the crest of the range Mount Whitney rises to 14,495 feet, the highest peak in the United States outside Alaska. All structural features of the east front of the range indicate that it is a huge fault scarp. The displacement did not take place along

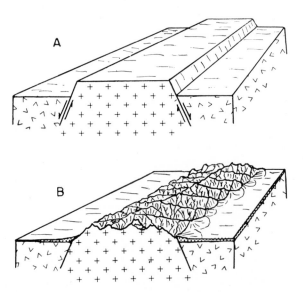

FIG. 436. Diagrams showing the mode of formation of block mountains. A, the earth's crust is fractured and faulted; B, erosion has sculptured the high block into mountainous topography.

a single fracture but rather along a zone with numerous compound faults that have left spurs and offsets in the present topography.

The Vosges and Black Forest mountains that form the walls of the Rhine Valley are fault-scarp mountains (Fig. 437). These mountains have escarpments that face each other across the valley. Before the valley was formed, the two ranges probably were welded together as a broad anticlinal ridge, composed of a core of ancient crystalline rocks overlain by younger sedimentary strata. Faulting caused the crest of the arch to subside, forming a troughlike valley by the depression of a series of small fault blocks.

Domed Mountains. In a number of mountainous regions where the mountains occur as irregular groups the central area of the group is composed of intrusive rock, such as granite, around which sedimentary rocks are found dipping in all directions away from the igneous core. The structure of the strata indicates that they once formed a continuous roof over the igneous mass. Such structures are formed where magma is injected into the earth's crust in such quantity that the surface strata are lifted into domelike structures, or laccoliths. Erosion removes the strata from the top of the dome, and irregular hills and mountains are carved from the exposed igneous core. In other mountain groups ancient igneous bodies such as granite masses were laid bare by erosion and subsequently covered by sedimentary beds.

The Black Hills in southwestern South Dakota and the adjoining portion of Wyoming are mountains which rise several thousand feet above the level of the surrounding plain (Fig. 438). They are carved from a domelike uplift that is nearly 100 miles long and approximately 50 miles wide. Before the sedimentary rocks were removed from the top of the dome, it must have risen at least 6,000 feet above the plains. The exposed ancient core of the dome is composed of granite that has been eroded to form many ridges and peaks that culminate in Harney Peak, which rises to more than 7,000 feet above sea level. Around the base of the igneous core is a ridge of limestone younger than the granite, with a steep escarpment facing inward toward the center of the hills. Beyond the limestone outcrops are hogback ridges of sandstone, which constitute

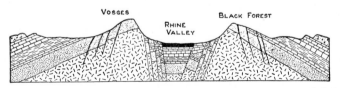

FIG. 437. Cross section of the Vosges and Black Forest ranges that parallel the valley of the Rhine. (Vertical scale greatly exaggerated.) (*After Penck.*)

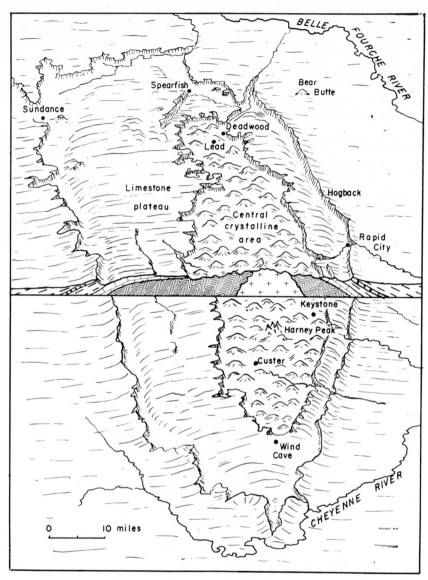

FIG. 438. Diagram of the Black Hills, South Dakota. A group of mountains formed by the dissection of a domelike uplift.

the outer rim of the domelike structure. The dome is not laccolithic in origin.

Not all mountains domed by intrusions have simple laccolithic structures. Some are produced by stocklike, cylindrical intrusive masses of igneous rocks that cut across the strata at depth but, nearer the surface, have bent and pushed the sedimentary rocks upward into symmetrical domes similar to those produced by laccoliths. Until erosion uncovers and removes much of the intrusive rock, the mountains formed from such a dome are indistinguishable from typical laccolithic mountains.

The Henry Mountains in southern Utah are typically domed structures. They stand singly or in clusters upon a desert plain that has an altitude of over 5,000 feet. They are a group of five individual mountains, the highest of which is Mount Ellen, which reaches over 11,000 feet above sea level. The domes show considerable diversity in the amount of erosion. Some are still partially or completely capped by overlying sedimentary strata, whereas in others the intruded igneous rock is exposed on the crest of the structure and the sedimentary strata appear in hogbacks or cuestas that encircle the uplift.

The intrusive masses responsible for the domelike structure of the Henry Mountains are not simple laccoliths but, rather, concordant tongues extending outward from a central, trunklike stock (Fig. 439). In form they are somewhat like semicircular lenticular fungus growths on tree trunks which make radial patterns around the trunks. In some

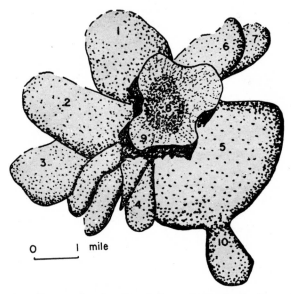

FIG. 439. Plan-view diagram showing the relations of intrusive bodies at Mount Ellen, Henry Mountains, Utah. Units numbered 1 to 7 and 10 are laccolithic masses connected with the Mount Ellen stock (8). A shattered zone (9) in the sedimentary rocks surrounds the stock. (*After Hunt.*)

instances dikelike ridges on the roofs of the intrusive masses trend away from the stocks.

Mountains of Marine Areas. Conspicuous mountain ranges are known to exist on the floor of the sea. The greatest of these is the Mid-Atlantic Ridge, which winds down the middle of the Atlantic Ocean from Iceland almost to Antarctica. It is thought to be the mightiest single mountain system on earth. It is at least 10,000 miles long and 500 miles wide, more than twice the width of the Andes, and with many peaks loftier than most continental mountains. Its summits lie 1 mile or more below the surface of the sea throughout most of its length, but some of the highest peaks are the scattered islands of the Atlantic, such as Ascension Island,

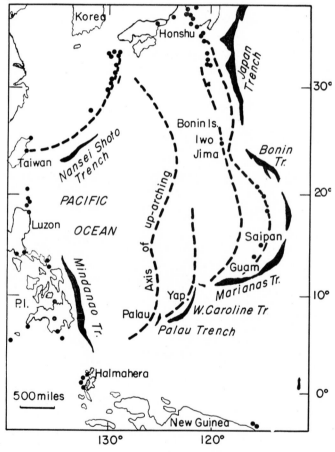

FIG. 440. Map of the western Pacific, showing island arcs (dashed lines), sea trenches (solid black), and active volcanoes (black dots). (*After H. H. Hess.*)

the Rocks of St. Paul, and the Azores. The highest of all, Mount Pico of the Azores, towers 7,613 feet above the surface of the sea and plunges 20,000 feet below the surface. Possibly only the peaks are true mountains and the remainder a submerged platform. Granite, however, occurs on some of the islands and probably makes up the bulk of the ridge.

The island arcs of the western Pacific represent zones of sharp mountain folds with great ocean deeps along the outer side of the arcs. These zones include a series of widely spaced geanticlines such as the Marianas, Iwo Jima, West Caroline, Palau-Kyushu, and Nansei Shoto. The island festoons represent high points, many of which are active volcanoes, along the crests of the geanticlinal arches (Fig. 440).

In addition to great ridges and volcanic chains the oceans conceal another type of submarine mountains referred to as flat-topped sea-mounts, or "guyots." They appear to be former volcanoes whose tops were planed smooth by wave action at some period when they stood above the sea. At present their truncated tops are submerged beneath about 1 mile of water, and it is believed that they sank either from their own weight or because of some general lowering of the ocean floor.

SUGGESTIONS FOR FURTHER READING

Billings, Marland P.: Structural Geology, 2d ed., Prentice-Hall, Inc., 1954.

Daly, R. A.: Accordance of Summit Levels among Alpine Mountains, *Jour. Geology,* vol. 13, pp. 105–125, 1905.

Fenneman, N. M.: Physiography of Western United States, McGraw-Hill Book Company, Inc., 1931.

Fenton, C. L., and M. A. Fenton: Mountains, Doubleday & Company, Inc., 1942.

Geikie, James: Mountains: Their Origin, Growth, and Decay, D. Van Nostrand Company, Inc., 1914.

Griggs, D.: A Theory of Mountain-building, *Am. Jour. Sci.,* 5th ser., vol. 237, pp. 611–651, 1939.

CHAPTER 21

Metamorphism

Every rock is the product of a definite environment, one in which the impelling factors are temperature, pressure, and chemically active fluids, vapors, and gases. The rocks that are in stable equilibrium under one set of conditions may be unstable under another set, and consequently an adjustment to the new environment tends to take place whereby new minerals and rocks are formed. Such transformed rocks belong to the third great division of rocks, called *metamorphic,* and the fact that they are the products of transformation or recrystallization implies that metamorphic rocks are formed from older, preexisting rock formations. Thus *metamorphism* may be defined as the sum of the processes that transform rocks and minerals. Some minerals, however, are stable under a wide range of conditions, and furthermore the transformation may proceed so slowly that a rock never attains a condition of complete equilibrium with its surroundings because environmental conditions may change again before the transformation is completed. Eventually some rocks may become so profoundly altered that little or no trace of their original structure and mineral association remains.

The most evident visible changes seen in metamorphic rocks are such things as an increase in grain size (Fig. 441), a partial reorganization of the chemical components to form a new mineral assemblage, and the development of new structural patterns, particularly those showing a parallel arrangement of minerals. The textures of most metamorphic rocks are different than those of igneous and sedimentary rocks; the chief difference is the way in which the minerals fit together. In igneous rocks, which crystallize in a more or less orderly sequence, the minerals are interlocked, the last minerals to form fitting into whatever spaces that remained after the previous ones had crystallized. In coarse-grained sedimentary rocks such as sandstone, one can observe readily that the grains are in simple contact and the spaces between them are filled by some cementing material such as quartz, carbonate, iron oxides, or other bonding materials. In metamorphic rocks, on the other hand, the minerals

524

fit together without interlocking and without introduced cement. There are a few exceptions, such as some marble and certain types of quartzite.

The textural pattern of a given metamorphic rock is determined by such variable factors as the nature of the original material, the type of metamorphic process or processes involved, and the intensity with which they have operated. If material is removed or introduced, it is transported either as a liquid or as a gas or even by the migration of ions or atoms by diffusion.

Processes or Factors Causing Metamorphism. Rocks are brought into new environments by any of the dominant geologic processes, namely, volcanism, diastrophism, and gradation. At some places they are subjected to the heat and pressure of volcanic intrusions; at other places they are

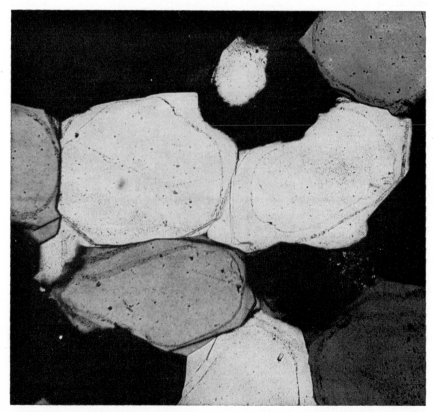

FIG. 441. Photograph of thin section of quartzite showing deposition of silica on quartz grains. The shape of the original grains is indicated by the concentric, dusty outlines in the white grains. If the silica was deposited from hot ground waters, the rock is considered a product of metamorphism. ($\times40$.)

more deeply buried under accumulating sediments or by deep folding; and at still other places they are being exhumed by erosion. The conditions to which the rocks are subjected determine the kind of metamorphic changes that take place. *Pressure* is one of the most important factors and is of two types. Static, or balanced, pressure is due to the weight of the overlying rock, and it increases with depth. Dynamic or unbalanced pressure causes and accompanies diastrophic movements. When the term metamorphism is used without qualification, generally it refers to such recrystallization as has been induced by pressure and the movement resulting from it.

Since a rise of *temperature* accelerates most chemical reactions, *heat* is a potent factor in causing metamorphism. The heat may come from hot intrusive magmas, or it may be the normal heat which prevails at depth. In regions where diastrophism is active, heat may be caused by the friction of movement within the rock that is being deformed. Hot liquids, vapors, and gases aid in the transfer of atoms to produce new mineral compounds. In fact, a certain critical temperature must be reached before an interchange of atoms begins and new minerals can form. Superheated water, under great pressure, is able to attack many minerals and produce new products of crystallization that will not form in an environment of dry heat alone. It has been demonstrated experimentally that vapors under great pressure will transfer atoms of metals from one compound to another. Furthermore, rocks which require a temperature of 2500°F. to melt in dry heat will melt at 750°F. when water is present as either a liquid or a vapor. Thus by lowering the melting point, hot solutions increase the plasticity of the minerals and thereby lower the pressure necessary to deform the rock masses in which they occur.

Liquids and vapors given off from magmas at high temperatures penetrate far into the country rock that is being invaded. Thus metamorphic changes are induced hundreds or even thousands of feet from the contact between magma and country rock. Such vapors are called *mineralizers*. They consist mainly of steam, chlorine, fluorine, boric acid, together with other chemically active agents. The extent of their influence depends upon the amount and kind of mineralizers, the pressure under which they react, and the porosity of the rock invaded.

Types of Metamorphism. On the basis of the agencies most active in producing the changes accomplished, the metamorphic processes may be classified as (1) geothermal, (2) hydrothermal, (3) igneous, or contact, and (4) dynamic, or kinetic. Since metamorphism may result from the effects of a single agency or of several, it follows that metamorphic rocks may show a series of gradations or various intermediate stages depending upon which factor or agency exercised the greatest influence during metamorphism. Furthermore, rocks may pass through more than one cycle of metamorphic processes and each may produce its distinctive characteristics.

Geothermal Metamorphism. Geothermal metamorphism is so called because the earth's heat produces the transformation without the intervention of heat from magmatic sources. It refers to the changes brought about by the high temperatures existing everywhere at considerable depths beneath the surface. Rocks formed at the surface may become deeply buried and depressed in the crust under a heavy load of overlying rocks. In the Appalachian Mountains, where a geosyncline filled with 30,000 feet of sedimentary rocks was folded, uplifted, and eroded, there are now exposed, at the surface, rocks that were once buried to a depth of nearly 6 miles. The minerals in these rocks are unstable at the surface and, from laboratory experiments they are known to form at temperatures of 500 to 1000°C.

Other examples, such as the potassium salt deposits of Germany, show similar changes. These salt beds were deposited on the floor of an evaporating lake, and later the floor of the basin in which they accumulated subsided and became filled with 15,000 to 20,000 feet of younger sedimentary rocks. The salts were unstable in the environment of deep burial and its accompanying higher temperature. Recrystallization took place, and many new and rare minerals were formed.

Hydrothermal Metamorphism. The terms hydrothermal metamorphism and hydrothermal alteration are used for the changes produced by hot magmatic waters. Magmatic heat also makes ground water of meteoric origin much more active chemically, either as a liquid or as a vapor. Such alteration is often accompanied by the addition of new substances, or by the removal of others, or by both. Ferromagnesian minerals are commonly altered to serpentine or soapstone, and orthoclase is altered to the fine-grained white mica called sericite. Many igneous rocks are changed so much that they are recognized with difficulty. In such metamorphism, replacement is common, and often such changes are attended by the deposition of ores of metals. A well-known example of hydrothermal metamorphism is seen at Butte, Montana, a copper-mining city built on granite. The waters that deposited copper ores altered the granite so much that practically no unaltered rock is found in the vicinity of the ores.

Igneous, or Contact, Metamorphism. The changes brought about by the action of intruding magmas and the emanation from them upon the invaded, or country, rock are classed as *igneous,* or *contact, metamorphism.* The high temperature and the high pressure under which magmatic solutions come out of intrusive magmas account for the pervasive character of this type of metamorphism. The changes are greatest near the contact with the intruded rock and become progressively less intense outward from the contact (Fig. 442).

Extrusive flows have but little effect upon the rocks or soils over which they move. The alteration consists in melting or baking a thin layer of the older rock, but such changes are not profound, and they rarely extend more than a few inches into the older rock.

Along small dikes and sills the invaded rocks are not changed very greatly, nor do the changes extend very far from the igneous body. However, beds of coal have been converted into coke by sills injected along bedding planes near them, and beds of clay have been "fired" or burned into a hard, red bricklike rock by dikes that intersect them.

The most extensive metamorphic changes accomplished by contact action are found around batholiths, particularly in the invaded rocks near the stocklike masses of the upper parts of batholiths. In such environments all rocks are changed—limestones, shales, sandstones, and older igneous rocks, if such are present. The most profound changes are generally in limestone and calcareous shales.

The alterations are caused not by readjustments due to pressure but rather by heat and mainly by hot fluids from the intruding rock. The altered contact zones around the intrusive at many places are 100 feet wide or more and at other places as much as 1 mile wide. At many places, however, the altered zone is wanting.

Whatever material is present in the invaded rock generally is utilized in making up its metamorphosed equivalent. If the limestone contains magnesium, a magnesium mineral like pyroxene is formed; if clay or some other aluminous material is present in the limestone, the new minerals, such as pyroxenes and garnet, will be of the aluminous varieties. In most contact zones, however, much new material is added. Silica and iron are very commonly introduced.

If the vapors and gas given off by the magma contain metals and have iron, zinc, lead, or copper in appreciable amounts, ore deposits of the metals may form in the invaded rocks (Fig. 443). Such deposits

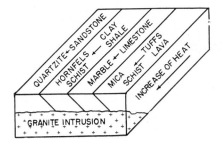

FIG. 442. Diagram showing the changes produced by the intrusion of a granite mass into various types of sedimentary and igneous rocks.

are formed most commonly in limestones and calcareous shales, but they may occur in any type of invaded rock.

At great depths the environments associated with igneous intrusions are those of very high temperature and intense pressure, and in some of the rocks formed under such conditions there is no clear line of distinction between igneous and metamorphic activity. This is true especially along orogenic belts where sedimentary rocks subsided or were dragged to great depths by diastrophic forces. Some granitic rocks now exposed in the cores of folded mountains appear to have acquired their characteristics in this zone while far below the mountain folds.

Where such rocks retain evidence of former sedimentary bedding, the process is referred to as *granitization*. Such granitized rocks may constitute a wide aureole around an intrusive granite batholith, with no definite contact between wall rock and granite. The granite grades gradually into the wall rock, which it appears to have replaced or transformed by the addition of emanations in gaseous or liquid form or by ions migrating upward by diffusion. Field evidence from a number of areas indicates that various types of igneous, sedimentary, and metamorphic rocks have been transformed into granite or granitelike rock by such metamorphic processes.

Kinetic or Dynamic Metamorphism. The term kinetic metamorphism is applied to changes induced by strong unbalanced or directed pressures without a notable increase in temperature. It is characteristic of zones of intensive folding at relatively shallow depths. Such differential stresses cause strata to be folded, crumpled, crushed, and stretched to the tearing point in some places and mashed together in others. The pebbles in Fig. 444 are drawn out into thin lenses. In such environments minerals are sheared and flattened, and if water is present, the atoms and molecules of which the minerals are composed are rearranged and

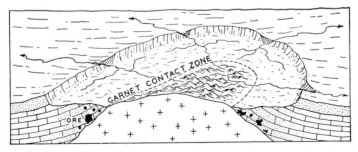

FIG. 443. Diagram showing contact-metamorphic zone of garnet rock and ore in the garnet zone.

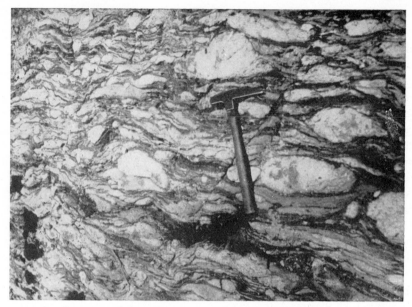

FIG. 444. Conglomerate schist with elongated pebbles. (*Photograph by F. J. Pettijohn.*)

new mineral compounds are formed. Such a finely granular mosaic of fragments is called a *cataclastic structure*.

All dynamic metamorphism implies movement, but rocks move differently in different parts of the lithosphere. The earth's outer shell may be regarded as divided in two zones: (1) an outer zone near the surface, called the *zone of fracture*, where consolidated rocks break when under great stress; (2) a deeper zone, called the *zone of flowage*, where even the stronger rocks are not strong enough to hold spaces open under the pressures that prevail.

Rocks differ greatly in their response to pressure. Wet muds do not fracture but flow at the very surface of the earth, and soft shales will flow at shallow depths. Quartzites and igneous rocks are strong enough to hold fractures open even when there is a weight of several miles of rock above them. At greater depths, even stronger rocks yield by flowage. Experiments were made by Adams and Bancroft in which they placed a cylinder of marble in a hollow cylinder of steel, and after the application of great pressure on the pistons, as indicated by the arrows in Fig. 445, it was found that the rock had changed its shape by "flowage." The flowage of rocks under these conditions is not like that of a liquid. The rocks do not become even malleable like some metals. The movement takes place very slowly by the formation of minute fractures and gliding planes, by shearing, by crushing, and by recrystallization.

Where the pressures result in strong differential movement along thrust-fault zones, the rocks near the fault surfaces are likely to be pulverized and the fragments strung out in the direction of movement along the fault. Such mechanical disturbance produces a streaky, compact rock called a *mylonite*, which is a strongly coherent mass of microscopic grains of minerals produced by the mashing of the original grains of the rock. In general, fault gouge and breccia form along such faults near the surface of the earth, where the confining pressures are comparatively small, whereas mylonite forms at greater depth, where the confining pressure forces the rocks to retain their coherence even though pulverized. A mylonite, therefore, may be thought of as a microbreccia that maintained its coherence during deformation.

Degrees of Metamorphism. Some metamorphic rocks are more intensely altered than others. In the transformation of shale to slate comparatively little recrystallization takes place, but from slate to phyllite, to mica schist, and finally to garnetiferous schist or gneiss each succeeding rock in the sequence represents a higher degree, or rank, in metamorphism. The chemical composition of the original shale and that of the end product of intensive metamorphism, the garnetiferous schist or gneiss, may be nearly identical, but their general appearance and mineral composition are vastly different. The degree, or rank, of metamorphism attained is determined by the intensity of action of the agents and other factors in the environment. In general, slates and phyllites, which are low-rank metamorphic rocks, are formed near the surface, whereas schists and gneisses, both high-rank metamorphic rocks, are formed at greater depth or near the margins of intrusive masses of magma.

An intensely metamorphosed rock such as a garnetiferous schist may be transferred by diastrophism into a new position which may have a different environment. At its new location the conditions of stability may be those which produce slates and phyllites. Thus the schist may return to the low-rank state of a phyllite. Such metamorphism has oc-

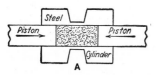 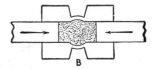

FIG. 445. Diagrams illustrating the deformation of marble by great pressure. The left figure shows a section of a hollow cylinder in which a small cylinder of marble is fitted. The right figure shows the same after great pressure has been applied by movements of the pistons. The deformation took place slowly, resulting in shortening and bulging out of the marble cylinder. It is deformed, but it is not crushed. (*After Adams and Bancroft.*)

FIG. 446. Garnet in schist, Stikeen River, Alaska. (*Courtesy of American Museum of Natural History.*)

curred in many mountainous areas where refolding and faulting of older metamorphic rocks have taken place.

STRUCTURES AND TEXTURES OF METAMORPHIC ROCKS

Metamorphic rocks are classified, on the basis of their structure and texture, into foliated and nonfoliated groups. Many metamorphic rocks are more or less foliated (Latin *folium*, a leaf), or arranged in bands. This structure is due to the parallel arrangement of their constituent minerals or to the elongation of bands, layers, or lenses of granular material. The rocks will split more readily on planes parallel to the planes of foliation than across them. Often these planes are highly irregular and undulating. In a coarse-grained metamorphic rock like a gneiss the planes are poorly defined, whereas in a fine-grained rock like slate or schist they are well-defined and closer together. This property of a rock which causes it to split, or break, in certain directions more easily than in others is called *rock cleavage*. The nonfoliated rocks are massive and do not cleave readily. If the minerals are arranged with their long dimensions parallel, the rock breaks so that the minerals separate on planes parallel to the long dimension of the grains. This type of cleavage is called *schistosity*, and the rocks that possess it are schists (Figs. 446, 449, 450).

If a mud or shale is examined under the microscope, it is found to consist of small particles of quartz which are mingled with finer particles of clay. Under great pressure the quartz grains are broken, and they are rotated so that their long axes lie in the direction of least pressure; the finer clayey material is recrystallized, and new minerals such as mica and amphiboles are formed. These new minerals have forms that are aligned with their long dimensions parallel to the direction of least pressure, as is illustrated by Fig. 447, in which A represents a shale greatly magnified and B shows the same rock after dynamic metamorphism. The direction of greatest pressure is indicated by the long arrows, and that of less pressure is shown by the short horizontal arrows. Because the pressure is less, the material of the rock tends to move out or to lengthen in that direction if free to move and to become shorter in the direction of greatest pressure. Because the mineral fragments are strung out in the direction at right angles to the lines of greatest pressure and because the flaky or fibrous minerals that are formed are aligned in that direction, the rock will break, or cleave, most readily in planes parallel to the long minerals. Thus a slaty cleavage is developed. Where bedded rocks are greatly compressed by folding, they take on a slaty cleavage, so that they often break across the beds, particularly at the axes of the folds (Fig. 448). Not all slates are formed from muds and clays; basalts and other igneous rocks also may be converted into slates. Shales are very readily changed to schists, because they are weak and also because they usually contain aluminum, potash, and iron, from which flaky minerals may form. If much potash is present, mica usually will be abundant in the product. Pure limestone and pure quartzite, on the other hand, do not so readily

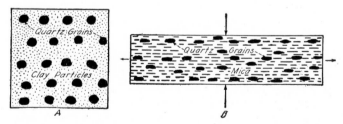

FIG. 447. A, mud, or shale, greatly enlarged, consisting of grains of fine quartz sand and of smaller clay particles; B, the same mud, or shale, metamorphosed by pressure to form slate. The quartz grains are broken, and the quartz fragments are oriented so that their long axes lie parallel to the direction of least pressure. Mica crystals form with flakes parallel to the direction of least pressure.

form schists, because they do not contain the materials for the formation of the platy minerals.

Foliates. The most common foliated rocks are those composed for the most part of micas and chlorite. These platy minerals are easily cleavable, and therefore a rock containing a large number of platy grains that are in parallel orientation will split readily in the direction parallel to that of the cleavage of the mineral grains. The most abundant foliated rocks are the slates, phyllite, schists, and gneisses.

Slates. A slate is a homogeneous, fine-grained rock which will split into thin or thick sheets with relatively smooth surfaces. The chief minerals are not readily distinguished by the naked eye. The surfaces are smoother than those of schists because of the finer grain. Some slates, however, have crumpled and folded cleavage surfaces. In some slates cleavage is parallel to the bedding, but at many places it intersects the bedding at high angles (Figs. 46, 448). The original bedding planes may appear as streaks, often more or less plicated and running at any angle with the slaty cleavage.

Slates range in color from gray through red, green, and purple to black. The gray and black colors generally are due to carbonaceous material in the original rock, the carbon compounds having changed to graphite. The red and purple shades are due to iron and manganese oxides, and the green to ferrous iron silicates. Slates commonly are named from the predominant color or most conspicuous mineral. There is no sharp boundary between slates and shales or between slates and phyllites.

Phyllites. A phyllite is a foliated, finely micaceous rock of nearly uniform composition. It is coarser and more lustrous than slate but too fine-grained to be classed as a schist. In phyllites generally the mica flakes are large enough to be distinguished with the unaided eye, but most of the other material is very fine-grained. Phyllites represent a degree of meta-

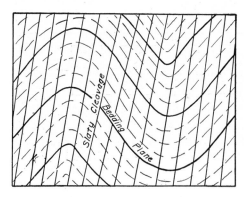

FIG. 448. Folded beds of slate with slaty cleavage developed across the beds.

morphism greater than that for slate but less than for schist. They may grade into either of these rocks.

Schists. In schists the mineral grains generally are sufficiently large to be identified with the naked eye. The individual leaves are not of uniform thickness but are flattened lenses that often are bent and curving, with their platy surfaces in parallel planes (Figs. 449, 450). At right angles to these planes, schists break with much greater difficulty, leaving irregular frayed edges.

Some Common Minerals of Crystalline Schists

Generally without marked elongation	Generally elongated in two dimensions, platy or tabular	Generally elongated in one dimension, needlelike
Quartz	Muscovite	Actinolite
Garnet	Biotite	Tremolite
Pyrite	Chlorite	Hornblende
Magnetite	Talc	

Schists generally are classified on the basis of their mineral composition. If micas are prominently developed, the rock is *mica schist*. If hornblende is the mineral responsible for the foliation, the rock, which is generally dark green to black with a silky luster, is *hornblende schist*. Schists

FIG. 449. A porphyry changed to a schist by pressure. Near Green Park, Caldwell County, North Carolina. (*Photograph by Keith, U.S. Geological Survey.*)

FIG. 450. Complex folding in quartzose schist on Boardman Hill, Clarendon, Vermont. (*Photograph by T. N. Dale, U.S. Geological Survey.*)

rarely have abundant feldspar. Commonly the various schists are formed from shales, but some are formed by the metamorphism of fine-grained igneous rocks such as felsites and basalts.

Gneisses. A gneiss is a banded, coarsely textured metamorphic rock with a rough foliation (Fig. 451) and the alternating bands, or layers, are commonly of unlike mineral composition. In most gneisses feldspar is a prominent constituent; often the presence of large feldspar crystals serves to distinguish a gneiss from a schist.

During movement under great pressure the crystals of a granite may rotate so that they lie with their long axes lined out in the direction of least pressure (Fig. 451). Recrystallization of micas takes place also, and these lie with their leaves parallel to the long axes of the crystals. The changes are brought about much less readily than the change from shale to slate, because the granite is a stronger rock; yet at great depths the granite may act as a somewhat plastic mass, and its minerals rotate much as others do when schist is formed. Gneisses have formed also from arkose sands by granulation and cementation of fragments of feldspar and other minerals which make up the sands. Certain granite gneisses appear to have formed by movement during the consolidation of the granite, probably just after the granite had cooled to a pasty mass but had not become completely solid. In such granites the feldspar and mica crystals are drawn out and arranged in lines so that the structure of the gneiss is

much like that of the granite gneiss formed by metamorphism. Such texture is called *flow banding*, and the rock is a *primary gneiss*. Recent work
has shown that primary gneisses are more common than was formerly
supposed and that they should not be classified as metamorphic rocks.

Where granitic batholiths are injected into slates and schists, great
numbers of sill-like injections of granite occur parallel to the foliation of
the invaded rock. Near the margin of the batholiths the amount of granite
may be as great as that of the foliated rock. The "sills" range in thickness
from a small fraction of an inch to several feet, and the rock between
them is completely recrystallized by the high temperature and the great
pressure of the injected magma. The resulting composite rock has a
gneissic, laminated appearance and is called an *injection gneiss*, or
granitized schist. Such rocks are common in the roof pendants of batholiths and around the cupolas that extend upward into the invaded rock
(Fig. 39). Many injection gneisses are so intricately folded and convo-
luted that one must conclude that both the granite and the host rocks
were in a mobile state at the time the folding occurred.

Nonfoliates. Not all metamorphic rocks have a foliated structure or
fabric such as is seen in the schists. Some are massive like igneous rocks
but can be distinguished from them by their mineral composition. Many
nonfoliated metamorphic rocks are the products of hydrometamorphism

FIG. 451. Granite gneiss (natural size). (*Courtesy of Security Printing Company, St.
Cloud, Minnesota.*)

in environments where solutions at either high or low temperatures are the dominant factors in producing the mineral alterations.

Marble. Marble is a crystalline calcareous rock formed by the metamorphism of limestone. The principal mineral is either calcite or dolomite, and the texture ranges from fine to grains that are clearly visible to the unaided eye. Marble is more compact than limestone, its porosity having been reduced by pressure and recrystallization. Pure marble is white, but impurities may give it a great variety of colors. Red, yellow, and brown marbles, many of which are very attractive when polished, owe their color to varying proportions of compounds of iron. Carbonaceous organic matter produces gray and black colors, whereas green shades are due to the presence of serpentine and chlorite.

Quartzite. Quartzite is sandstone that has been thoroughly cemented by quartz which was brought into the rock in solution and deposited around the sand grains. A broken surface of quartzite shows a glassy luster and a splintery or conchoidal fracture. Impure sandstones, especially those containing clayey minerals, form quartzose schists when subjected to dynamic forces due to earth movements. Thus there are sand-

Sedimentary Rocks and Their Metamorphosed Equivalents

Unconsolidated	Consolidated	Metamorphosed
Gravel	Conglomerate	Conglomerate schist
Sand	Sandstone	Quartzite, quartz schist
Mud, clay	Shale, argillite	Slate, phyllite, mica schist
Calcareous ooze	Limestone	Marble, calcareous schist
Peat	Lignite, bituminous coal	Anthracite coal, graphite

Igneous Rocks and Their Metamorphosed Equivalents

Igneous rocks	Metamorphosed equivalents
Granite	Granite gneiss
Syenite	Syenite gneiss
Diorite	Diorite gneiss
Gabbro	Gabbro gneiss
Peridotite	Serpentine
Rhyolite	Mica schist
Andesite	Hornblende schist
Basalt	Slate, hornblende schist, biotite schist, chlorite schist

stones showing various degrees and types of metamorphism. Quartzites formed by simple deposition of quartz from cold ground waters are not considered to be metamorphic rocks.

Soapstone. Soapstone is a rock composed essentially of talc but commonly containing some mica, tremolite, chlorite, and quartz as accessory minerals. The rock is light bluish gray or grayish green in color and has a greasy feel. It is a product of hydrothermal alteration and consequently contains various hydrous silicates.

Metamorphism of Coal. Coal is formed by the consolidation and induration of plant remains which, as subjected to progressively greater pressure during metamorphism, form (1) peat, (2) lignite, (3) bituminous coal, (4) anthracite coal, and (5) graphite. Each member of this series contains more carbon and less gas and water than the member preceding it. At many places coal-bearing formations may be followed from the plains, where they lie nearly flat, to mountains, where they are highly folded. As the amount of folding increases, the character of the coal changes. In the western plains, where the beds lie nearly horizontal, lignite only is present; toward the mountains the lignite has changed to bituminous coal, and where the coal beds have been more intensely folded, the coal has become anthracite.

SUGGESTIONS FOR FURTHER READING

Fenton, Carroll Lane, and Mildred Adams Fenton: The Rock Book, Doubleday & Company, Inc., 1940.

Harker, Alfred: Metamorphism: A Study of the Transformations of Rock-Masses, Methuen & Co., Ltd., London, 1939.

Kemp, James Furman: Handbook of Rocks, 6th ed., rev. by Grout, Frank F., D. Van Nostrand Company, Inc., 1940.

CHAPTER 22

Earthquakes and the Interior of the Earth

Earthquakes are tremors from the passage of a series of vibratory waves through the rocks of the earth. They have been known to man and feared since very ancient times. They are among the most destructive of natural phenomena and often are even more terrifying than the eruptions of volcanoes, because earthquake shocks take place on the ground, which from childhood men generally have regarded as stable.

EXAMPLES

Lisbon, 1755. On All Saints' Day, Nov. 1, 1755, thousands of persons were congregated in the cathedrals of Lisbon, Portugal, when at 9:40 A.M. the city was struck by a violent earthquake, 6 or 7 minutes long, that virtually destroyed the churches and other buildings of the city and killed tens of thousands. Some of the survivors, many of them seriously injured, sought refuge on a new marble quay at the waterfront, where a second shock about 20 minutes after the first one plunged the quay and people into the water. A third severe earthquake at noon added to the havoc.

The kick imparted to the Atlantic Ocean caused its water first to leave the harbor and then about 10 A.M. to slosh back on land as a great wave, variously estimated to be 16 to 50 feet high, that reached inland ½ mile. In its return the wave washed ships, buildings, bridges, and people out to sea. Three other such waves about 16 feet high returned in the next 4 hours.

Altogether about half the city was destroyed. The aftershocks of the quake continued for several months.

The earthquake was felt over an area of at least 1,250,000 square miles. The shock disturbed lakes and rivers over much of western Europe. Loch

Lomond, Scotland, 1,220 miles from Lisbon, rocked back and forth every 10 minutes in seiche waves about 2 feet high that continued for 1½ hours.

New Madrid, 1811–1812. A little after 2 A.M. on Dec. 16, 1811, a major earthquake struck the region of New Madrid, Missouri. There followed 27 aftershocks before dawn and a declining series of shocks for days afterward. On Jan. 23, 1812, a second great temblor struck, and on Feb. 7,

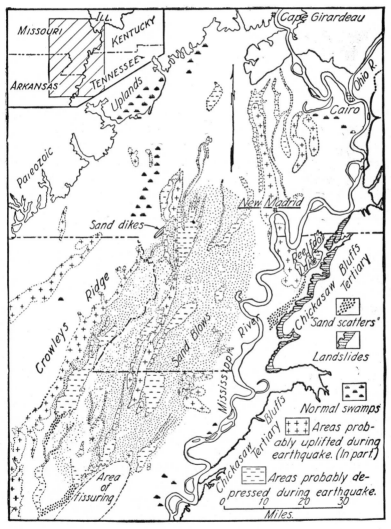

FIG. 452. Map of part of region affected by the earthquakes of 1811 near New Madrid, Missouri. (*After Fuller, U.S. Geological Survey.*)

1812, a third rocked the area the most severely of all. In 3 months' time a total of 1,874 shocks was noted at Louisville, Kentucky, 200 miles away. Chimneys were toppled in Cincinnati, Ohio, 400 miles away. The alluvial fill on the Mississippi River flood plain was thrown into waves and cracked; parts of it were elevated, and an area of about 5,750 square miles, including the newly created basin of Reelfoot Lake, Tennessee, sank several feet; and the course of the river was changed (Fig. 452). The affected area displayed an array of newly formed fissures, sand dikes, sand extrusions, elevated domes, landslides, sunken ground, lakes, and swamps. The earthquake was felt from the Rocky Mountains to the Atlantic Coast and from Canada to the Gulf of Mexico. The American seismologist Perry Byerly regards the New Madrid earthquake as the greatest one on record in the United States. A repetition of it would cause prodigious damage because of the subsequent growth of population and cities within its potential reach.

Charleston, 1886. On Aug. 31, 1886, a violent earthquake shook the city of Charleston, South Carolina, for about 70 seconds. Buildings on filled-in ground were heavily damaged, roads and railroads were twisted about, air and water spurted out of the ground, and sand mounds were built up at many places. The earthquake was felt over most of the eastern part of the United States, from Boston to Milwaukee to New Orleans. The intensity of the shock decreased with distance from the source, as is indicated by Fig. 453. Aftershocks continued for more than a year. This quake is noteworthy for its occurrence in a region generally free from shocks, the wide range of the area in which it was perceptible, and the moderate damage and loss of life for a shock of such pronounced intensity.

Assam, 1897. At about 5:15 P.M., June 12, 1897, an earthquake severely shook the region of the province of Assam in eastern India. Inasmuch as damage to buildings was almost total over an area of about 30,000 square miles and the acceleration was great enough to overcome gravity and project stones vertically off the ground, this earthquake may be the most severe one known, although only a moderate number of persons were killed. The shock started great landslides, opened fissures, displaced alluvial soils, ruined forests and rice fields, and produced visible waves on the ground. Several thousand aftershocks were noted in the next 2 years.

Another unusually severe shock occurred in Assam in 1950.

California Earthquake. On Apr. 18, 1906, California was shaken by the most severe earthquake in the history of the state. About 700 persons were killed, buildings were destroyed, and in a fire that followed the earthquake a large part of San Francisco was burned. Piers in harbors nearby were destroyed, and landslides occurred. The first snap, or movement, of the earth was recorded at the observatory of the University of California and was found to be 3 inches in a horizontal and 1 inch in a vertical direction. Quickly following the first snap were rebounds over the greatly disturbed area on both sides of a fault line. These movements, or "temblors," brought down chimneys and towers. The shocks were felt from Coos Bay, Oregon, to Los Angeles and were recorded at Washington, D.C.; at Potsdam, Germany; Irkutsk, Siberia; and other places.

The San Andreas fault (Fig. 460) that caused the California earthquake is approximately vertical, and the movement along it was approximately horizontal. In general the effects were most severe nearest the fault, although they varied considerably with the character of the rock. Buildings on rocky hills were little damaged, whereas those on made ground collapsed. Where foundations were laid on piles driven into the ground, the destructive effects were generally slight, even in the area of made ground. The buildings that were most affected by the shocks were on raftlike foundations on the loose mantle-rock or fill.

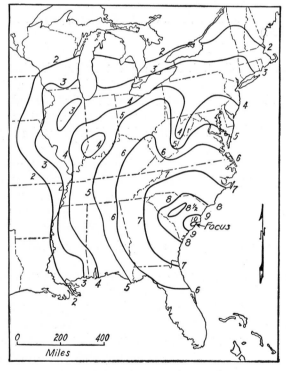

FIG. 453. Map of eastern part of United States, showing lines of equal intensities of shocks caused by Charleston earthquake of 1886. (Calculated on the Rossi-Forel scale.) (*After Dutton, U.S. Geological Survey.*)

FIG. 454. Irregular "mole track" developed in alluvium from movement on White Wolf fault near base of Bear Mountain, Kern County, California, July 21, 1952. (*California Division of Mines.*)

Sagami Bay. On Sept. 1, 1923, a great earthquake destroyed Yokohama and a large part of Tokyo, Japan. At 11.58:44 A.M. a violent shock shook the houses and other structures. Other shocks followed, and fire was kindled at scores of places. Owing to the bursting of water mains the fire could not be extinguished. At 4 P.M. a high wind swept the city. By nightfall 1 million persons in Tokyo were left homeless. Sea waves destroyed shipping along the shores. The loss of life, partly by fire, was more than 100,000. The bottom of Sagami Bay, which is about 1 mile deep, had been mapped by soundings before the earthquake, and it was mapped again after the earthquake. At some places the movements of the sea bottom, partly upward but mostly downward, amounted to hundreds of feet, probably as a consequence mainly of shifting of loose sediments on the floor of the bay.

Long Beach, California. At Long Beach, California, there was a shock Mar. 10, 1933. At short distances away it was not a strong shock as recorded by seismographs, but it was severe locally, and since there is deep alluvium over much of the area, there was heavy damage and some loss of life. The point of origin was a little offshore. There was no sea wave and no notable disturbance of water, although vessels nearby felt the tremors.

Helena, Montana. Some earthquakes consist of a large number of small shocks. These are *swarm earthquakes*. At Helena, Montana, from

Oct. 18, 1935, to Jan. 1, 1936, there were nearly 1,300 shocks; strong shocks on Oct. 18, Nov. 28, and Dec. 31 were destructive. Forty houses were ruined, 200 considerably damaged, and 80 per cent of the houses in the city suffered some damage. In mines nearby the shock was felt strongly, but no damage was done to them.

Arvin-Tehachapi, California. The strongest California earthquake since 1906 struck the Arvin-Tehachapi area at the south end of the San Joaquin Valley, California, on July 21, 1952. It had a maximum intensity of XI, but only 14 lives were lost, as the area is thinly settled. It was followed by numerous aftershocks, including seven strong ones within a few weeks, one of which on Aug. 22 damaged Bakersfield. The series of shocks did extensive damage to wells, pipe lines, irrigation reservoirs, ditches, roads, railroad tunnels, and other structures, mainly from lurch-

FIG. 455. Earthquake crack near Mammoth Lakes, California. (*Photograph by Frashers.*)

ing of alluvium. The quakes were started by movement on the White Wolf fault near the base of Bear Mountain (Fig. 460). Numerous fractures and scarplets were formed in the alluviated lowland (Fig. 454), on the higher slopes fissures formed in solid rock (Fig. 455), and several landslides broke loose.

Orleansville, Algeria. About 1:07 A.M., Sept. 9, 1954, a severe earthquake occurred at Orleansville, in northern Algeria, wrecking much of the city and killing more than a thousand of the 32,500 population. The earth fractured, and open fissures appeared for 60 miles around. The major shock was followed by a series of minor quakes continuing over the following week.

Other Earthquakes. References to earthquakes appear in ancient and medieval writings of Greece, Italy, and other countries, as well as in modern records. It has been estimated that in 10 great shocks since A.D. 1000 more than 1½ million persons have lost their lives and that in 4,000 years more than 13 million persons have been killed.

Some outstanding earthquakes are listed in the accompanying table, but the list might be extended manifoldly.

Other Examples of Destructive Earthquakes

Year	Place	Remarks
1450 B.C.	Cimini, Italy	City engulfed in Lake Cimini
224 B.C.	Rhodes, eastern Mediterranean	Colossus, bronze statue of Apollo, 105 feet high, one of the Seven Wonders, at harbor entrance destroyed
811 A.D.	Rome, Italy	Basilica of St. Paul's destroyed
1170 A.D.	Sicily	15,000 lives lost
1303 A.D.	Alexandria, Egypt	Pharos, 370-foot first lighthouse, another of the Seven Wonders, 1,500 years old, destroyed
1456 A.D.	Naples, Italy	60,000 lives lost
1693 A.D.	Naples, Italy	93,000 lives lost
1731 A.D.	Peking, China	100,000 lives lost
1891 A.D.	Mino-Owari, Japan	Horizontal and vertical movements on faults readily apparent
1899 A.D.	Yakutat Bay, Alaska	Seacoast uplifted as much as 47 feet, and glaciers affected
1906 A.D.	Colombia-Ecuador	One of the largest of the last half century
1908 A.D.	Messina, Italy	125,000 people killed
1911 A.D.	Tien Shan Mts., Asia	Of large magnitude
1920 A.D.	Kansu, China	100,000 persons killed, mainly by landslides of loess
1922 A.D.	Chile	Of great severity; great sea wave in the Pacific
1927 A.D.	Murchison, New Zealand	Vertical faulting of 14 feet, great landslides, and a seismic sea wave
1929 A.D.	Grand Banks, off Newfoundland	12 transatlantic cables broken, submarine slides started, 50-foot sea waves set up
1931 A.D.	Hawkes Bay, New Zealand	Originated offshore; damaged cities and harbors; coast uplifted several feet
1939 A.D.	Turkey	40,000 people killed
1950 A.D.	Assam, India	Of unusually high magnitude

GENERAL FEATURES OF EARTHQUAKES

Intensity. The intensity of an earthquake is measured by its effects on man, its damage to buildings and other structures, and the changes in rock and soil at the earth's surface. The intensity differs not only from place to place but also at the same place, because of differences in the stability of the foundations, the manner of construction, and other variables. Macelwane states that destructivity depends upon the geological character of the ground, on the size and shape of the structures, on the character of their materials, on their design and workmanship, on the acceleration of the earthquake wave, on its period, on its velocity, and on its duration.

In a severe earthquake buildings are shaken down, cornices fall off, chimneys topple, bridges collapse, pavement is broken, roads and railroads are buckled and twisted (Fig. 456), telephone and telegraph wires and cables are broken, power lines are downed, fires are started, water towers and tanks give way, gas and water mains are severed, and so on, so as to disrupt almost completely the life of an urban community.

The Mercalli Scale, as modified by Wood and Neumann in 1931, is

FIG. 456. Rails of track twisted by earthquake in Arvin-Tehachapi area, California, in 1952. North end Tunnel No. 4 of Southern Pacific Railroad. (*Photograph courtesy W. M. Jaekle.*)

the intensity scale most used in the United States. An abridged form of it is as follows:

Modified Mercalli Intensity Scale

I. Not felt except by a very few under especially favorable circumstances.

II. Felt only by a few persons at rest, especially on upper floors of buildings. Delicately suspended objects may swing.

III. Felt quite noticeably indoors, especially on upper floors of buildings, but not recognized by many people as an earthquake. Standing motor cars may rock slightly. Vibration like passing of truck. Duration estimated.

IV. During the day felt indoors by many, outdoors by few. At night some awakened. Dishes, windows, doors disturbed; walls made cracking sound. Sensation like heavy truck striking building. Standing motor cars rocked noticeably.

V. Felt by nearly everyone; many awakened. Some dishes, windows, etc., broken; a few instances of cracked plaster; unstable objects overturned. Disturbance of trees, poles and other tall objects sometimes noticed. Pendulum clocks may stop.

VI. Felt by all; many frightened and run outdoors. Some heavy furniture moved; a few instances of fallen plaster or damaged chimneys. Damage slight.

VII. Everybody runs outdoors. Damage *negligible* in buildings of good design and construction; *slight* to moderate in well built ordinary structures; *considerable* in poorly built or bady designed structures; some chimneys broken. Noticed by persons driving motor cars.

VIII. Damage *slight* in specially designed structures; *considerable* in ordinary substantial buildings with partial collapse; *great* in poorly built structures. Fall of chimneys, factory stacks, columns, monuments, walls. Panel walls thrown out of frame structures. Heavy furniture overturned. Sand and mud ejected in small amounts. Changes in well water. Persons driving motor cars disturbed.

IX. Damage *considerable* even in specially designed structures; well designed frame structures thrown out of plumb; *great* in substantial buildings, with partial collapse. Buildings shifted off foundations. Ground cracked conspicuously. Underground pipes broken.

X. Some well-built wooden structures destroyed; most masonry and frame structures destroyed with foundations; ground badly cracked. Rails bent. Landslides considerable from river banks and steep slopes. Shifted sand and mud. Water splashed (slopped) over banks.

XI. Few, if any (masonry), structures remain standing. Bridges destroyed. Broad fissures in ground. Underground pipelines completely out of service. Earth slumps and land slips in soft ground. Rails bent greatly.

XII. Damage total. Waves seen on ground surfaces. Lines of sight and level distorted. Objects thrown upward into the air.

The intensities at different places are rated by trained seismologists on the basis of field surveys and of returned postcard questionnaires distributed by the U.S. Coast and Geodetic Survey or by local collaborators.

The intensity at each locality is plotted on a map, and *isoseismal lines* then are drawn at the boundaries of areas of different intensities (Fig. 457). Such an isoseismal map shows the area of maximum damage, surrounded by more or less concentric belts of progressively less damage. Its principal value is to call attention to areas of poor geologic foundations, of unstable methods of construction, or of other hazards which need to be taken into account to reduce destruction in future earthquakes.

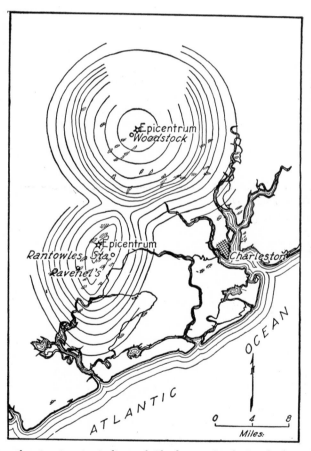

FIG. 457. Map showing isoseismic lines of Charleston, South Carolina, earthquake of Aug. 31, 1886. The stars mark the epicentral tracts. The dotted areas show regions of craterlets. (*After Dutton, U.S. Geological Survey.*)

FIG. 458. Alluvium cracked by an earthquake near Arvin, California, July 21, 1952. The house was shifted off its foundation and severely damaged structurally. (*California Division of Mines.*)

Geologic Effects. The foregoing accounts mention some of the geologic effects of earthquakes—fissuring of the ground, sunken ground, raised hummocks, slumping, earth slides, mudflows, eruptions of water and sand, seismic sea waves, and seiches on lakes (Figs. 452, 454, 455, 458, 459). Other effects include disturbances of the ground-water circulation so as to muddy the waters of wells and springs, to stop some springs, and to start others. Earthquakes may start avalanches of snow, release icebergs from tidewater glaciers, and perhaps affect glaciers in other ways.

It will be seen that these effects are relatively superficial, largely local, and generally of minor geological consequence. Hence we may conclude that in spite of their destructiveness earthquakes are comparatively unimportant as geologic agents. In the science of geology, however, as noted below, they serve as important clues to the internal structure of the earth.

Causes. Earthquake waves may be set up (1) by *percussion*, or sudden blows, as from an explosion (quarry blast, A bomb, volcanic eruption), from traffic (trucks, tanks, trains), or from rockfalls (from cliffs, water-falls, caverns, or mines); (2) by *fracture* of the rocks (as of a stick, a bat, or a tool handle) by faulting or by volcanic explosions; and (3) by *rubbing* together two uneven surfaces (as by rubbing two files together, or pushing a heavy table across the floor) in faulting, landslides, ava-lanches, and submarine slumping of sediments.

It has been found that the principal cause of earthquakes is *faulting,* either the initiation of a new fault or repeated movement on a previous fault. Nontectonic causes are responsible only for local and mostly

FIG. 459. Landslide scars in Sycamore Canyon, Kern County, California, after the Arvin-Tehachapi earthquake of July 21, 1952. The mountain in the background is Bear Mountain. The White Wolf fault zone, along which movement took place, caus-ing the earthquake, lies to the left (northwest), a fraction of a mile. (*Photograph by Robert C. Frampton.*)

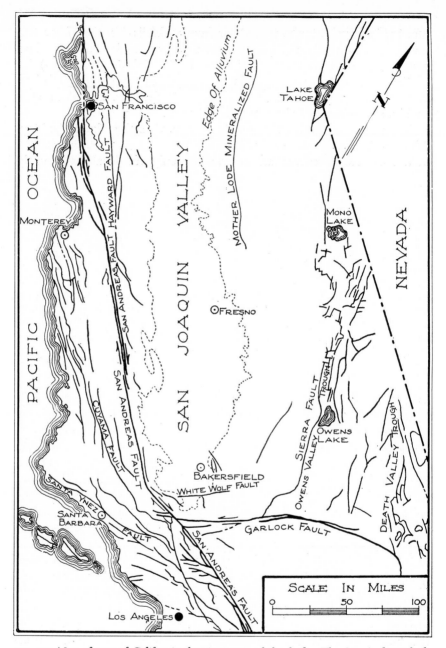

FIG. 460. Map of part of California showing some of the faults. The San Andreas fault is outstanding. (*After Tectonic Map of the United States, American Association of Petroleum Geologists, 1944.*)

minor tremors. Most volcanic explosions, even the giant firecracker outbursts of Krakatao in 1883 and of Katmai in 1912, have only small, local,
shallow, and weak effects.

The association of earthquakes with faulting was especially well-shown
by the California earthquake of Apr. 18, 1906, when the San Andreas fault
broke over a length of at least 270 miles (Fig. 460). The fault is vertical,
but the movement was almost entirely horizontal and parallel to the trend
of the fault.[1] The block on the southwest side shifted northerly with reference to the opposite side (Fig. 461). The maximum measured displace-

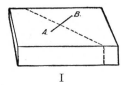
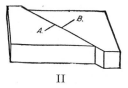

I   II

FIG. 461. I, diagram showing the direction of movement on the San Andreas fault,
which caused the California earthquake of 1906. The broken line represents the fault.
AB is a straight line crossed by the fault. II, the same after faulting. The horizontal
movement was 2 to 21 feet, and the vertical displacement 0 to 3 feet. The southwest
block was elevated. (*After G. K. Gilbert, U.S. Geological Survey.*)

ment of 21 feet was found by the offset of a road near the head of
Tomales Bay northwest of San Francisco.

In connection with the Imperial Valley earthquake of California in
1940, roads and row crops similarly were offset horizontally at least 15
feet. A 35-mile fault in Sonora, Mexico, showed 26 feet of vertical displacement with an earthquake in 1887. The Chedrang fault in Assam,
India, in 1897 had a vertical displacement of 35 feet. The displacement
on the Mino-Owari earthquake fault, several tens of miles long in Japan,
in 1891 was 13 feet horizontally and 20 feet vertically. These faults
caused the earthquakes, not the reverse. Although thousands of faults are
known, only a small number seem to be active sources of earthquakes.
Many earthquakes must originate from concealed faults.

The association of earthquakes with faulting is explained by the *elastic-
rebound* theory developed by H. F. Reid and others after the California
earthquake of 1906. According to this theory the rocks beside the fault,
held tightly together, are able gradually to undergo accumulating strain
by changing shape until their elastic limit finally has been reached. Then

---

[1] The San Andreas fault is therefore an example of a rift fault. To one facing the
opposite side the apparent shift of that side was toward the right; hence the description of its movement as "right lateral." The vertical displacement was negligible.

they suddenly snap, and much of the pent-up energy is released in earth-quake waves. The rocks resume their original shapes but in faulted or different relative positions, and then the process may be repeated.

The method of operation of elastic rebound is shown diagrammatically in Fig. 462. The point O lies on the fault, and A and B are points on opposite sides thereof. In stage 1, before any strain has accumulated, the line AOB is straight. In stage 2, after strain has accumulated but before an earthquake, A and B have been displaced in opposite direc-tions, and the line AOB is bent. The situation then is somewhat analogous to a bent steel spring. In stage 3, after an earthquake, the points formerly adjacent to O have shifted to O' and O'', faulting has occurred, the seg-ments AO' and $O''B$ are straight, and the strain is relieved.

Comparisons of the results of careful surveying of the relative posi-tions of points determined many years before and again just after the California earthquake of 1906 showed that points on the northeast side of the San Andreas fault were displaced 2 to 5 feet southerly (according to their nearness to the fault) and that points on the southwest side had shifted 6 to 10 feet northerly. Thus the elastic-rebound theory was con-firmed. Two subsequent surveys show that the differential displacement is taking place again at a rate of about 2 inches a year. How long can this go on before the fault snaps loose again?

Geographic Distribution of Earthquake Areas. Although earthquakes are transmitted over the entire earth, their places of origin are in limited areas. The regions of most violent earthquakes (Figs. 463, 465) lie in two main belts. One circum-Pacific belt extends through Chile, Peru, Central America, two loops in the Caribbean-Antillean area, Mexico, California, Puget Sound, Vancouver and Queen Charlotte Islands, Aleutian Islands, Kamchatka, Japan, Philippines, Indo-nesia, New Zealand, and certain of the associated arcuate island groups. The second major belt, the Alpine–Mediterranean–trans-Asiatic belt, in-cludes northern Africa, Spain, Italy, Greece, Turkey, Iran, northern India, and Burma. These two belts nearly coincide with the volcanic belts of the earth, as if related to a common cause. Minor belts are along sub-

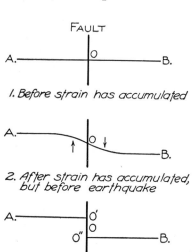

FAULT

1. Before strain has accumulated

2. After strain has accumulated, but before earthquake

3. After earthquake; strain relieved

FIG. 462. Elastic rebound. (*After Reid.*)

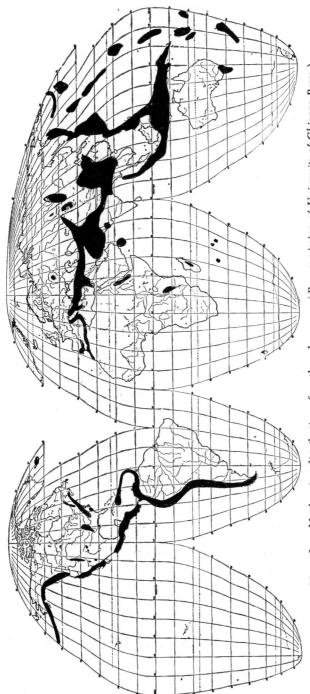

FIG. 463. Map of world, showing distribution of earthquake areas. (*By permission of University of Chicago Press.*)

marine ridges in the Arctic, Atlantic, and Indian Oceans, and in the rift zones of eastern Africa and east central Siberia.

Gutenberg and Richter state that of several thousand major shocks occurring between 1904 and 1946 the circum-Pacific zone includes about 80 per cent of the shallow shocks (originating at depths of less than 60 kilometers), 90 per cent of the intermediate shocks (70 to 300 kilometers), and all deep shocks (those originating below 300 kilometers) and the Alpine–Mediterranean–trans-Asiatic belt includes most of the other large shallow and intermediate shocks. The circum-Pacific zone is thus by far the principal source.

These active zones of the earth in the main are regions where young mountains have been uplifted in late geologic time, where steep slopes exist on the earth's crust, or where rift faulting prevails. Apparently the zones where the high segments and the low segments of the earth come together are zones of weakness and the zones of greatest and most deep-seated movement. By contrast the interiors of geologically old areas of east central Canada, Brazil, Scandinavia, part of Siberia, much of Africa, southern India, and western Australia, except in rift zones, are comparatively free from earthquakes, but not wholly so. The interior of the Pacific Basin, outside the Hawaiian Islands, also is nearly inactive.

Not all earthquakes, however, are in the great deformation belts of the earth. Some are situated in areas remote from present-day volcanoes and late mountain building. New Madrid, Missouri, is far from volcanic centers and far from high mountains, and so is Charleston, South Carolina. Some minor earthquakes occur in areas of delta building, presumably from loading of the earth's crust, and others in areas of recent continental glaciation, presumably from unloading by removal of the ice sheets.

Frequency of Earthquakes. As earthquakes occur somewhere on the earth every few minutes, the earth is said to be in a state of "perpetual

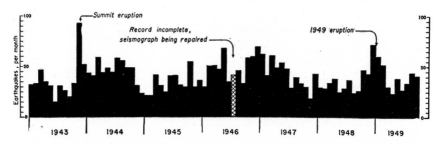

FIG. 464. Earthquake frequency on the volcanic island of Hawaii, January, 1943, to September, 1949. During the period shown earthquakes averaged several tens a month and had a maximum of about 90. Unrest continues between eruptions. (*From Macdonald and Orr, U.S. Geological Survey.*)

tremor." Severe shocks come every week or two. Large numbers of minor shocks attend volcanic activity on the island of Hawaii (Fig. 464). According to Gutenberg and Richter the annual average for the whole earth is about 2 great shallow shocks per year and 17 other major ones, of which 5 are of intermediate and 1 of deep origin. As a rough estimate, it may be said that, for each shock of intensity VII, there are 10 of intensity VI, 100 of intensity V, and so on, in increasing numbers down the scale. Hence earthquakes are very numerous and frequent, but many of them are so slight as to be negligible.

Possibility of Predicting Earthquakes. Earthquakes recur, but apparently not in any regular cycle. Even when we know, for example, that elastic strain has been accumulating along the San Andreas fault in California since 1906, we are unable to tell when the limit will be reached. So we cannot predict the year, much less the day or hour, when another shock may be expected from its release.

There is some evidence that full moon, high tides, heavy rainfall, sharp

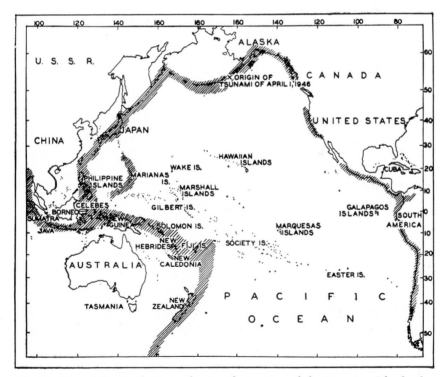

FIG. 465. Map of the Pacific Basin showing the position of the Hawaiian Islands, the place of origin of the seismic sea wave of Apr. 1, 1946, and the distribution of seismically active belts around the Pacific. (*After Macdonald, Shepard, and Cox.*)

changes in barometric pressure, and, better yet, another earthquake elsewhere act as "triggers" for earthquakes, but detailed studies by seismologists, especially in quake-ridden Japan, have failed so far to make useful predictions possible. We can be sure only that earthquakes come again and again, and so our structures should be built to meet the hazard.

Protection from Earthquakes. In many earthquake regions nearly every house in the areas of origin of the shock is damaged, and many are destroyed. The destructive effects result from the falling of roofs and chimneys and from the breaking of foundations and walls. A so-called earthquake-proof house, according to Milne, should be constructed with rafters running from ridgepole to floor sills and with iron straps and sockets replacing mortises and tenons. Light roofs and chimneys are recommended.

Potentially dangerous are heavy cornices, parapet walls, unnecessary ornaments (especially over doorways), old lime mortar, unanchored roofs and roof trusses, unanchored brick veneer, loose shelving and partitions, unreinforced chimneys, unstiffened elevator shafts and frames, unreinforced stair wells, party walls in adjoining buildings of different size, poorly supported water, gas, steam and sewer pipes, free-standing elevated water tanks, and similar structures subject to rupture by differential movement.

Examinations of ruins of the San Francisco earthquake of 1906 showed that many of the bricks had been laid dry in mortar. They were poorly bonded and had clean surfaces, and the mortar showed little adhesion. Walls laid in cement with wet brick stood the test of the earthquake better. Reinforced-concrete buildings have proved relatively stable, but wood, steel, and reinforced-masonry structures can be earthquake-resistant if well-designed and well-built, with the use of adequate reinforcements and appropriate ties, bracing, struts, and anchor bolts. The most secure structure is one that will move as a unit.

Bridges and tall buildings require special consideration of the distribution of their weight (to obtain a low center of gravity), of their resistance to horizontal forces, of their "free period" (to avoid harmonic resonance with an earthquake), and of their internal balance. For large structures soft ground should be avoided. River bluffs and sites near deep excavations also are undesirable.

Seismic Sea Waves. The seismic sea waves, or "tsunamis" (Japanese) which accompanied the Lisbon earthquake of 1755 have already been mentioned. These waves swept at an average speed of about 400 miles an hour 3,540 miles across the Atlantic Ocean to Antigua, in the southeastern West Indies, where they were 12 feet high.

On Aug. 13, 1868, the west coast of South America was shaken from Guayaquil, Ecuador, to Valdivia, Chile, the most violently shaken region being in the neighborhood of Arica, a city on the west coast, where many buildings were destroyed. A few minutes after the destructive shock the sea slowly receded from the shore, and ships anchored in 42 feet of water were left dry. Later the water returned as a great wall, caught up the ships, and swept them inland as if they had been chips of wood. The United States steamer "Wateree" was carried inland ¼ mile with little damage and left ashore.

In 1877 another earthquake in Chile set up a succession of sea waves which traveled across the Pacific to Japan, where for several hours the water rose and fell a maximum of 8 feet at intervals of about 20 minutes. Great sea waves also attended the earthquake accompanying the eruption of the volcano Krakatao in August, 1883. The waves were 100 feet high and destroyed towns along the coasts of Java and Sumatra.

In 1896 a series of waves as much as 30 meters (98 feet) high dashed up on the shores of Japan and destroyed thousands of houses and tens of thousands of lives. The waves crossed the Pacific in about 10½ hours at an average velocity of 450 miles an hour. In 1923, great sea waves accompanied the disastrous earthquake of Sagami Bay, Japan.

With the Messina earthquake of 1908, seismic sea waves rose 25 to

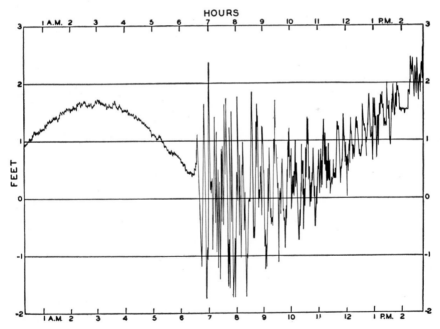

FIG. 466. Record produced on the tide gauge in Honolulu Harbor by the seismic sea wave of Apr. 1, 1946. (*From Macdonald, Shepard, and Cox, Pacific Sci., January, 1947.*)

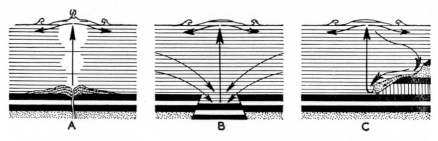

FIG. 467. Diagrammatic sketches showing causes of seismic tidal waves or tsunamis. *A*, submarine volcanic eruption; *B*, submarine faulting; *C*, submarine slumping of sediments. (*After Sieberg.*)

35 feet above the still-water level, flooded many villages, and greatly added to the destruction.

Another tsunami on Apr. 1, 1946, originating in the Aleutian area, destroyed a lighthouse at Dutch Cap, Alaska, about 100 feet above sea level, and crossed 2,300 miles of ocean to the Hawaiian Islands at an average speed of 470 miles an hour (Figs. 465 to 467). At sea the waves were only a few feet high and 90 miles long, but near shore they rose 10 to 20 feet and in places were funneled to elevations of 30 to 50 feet above sea level. Such walls of water did great damage to buildings, roads, railroads, bridges, piers, breakwaters, and ships. The total property damage in the Territory of Hawaii was estimated at 25 million dollars.

Thus seismic sea waves are characterized by their great length, moderate height, high velocity, and great potential destructivity. They are not to be confused with *seaquakes*, which are short-period tremors of the water itself that result from refraction of earthquake waves from the rocks underneath and whose effects are merely the shaking of ships, stunning and killing of fish, and rippling the surface of the sea.

INSTRUMENTAL STUDIES OF EARTHQUAKES

Seismographs. The instrument used to record earthquakes is called a *seismograph*. It consists of (1) a vibrating system, or seismometer, and (2) a recording device.

The vibrating element must be well-anchored, ordinarily on solid rock, so that it moves with the ground. It usually is damped, either mechanically, as by a plunger in a fluid, or magnetically (or electromagnetically), as by a copper vane in a magnetic field.

Vibrating systems are of many kinds. One variety uses a simple horizontal pendulum, free to move in a fixed direction, north-south or east-west (Fig. 468). As the mass of the pendulum may be either very heavy or relatively light and damped or undamped, the natural periods, sensitivities, and magnifications of these instruments differ considerably. The

Milne-Shaw seismograph is a much-used, simple, light, compact horizontal-pendulum instrument.

Another type (Galitzin) uses a pendulum also, but coils of fine wire
are wound around it, and strong permanent magnets are attached to the
framework. When the pendulum swings through the magnetic field, the
motion of the coil generates an electric current in the coil in proportion to
the movement. Wires lead from the coil to a recorder.

In a third type (Wood-Anderson) the pendulum is a small copper
cylinder suspended off center by a very fine vertical wire. When the
ground underneath it moves, the cylinder is twisted back and forth
(Fig. 469). This torsion pendulum has a natural period of about 1 second,
is quite sensitive, and may be used to give high magnification of the
real movement. Hence it is not well-adapted for use in a strong earthquake area but finds its principal place outside the main earthquake belts
to obtain records of distant earthquakes or of nearby earthquakes of
moderate intensity and short period.

A still different type of instrument, having no pendulum, has been
set up at Pasadena, California, to measure the changes in the linear

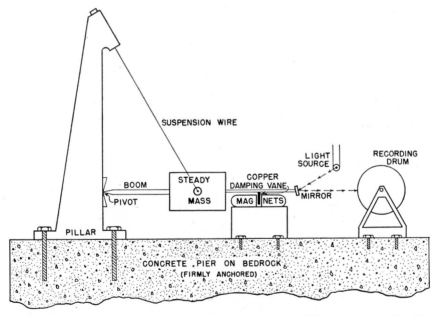

FIG. 468. Sketch of the main elements of a horizontal-pendulum seismograph. The
suspension of the steady mass resembles a sagging gate, free to swing horizontally as
the earth moves underneath it. It is damped magnetically and restored by gravity.
The swing of the mirror attached to the end of the boom is recorded photographically
on the revolving drum. Many variations and adjustments are possible.

strain in the ground between two points about 20 meters apart as an earthquake passes by.

The instruments described above measure only the horizontal components of the earthquake waves. The vertical component is more difficult to get, mechanically, and its amplitude ordinarily is small. A heavy inverted pendulum on springs may be used, and the Galitzin galvanometric device may be adapted to the purpose. In the Benioff vertical-component seismograph a large, heavy horseshoe permanent magnet is suspended as a vertical pendulum from a spiral spring at a distance of about 1 millimeter over a soft iron bar attached to the ground. Coils of wire are wound around the pole pieces of the magnet. When an earthquake moves the iron bar vertically toward or away from the pole pieces, the magnetic flux is changed accordingly and so a current is generated in the coils. The resulting current is conducted by wires from the coils to a galvanometer.

The recorder may use mechanical, optical, or electromagnetic devices, or combinations of them, to transfer the vibrations to paper clamped on a revolving drum driven by a synchronous motor. The earliest ones used a pen on a clock-driven drum. In some modern designs a point of light is reflected from a mirror attached to the seismometer directly upon photographic paper. In another and very sensitive design (Galitzin type) the electric current set up by movement of a coil on a pendulum set in a strong magnetic field actuates a galvanometer to which a tiny mirror is attached whereby light is reflected to the photographic paper. The

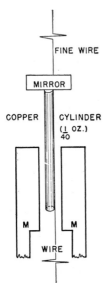

FIG. 469. Sketch of a Wood-Anderson torsional seismograph. Horizontal movement of the ground causes the cylinder and attached mirror to twist on the fine wire suspension. Damping is done by means of an adjustable magnet (M). A point of light reflected from the mirror to photographic paper on a revolving drum records the twist as the mirror swings back and forth with an earthquake. A slightly inclined suspension allows control both by torsion and by gravity.

movement of the drum is such that in the absence of an earthquake the light describes a fine line in the form of a helix around the drum, because the drum moves a short distance longitudinally as it rotates. When an earthquake occurs, the moving mirror transfers the motion to the recording paper as a seismogram (Fig. 470).

Magnification of the movement is brought about mechanically by levers or optically by increasing the distance from the mirror, so that the point of light swings through a larger arc. Magnifications vary on different instruments, but those in the range of a few hundred to several thousand times the actual movement are commonly used.

Exact timing of the record is very important; so an arrangement is made to put a break, or jog, in the recording line once a minute, based on radio time signals, as from the U.S. Naval Observatories. Drum speeds differ, but the usual speed is about ¼ inch to 1 or 2 inches per minute.

It should be noted that there is no universal seismograph. Some instruments are very sensitive, others are sluggish; some give low magnifications, others high; and so on. Different instruments meet different needs at different places. A "strong-motion accelerograph," for instance, is a special type, so constructed as to begin recording only when started by a movement of large, predetermined amplitude and then only for a fixed period of, say, 60 or 70 seconds, unless the motion continues longer. It will supply a record in a strong earthquake area when more delicate instruments may have been thrown out of commission by a heavy shock.

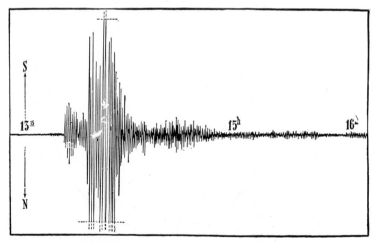

FIG. 470. Seismogram of the San Francisco earthquake of 1906, registered by a horizontal-pendulum seismograph at Irkutsk, Siberia. The oscillations recorded are made by earthquake waves that have passed deep into the earth. (*After Report of California Earthquake Commission, 1906.*)

For obvious reasons its light and power sources are independent of public utilities.

Earthquake Waves. The seismograms show that earthquakes consist of the passage of a series of waves. The amplitude of these waves from a nearby earthquake may be large, but at a distance they are so small as to require magnification. In the Imperial Valley earthquake of May 18, 1940, at El Centro, California, the maximum horizontal movement was about 15 inches in somewhat less than 3½ seconds, and the maximum vertical motion was 4 inches in 2½ seconds—exceptionally large ranges of movement.

Earthquake waves are of three main types: (1) *P*, or *primary* (fast), waves, which are transmitted by alternate push-pull changes of volume (dilatation), or compression and rarefaction in the direction of propagation; (2) *S*, or *secondary* (slow), waves, which shake, shear, twist, and distort by changes of shape; (3) *L*, or *long* (last), waves, which are complex sinuous or undulatory gravity waves that travel along the surface of the earth (Figs. 471, 472).

The *P* waves are like sound, but are far below audible frequencies. Most of them vibrate only once in 2 or 3 seconds, the longest ones once in 25 seconds or more, and those of shortest frequency only about 10 times a second, whereas the frequency of middle C on a piano is 256 per second.

The *L* waves include Raleigh waves vibrating vertically in the direc-

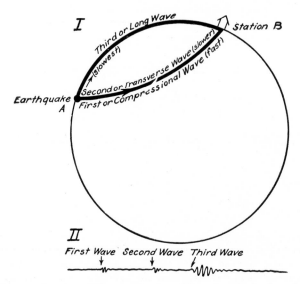

FIG. 471. Diagram showing difference in the times of arrival of various types of seismic wave at seismograph station. (*After N. H. Heck.*)

tion of propagation and transverse Love waves vibrating horizontally. These waves lengthen out to periods of 2 or 3 per minute in traveling one-quarter of the way around the earth and to 1 per 3 minutes in going entirely around it.

The *P* waves travel at velocities of about 5.5 to 13.8 kilometers (3.4 to 8.5 miles) per second, increasing with depth; the S waves, 3.2 to 7.3 kilometers (2.0 to 4.5 miles) per second; and the *L* waves, about 4.0 to 4.4 kilometers (2.5 to 2.7 miles) per second. Because of their different velocities and different routes of travel the three sets of waves arrive at a seismographic station at different times, and so a simple record of a not too distant earthquake is a threefold set of signals. Thus if there is an earthquake at *A* (Fig. 471), a station at *B* will record (1) the time of arrival of the fast longitudinal *P* wave, (2) the time of arrival of the slower transverse *S* wave, and (3) the time of arrival of the *L* wave that passes around the earth. As the interval between the arrivals of *P* and *S* waves increases proportionately with the distance, the time lag (*S* minus *P*) may be used to compute the distance to the source (Fig. 472).

When the travel times of the different waves are plotted against the surface distances from the source, we find that the travel times of the *L* waves are almost directly proportional to the surface distances; hence the inference that they follow the surface. They do, however, travel some-

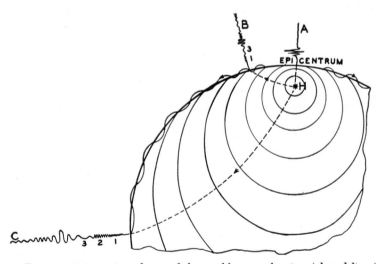

FIG. 472. Diagrammatic section of part of the earth's crust showing (*dotted lines*) the direction of propagation of elastic waves from the focus of an earthquake at *H*. The wave fronts are not spherical because the impulse travels more rapidly with depth. The nature of the vibrations at the epicentrum are shown at *A*. Those not far distant are indicated at *B*, and those which have traveled a great distance are recorded at *C*. (*After Sieberg.*)

what faster in the rocks beneath the oceans than they do under the continents, and at slightly different rates in areas of different kinds of rock. On the other hand, the travel times of the P and S waves decrease, and the velocities increase, as the surface distances from the source become greater. Therefore we infer that they travel, not along surface arcs, but along paths within the earth, where (within limits) their velocities increase as their paths reach greater depths.

Seismograms indicate that the travel of waves within the earth is greatly complicated, however, by refraction, by reflection, by diffraction, and by dispersion. Very complex wave patterns result, but professional seismologists are able to identify and classify most of them.

Focus and Epicenter. The point of origin of an earthquake is its *focus*, and the point on the surface directly above the focus is its *epicenter*. As the intensity of an earthquake dies out inversely as the square of the distance from the source, one may compute the depth of focus from the records of intensities at different places.

At least 75 per cent of all earthquakes originate within 50 kilometers (31 miles) of the surface—some seismologists say more than 90 per cent. The depth of focus of most of these is less than 5 miles. The remainder, those of "intermediate" and "deep-focus" types, originate at depths of 50 to 700 kilometers (31 to 434 miles).

The existence of deep-focus earthquakes was discovered from the early arrival of P waves on the opposite side of the earth and from discrepancies in the arrival times of P and S waves, which made the estimated epicentral distances to disagree even by hundreds of miles. Surface waves also are weak or lacking from a deep source. From a deep focus the waves not only follow the usual direct courses through the earth but also travel up to the surface, whence they are reflected back to the receiving station. The extra time, ranging from a few seconds to about 1 minute, required by the roundabout route is a measure of the depth of

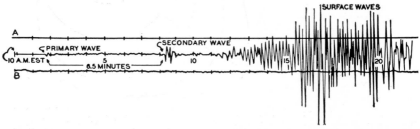

FIG. 473. Seismogram of an earthquake nearly 3,000 miles from the seismograph that recorded it. A shows the undisturbed line recorded 1 hour before the quake; B is a record of the minor waves still arriving 1 hour after the quake. (*Courtesy of Harvard University Press.*)

the focus. Such deep-focus earthquakes show that the rocks of the earth are highly rigid, can accumulate strain, and can fracture even at great depths. These deep-focus earthquakes are confined to the margins of the Pacific Basin.

Location of Distant Epicenters. The method most used for the geographic location of distant epicenters is the three-circle method. After first finding the epicentral distances from three stations by the interval between the arrival times of *P* and *S* waves at each station, a circle is drawn about each station, preferably on a globe, with the radius appropriate to each. The three circles intersect at the point sought (Fig. 474).

The location of distant earthquakes also may be computed from known travel-time curves, when one knows accurately the arrival times of the *P* waves at several stations, especially if pairs of stations show nearly identical arrival times.

The direction to the source also may be indicated at a single station by a record good enough to show the first push or pull. This direction and the epicentral distance obtained from the *S* minus *P* arrival times give at least an approximate location of the source.

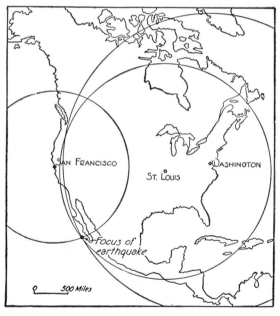

FIG. 474. Map showing the method of locating the focus of an earthquake from seismograph records at three stations. The distances from San Francisco, St. Louis, and Washington are determined from the time elapsed between the arrival of the first and second seismic waves. Using the calculated distances as radii of circles drawn about the stations, they intersect near the coast of Lower California.

Instrumental Magnitude of Earthquakes. The scale of earthquake magnitudes, originated by Richter in 1935, is based on the logarithms to base 10 of the maximum amplitudes traced on a seismogram by a standard Wood-Anderson seismograph of specified free period, magnification, and damping, at a distance of 100 kilometers from the epicenter. Corrections are made for other instruments and for other distances. On this scale earthquakes range in magnitude from 0 (barely recorded) to about 8.5 (for the world's greatest shocks).

Microseisms. On the records of many sensitive seismographs of high magnification there commonly appear tiny quivers from earth waves of small and irregular motion. These waves are termed *microseisms*. They come and go, but commonly they continue for hours or even days at a time and become a nuisance. They have been ascribed to the pounding of the surf on seacoasts, to hurricanes, typhoons, and other storm centers, and to monsoons and trade winds. From the microseisms at specially

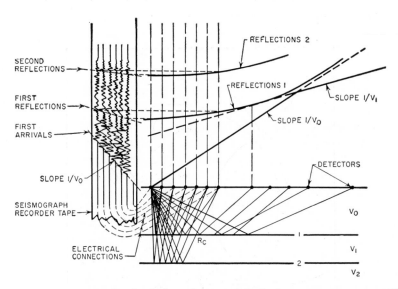

FIG. 475. Diagrammatic sketch of the reflection method of seismic prospecting. The lower right-hand portion of the diagram is a vertical cross section. Waves spreading out from the shot point at its left are reflected from surfaces 1 and 2 (where velocities change abruptly) back up to a series of carefully spaced detectors at the surface. The corresponding records of the first arrivals by direct horizontal routes and of the first and second reflections are shown at the left. The time-distance curves are plotted in the upper right. Waves to the right of R_c (corresponding to the angle of total reflection) undergo refraction instead of reflection. (*Reprinted by permission from Nettleton, Geophysical Prospecting for Oil, 1st ed., copyright 1940, McGraw-Hill Book Company, Inc.*)

equipped stations it has been found possible to locate a hurricane at sea, but how a hurricane can propagate them is not known. Storms on land seem to have little comparable effect.

Seismic Prospecting. Small artificial earthquakes are put to work probing the structure of the outer part of the earth's crust, especially in the search for petroleum. Small charges of explosives are detonated in shallow holes specially bored for the purpose, and the resulting waves are picked up by a series of geophones carefully spaced along the line of a traverse. Recording equipment is housed in an accompanying truck. Timing of the record must be very precise, and relatively high drum speeds are used.

The rates of travel of the waves underground differ in different kinds of rock; so the travel times afford clues to at least the general character of the underlying rocks. Principal dependence is placed, however, upon the reflections and refractions which the waves undergo, because these changes of direction of wave travel serve as clues to the position of the contacts between different bodies of rock, especially layered ones, underground (Fig. 475). From a series of shots it is possible to compute the depth of a reflecting or refracting layer at different places and thus to work out the structure of the rocks below the surface.

REVELATIONS FROM THE SEISMIC RECORDS

Discontinuities. The velocities at which earthquake waves travel at various depths are shown by Fig. 476. These travel times show sharp changes in velocity at certain depths within the earth. The buried surfaces where these changes occur are called *discontinuities*. The principal ones lie at depths of (1) 10 to 15 kilometers on land (6 to 9 miles); (2) 30 to 40 kilometers (18 to 24 miles), the Mohorovičić discontinuity; and (3) 2,900 kilometers (1,800 miles), the Dahm discontinuity; less abrupt ones occur at 400 kilometers (250 miles) and 700 kilometers (435 miles).

These discontinuities indicate that the earth is made up of a series of concentric shells, of different material or of different state, surrounding a central core, each having a different earthquake conductivity. As the velocities depend upon the elastic properties and the density of the material through which the waves pass, the different velocities are explained as the effect of a combination of different composition, different density, and possibly different state, especially in the core.

Structure of the Earth's Crust. The earth's crust is double. The P waves in its outer part travel about 5.6 kilometers per second. Partly because this rate corresponds to the rate found by experiment to be characteristic of granite and partly because granite is observed to be abundant at the earth's surface, this outer layer, generally 10 to 15 kilometers thick, therefore is called the *granitic layer*. The sedimentary film is included with it, although velocities in most sedimentary rocks are slightly less than those in granite.

The inner layer of the crust, extending to a depth of 30 to 40 kilometers, corresponds to basalt in its density and earthquake velocities, and so it is called the *basaltic substratum*. Velocities of *P* waves in it range from about 6 kilometers per second near the top to about 8 kilometers per second near its base.

Continents versus Ocean Basins. The speed of surface seismic waves indicates that the granitic layer of the crust is absent from the Pacific Ocean Basin and is thin or missing in the other ocean basins. Hence we infer that the continents owe their existence primarily to the masses of relatively light platforms of granite which compose them.

Mountain Roots. It has been found that *P* waves traveling in the basaltic substratum from epicenters in western California are not received on seismographs in Owens Valley immediately east of the Sierra Nevada. Hence we infer that the Sierra Nevada must have deep-seated "roots," or downward extensions of granitic rocks, which cut off these waves. Elsewhere also the granitic layer is found to be thicker beneath mountains and plateaus than it is under low-lying plains.

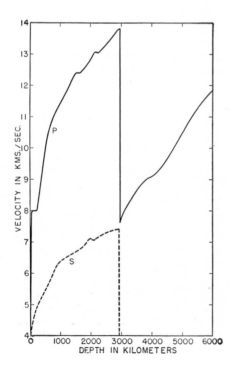

FIG. 476. Diagram showing the velocities of seismic waves in the interior of the earth. *P* = compressional waves, *S* = transverse waves. (*After Gutenberg and Richter, 1935.*)

The Deep Interior of the Earth. That part of the earth which lies at depths between 30 to 40 kilometers and 2,900 kilometers is called the *mantle*. The velocities of P waves in it increase from about 8 kilometers per second at its top to almost 14 kilometers per second at the bottom.

Below a depth of 2,900 kilometers is the *core*. Its surface is a remarkable discontinuity where P waves are easily reflected and are sharply refracted and where their velocity drops abruptly from nearly 14 kilometers per second to about 8 kilometers per second. Because S waves, incapable of transmission through liquids, are not known to pass through the core, the core may be liquid, in spite of the high pressure prevailing there. There are suggestions of differences within the core itself at a depth of about 5,000 kilometers.

The extensive reflections and refractions of P waves caused by the core leave a ring-shaped *shadow zone* 3,000 miles wide between 105 and 142 degrees (7,000 to 10,000 miles) from the epicenter (Fig. 477).

Combining our knowledge of densities with this picture of the earth's layered internal structure, we may envision a model of the composition of the earth to meet these requirements. A model (Fig. 478) which fits

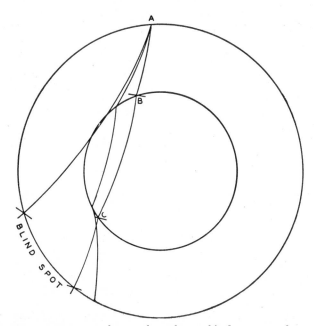

FIG. 477. Diagrammatic section showing how the earth's dense core changes the direction of travel of seismic waves. Vibrations set off below the surface at A are refracted at B and C. Seismic stations in the "blind-spot" area do not receive penetrating waves. (*After Lynch.*)

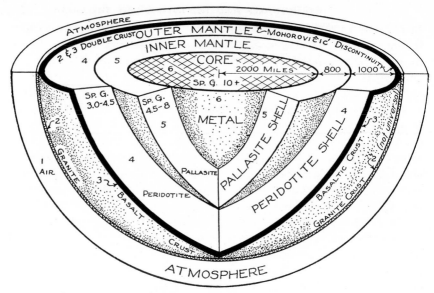

FIG. 478. Sketch showing the inferred composition of the interior of the earth. The ocean is too shallow to be shown at this scale.

the known facts consists of (1) the atmosphere and ocean; (2) the granitic layer of the continents; (3) the basaltic substratum; (4) an outer and an intermediate mantle of heavier, more basic rocks, ranging in composition from peridotite on the outside to pallasite (a mixture of the minerals of basic rocks and metallic iron) at greater depths; and (5) a core of metallic iron or iron and nickel, possibly partly in a liquid state.

Such a model is consistent with inferences based on the earth's equatorial bulge, its body tides, its moment of inertia about its axis of rotation, and the composition of meteorites.

OTHER FACTS AND INFERENCES REGARDING THE INTERIOR

Distribution of Densities. As the mass of the earth is 5.98×10^{27} grams and its volume is 1.083×10^{27} cubic centimeters, its average specific gravity (mass divided by volume) is 5.52 times that of water, not far from the figure obtained by Lord Cavendish in his famous experiment of 1799 in weighing the earth.

Because the familiar rocks of the earth's crust have densities generally of only 2.6 to 3.0, their moderate density must be more than matched by much heavier rocks at depth so as to give an average density of 5.52. Volume relations are important. The core, with a diameter of about half that of the earth as a whole, has a volume of only about one-eighth that of the earth. To help meet the density requirements, we infer (partly by analogy with meteorites) that the core is composed mostly of iron (or iron and nickel) and that the density of the iron, normally 7.8 at the earth's surface, may be increased by compression to about 10 or more. Even so, a great deal of the extra weight must be in the mantle, because of its large volume. So we infer further that the rocks of the mantle are composed of heavy peridotite and pallasite and that their densities, somewhat increased by the weight of the overlying load, range from about 3.0 on the outside to about 8.0 just above the core. As thus adjusted the model of the earth seems reasonable (Fig. 479). The density of the crust is thought to range from about 2.65 (granite) at the surface to about 3.3 (peridotite) at a depth of 30 kilometers.

Temperature. It is known that the interior of the earth is hot, for hot materials are expressed from it. Thermometer measurements of the temperatures in mines and oil wells show that the temperature of the earth's crust increases steadily downward. In regions of hot springs the increase is as high as 1°F. per 30 or 40 feet. In mines that have been opened for some time, where the rock is cooled by air circulation, the increase with depth is much less rapid. The average increase is about 1°F. per 60 or 65 feet, or approximately 1°C. per 100 feet.

If this increase continued to a depth of 100 kilometers, or 62 miles, the temperature would be about 3000°C., which is far above the melting

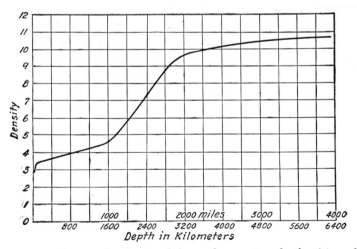

FIG. 479. Diagram showing the density of the earth at various depths. (*According to estimates of Adams and Williamson.*)

points of ordinary rocks at the earth's surface, but because of pressure the rocks are mainly in a solid state. Very little is known of the temperatures deep within the earth. It is improbable that they increase downward at a uniform rate. Most estimates for the temperature at the center of the earth range between 2000 and 4000°C. It is certain that most of the earth is essentially solid, for most of it transmits earthquake waves of a character that do not pass through liquids. If, by compression or radioactivity, parts of the earth become molten, it is probable that some of this hot material rises toward the surface and carries heat with it. It is not unlikely that the outer part of the earth has a relatively high temperature as a result of this process.

Pressure. The pressures within the earth are very high owing to the weight of the rocks. The densities of rocks are known, and so these pressures can be calculated. At the center of the earth the pressure is more than 3 million atmospheres, or more than 20,000 tons per square inch.

Magnetism. The earth is a gigantic magnet. If a magnetized needle is mounted so that it is balanced on a pin, it will be acted upon by the earth's magnetism, orient itself parallel to the earth's magnetic field, and point to the earth's magnetic pole. A needle so mounted is known as a magnetic compass, and it is used to point directions on land and on sea. At the magnetic poles the magnetic needle points directly downward.

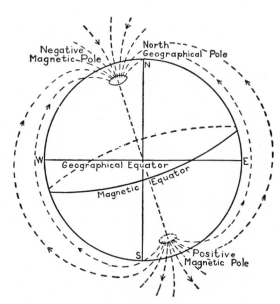

FIG. 480. Diagram showing the relative positions of the magnetic and planetary poles of the earth. (*Based on a figure by Black and Davis.*)

The magnetic poles are not points but small areas. The earth's magnetic poles do not coincide with the north and south axial poles (Fig. 480). The magnetic pole in the Northern Hemisphere is located among the islands of northern Canada and is approximately at 70°5′N. and 96°46′W., and the opposite magnetic pole at about 72°40′S. and 152°30′E.

In the magnetic compass the needle is mounted to swing horizontally, and the compass box is graduated in a 360-degree circle. Other needles, called dip needles, are mounted to swing in a vertical arc, and this arc also is graduated to read 360 degrees. Readings on both compass and dip needles are different at different places over the earth's surface, but the variations of the compass in general are well-known (Fig. 481), so that when it is used for finding directions, allowances are made for the declination or the variations which result in part from differences in the earth's geographic and magnetic poles.

The magnetic needle is a very useful instrument for the mariner and for the geologist, although at places it is unreliable owing to local magnetic attraction. The dip needle shows great variations. Thus a needle will read different intervals on the arc on different days and at different times during the same day. The dip needle is used for locating magnetic masses near the surface of the earth. Some of these magnetic bodies are valuable ores. Certain beds that contain small quantities of magnetic substance may be followed by dip-needle readings, and by using these

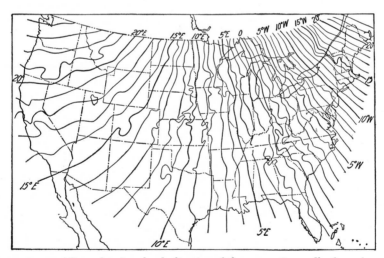

FIG. 481. Isogonal lines showing the declination of the magnetic needle throughout the United States. East of the zero line the north end of the compass needle points to the west of north; west of that line it points east of north. (*After U.S. Coast and Geodetic Survey.*)

the positions of the various rocks may be discovered and the geologic structure worked out in an area, even where the beds at most places are concealed by mantle-rock. Reconnaissance magnetometer surveys now can be made rapidly from airplanes.

The iron-nickel in the core of the earth and in the pallasite zone presumably is the main seat of the earth's magnetism, but the polarization is unexplained. Movements in the core may be responsible for the gradual changes in the earth's magnetic field.

Isostasy. If a plumb bob is hung from a string suspended above a great, flat plain, it points approximately toward the center of the earth. If the plumb bob is hung above a plain near a great mountain range, it is attracted also by the mountain and is deflected from the vertical, albeit minutely, by the mass of the mountain nearby. In Peru, India, and elsewhere, however, it has been found that the deflection is less than the value should be as computed from the known size, shape, and density of the mountains. Hence the discrepancies must be caused by deficiencies of mass underneath the mountains. So we infer that mountains stand high because they are the upper portions of masses of relatively light rocks and, conversely, that ocean basins are low because they are underlain by comparatively heavy rocks.

The pendulum also may be used for measuring the pull of gravity at various places on the earth's surface. The period of a pendulum of a given length depends upon the pull of gravity, which varies with the mass of material below the pendulum. The stronger the pull, the faster the pendulum vibrates. The vibrations are recorded by a clock. If the pull is abnormally strong, the pendulum vibrates faster and the clock gains time; and if the pull is abnormally weak, the pendulum vibrates more slowly and the clock loses time. By allowing the clock to run over long periods even small differences of the pull of gravity can be measured. Stations have been established at many places over the earth's surface and gravity observations made.

Thousands of measurements of gravity both on land and from a submerged submarine at sea tend to confirm the suspected distribution of mass in the earth's crust. These observations show a deficiency of mass, not only in or below mountains, but in and under continents as well. Although there are gravity anomalies, that is, departures from the computed values, these anomalies tend to cancel out when areas of a square degree or more are considered.

In explanation of these relations, the theory of *isostasy* (equal standing or equal weight) holds that different masses of the earth's crust stand in equilibrium with each other at some depth within the earth, where the weights of all columns of rocks of equal area are the same, regardless of mountains or plains, shallow or deep seas at the surface. If the equilibrium is disturbed, as by the long-continued erosion of a continent, the loss of mass should be met by the plastic flow of heavier material into the area underneath it. Such a process is *isostatic compensation*.

The theory of isostatic compensation is illustrated by Fig. 482. The three columns represent three prisms of the earth. In one the surface of the ground is above sea, in another it is at sea level, and in the third it is below sea. The three prisms are of equal mass and weight; the longest is made of the lightest material, and the shortest is of the heaviest material. The line on which the blocks rest is called the *level of compensation*. It is a theoretical plane, or zone, and the rock columns above it are supposed to be of equal weight. Below the bases of the three columns the earth is solid, but because of the great pressures it is believed to yield easily as a plastic or highly viscous liquid does.

An illustration of an isostatic condition is shown by Fig. 483. Blocks of various materials of different densities are immersed in quicksilver, which has a density 13.6 times that of water (specific gravity, 13.6+). The blocks weigh the same and have the same cross section but are of different lengths. The densities of the materials are shown on the blocks. The blocks of the lighter materials extend higher above the surface of the mercury than those of heavier materials. In Fig. 484 all the blocks are of copper (specific gravity, 8.9) but are of different lengths. The

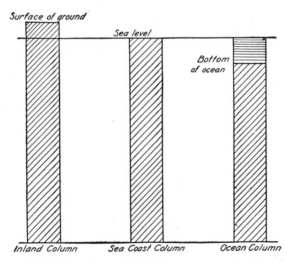

FIG. 482. Diagrams showing three columns of rock, one extending above sea level, another to sea level, and a third to the bottom of the sea. According to the interpretation of isostatic compensation, the weight of the first column equals that of the second and also that of the third column plus the weight of the column of water above the third column. (*After Hayford and Bowie.*)

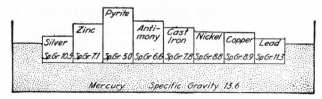

FIG. 483. Ideal illustration of the isostatic assumption that differences in altitude of large parts of the earth's crust are compensated by differences in density. The blocks are equal in cross section and in weight and thus sink to equal depth. (*After Bowie.*)

longer ones sink deeper and also extend farther upward than the short ones. If material is taken from the top of a high block and is added to a low one, the base of the high block will rise and the base of the low one will sink. Adjustment is attended by the movement of the mercury from the bottom of the depressed block to the bottom of the elevated block.

According to the hypothesis of Pratt the bottoms of the columns are even, and the level of compensation is uniform, as in Fig. 483; if so, the depth of compensation would be 60 to 100 kilometers (37 to 62 miles). By the hypothesis of Airy the light masses float freely in the heavier substratum; so each column displaces a quantity equal to its own mass, as in Fig. 484. Thus high columns (continents and mountains) would have deep extensions downward and low columns (ocean basins) short ones, and the level of compensation would be uneven. The Airy concept fits the geologic record fairly well and is consistent with the behavior of surface seismic waves.

How well isostatic compensation works is a moot point. It is certain that the earth is rigid and can accumulate strains over long eons of time. It tends, however, to assume a shape in accord with the theory, but perhaps imperfectly so. That it accumulates stresses through long periods without important adjustments is shown by peneplanes developed by erosion. Peneplanes are common features that have formed again and

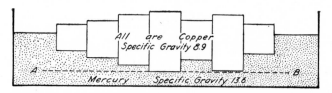

FIG. 484. Diagram showing seven copper blocks of equal cross sections but of different heights; all are immersed in mercury. The longest blocks rise highest and also extend to the greatest depths. According to the theory of isostasy, higher mountains are underlain by lighter material than low ones, and both are in balance. (*After C. R. Longwell.*)

again in the geologic past. If the earth's surface responded quickly and perfectly to changes of load, a peneplane could not readily form. As soon as a mass of rock was eroded from a high area, that area would rise again and it would be subjected to renewed erosion. If peneplanation occurs even in spite of such an isostatic adjustment, the quantity of rock to be removed to produce a peneplane is increased about tenfold.

A greater difficulty is posed by the rejuvenation of peneplanes. Old erosion surfaces have lain low for a long time and then have been uplifted hundreds or even thousands of feet. How does compensation work then?

Notwithstanding these difficulties, it seems to be true that the earth does respond to great load stresses by subsurface adjustment, though its strength and rigidity are perhaps great enough to resist at least minor changes in equilibrium.

SUMMARY REGARDING THE EARTH'S INTERIOR

We *know* that the interior of the earth is (1) hot, (2) heavy, (3) solid (except perhaps the core), (4) highly elastic, (5) magnetic, (6) under great pressure, (7) different at different depths, and zoned or layered as to elasticity, (8) responsive to tides, (9) radiating heat very slowly, (10) overlain by light rocks at the surface, (11) composed of columns of different density at different places, and (12) isostatically balanced.

We *infer* that (1) the temperature gradient declines rapidly, (2) the zoning is caused by changes in composition and density, (3) the outermost thin shell is granite, (4) most of the crust is basalt, (5) the bulky mantle is peridotite and pallasite, (6) the core is nickel-iron, (7) the central density is about 10, and (8) the deep-seated solid rocks yield isostatically mainly by plastic flow. We also think that earth heat is caused principally by compression and radioactivity and that magma forms when and where the pressure temporarily is reduced in an otherwise solid earth.

SUGGESTIONS FOR FURTHER READING

Birch, Francis: Elasticity and Constitution of the Earth's Interior, *Jour. of Geophys. Research*, vol. 57, pp. 227–286, 1952.

Bullen, K. E.: An Introduction to the Theory of Seismology, Cambridge University Press, 1947.

Byerly, Perry: Seismology, Prentice-Hall, Inc., 1942.

Gutenberg, Beno: Internal Constitution of the Earth, McGraw-Hill Book Company, Inc., 1939.

Gutenberg, Beno, and Charles F. Richter: Seismicity of the Earth, Princeton University Press, 1949.

Heck, N. H.: Earthquakes, Princeton University Press, 1936.

Leet, L. D.: Practical Seismology and Seismic Prospecting, Appleton-Century-Crofts, Inc., 1938.

Lynch, J.: Our Trembling Earth, Dodd, Mead & Company, Inc., 1940.

Macelwane, James B., S.J.: When the Earth Quakes, The Bruce Publishing Company, 1947.

CHAPTER 23

Mineral Resources

In our modern industrial civilization, mineral resources play a role second only to that of agriculture, and consequently an appreciation of their mode of occurrence is of vital interest. Economic mineral deposits are those portions of the lithosphere which are of value to man because they contain certain mineral substances, such as coal, oil, gas, metals, mineral fertilizers, and various salts. These materials are used by essentially all civilized peoples, and many of them were used by man before the beginning of the Christian era. Today more than half the value of mineral production of the United States is supplied by the mineral resources that supply energy, namely, the *mineral fuels*—coal, petroleum, and natural gas. Mineral resources other than fuels include the *metalliferous deposits* from which metals are extracted and the *nonmetallic* deposits such as phosphate rock, gypsum, sulfur, graphite, cement rock, and many others. At present the total annual value of mineral products in the United States is more than 10 billion dollars (Fig. 485). The mineral fuels account for about 75 per cent of the total (Fig. 486), the metals about 10 per cent, and the nonmetals about 15 per cent.

Various geological conditions determine the localization of mineral resources in the earth's crust. In fact virtually all the major geologic processes, such as weathering, transportation, sedimentation, igneous intrusion, and metamorphism, have been responsible for valuable concentrations of minerals in certain environments. Even though mineral deposits result from such normal geological processes, they are nevertheless very unevenly distributed over the earth. For example, diamonds occur only in very small, isolated spots; nearly all the world's production of nickel comes from a few mines at Sudbury, Ontario; and one mine in Colorado produces nearly 90 per cent of the world's molybdenum. Even coal and oil, which have a more widespread geographic distribution, underlie no more than a very small fraction of the continental areas of the earth.

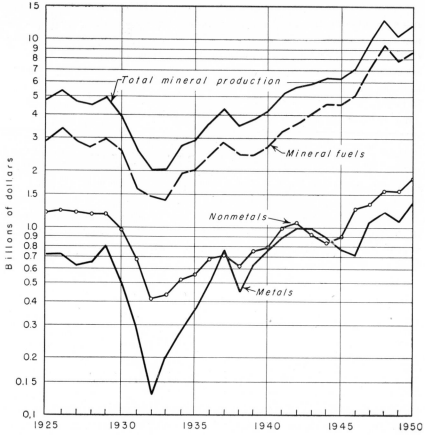

FIG. 485. Graphs showing value of mineral production in continental United States, 1925–1950. (*From U.S. Bureau of Mines Yearbook* 1950.)

The distribution of mineral deposits is governed by definite geologic laws, and the deposits were formed at certain times and at certain places because the environments were favorable for their formation. Their origin and location are definitely related to processes and events of earth history, and when these are understood, it becomes apparent that there are large parts of the world in which it is unreasonable to expect that valuable mineral deposits ever will be found.

Coal. Coal is a sedimentary rock composed mainly of unoxidized carbon derived from plant tissues. It occurs in layers, or beds, that range from a fraction of an inch to many feet in thickness, interstratified with shale, sandstone, and other sedimentary rocks. Even thin beds of coal represent long periods of growth and accumulation during which the remains of vegetation were preserved from the ordinary processes of decay by being buried beneath shallow water of peat bogs and subsequently beneath layers of mud and sand. Most individual beds of coal are not of great areal extent, and only a few are of sufficient size so that the same bed can be traced underground for many miles. A typical example of such a bed is the famous Pittsburgh coal bed, which is workable over an area of more than 6,000 square miles. Its limited distribution indicates that the coal was formed in groups of small, swampy basins. That these basins stood relatively near sea level is suggested by the fact that coal-bearing strata ordinarily include many alternations of marine and nonmarine beds. The coal is associated with the nonmarine strata, and in some coal fields a half dozen or more coal beds are known to lie one above another, separated by various thicknesses of other sedimentary rocks (Figs. 487, 488).

It may be assumed that all coal began as the swamp vegetation which produced peat and that the higher forms of coal represent successive stages in its transformation because of the weight of overlying rocks or because of diastrophic forces or other processes that involve compres-

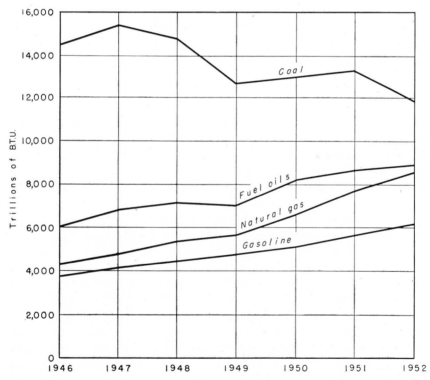

FIG. 486. Diagram showing the marked increase in the use of natural gas and the decrease in the consumption of coal during the postwar years. (*Courtesy of American Petroleum Institute.*)

FIG. 487. Strata of coal (*black*) interbedded with other sedimentary rocks along the valley of the Healy River, Alaska. (*Photograph by Evans.*)

sion. Thus, there is a series: (1) vegetable tissues, (2) peat, (3) lignite, (4) subbituminous, (5) bituminous coal, (6) anthracite coal. In this series, in the order named, water and gas decrease, and so there results a proportionate increase of carbon and ash, although the total amount of carbon has been reduced, as by removal of marsh gas. Anthracite coal is very high in carbon (90 per cent or more on an ash-free basis), and most of it contains 8 to 10 per cent ash but very little water or gas. The heating value of a coal depends on its content of fixed carbon and volatile combustible matter. Moisture, ash, and sulfur are undesirable constituents.

Coal Reserves. The coal reserves of the world are difficult to estimate because, in computing reserves, various limits of thickness, depth, and quality are employed. The best available figures, including all ranks of coal, give the staggering total of more than 7,000 billion tons. These reserves are mainly in the United States, Manchuria, China, Germany, Great Britain, France, Poland, the U.S.S.R., Belgium, Canada, and Australia. The reserves in the United States are estimated to be 4,200 billion tons (Fig. 489). This total includes about 800 billion tons of low-grade lignite and subbituminous coal, nearly all of which is located in Wyoming, Montana, and the Dakotas. These low-grade coals are considered also as a reserve of a petroleum substitute, because by a process of hydrogenation the coal can be liquefied to yield crude hydrocarbon compounds which can be distilled to yield gasoline.

Petroleum. Geologists agree that petroleum is formed from animal and plant remains that accumulated on the floor of the sea along with the clays, silts, sands, and calcareous oozes that formed sedimentary rocks. The evidence for such organic origin seems conclusive. In the first place, it is a mixture of organic chemical compounds with characteristic optical properties, and furthermore all extensive occurrences of crude oil are associated with marine sedimentary rocks. It is rarely found in igneous or in metamorphic rocks or in freshwater sediments and then only where associated with marine sedimentary strata. Where found in such rocks, the oil has migrated from marine source beds.

Extensive studies on recent sediments have shown a definite relationship between the organic content of sediments and their texture. More organic matter is preserved in fine sediments because they are generally deposited in deep, quiet water, which contains less oxygen than shallow, agitated water. A study of several thousand sediments from many different environments has led to the conclusion that shales or calcareous shales should be the best source beds of petroleum. Such sediments contain an average of 2.5 per cent by weight of organic material. The conversion of this material into hydrocarbon compounds may be brought about, at least in part, by the action of sulfate-reducing bacteria that thrive under anaerobic conditions and thus remain active even after the sediments are buried under younger deposits.

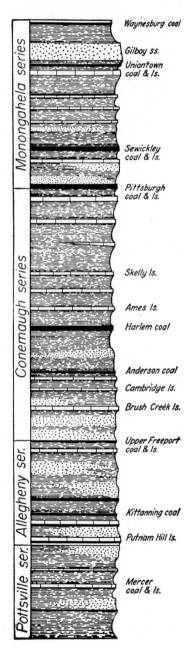

FIG. 488. Diagram showing the repeated alternations of coal, sandstone, shale, and thin limestone in eastern Ohio. Total thickness of strata nearly 900 feet. (*After Dunbar.*)

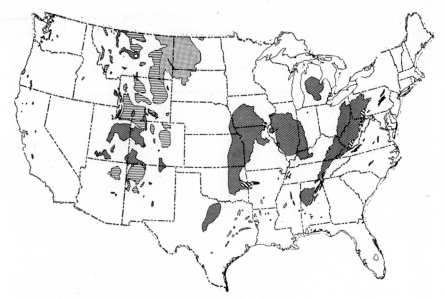

FIG. 489. Map showing major coal-producing areas of the United States. Diagonally and horizontally ruled areas produce bituminous coal, stippled area lignite, and small black areas anthracite coal.

Natural gas and salt water are nearly always associated with petroleum. It is the pressure of the gas that makes oil rise in wells and issue from gushers, or flowing oil wells. The salt water is believed to be sea water that filled the openings in the rocks when the sediments were laid down. Most oil-field waters, however, do not resemble sea water very closely in composition, and if it is ancient sea water, as believed, it has changed by reacting with rocks and with petroleum during the long ages when it was stored with oil in the rocks.

Oil Pools. Even though petroleum generally originates in clays and shales, it cannot ordinarily accumulate in commercial quantities in such sediments because suitable openings are not available. As a rule, it accumulates in sandstone or in porous limestone and dolomite. The oil and gas seldom are distributed uniformly throughout the entire extent of the rock in which they accumulate but occur in limited areas, called *pools* (Fig. 490). The pools are units of a porous rock formation in which the pore spaces of the rock are filled with oil instead of with ground water. Such pools occur in structural traps, or pockets, in which the oil and gas collect but from which they cannot escape. There are many kinds of structural trap (Fig. 491), such as the tops of anticlines and domes which are capped by clays, shales, or other impervious rocks that prevent the upward escape of the oil and gas. In such structures the gas occupies the upper or central part of the structure. The oil lies

FIG. 490. Signal Hill Oil Field, Long Beach, California. (*Spence Air Photos.*)

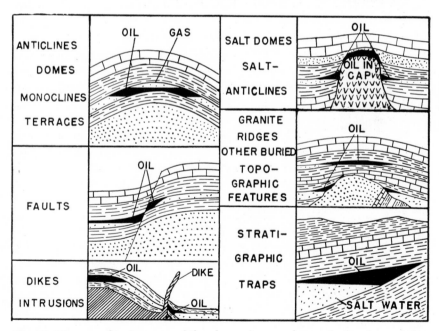

FIG. 491. Diagrams showing some of the places of accumulation of oil and gas. (*After Heiland.*)

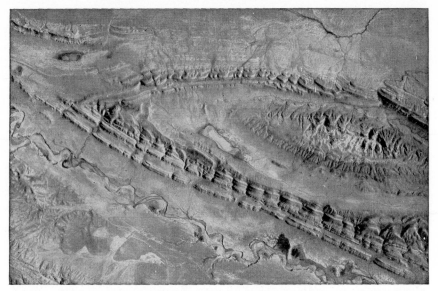

FIG. 492. An oil-producing anticline in western Wyoming. (*Courtesy of U.S. Department of Agriculture, Production and Marketing Administration.*)

below the gas on each flank of the fold; and salt water may be found lower down on each flank. Other pools are found in pockets, or lenses, of many shapes and origins into which the oil or gas has migrated from surrounding areas (Fig. 492). The migration into structural traps took place during the long geologic past and may still be taking place because the oil and gas are lighter than water and tend to rise through it until they are caught and held beneath a barrier of some impervious formation.

Briefly the conditions that are necessary for the formation of a large accumulation of oil are:

1. Strata containing organic matter to provide sources of oil.

2. A rock with openings to serve as a reservoir.

3. An impermeable cover to prevent the escape of the oil.

4. A suitable elevated structural feature to facilitate the separation of oil, water, and gas.

Natural Gas. Natural gas, or rock gas, is an aeriform mixture that is found at or beneath the surface of the earth and is used as an illuminant, for fuel, for generating power, and for making carbon black (soot). Most natural gas has a high heating value, and it is superior to artificial gas made from coal. Nearly every oil field yields some gas, although there are a few gas fields that produce no oil. As a rule the gas stored in the rocks is under strong pressure. When the natural reservoir is penetrated by a well, the gas issues violently and at places it has caused great destruction. Because it is under high pressure, the gas well can be connected directly with a pipe line, and its own pressure serves as the means of transporting it. A large part of the natural gas that is produced contains a vapor of gasoline, and by compressing or freezing the gas or by passing it through a heavy oil this gasoline may be recovered.

In addition to the combustible gases, others are encountered in the earth. Among these are hydrogen sulfide, sulfur dioxide, and carbon dioxide. The last is a heavy gas and therefore collects in ravines and low places in the topography where occasionally the quantity becomes sufficient to cause death to animals. Some of the petroleum wells of Colorado and Utah produce, with oil, large quantities of carbon dioxide at such low temperature that the oil comes out as a partly frozen slush that is very difficult to handle. In Utah, California, and elsewhere carbon dioxide is compressed to make dry ice. Certain wells in the United States produce helium. It is a light gas, is not inflammable, and is used for inflating balloons.

Petroleum Reserves. Notwithstanding the enormous production of petroleum in recent decades the discovery of additional reserves has more than kept pace with depletion, and so the known reserves are at their highest level in history. How long the discovery rate can exceed production is, of course, uncertain, but the industry is optimistic. The proved reserves are mostly in the United States, Canada, Venezuela, Peru, Colombia, Saudi Arabia, Iran, Iraq, the U.S.S.R., and the Dutch East Indies.

Potash Salts. The term "potash salts" is used commercially for all the compounds of potassium used in the fertilizers and munitions industries. The naturally occurring compounds are mainly chlorides, sulfates, and carbonates. Some are double or triple salts of potassium with calcium and magnesium. The large deposits of potash of inorganic origin are products of the evaporation of saline waters such as sea water or the waters of some highly saline lakes or seas such as Searles Lake in California and the Dead Sea. The largest and most important known deposits of this class are those of the Stassfurt district in Germany, where they are associated with beds of gypsum and anhydrite. These deposits cover an area of approximately 100 square miles, and it has been estimated that they occupy a volume of 10,790 million cubic meters, containing 20,000 million metric tons of potash salts, a quantity sufficient to supply the world's needs for 2,000 years at the present rate of consumption.

The potash industry in the United States began with the production of potassium carbonate from wood ashes, but after the discovery of the Stassfurt deposits in Germany the natural mineral potash soon displaced that from organic sources. In 1915 Germany placed an embargo on the export of its potash, and the United States was obliged to find other sources. This resulted in systematic surveys and exploration projects which eventually resulted in discoveries of such magnitude as to make the United States permanently independent of foreign imports.

The largest deposits in the United States are in the salt basins of New Mexico, West Texas, and adjoining states, where it is associated with beds of salt and gypsum. The potash beds occur several thousand feet below the surface, where they are mined by modern mechanized methods.

Phosphate Rock. The phosphate rock used as a fertilizer is an earthy substance varying from a hard rock to a granular, loosely consolidated mass, consisting of more or less impure noncrystalline calcium fluorophosphate. It occurs as sedimentary beds, as concretionary nodules or irregular masses, and as a poorly cemented clastic sediment. Because it occurs in such a wide variety of forms and under such differing conditions, it is not thought that all deposits have a common mode of origin, but it is generally believed that the larger deposits are directly or indirectly traceable to animal remains. Some of the small deposits may have resulted from a segregation by meteoric waters of phosphatic matter from igneous rocks. The Russian deposits on the Kola Peninsula are in an intrusive mass in which apatite and nepheline are the most abundant constituents.

Phosphate rock is widely distributed on all the continents of the earth, and its value in the manufacture of chemical fertilizers is so great that it forms a very important item in world commerce.

Sulfur. Sulfur has been obtained for many years from deposits associated with recent volcanic activity. Small amounts are still being mined from these sources in Japan, Spain, Italy, and Chile. The most important commercial deposits, however, occur in sedimentary beds associated with gypsum, anhydrite, and other sulfates and carbonates. It is thought that the sulfur is formed by the reduction of sulfates, but at present the reducing process is not clearly understood. Undoubtedly bacteria play a part in the reduction, but chemical reduction by other means is possible. The deposits formed at the craters of volcanoes or near the vents of hot springs are produced by the oxidation of hydrogen sulfide or by the interaction of sulfur dioxide fumes given off by the volcano.

The United States produces more than 90 per cent of the world's output of sulfur, and most of it is obtained from the "salt-dome" structures of the Gulf Coast region in Louisiana and Texas. There the sulfur is recovered by means of wells through which superheated water is pumped underground to the sulfur beds and molten sulfur is returned to the surface.

Dimension Stone. Dimension stone is a term applied to stone sold in blocks or slabs of specified shapes and sizes. It includes monumental stone, building stone, paving blocks, and rough-cut stone for various structural purposes. Nearly every kind of rock can be used in some way in stone construction. The requirements of a dimension stone depend upon the use for which it is intended. The essential qualities are strength, durability, workability, color, and beauty. For bridge spans great strength is essential; for monuments and other outdoor structures appearance and resistance to weathering are required; and for interior decoration pleasing color and adaptability to carving and polishing are the most important properties.

In the building trade the term granite is used to include nearly all crystalline igneous and metamorphic rocks. These rocks have low porosity and great strength and durability. In fact most of them are much stronger than necessary to meet all demands likely to be made upon them. Architectural granites are quarried extensively in Vermont and Maine in the East; in Upper Michigan, Wisconsin, and Minnesota in the Middle West; and in Colorado and California in the West.

Limestones and dolomites are the sedimentary rocks used most extensively for building purposes (Fig. 493). Limestone necessarily has the same hardness as that of its chief constituent calcite (hardness 3) and hence can be worked far more easily than igneous rocks, most of which are twice as hard. Limestone is quarried chiefly in the interior

FIG. 493. Limestone quarry in wall of Minnesota River Valley at Mankato. The quarried blocks are sawed into dimensions used as building stone.

states, between the Rocky and the Appalachian Mountains. Where limestone strata are included in the mountain folds, much of the rock is recrystallized to marble. The stone industries do not use the term "marble" in the strict sense of being a metamorphic rock. The term is applied to any calcareous rock capable of taking a polish. Vermont, Tennessee, and Georgia are the principal marble-producing states.

Some sandstones are used as building stones, but their adaptability to construction work depends very largely upon how well their grains are cemented. A thoroughly cemented sandstone or quartzite makes very durable building material.

Slates provide a valuable roofing material. Uniform slaty cleavage is the most desired characteristic of commercial slates. A good slate may be split in one direction only, into flat sheets with smooth surfaces, as thin as $\frac{1}{16}$ inch. The market value of a slate depends very largely upon its color and on the permanence of the color. Some slates fade or discolor rapidly, while others retain their original colors for many years. The more common colors are various shades of green, red, blue-gray, and gray to black.

Crushed Stone. Crushed stone is prepared in large tonnages from a variety of rocks and is used as an aggregate in concrete for many types of structures. The absence of natural aggregates, such as sand and gravel, in many large areas makes the use of crushed stone a necessity.

Sand and Gravel. The most extensive deposits of sand and gravel occur in the regions of recent continental glaciation. They were deposited in outwash plains, valley trains, eskers, kames, alluvial terraces and other types of glacial deposit which are distributed over a very large area. In nonglaciated areas well-sorted sand and gravel are more limited in distribution and tend to be confined to land forms produced by stream aggradation and by wave action.

Sands may be classified in many different ways, for example, by mineralogical composition, by origin, by grain size, by uses or by combinations of two or more of these methods. Sand has many uses, among them are high-silica sands used in making glass and fiberglass; molding sands for foundry molds; sand for concrete blocks and concrete pavements; filter sands for filter beds in water-supply systems, and many others.

Limestone. In addition to being one of the important building stones and a source of crushed stone for concrete, limestone is quarried and mined extensively for the manufacture of cement, as a flux for blast furnaces, and for the manufacture of quicklime, hydrated lime, soda ash, and other products that are used on a large scale in the chemical industry. Of its many uses the manufacture of cement is by far the most important as it accounts for approximately one-third of the total value of the nonmetallic mineral resources produced annually in the United States. The raw materials most commonly used in making cement are mixtures of limestone and clay which are heated to form a clinker. A small amount of gypsum is added to the clinker before it is finely ground and ready to use to make concrete.

Salt and Gypsum. Under arid conditions salt and gypsum are precipitated in bodies of water that have been cut off from the sea or in embayments that extend landward from the sea where the water flows into the embayment and is evaporated. Great beds of salt and gypsum are interbedded with sedimentary rocks in Texas, Kansas, Michigan, Ohio, New York, southeastern Ontario, and many other places. Salt is obtained also from natural brines such as brine springs, salt lakes, and sea water. For example, nearly all the salt produced in California is made by the solar evaporation of sea water. Similar salt industries flourish at Great Salt Lake in Utah, Owens and Searles Lakes in California, and the Dead Sea of Palestine. In the United States, however, nearly 25 per cent of the production is now mined rock salt.

Gypsum is more widely distributed than rock salt because it is less soluble and therefore its saturation point is reached before that of common salt. This resulted in the precipitation of gypsum in many basins of evaporation that failed to reach the concentration necessary for salt to be precipitated. In the United States gypsum is produced commercially in 17 states. At present the state of Michigan is the leading producer of raw gypsum, but both New York and Texas have many active gypsum mines.

The largest tonnage of raw gypsum rock is used as a retarder in the manufacture of portland cement. The second largest use is as agricultural gypsum, sometimes called land plaster. Its chemical action in the soil is very complex but valuable to the growth of many plants. Much gypsum is used also in making a prefabricated wallboard, and it is also ground and used as a carrier of insecticides and as a filler in the manufacture of paper.

Clay. Clay deposits are of two general types, residual and transported; but in all cases the clay is of secondary origin, that is, it was formed by the alteration of some other rock. Clays have been classified upon many different bases and in many different ways, but the behavior of a clay, and therefore its value and suitability for any specific use, depends upon its chemical and physical properties. The most important physical properties of clays intended for ceramic use are such things as plasticity, cohesion, tensile strength, texture, drying shrinkage, etc. Chemically the clay minerals are complex hydrous silicates of aluminum. Some of them contain small amounts of potassium, sodium, magnesium, and iron. The

FIG. 494. Clay pit and plant near Joliet, Illinois. (*Courtesy of Illinois Clay Products Co.*)

chemical composition of a clay gives little indication of its physical properties or of its value in industry, but it may reveal the presence of impurities that would be harmful for certain uses.

The chief use of clay is in the making of brick, and clays suitable for this purpose are very widespread (Fig. 494). A pure fine-grained white clay is required for the manufacture of the better grades of pottery, chinaware, and porcelain. A type of clay that withstands high temperatures is called fire clay. It owes its refractory properties to the fact that it contains only very small quantities of elements which act as fluxes. Its principal uses are in making firebrick and other heat-resisting materials such as the furnace linings required in the iron and steel industry and in making coke.

Certain clays possess the ability to decolorize, or bleach, oils, fats, and greases. Such absorbent clays, or fuller's earths as they are commonly called, are characterized by exceedingly fine shreds and thin plates of a clay mineral, called montmorillonite, that contains small amounts of sodium and potassium. It is used extensively for decolorizing and stabilizing petroleum lubricants and in the fat and vegetable-oil industry.

Another clay known as "bentonite" is not only absorbent but possesses the ability to swell enormously when wetted with water. Some bentonites absorb up to five times their weight or fifteen times their volume of water. Such clays are regarded as alteration products of volcanic ash. They are used most extensively in preparing oil-well drilling muds, in oil refining, and as a bonding material in molding sands.

Graphite. Graphite is very widely distributed geographically, and commercial deposits have been formed by various geologic processes. The crystallized flake graphite of Alabama and Pennsylvania resulted from the alteration of carbonaceous matter in sediments, whereas the deposits of Quebec were formed by igneous emanations. Some of the deposits in Mexico and in Austria represent coal beds that have been altered by the intrusion of igneous rocks. The island of Madagascar is the leading producer of high-grade flake graphite. There it occurs as lenses, veins, pockets, and large masses in crystalline metamorphic rocks.

One of the chief uses of graphite is in the making of crucibles employed in the manufacture of crucible steel and in melting brass and other nonferrous alloys. Such crucibles are composed of approximately 50 per cent graphite, which is bonded with clay and sand. Finely pulverized graphite is used in foundries to give the surface of molds a smooth finish, and in various types of lubricant. It has a great variety of other uses. Recently a substantial tonnage has been employed in the atomic pile as a moderator or as a retarding agent for neutrons.

Asbestos. The term "asbestos" is not the name of a specific mineral but a commercial term applied to any mineral that can be readily separated into more or less flexible fibers. One such mineral is a fibrous form of serpentine called chrysotile (Fig. 35). It occurs in aggregates of fine, crystalline, silky fibers, which are flexible and have good tensile strength. Such fibers usually range in length from less than $\frac{1}{8}$ inch to 2 inches, but fibers as much as 24 inches in length have been found.

The types of material to which the term asbestos was originally given are amphiboles, such as tremolite and actinolite, which may occur as long silky fibers, but they usually have little tensile strength. A soda-iron amphibole called crocidolite is highly fibrous like chrysotile, and it has a higher tensile strength but a much lower resistance to heat.

Deposits of asbestoslike minerals are widely distributed geographically, but there are only a few localities in which high-grade spinning fibers have been found in sufficiently large deposits to have become important commercial sources. Quebec produces more asbestos than any other area in the world. There it occurs as narrow veins in an area of serpentine rocks. The fibers extend across the veins from wall to wall, and most of the veins are less than 2 inches wide.

The main uses for asbestos are in asbestos yarns and papers, asbestos shingles and siding, and in heat-insulating materials. Automobile brake band linings and various types of gasket are very important and essential uses of asbestos.

Bauxite. Aluminum is extracted from bauxite, an earthy mineral which occurs in a variety of forms and colors. It often shows a pisolitic or oölitic structure with rounded concretionary grains embedded in an amorphous or claylike mass. Some deposits are decomposition products of granites, syenites, and gneisses, but others are thought to be derived by solution of alumina from sediments, followed by its deposition as nodules and irregular pockets in limestone and dolomites.

More than 90 per cent of the production of bauxite in the United States comes from the central part of Arkansas, where the deposits were derived by the alteration of syenites and the replacement of silica by alumina. In tropical countries bauxitic laterites are very widespread, but high-grade bauxite deposits of large size are not common. British Guiana and Dutch Guiana have the largest known deposits in South America, and both France and Italy are large producers in Europe.

Other Useful Nonmetals

Mineral	Uses	Geologic sources	Geographic sources
Abrasives	Grinding wheels, drills, loose powders	Forms of SiO_2, garnet, corundum, diamonds	New England, Ohio, Arkansas, Scotland, Belgium
Asphalt	Paving, roofing, waterproofing, etc.	In petroleum, in lake emulsified with water	Texas, California, Trinidad
Barite	Oil-well drilling mud, paints, rubber, glass	Replacements in limestones, residual nodules, veins	Arkansas, Missouri, Georgia, Nova Scotia
Bentonite	Oil refining, rotary drilling mud, foundries	Claylike minerals of volcanic origin	Wyoming, South Dakota, Mississippi, Montana
Boron minerals	Glass, porcelain enamel, fluxes, alloys	Brines, evaporites, hot springs, fumaroles	Searles Lake and Kramer, California
Bromine	In making tetraethyl lead	Sea water and the Dead Sea	Offshore from Texas
Calcium chloride	Stabilizing dirt and gravel roads, refrigerating plants	Natural bitterns	California, Michigan, West Virginia
Feldspar	Glass, ceramics	Pegmatite dikes	South Dakota, Wyoming, Colorado, North Carolina
Fluorspar	Open-hearth steel, flux	Replacements in limestones	Illinois, Kentucky, Colorado
Magnesite	Refractories, Sorel cement, Metallic magnesium	Alteration of serpentine, replacement of limestone, sea water	Washington, California, Nevada
Pumice	Lightweight concrete blocks	Volcanic ash	Kansas, California, Saskatchewan
Talc	Paint, rubber, ceramics, roofing, cosmetics	Alteration of magnesium silicates	New York, California, Vermont, Georgia

METALLIC ORES

An ore deposit is a concentration of one or more metallic minerals sufficiently rich in some metal to make its mining profitable. Some metals such as gold and platinum are found in the metallic state, but more commonly the metallic elements occur in chemical combination with other elements in the form of such compounds as sulfides, oxides, and carbonates.

Ore deposits are formed by the same processes that form other rocks, that is, by gradation and vulcanism. Like other rocks they are deformed by diastrophism, and where exposed at the surface of the earth they are weathered. Certain mineral deposits are igneous rocks in the strict sense. Other deposits are sedimentary beds that contain valuable materials. These include iron-ore beds, gold-bearing gravels, etc. In ore deposits the same materials are found that are present in other rocks, but they are sufficiently concentrated to be of economic value.

There is, however, an important group of mineral deposits that are neither igneous rocks nor sedimentary rocks. These are mineral veins which have been formed by water solutions moving through openings, chiefly through fissures, and depositing valuable minerals in and along them. These mineral-depositing waters are in part ordinary ground waters that contain the metals or other valuable materials in solution. The great majority of mineral veins, however, are found in and near intrusive igneous rocks, and their relations to igneous rocks are such as to warrant the conclusion that the veins are connected in origin with the intrusives. It is the belief of many students of ore deposits that solutions that deposited most of the veins have been derived from the cooling igneous intrusives.

An *ore mineral* is one that contains a valuable metal. In most deposits the ore minerals are associated with large amounts of material consisting of gangue and country rock. The *gangue* is the valueless material deposited along with the ore and usually is earthy or nonmetallic. The

Kinds of Ore Deposits

Veins and similar deposits	Formed by mineral-bearing waters moving along fissures and other openings
Pegmatites	Formed by "aqueo-igneous" solutions derived from igneous intrusives
Contact-metamorphic deposits	Formed by solutions from igneous intrusives replacing invaded rocks
Magmatic segregations	Formed by consolidation of magmas
Sedimentary beds	Formed by processes of aggradation

Common Ore Minerals

Metal	Mineral	Elements present	Percentage of metal	Formula
Iron	Hematite	Iron, oxygen	70	Fe_2O_3
	Magnetite	Iron, oxygen	72.3	Fe_3O_4
	Limonite	Iron, oxygen, water	59.8	$2Fe_2O_3.3H_2O$
	Siderite	Iron, carbon, oxygen	48.3	$FeCO_3$
	Pyrite	Iron, sulfur	46.6	FeS_2
	Pyrrhotite	Iron, sulfur	60.4	Fe_7S_8
Copper	Native copper	Copper	100.0	Cu
	Chalcopyrite	Copper, iron, sulfur	34.6	$CuFeS_2$
	Chalcocite	Copper, sulfur	79.8	Cu_2S
	Cuprite	Copper, oxygen	88.8	Cu_2O
	Malachite	Copper, carbon, oxygen, hydrogen	57.4	$Cu_2(OH)_2CO_3$
Zinc	Sphalerite	Zinc, sulfur	67	ZnS
	Smithsonite	Zinc, carbon, oxygen	52	$ZnCO_3$
	Calamine	Zinc, silica	54.2	$Zn_2H_2SiO_5$
Lead	Galena	Lead, sulfur	86.6	PbS
	Cerussite	Lead, carbon, oxygen	77.5	$PbCO_3$
	Anglesite	Lead, sulfur, oxygen	68.3	$PbSO_4$
Tin	Cassiterite	Tin, oxygen	78.6	SnO_2
Silver	Native silver	Silver	100	Ag
	Argentite	Silver, sulfur	87.1	Ag_2S
	Cerargyrite	Silver, chlorine	75.3	$AgCl$
Gold	Native gold	Gold	50 to 100	Au
Uranium	Uraninite	Uranium, oxygen	.....	$UO_2.UO_3$
	Carnotite	Uranium, vanadium, potassium, oxygen, hydrogen	Variable	$2U_2O_3.K_2O.V_2O_5.3H_2O$

Common Gangue Minerals

Mineral	Elements present	Composition
Quartz	Silicon, oxygen	SiO_2
Calcite	Calcium, carbon, oxygen	$CaCO_3$
Dolomite	Magnesium, calcium, carbon, oxygen	$MgCO_3.CaCO_3$
Barite	Barium, sulfur, oxygen	$BaSO_4$
Fluorite	Calcium, fluorine	CaF_2
Feldspar	Potassium, aluminum, silicon, oxygen	$K_2O.Al_2O_3.6SiO_2$
	Sodium, aluminum, silicon, oxygen	$Na_2O.Al_2O_3.6SiO_2$
Garnet	Calcium, iron, silicon, oxygen	$Ca_3Fe_2(SiO_4)_3$
	Magnesium, iron, silicon, oxygen, etc.	Many of complicated formulae
Tourmaline	Iron, silicon, aluminum, boron, oxygen, etc.	Variable

country rock is the rock that encloses the ore deposit. In many deposits the ore grades into the country rock, and much of the latter is removed by mining the ore. Certain ore and gangue minerals are listed in the accompanying tables. In some ores the valuable metal predominates, but in most deposits the ore minerals are present in subordinate amounts. An iron ore generally contains between 50 and 70 per cent iron, a zinc ore generally between 3 and 25 per cent zinc, and a lead ore between 3 and 15 per cent lead. Copper ores are generally low in copper, and the bulk of the metal is derived from ore that carries between 0.75 and 5 per cent copper. Silver ores carry between 8 and 30 ounces or more of silver per ton, and gold ores generally contain between $3 and $10 per ton gold. Many ores contain two or more metals. Thus the copper ores of Butte, Montana, carry important amounts of silver and gold, and there are few copper ores that do not contain small amounts of the precious metals. Lead and zinc are very commonly found in the same deposit, and lead and silver are common associates. In general, in the present practice of treating ores by milling and smelting them, two or more metals are recovered from the ore, and ores that contain less than the amounts of the metals stated above often are utilized.

Mineral Veins. Mineral veins are the most numerous mineral deposits and are among the most valuable ones. They are formed by waters moving through fissures and other openings, which deposit ore in the openings and soak into the wall rock, altering it and at places depositing ore by replacement in the wall rock near the openings. Veins exist in an almost infinite variety. They differ as to structure, texture, composition, and arrangement.

Structures of Veins. The structures of veins depend largely upon the character of the openings that were prepared to receive the solutions that deposited the veins. Some veins fill single openings, as is illustrated by Fig. 495. Others fill closely spaced parallel openings. Still others fill irregularly fractured bodies of rocks and are called fractured zones. Along many veins the country rocks near the veins are partly replaced by ore. In certain irregularly fractured rocks small veins (veinlets) are

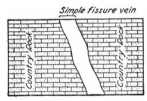

FIG. 495. A cross section showing a simple fissure vein.

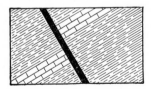

FIG. 496. Cross section of a vein in a fault fissure.

closely spaced, and the rock is replaced between the fractures, so that the entire rock may be regarded as ore. Some veins occupy fault fissures (Fig. 496); others follow certain beds that are brittle and easily fractured and therefore after movement offered favorable channels for waters. Certain beds are followed because they were easily replaced by the mineral-bearing waters that deposited the veins. Many deposits along fissures replace limestone beds below shales but do not replace the shales, because the shales are relatively impermeable (Fig. 497). Because the contacts of two rocks commonly are planes of weakness, they are often fractured and mineralized (Fig. 498).

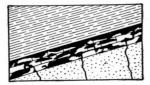

FIG. 497. Cross section of a vein replacing a bed.

FIG. 498. Diagram showing a vein at the contact between a rhyolite and a quartz-porphyry dike.

Textures of Veins. Some veins are made up of one mineral or of two or more minerals so intergrown that the vein is essentially uniform throughout. Others consist of banded layers (Fig. 499). In certain veins these layers appear in the same order from the two walls to the center of the vein, that is, in symmetrical order. The waters moving through the fissure have deposited minerals layer upon layer on opposite sides of the channel, and the layers last deposited may come together and fill the channel. Where they do not come together, they leave an opening which is called a *vug*, or *druse*. Certain veins fill fissures without greatly altering the wall rock and without replacing it with ore. Such veins generally have sharp, regular contacts.

Many veins do not have sharp, clean-cut walls, but they grade into the

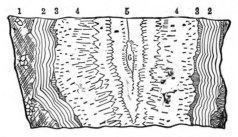

FIG 499. Section of a vein with symmetrical crustified banding. Creede, Colorado.

wall rock in such a way that it is difficult to determine where wall rock ends and vein begins. This is noted in many veins where the vein-forming waters soaked into the wall rock and replaced some of it by ore. The changes that are brought about in the wall rock by hot waters moving along fissures are due to hydrothermal metamorphism.

Composition of Veins. Veins are the chief sources of most of the metals. The veins and nearly related deposits of ore formed in and along openings include the most valuable sources of gold, silver, copper, lead, zinc, mercury, and many other metals. Certain veins produce one metal; others produce two or more. In some veins the metals occur in the native state. This is true of most gold-bearing veins and of some copper-bearing ones. Many of the metals occur combined with other elements. Thus lead is found mainly as the sulfide galena; zinc as the sulfide sphalerite; and copper as the sulfides chalcopyrite and chalcocite. Tin is found chiefly as the oxide cassiterite; and certain other metals often occur in compounds with arsenic. Iron is found in veins and beds. The iron-bearing minerals include the sulfides pyrite and pyrrhotite and the oxides hematite and magnetite. In the great majority of veins the metals are present as sulfides or in association with sulfides.

As veins are worked out, often it is found that a single vein changes in composition at successive depths. Certain lead veins change downward to zinc veins; certain zinc veins become copper veins with depth; and certain copper veins become tin veins. The order is essentially the same if the same metals are present, and the reverse order is rare. A tin vein does not pass downward into a vein of copper, lead, or zinc, nor does a copper vein change to a lead vein with depth. These different parts of veins in which one metal predominates are called *zones,* and the zonal arrangement is a common feature of many veins. In some veins similar changes are found along the strike. Thus one may follow a vein along the surface through zones in which tin ore gives way to copper ore and copper to zinc ore. These arrangements of zones of ore are due to precipitation of different metals by solutions under changing conditions of temperature and pressure.

Sources of Vein-forming Waters. Many veins are deposited by ordinary rain water, which soaks into the ground and dissolves metals from the rocks. The water circulating along cracks and fissures deposits the material it has gathered, and thus the ore is concentrated in and along the fissures. Veins of nickel ore in nickel-bearing basic rocks in New Caledonia have formed by this process, and iron and manganese ores have been concentrated in veins in rocks that contain iron and manganese. Certain valuable lead and zinc deposits generally are believed to have been concentrated by ground water and to have no connection with igneous processes.

The element uranium is widely distributed in exceedingly small amounts in both igneous and sedimentary rocks, but the bulk of commercial production has been derived from local concentrations of the minerals uraninite and carnotite. The massive form of uraninite called pitchblende occurs most commonly in veinlets in massive igneous rocks or as impregnations in schists and gneisses. The largest known deposits of this type are those at Joachimsthal in Czechoslovakia, Great Bear Lake in Canada, and in the Belgian Congo. Carnotite occurs as canary-yellow amorphous earthy masses and granules in sedimentary rocks. The origin of the uranium-bearing waters has not been established. The principal productive area in the United States is the Colorado Plateau where the mineral is found encrusting fossilized carbonaceous fragments and as fossil logs in sandstones. The deposits are small and widely scattered over an area roughly 200 miles in diameter. The average ore contains from less than 0.1 to 0.3 per cent of U_3O_8 and from 0.5 to 2.5 per cent V_2O_5.

The great ore veins are believed to have been formed, in the main, by ascending hot fluids that have escaped from cooling igneous masses. When deposits are associated with shale, they generally are found below the shale (Fig. 500). Shales are relatively impervious to water and form the great natural barriers to solutions. Limestones are replaced readily by ore; and if the ores are in limestone near shale, they are nearly everywhere below the shale, which suggests that the ore-bearing waters rose in the limestone and were halted by the shale where the ores were deposited. At places the rocks are arched, and the ores occur in anticlines in limestone below the shales. Ascending waters would converge in the upfolds and deposit ore below the impermeable shale barriers (Fig. 501).

The waters that deposited the ore veins are believed to have been hot, because the larger number of veins are associated with igneous rocks, and moreover the wall rocks near the veins show alterations that are characteristic of hot waters (hydrothermal metamorphism). Steamboat Springs, Nevada, is a good example of metallic sulfides now being formed by hot-water deposition.

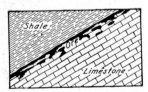

FIG. 500. Ore deposit formed at and below the contact of shale and limestone.

FIG. 501. Cross section showing ore near the axis of an anticline replacing limestone below shale.

While it is obviously not possible to observe the deposition of ores around deep-seated intrusives or to examine the whole of such intrusives and their associated ores, one may study many different intrusives and associated ores at many different stages of erosion. The study of many of these deep-seated intrusives, or batholiths, shows that they have upper parts called "roofs" that are very irregular and generally broad. Their contacts with invaded rocks generally slope away from the mass so that they become broader downward. Many metalliferous veins are found in and around granitic batholiths, and it is believed that the solutions that deposited them were expelled from the cooling magmas that solidified to form the batholiths (Fig. 39).

Pegmatites. Pegmatites (Fig. 502) are magmatic-differentiation products, but they represent, in general, the lighter rather than the heavier products of the magma. Generally they are composed of large crystals, and of these feldspar, quartz, and mica greatly predominate. They have been called "giant granites." Some contain crystals of tourmaline (a boron mineral) and of apatite, which contains fluorine and chlorine. It is believed that the boron, fluorine, and chlorine, probably as gases, aided the growth of the large crystals, for it is known that these substances and also steam tend to keep the magma liquid, and this allows the crystals greater freedom of formation and results in the development of larger crystals.

FIG. 502. Granite pegmatite at Elk Mountain Mine, New Mexico. (*Photograph by R. H. Jahns.*)

Because the parent magmas of pegmatites are believed to contain much water, they are called *aqueo-igneous* solutions. Pegmatites are found as dikes in the roofs as well as in the upper parts of batholiths. A few of them are associated with basic rocks. They are the chief sources of the micas, lithium minerals, and feldspars of commerce; they contain also gems, such as tourmaline, ruby, diamonds, and other substances of value. On the other hand, pegmatites are rarely important as sources of the metals. A few are banded, like quartz veins, and some of them grade into quartz veins, but they are very rarely found grading into veins that carry commercial amounts of the precious metals.

Contact-metamorphic Deposits. Contact-metamorphic deposits are replacements of invaded rocks formed by solutions that are expressed from the invading rocks. They are found in the garnet or other contact zones in both sedimentary and igneous rocks but mainly in sedimentary rocks, particularly in limestones and calcareous shales (Fig. 503). Many of them lie against the intruding igneous rock, and they are rarely as much as 1 mile away from it. Contact-metamorphic deposits carry ores of copper, iron, zinc, and, more rarely, gold, silver, and lead. The gangue minerals include garnet, amphiboles, pyroxenes, and quartz. The sulfides, such as pyrite, chalcopyrite, and pyrrhotite; the oxides, such as hematite and magnetite; and the heavy silicates, such as garnet and amphibole, are mutually intergrown and have formed at about the same time. Some contact-metamorphic deposits follow beds, others cut across beds, but as they do not follow well-defined fissures they differ from fissure veins.

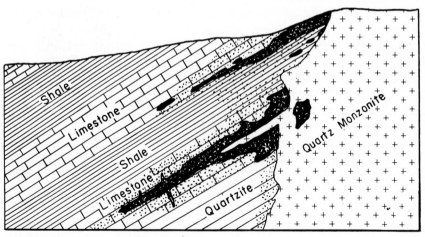

FIG. 503. Section of contact-metamorphic ore deposit. Ore, black; altered rock, stippled. The alteration was induced by the intrusion of the magma that formed the quartz monzonite.

The solutions that carried the ores, moved out from the intruding masses, and deposited material in the invaded rocks were at high temperatures and under strong pressures, so that they seemed to be able to penetrate minute joints and the cleavage planes of minerals. For this reason the contact-metamorphic deposits are generally very irregular in shape and are rarely tabular, like veins. As a rule, the minerals of contact-metamorphic deposits form coarse aggregates.

Magmatic Segregations. Magmatic segregations are deposits formed by magmatic differentiation. The heavier minerals generally are found below the lighter ones. Differentiation is most easily discovered and studied in laccoliths and sills, because they have "floors" on which the heavier differentiates rest. The heaviest material sinks, the lightest material rises, and the constituents of intermediate weight occupy an intermediate position. At places where igneous magmas have risen to form lopoliths, the latter have slumped down. Thus certain lopoliths are basin-like sheets, and after erosion they present at the surface a ring of the heaviest material, inside which is a ring of lighter material, and inside that a ring of still lighter material such as granite. The Sudbury, Ontario, eruptive mass is said to show such relations, where a heavy ore consisting of sulfides of iron and nickel is found below gabbro, and above the gabbro is granite.

In certain regions there are dikes of iron ore which fill fissures believed to extend downward to bodies of ore that have formed by the differentiation of a deeply buried and invisible rock magma. These dikes of ore, also, are believed to be magmatic differentiations. Deposits that have formed by magmatic differentiation include ores of nickel, iron, titanium, chromium, platinum, and subordinate deposits of copper and gold. Diamonds and other gems also are formed in magmatic segregations.

Sedimentary Deposits. When rocks weather and are eroded, their materials often are separated. Thus a granite which is composed of quartz, feldspar, and mica will break down and form quartz sand and clay, which go to make up sandstones and shales. The iron in dark mica may be carried by streams to the sea and be deposited along with iron from other sources to form sedimentary beds that contain iron. The quartz that is liberated as sand is valuable for making glass and for other purposes, the clay for making pottery, and the iron ore for making iron and steel. In the granite these materials were not sufficiently concentrated to be of commercial value. Thus running water, the lakes, seas, etc., which collectively constitute the hydrosphere, may be regarded as a giant concentrating mill. By processes of gradation, deposits of coal, petroliferous beds, gypsum, iron ores, manganese ores, gold, platinum, tin, salt, phosphate rock, and many other valuable materials are formed. Some of these are carried along mechanically by the water and are deposited along streams

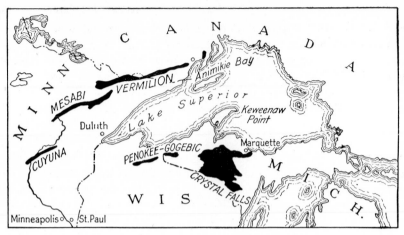

FIG. 504. Map showing distribution of iron ranges in Lake Superior region.

and in the lakes and seas. Others, such as phosphate rock and some iron ores, are deposited by chemical precipitation from the waters. At many places gold, platinum, and tin ore are washed by water from the tops of deposits and are concentrated by water as placers in ravines and creeks near their sources. At other places the materials that were eroded from the parent sources are carried far away.

Deformation of Mineral Deposits. Ore deposits, like other rocks, are deformed by earth movements. They are faulted or folded, or where deeply buried they may be deformed by dynamic metamorphism. Certain veins are broken into small blocks by systems of parallel faults; others are folded to form anticlines or synclines. All types of ore bodies may be deformed in various ways. When folded at great depths, ore deposits take on the characteristic structures of gneisses and slates. Thus certain iron ores of the Vermilion Range, Minnesota, have been folded at great depth, and in the ore a slaty cleavage has developed by rearrangement of the flat crystals of hematite. Certain sulfide ores composed of quartz, hornblende, and pyrite have been deformed so that they now have the structure of gneiss.

Weathering of Ores. Ores, like other rocks, are subject to weathering at the earth's surface. Where exposed to the action of air and water, the deposits break down and form new minerals. In certain deposits value-less materials are carried away by ground water, leaving the valuable material in a more highly concentrated state. In the Lake Superior iron-ore districts beds of the iron-ore formations with about 25 per cent iron, by removal of material other than iron by surface waters, have been converted into ores with 50 per cent iron or more (Figs. 504, 505). Near Little Rock, Arkansas, a highly aluminous igneous rock has been weathered and leached of silica so that it is now a high-grade aluminum ore.

Nearly all the veins with ores of copper, silver, lead, zinc, and other metals contain sulfides. Pyrite, iron sulfide, is nearly always present. Where the veins are exposed at the surface of the earth, they are attacked by air and water and they undergo a series of changes. Thus pyrite will be oxidized, forming sulfuric acid and iron sulfate.

$$FeS_2 + H_2O + 7O = H_2SO_4 + FeSO_4$$

The sulfuric acid that is formed will dissolve copper, zinc, and certain other metals, which are carried downward. The iron sulfate will be further oxidized and will break down and form iron hydroxide, which is insoluble and will remain at the outcrop. Thus nearly all deposits that

FIG. 505. An open-pit iron mine on the Mesabi Range, Minnesota.

carry iron sulfides will be marked by iron hydroxide, which stains the croppings of the vein, giving it a rusty appearance. This altered iron-stained material is called an "iron hat," or "gossan." As a rule, the out-crops of copper sulfide veins carry very little copper. Gold, unlike copper, is not soluble in sulfuric acid, and gold-bearing veins are generally as rich in gold at the outcrop as at depth or even richer. Copper is carried downward as copper sulfate, for in the presence of air and water copper is highly soluble in sulfuric acid.

Where gold veins are exposed at the surface, the gold commonly will accumulate in the outcrop, to be washed away by running water. Thus the particles of gold will be strung out along the surface below the vein cropping and will be washed into the beds of the streams, as is shown by Fig. 506. The stream gravels are washed into long wooden boxes, or sluices, and the gold, being heavier than rock, settles to the bottom of the box and is recovered. This method of recovering gold is "placer" mining,

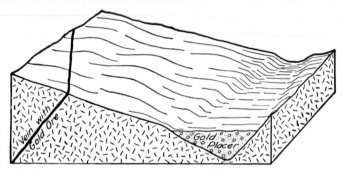

FIG. 506. A vein with gold ore cutting granite. Owing to degradation of the vein a gold-bearing placer deposit was formed along a nearby stream.

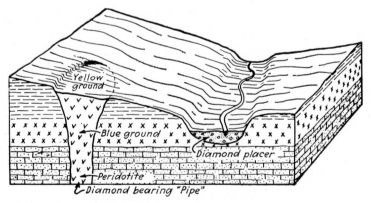

FIG. 507. A diamond-bearing pipe. Diamonds removed from its eroded upper portion are deposited in gravels along a stream near the pipe.

FIG. 508. The Kimberley Diamond Mine, South Africa. The mine is about 1,500 feet in diameter at the surface, and the main shaft is 3,520 feet deep. From 1888 to 1914 when operations were discontinued, about 16 million tons of diamond-bearing "blue ground" was taken from the mine and yielded 6,404 pounds of diamonds. (*Courtesy of N. W. Ayer and Son, Inc.*)

and gold-bearing gravels are *placer deposits*. All ore minerals that are heavy and not easily dissolved by ground water are likely to be accumulated in placer deposits. These include gold, platinum, tin oxide, diamonds, rubies, and other gems. Figure 507 illustrates the accumulation of a diamond placer by erosion of diamond-bearing material from a peridotite intrusive (Fig. 508).

Sulfide Enrichment. The water that dissolves copper and other soluble metals from the outcrops of copper sulfide deposits moves downward, carrying the copper with it; and when it reaches the water level, it enters a changed environment. The water level, as already stated, is the level below which the openings in rocks are filled with water. The water seals out the air, which is present in openings above the water level, and consequently below the water level air is absent. Copper is readily dissolved by acid in the presence of air, but the solution in the absence of air loses its copper, which is precipitated by pyrite or by pyrrhotite or by many other minerals.[1]

[1] Reactions forming copper sulfides are

$$FeS + CuSO_4 \rightarrow CuS + FeSO_4$$
$$ZnS + CuSO_4 \rightarrow CuS + ZnSO_4$$

As a rule, some copper carbonate or copper oxide will form just above the water level, so that the copper vein after oxidation and weathering will show a series of standard changes from the surface downward. This is illustrated by Fig. 509. Near the surface is found the gossan, or iron hat, which carries little or no copper. A pit sunk through this will encounter first the oxidized copper ore with carbonates and oxides of copper. Still deeper it will encounter the level of ground water; and near that secondary copper sulfide ore will appear. At still greater depths the sulfide ore is found in its original state, and it is reasonable to suppose that the entire deposit from the surface downward was once like the primary ore and that it has been changed by ground water to the various types of ore that are found above it. The process by which the rich secondary sulfide ore is formed is called sulfide enrichment. Deposits of ores of other metals also show changes that are brought about by surface alteration, but each metal behaves in its peculiar way, depending upon its chemical properties.

Summary. There are certain ore deposits which have no direct connection with igneous activities. These include the sedimentary beds and the products of weathering and concentration of sedimentary beds and other rocks. Such deposits may be found wherever conditions were suitable for the deposition of such rocks. They commonly are situated in structural basins far from mountain ranges, and some of them are far from areas of igneous activity. Another group of deposits includes the veins and closely related deposits that have been concentrated by ground water, which dissolves the metals from rocks in which they are scattered and concentrates them in and along the fractures through which ground

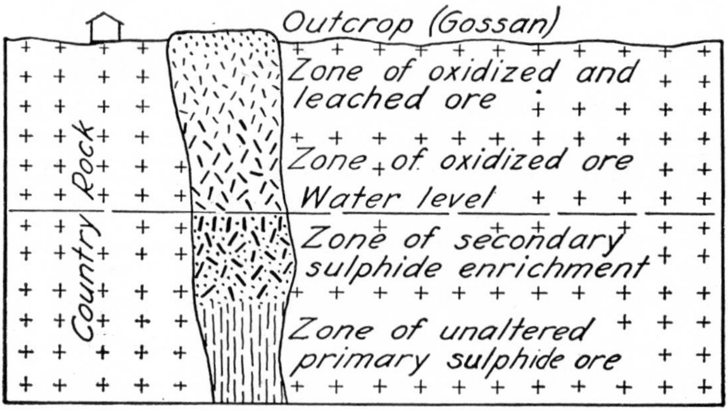

FIG. 509. Diagram illustrating zones forming in a sulfide lode because of weathering and sulfide enrichment.

water moves. These deposits often are found far from igneous rocks, and many seem to have no close relation to the distribution of igneous rocks.

The great majority of mineral deposits, however, are directly related to the igneous rocks and have formed by processes connected with igneous intrusions. These include the magmatic segregations, pegmatites, contact-metamorphic deposits, and the majority of mineral veins. Many veins are formed doubtless by solutions originating in igneous bodies. The intrusives contain water and other fluids which during cooling are expelled from the intrusives. Where they find suitable openings, they flow through them. On cooling or through reactions with the wall rocks the metals are deposited.

The mountain regions are, in general, the regions where intrusive rocks are most common and where strong fracturing and faulting of the rocks prevail. The intrusives provide sources of the metals, and the fractures afford openings for movements of fluids that deposit the metals. Consequently the mountain areas are generally the areas in which mineral deposits are most common, and these areas therefore supply the bulk of the metals. At certain places, however, the mountains have been worn down to near the elevation of the surrounding areas, and only their roots remain. At such places, also, mineral deposits often are concentrated because the original deposits extended downward to depths below the present erosion surfaces.

SUGGESTIONS FOR FURTHER READING

Bateman, A. M.: Economic Mineral Deposits, John Wiley & Sons, Inc., 1942.

Ladoo, R. B., and W. M. Myers: Nonmetallic Minerals, 2d. ed., McGraw-Hill Book Company, Inc., 1951.

Lalicker, C. G.: Principles of Petroleum Geology, Appleton-Century-Crofts, Inc., 1949.

Levorsen, A. I.: Geology of Petroleum, W. H. Freeman & Co., 1954.

Lindgren, W.: Mineral Deposits, 4th ed., McGraw-Hill Book Company, Inc., 1939.

Lovering, T. S.: Minerals in World Affairs, Prentice-Hall, Inc., 1943.

Maps, Topographic and Structural

TOPOGRAPHIC MAPS

Topographic maps show the configuration of the land surface, that is, the size and shape of the hills and valleys, as well as their location with respect to each other. The term *relief* refers to the difference in elevation of features within the map area. *Elevation* is the vertical distance above some datum plane which is used for the level of zero elevation. For practically all the maps of the U.S. Geological Survey mean sea level is the datum plane. The term *height* has a different meaning. It is the distance vertically between the base and the top of a feature. A hill 500

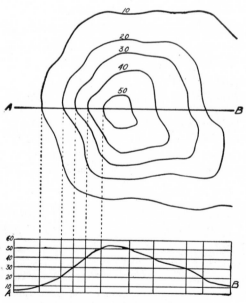

FIG. 510. Diagram showing a contoured hill. The contour interval is 10 feet. The lower diagram is a profile of the hill along the line *AB*.

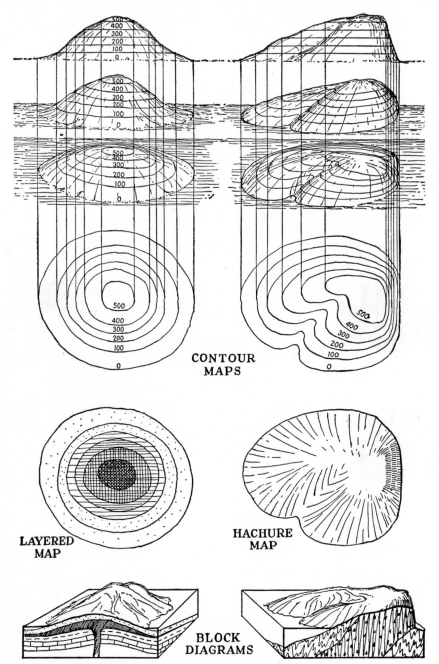

CONTOUR MAPS

LAYERED MAP

HACHURE MAP

BLOCK DIAGRAMS

FIG. 511. Methods of showing relief. (*Reprinted by permission from Lobeck, Geomorphology, 1st ed., copyright, 1939, McGraw-Hill Book Company, Inc.*)

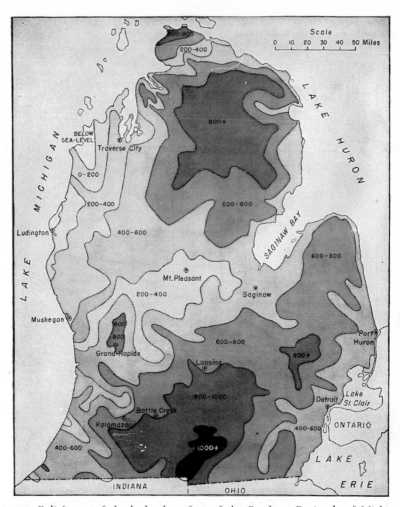

FIG. 512. Relief map of the bedrock surface of the Southern Peninsula of Michigan. Contour interval 200 feet. (*Courtesy of Michigan Geological Survey.*)

feet high might stand on a coastal plain which itself has an elevation of 300 feet. The top of the hill, then, would have an elevation of 800 feet, and the base of the hill would have an elevation of 300 feet. A similar hill, 500 feet high, might stand on the surface of a plateau which has an elevation of 5,000 feet above sea level. In the second case the elevation at the top of the hill would be 5,500 feet, and the elevation at the base of the hill would be 5,000 feet. The height of the hill is 500 feet in either case.

Four different methods are used to represent relief on a flat sheet of paper or on a map. These are by color, by shading, by hachures, and by contours (Figs. 510 to 513). The contour method is the commonest and most nearly accurate. A contour line on a map represents an imaginary horizontal line that passes through all points on the surface of the area mapped that have the same elevation above a given datum—usually sea level. The lines are drawn to indicate a certain regular difference in elevation, and this difference is called the contour interval. Figure 510 represents a contoured conical hill. The contour interval is 10 feet. Contours bend, or "loop," upstream in valleys. They are closely spaced on steep slopes and distantly spaced on gentle slopes. They encircle conical hills and are paired on opposite sides of parallel ridges. The contours near the crests of hills are relatively short, closed curves.

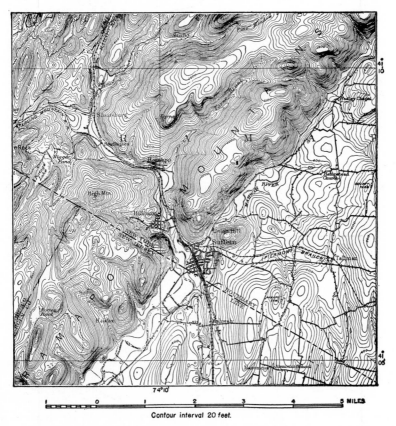

Contour interval 20 feet.

FIG. 513. Topographic map showing the contrast between low hills with gentle slopes (*lower right*), and high ridge with steep slopes (*upper right*) near New York–New Jersey boundary. (*Courtesy of U.S. Geological Survey.*)

STRUCTURAL CONTOUR MAPS

For making a structural contour map the surface chosen is that of the top or bottom of some bed which is easily recognized, is persistent over a large area, and is not too far below the surface of the land. The elevation of this bed, or datum, as it is called, above sea level is obtained in the field at as many points as possible, both at actual outcrops and from the records of drill holes. At some locations, rocks above the key bed, or datum, which is being contoured are exposed. If the thickness of the intervening strata

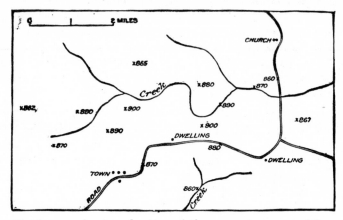

FIG. 514. Sketch map showing elevation of the same stratum at different points, marked by crosses. (*After Gardner.*)

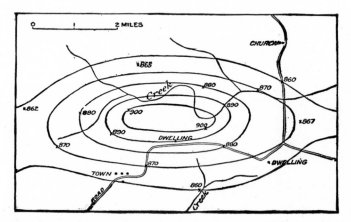

FIG. 515. Sketch map showing elevations of same stratum at different points marked by crosses as in Fig. 514. The structure contours connect points of equal elevation, thus outlining an elongated dome. (*After Gardner.*)

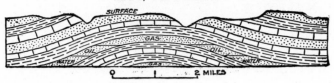

FIG. 516. Lengthwise section of elongated dome shown in Fig. 515. Vertical scale greatly exaggerated. (*After Gardner.*)

is known, the depth to the key bed may be calculated. Likewise, if the rocks exposed are those which lie below the bed that is contoured, then the position of the latter before it was removed by erosion may be determined. These data are plotted at their proper locations on a map of the region, and lines are drawn through points of equal elevation (Figs. 514, 515). Such structure contour lines show the approximate position of the key bed below the surface at all points over the entire area of the map. Since the other beds included in the folds lie parallel to it, the contour map will show the position of all beds of the series.

A section through the area contoured is shown in Fig. 516. Since most of the world's petroleum is found in domes, the mapping of oil-bearing areas by structural contours is a great aid to the search for petroleum. Contour maps showing structure are used also in the explorations for coal, iron ore, phosphate rock, and other valuable beds.

APPENDIX B

Map Symbols, Columnar Sections, and Structure Sections

Map Symbols. For representing certain rocks on geological drawings, certain symbols are in general use (Fig. 517). The groups of beds make up the geological formations, and groups of formations make up the rock systems. From these is constructed a standard geologic column which shows the relative ages of the rocks, the younger ones appearing above the older ones in the table (Fig. 518). The table, read from the bottom up, may be regarded as the table of contents of the history of the earth. The beds are the leaves, the formations are the signatures, and the rock systems are the chapters of the history. After the age relations are established, a structure section can be constructed (Fig. 519).

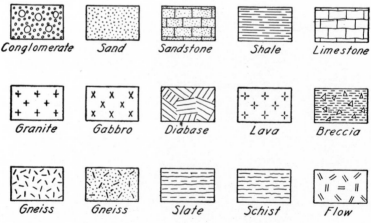

FIG. 517. Conventional symbols used in geological cross sections. Those shown in upper row are very generally used to show rocks listed. The other symbols are used with less uniformity.

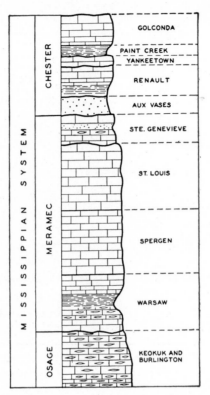

FIG. 518. A columnar section showing the chronological succession of the Mississippian rock formations in the Ste. Genevieve County, Missouri. (*After Stuart Weller.*)

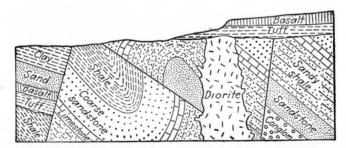

FIG. 519. A geologic cross section showing the subsurface structural relations of the rock formations. (*Reprinted by permission from Krauskopf, Fundamentals of Physical Science, 1st ed., copyright, 1941, McGraw-Hill Book Company, Inc.*)

Conventional Signs Used on Geological Maps

⤨ 70°	Strike and dip with record of amount of dip
⌀	Strike with record of vertical dip (90 degrees)
⊕	Record of flat-lying beds
⤬	Record of axis of anticline
⤲	Record of axis of syncline
20° 50° 60°	Record of axis of anticline and amount of plunging of axis
25° 40° 50°	Record of axis of syncline and amount of plunging of axis
⤲	Record of axis of overturned fold and of plunge of axis

Geologic Time

Table of Geologic Time Divisions

Eras	Periods	Some outstanding physical events	Life development
Cenozoic (60 million years)	Pleistocene	Postglacial changes	Advent of man
		The Great Ice Age and recent changes	Flowering plants dominate vegetation
	Pliocene	Formation of Coast Ranges	
	Miocene	Formation of the Alps and many other mountain chains	Primitive horses and other ungulates
	Oligocene		
	Eocene	Extensive volcanic activity in western United States	Apes appear
	Paleocene		First placental mammals
Mesozoic (130 million years)		LARAMIDE REVOLUTION	
	Upper Cretaceous	Early folding to form Rocky Mountains	Extinction of dinosaurs at close
			Climax of reptiles on land, air, and sea
	Lower Cretaceous	Central cordilleran disturbance	First flowering plants, trees, and grasses
	Jurassic	Beginning of Sierra Nevada uplift	First birds
	Triassic	Extensive volcanic activity in New England, Pennsylvania, and New Jersey	First dinosaurs and primitive mammals
Paleozoic (360 million years)		APPALACHIAN REVOLUTION	
	Permian	Folding to form Appalachian Mountains, glaciation over wide area	Rise of reptiles
	Pennsylvanian	Extensive coal-forming swamps	Large nonflowering plants
	Mississippian	Paleozoic Alps	First land vertebrates
	Devonian	Acadian Mountains	Age of fishes
	Silurian	Caledonian uplift	Rise of land plants
	Ordovician	Taconic Mountains	First known fishes
	Cambrian	Green Mountains disturbance	Age of invertebrate dominance
Proterozoic (900 million years)		LIPALIAN INTERVAL PENEPLANATION, GLACIATION KILLARNEY REVOLUTION	Probable development of shells on invertebrates
	Keweenawan	Extensive lava flows	Scanty record of primitive plants and animals
	Huronian	Ocoee Mountains (Schuchert)	
	(Animikean)	Oldest evidence of glaciation	
	Algoman	Folding connected with igneous intrusions	
	Timiskamian		Algae fairly common
Archeozoic (550 million years)		LAURENTIAN REVOLUTION	
	Laurentian Keewatin	Rocks much altered and history obscured	Primitive life probable

Samples Dated by Uranium-Lead Ratio

Mineral	Locality	Geologic age	Probable age, millions of years
Pitchblende	Gilpin County, Colorado	Early Cenozoic	60
Pitchblende	Bohemia	Late Permian	215
Pitchblende	Oslo, Norway	Early Permian	230
Samarskite	Connecticut	End of Devonian	255
Cyrtolite	New York	End of Ordovician	350
Kolm	Gullhogen, Sweden	Upper Cambrian	440
Pitchblende	Katanga, Belgian Congo	Pre-Cambrian	580
Uraninite	Besner, Ontario	Pre-Cambrian	760
Bröggerite	Moss, southern Norway	Pre-Cambrian	860
Uraninite	Wilberforce, Ontario	Pre-Cambrian	1,035
Cleveite	Aust-Agder, Norway	Pre-Cambrian	1,075
Pitchblende	Great Bear Lake, Canada	Pre-Cambrian	1,330
Uraninite	Keystone, South Dakota	Mid-pre-Cambrian	1,420
Uraninite	Northeast Karelia, U.S.S.R.	Early pre-Cambrian	1,800
Pitchblende	Winnipeg River, Manitoba	Early pre-Cambrian	2,300

MEANS OF MEASURING GEOLOGIC TIME

Various methods of measuring geologic time in years have been suggested, but the only one that seems at all reliable is based on the rate of atomic disintegration. Some of the elements, such as uranium and thorium, have unstable atomic nuclei, which undergo constant, spontaneous disintegration resulting in various more stable end products. Thus uranium gradually changes to radium. The radium breaks down into helium nuclei (alpha particles), gamma radiation, and an isotope of lead. The lead formed from radium has a slightly different atomic weight from that of ordinary lead deposited from magmatic solutions and vapors.

The rates of atomic disintegration are well-established, and, regardless of the physical or chemical conditions under which it operates, the rate for a given substance is constant. It therefore becomes a means of determining the lapse of time during which the disintegration has continued. The actual determination both by direct count and by sensitive automatic electronic devices gives the number of helium nuclei emitted by a measured amount of uranium in a given unit of time. Thus it is found that 1 gram of uranium, by loss of helium and gamma radiation, will result in 1/7,600,000,000 gram of lead per year, and U grams of uranium will yield U times as many, or $(U \times 1)/7,600,000,000$ grams of lead in 1 year. In T years the U grams will yield $TU/7,600,000,000$ grams of lead. That is, Pb in grams $= TU/7,600,000,000$; solving this equation for time, $T = Pb \times 7,600,000,000/U$ in years. If, therefore, the quantities of uranium and lead of uranium origin are determined in an igneous rock, the age in years is easily determined by simple substitution in this equation. By this means age determinations have been made for rocks from widely scattered locations.

Radioactive Transformations in the Series Uranium-Radium-Lead

Element	Group in periodic table	Atomic weight	Half life	Particle emitted during transformation
Uranium	VI	238	4.4×10^9 years	Alpha particle
Uranium X_1	IV	234	24.5 days	Beta particle
Uranium X_2	V	234	1.14 min	Beta particle
Uranium II	VI	234	3×10^5 years	Alpha particle
Ionium	IV	230	8×10^4 years	Alpha particle
Radium	II	226	1590 years	Alpha particle
Radon	0	222	3.82 days	Alpha particle
Radium A	VI	218	3.05 min	Alpha particle
Radium B	IV	214	26.8 min	Beta particle
Radium C	V	214	19.7 min	Beta particle
Radium C'	VI	214	10^{-6} sec	Alpha particle
Radium D	IV	210	22 years	Beta particle
Radium E	V	210	4.9 days	Beta particle
Polonium	VI	210	140 days	Alpha particle
Lead	IV	206		

SUGGESTIONS FOR FURTHER READING

Evans, R. D., *et al.*: Radioactivity: The Earth's Heat and Geological Age Measurements, *Geol. Soc. America Special Paper* 36, pp. 267–277, 1936.

Knopf, Adolph, *et al.*: The Age of the Earth, *Nat. Research Council Bull.* 80, 1931.

Libby, Willard F.: Radiocarbon Dating, University of Chicago Press, 1952.

Zeuner, F. E.: Dating the Past—An Introduction to Geochronology, Methuen & Co., Ltd., London, 1946.

Index

625

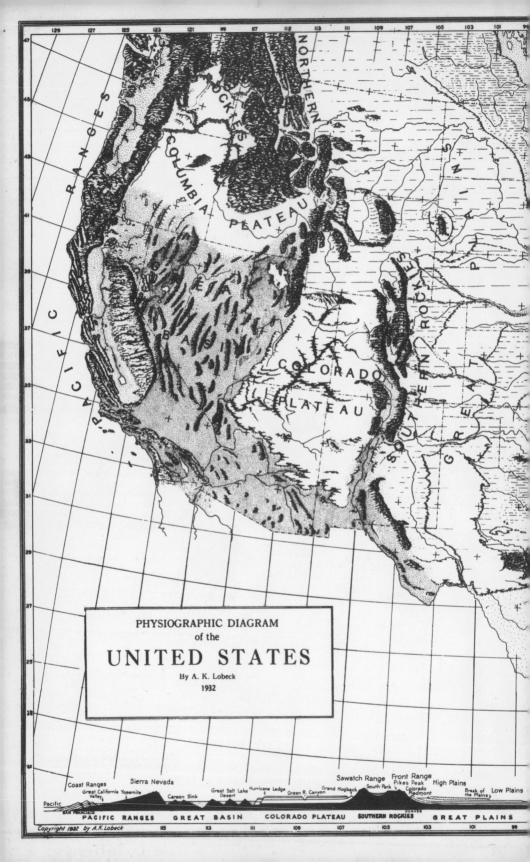

PHYSIOGRAPHIC DIAGRAM
of the
UNITED STATES

By A. K. Lobeck
1932